INDEPENDENT MAN

BOOKS BY HARRY BARNARD

INDEPENDENT MAN: *The Life of Senator James Couzens*

EAGLE FORGOTTEN: *The Life of John Peter Altgeld*

RUTHERFORD B. HAYES AND HIS AMERICA

SENATOR JAMES COUZENS

INDEPENDENT MAN: THE LIFE OF
Senator James Couzens

BY

HARRY BARNARD

CHARLES SCRIBNER'S SONS

NEW YORK

FOR PERMISSION TO QUOTE BRIEFLY FROM THE FOLLOWING SOURCES, THE AUTHOR MAKES
GRATEFUL ACKNOWLEDGMENT.

America in Midpassage by Charles A. and Mary R. Beard (The Macmillan Company,
1939)

Inside U. S. A. by John Gunther (Harper and Brothers)

Letters of Franklin D. Roosevelt by permission of Mrs. Franklin D. Roosevelt

"Michigan Magic" by John T. Flynn (Harper's Magazine, December 1933)

Wild Wheel, The by Garet Garrett (Pantheon Books, Inc.)

FOR

Alfred P. Solomon
AND *Esther,* TOO

FRIENDS
AND
COUNSELLORS

CONTENTS

PROLOGUE:

October 12, 1915

OCTOBER 12, 1915

WHEN the story broke, it shoved the European war dispatches into a subordinate position in newspapers all over the world. In London as well as in Copenhagen, not to mention New York, Chicago, St. Louis, and Los Angeles, this was true. The newspapers in Detroit put out extras with big headlines:

COUZENS LEAVES FORD!

Days afterward, from one coast of the United States to the other, the press continued to feature special commentaries and so-called "inside" stories about the man who left Ford.

There were stories, too, about the reasons (true, speculative, or imagined) for the startling separation that concerned the world's most conspicuous industrial enterprise—the Ford Motor Company of Detroit, U.S.A. If Henry Ford himself had quit, or had even simply disappeared, the sensation could scarcely have been greater.

"But none of the stories, then or later, of why it happened, came within one and one-half percent of the truth." So, years after, said John C. Lodge, the venerable ex-councilman and ex-mayor of Detroit. He was one of the very few people in all the world who knew both principals in the stories well enough to call the one "Jim" and the other "Henry." And Lodge believed that he at least had heard the "whole truth" from the lips of both "Jim" and "Henry"—but he wasn't telling, for he had been "pledged" not to tell.

Yet the whole truth was that no one really had told the whole truth—not "Jim" and not "Henry," not even when they had in fact tried to unburden themselves of the full story to old John Lodge. This is not strange. In such matters, the truth is almost always linked with, and enveloped in, motives and aspects deeply psychological, things usually veiled—veiled most of all, perhaps, from the principals themselves. They can tell of the incident itself, the "what" of the occurrence. But they are not able to tell of all that really lay behind it—the "why." Such, clearly, was so in the case of James Couzens and Henry Ford—without either of whom the company that bore the name of Ford would never have been of interest to anyone outside of Detroit.

The "what"—the bare facts—may be pieced together briefly.

On the evening of October 11, 1915, Charles A. Brownell, who uneasily wore the title of advertising manager, had stepped, just before closing time, into the office of the Vice President, Treasurer, and General Manager of the Ford Motor Company.

Brownell, usually the opposite of a timid man, made his entrance with the attitude of caution and wariness customarily adopted by nearly everyone who went into that office. For Brownell had come to see "Jim"—though, to be sure, he did not refer to the Vice President, Treasurer, and General Manager of the Ford Motor Company as "Jim," but rather as "Mr. Couzens." His mission was to get Couzens' approval of the page proofs for the next issue of the Ford Motor Company magazine, the *Ford Times*. He was acting in accordance with a rule that everyone in the Ford organization understood in those days—that Mr. Couzens had to approve everything (or nearly everything) the company did, and of late this had applied especially to articles in the *Ford Times*.

Brownell handed Couzens a set of the proofs. In his characteristically quick way, Couzens thumbed through them, while Brownell held his breath. Nothing objectionable to Couzens turned up—until his eyes fell upon one particular article.

The effect on him of glancing at this article was an almost instantaneous—and characteristic—reddening, first of his neck and then of his face—danger signs that all who knew him well understood.

The article that produced this redness contained the substance of remarks previously published in the Detroit *Free Press* and credited to Henry Ford, remarks concerning the war in Europe and the "preparedness movement" in the United States.

The tenor of these remarks was distinctly "pacifist"—of the kind that led a little later to Ford's being persuaded to sponsor his celebrated *Oscar II* "peace ship" venture.

"You cannot publish this," Couzens told Brownell.

"But Mr. Ford himself—"

"You cannot publish this! Hold it over."

"But Mr. Ford said—"

"These are Mr. Ford's personal views, not the views of the company. This is the company paper. He cannot use the *Ford Times* for his personal views. I will talk to Mr. Ford tomorrow."

Brownell withdrew without saying anything more. He knew a decision had been made at the Ford company—when Couzens had made it.

After Brownell had departed, Couzens turned his swivel chair away from his flat-top desk and shut violently the roll top of his "aft" desk.

These two desks formed the nerve center of the Ford Motor Company. To them came the reports from the 6,700 Ford agents, the thirty-five Ford branches, the twenty-six Ford assembly plants, the forty-eight American banks, and the two foreign banks in which the Ford company millions were deposited. From these desks came the decisions that guided the company's affairs throughout its already vast empire in the United States and abroad, every place, in fact, except in the main shop and in the laboratory (Mr. Ford's particular bailiwicks)—and sometimes in these places as well.

Couzens got up briskly. He walked over to his clothes rack and planted a black derby firmly on his prematurely gray head. For a moment he stopped before the mirror over the wash basin to adjust his necktie knot to a precisely correct position in his high, stiff collar, flicked away some dust that may or may not have been on his jacket sleeves, thriftily turned off the office lights, and, in an instant, with his usual quick gait, left the office of the Ford Company for his home.

His movements that evening, down to the last gesture, were all routine for him. He had gone out of the Administration Building that same way night after night since it had been built. But, after arriving home, he went to bed earlier than usual that night, explaining to his wife, Margaret, that he had one of those headaches which his doctors called "migraine."

At ten o'clock the next morning, Henry Ford came into Couzens' office. "He was perfectly good-natured. He sat and visited awhile," Couzens later described the meeting.

The two "partners," as they were known, talked of Couzens' recent trip to California, of Ford's plan to attend the San Diego Exposition there with Thomas A. Edison. Then Couzens said to Ford, "I held up the *Times* because of your article in it about the war."

Suddenly, as if a match had been touched to gunpowder, the calm and friendly atmosphere in the office exploded.

Ford's geniality changed swiftly into something else—a belligerence not usually associated with Henry Ford in those days, an attitude he had certainly never before shown so sharply to Couzens, although others in the company already knew that Ford was capable of such a transformation. As Couzens himself said some time later, "Mr. Ford just flew off the handle . . . I was shocked . . . aghast."

Couzens did not recall in detail everything Ford said on that occasion. But he did remember Ford's having snapped:

"You cannot stop anything here!"

"Well, then, I will quit," Couzens replied.

Ford suddenly seemed to calm down.

"Better think it over," he said.

"No, I have decided," Couzens said.

"What will you tell the papers?" Ford asked.

"That we disagree about the war."

"All right, if you have decided," said Ford.

So these two—"Jim" and "Henry," who had been referred to in a business publication only a few weeks earlier as "The Damon and Pythias of the Ford Motor Company"—had separated.

And it all happened in less time than it takes to set it down.[1]

For some time a few persons in the automobile industry had known that there was trouble between the "partners," but no one ever assumed that matters would come to this. A Ford Motor Company without James Couzens would have then been as unthinkable as a Ford Motor Company without Henry Ford. Indeed, there were those who said that the Ford Company up to then *was* mainly Couzens. Of course, this was not true. Henry Ford could not be dismissed so casually. Conjecture about a Fordless Ford Motor Company is unrealistic. The Ford certainly was Ford's car, though, to be sure, C. Harold Wills, as well as certain other mechanics and designers including the Dodge brothers, John and Horace, had contributed to its creation. Similarly, the Ford ideas of factory production were more Henry Ford's than anyone's else, even though Walter Flanders, the Dodges, W. F. McGuire, Wills, Charles E.

Sorensen, and others contributed to their development and practice. Yet, indisputably, Couzens had played a role in the company that was decisive—as decisive as Ford's.

It was Couzens, for example, who had been responsible for the five-dollar-a-day wage plan which electrified the world in 1914. More than anything else, this plan gave the Ford Company its first international reputation. Ford himself once wrote (or had written for him):

"Ideas are of themselves extraordinarily valuable, but an idea is just an idea. Almost anyone can think up an idea. The thing that counts is developing it into a practical product."

And that was where Couzens figured in the Ford Company picture.

Norval Hawkins, the Ford sales manager in the halcyon days of the Model T success, once summed up the story quite accurately. "Mr. Couzens was a very remarkable man, as remarkable, in many ways, as Mr. Ford. Mr. Couzens was responsible for at least half of the success of the Ford Motor Company . . . Mr. Ford required just the type of man that Mr. Couzens was to occupy the front seat, and had Couzens been a less indefatigable worker, or a man who paid less attention to the details of that business . . . it might not have been as successful as it is today. . . ." [2]

Barron's, the financial weekly, said of Couzens in 1915:

"For twelve years he was with Henry Ford and it is an open question if the reverse order of the statement might not be fairly accurate. . . . The public thought of him all the time as entitled to equal credit with 'Henry' for the marvelous success of the motor enterprise."

John Wendell Anderson, one of the two Detroit lawyers who were among the original stockholders (and to whom it was worth literally millions of dollars, on the basis of a $5,000 investment, to watch the affairs of the company closely from the very start) said:

"It was due to his [Couzens'] efforts that the company became a success. The team work of himself and Mr. Ford contributed to its success to a much greater extent than either one of them could possibly have done alone." [3]

Many more such statements from those who knew how the company had been created and guided in its formative years could be compiled. But such compilation was not at all necessary in 1915— the very year, incidentally, in which the millionth Model T came off the assembly line at the Highland Park plant, a production and sales record that seemed incredible at the time—for the facts about Couzens' role in the company were widely known in the world of commerce and industry.

Then, suddenly, Couzens was out of the Ford picture.

Everywhere the question was asked: "What will become of the Ford Company?"

Some predicted that the Ford Company would go the way of hundreds of other motorcar manufacturing companies, the names of which only antiquarians in the field would now remember. Recalling what they knew (or thought they knew) of Henry Ford and his commercial views, they shuddered over what they *supposed* would be the future of the company. James Couzens himself, however, knew (or thought he knew) the answer to the fears expressed for the company. Just after October 12, 1915, he said:

"I hope I have assisted in so perfecting the organization of the company that my resignation will not make a pin's worth of difference. Mr. Ford agreed that his own resignation would not make a pin's worth of difference. The momentum of the business is too great . . ."

And this, of course, proved absolutely true. Indeed, as would be demonstrated around 1928, when Henry Ford was still clinging tenaciously to the Model T long after the public had begun to reject it, and again as demonstrated in another crisis period of the 1940's, the company had been built on such a strong foundation that not even Henry Ford himself could wreck it.

"What will Couzens do?" was another question widely asked.

He was then only forty-three. Financially he was worth anywhere from forty million dollars to fifty or even sixty million, depending on the value of his Ford stock and on investments he had made with Ford dividends and his salary. He was energetic and intellectually alert. In this respect, in fact, he was in his prime. But he had come to the end of his road—or so he thought. It seemed clear to others, however, if not to himself at just that moment, that a man who could walk out deliberately, as he had just done, on a business that was acclaimed "The Seventh Wonder of the World," undoubtedly would find another road, perhaps an even more rewarding and satisfying one. His role in the development of the Ford Company, important as it was, actually was but prelude for an even more important role on the stage of the modern industrial era—the motor age—which he had helped to usher into being in America.

BOOK ONE

The Money-Making Machine

CHAPTER I

THE BEGINNING

PROPERLY the story of James Couzens had its real beginning in the fall of 1870, two years before he was born. This was when his father stepped off a train in the windswept little town of Chatham, Ontario Province, Canada.

An immigrant tossed up by economic depression and also propelled by deep-seated inability to get along with his own father, this traveler, then twenty-one, had been en route to the United States from London, England. His goal was a better living than he believed he could achieve at home, for he was convinced that London in 1870 was "finished and had no future." [1]

To be sure, this precise-looking, sober-miened Englishman named James Joseph Couzens was not so dull as to believe with any strong faith that nondescript, tiny Chatham really promised a much better future for him than had London. The fact was that he had not even heard of Chatham in Ontario before arriving there by the slow train he had boarded at Levis, Quebec, where his ship had docked.

But he had rechecked the contents of his purse and concluded that the little funds he had left made it impractical for him to travel the fifty miles farther to Detroit, his original destination. So with British prudence he decided to stay right there at Chatham.

2

This was a mistake. Though not a man to admit error readily, he sometimes conceded this in after years, especially since his decision deprived his children, in particular his first son, of something that might have made a great difference: United States citizenship by birth.

However, he did have a sentimental rationalization to justify the error. He asserted later that he had rather fancied the idea of settling in a town, even an unattractive one, that bore the same name as the great naval-station city of Chatham in England, which was the home of the girl to whom he had become betrothed just before leaving London. But if this was a factor, one can be sure that not often afterward did James Joseph Couzens permit any such romantic notions to shape his conduct. Practicality was stamped all over him.

3

His training was that of an ordinary grocer's apprentice, and he knew his status. Yet in his manners and bearing there was a kind of special promise, a certain aristocratic air, a kind of self-assured dignity almost out of place, even somewhat humorously incongruous, in Chatham at that time, especially for an immigrant, job-seeking grocer's clerk. Years after he had left Chatham, people there still remembered this characteristic that had marked him when he first arrived. They also remembered the fact that, very early, he revealed an ingrained streak of belligerence (something he was destined to pass on to at least one son), the trait that had made his relationship with his father, a bailiff, less than tolerable.

He had a way of speaking that of itself set him off from others. He spoke in an especially polite and trimmed way. His style was not, to be sure, the cultivated one of Mr. Gladstone, the Prime Minister. But neither was it the cockney style of the submerged London masses. It was something in-between. And this was interesting, for he really had had only a little schooling.

He carried himself, too, with uncommon erectness. Clearly, he thought well of himself. Yet when he set about getting a job in Chatham, he made no pretense of seeking more than an ordinary one. He was satisfied to start at something even lower than what he had had in London and soon he was working as a handyman in a grocery owned by one Andrew Crow, a crude, shantylike establishment of the kind one associates with a general store at some crossroads in, say, Kansas, or in a mining camp in the Colorado territory of that same period.

4

Chatham, Ontario, did in fact seem just then like a Western outpost, a settlement in a state of arrested erosion. Years before, it had had a period of growth, even of excitement. It had been intended, by its original settlers, as a shipbuilding center for a Canadian navy because of its location on a river called the Thames. Hence its proud name, after the naval center on the Thames in England. But nothing came of the shipbuilding idea. As stated in a town chronicle, "Several gunboats were built, but it is questionable if they ever left the stocks." [2] In 1870, it was just a seamy settlement, quite as ordinary as its newcomer.

Yet the town had been brushed by history. During the War of 1812, the battle in which Chief Tecumseh had been killed was fought nearby. In this same war, a regiment composed largely of Chathamites helped to capture Detroit. Some years later people quipped that this was not the only time "Chatham captured Detroit." A second capture occurred, they said, when a man born in Chatham and named Couzens became its mayor.

5

In the 1850's, the organized Abolitionists in the United States selected the town as the end of the line for the Underground Railroad that helped slaves to freedom. In consequence, for a period, Chatham's population was comprised more of blacks than of whites. In search of material for *Dred*, her sequel to *Uncle Tom's Cabin*, Harriet Beecher Stowe visited there.

In 1858, John Brown held a meeting in Chatham for the purpose of organizing an armed invasion of the United States. Of course, nothing came of Brown's "Chatham Plan," and after the United States had fought the Civil War, most of the Negroes left town. The former Abolitionists ceased to visit Chatham—and also stopped sending funds to help the colony of black freedmen there. Then the town became as slow-paced and inconsequential as its meandering little Thames. When James Joseph Couzens settled there, it had acquired a nickname: Mudtown.

6

A year later, young Mr. Couzens, now wearing a beard, sent for the girl who had been waiting patiently in England for his summons —and a passage ticket.

Emma Clift, of the other Chatham, was the daughter of Thomas Clift, who had served in the Crimean war as a member of a commissary unit. After that war he had prospered moderately as a confectioner and may have sold some of his sweets to Charles Dickens, then living in Chatham, England. The war service of Emma Clift's father provided what was perhaps the one bit of "color" in the Couzens-Clift family history up to then. Moreover, Florence Nightingale had visited his regiment, led the soldiers in some singing, and asked Tom Clift to stand with her on his trunk while doing so. Emma's father liked to talk of that incident, as did some of his descendants.

Blue-eyed Emma Clift brought with her the "Nightingale trunk," when she made her own trip from Chatham, England, to Chatham, Ontario, to marry James Joseph Couzens.[3]

The couple set up housekeeping in a boxlike little brick "row-house" in "the cheapest and muddiest district" of the town. There, on August 26, 1872, a boy, blue-eyed and full-faced like Emma Clift Couzens, was born to them.

One thing only seemed remarkable about the birth of the couple's first child. James Joseph Couzens, Junior (as the boy was christened in the St. Andrews Presbyterian Church), was born with a caul, a fact, according to the old folk legend, that foretold special good fortune in life.

7

Young James grew up fully conscious of the supposed meaning of his caul. It was often a topic of conversation in the family and among the neighbors. His mother saved the caul, keeping it in a little silk sack that she made for it, and parted with it only when he married, presenting it to his bride, who also saved it.[4] After he had reached maturity, he scoffed at the superstition—"That nonsense!"—concerning his caul. Yet almost from the beginning of his life, his outlook toward the world, and his estimate of himself and his destiny, may well have been influenced by the story.

It is certain that for a boy who grew up in the forlorn neighborhood of Elizabeth and Grand in Chatham, he carried himself as if aware that a special destiny of fortune was his. Perhaps this was something acquired in part from his father. But, if so, it was more than just emulation. His pronounced assurance, apparent quite early, that he was an especially favored child of fortune plainly was one dominant factor that helped to make his later life so extraordinary, even startlingly so, in view of how and where it had begun. But that was all in the future.

That hot summer of 1872, when he was born, nobody in Chatham would have wagered twopence that the new baby out on muddy Grand Avenue would leave any special mark any place.

CHAPTER II

THE CANADIAN BOY

WHEN the boy was four or five, his father became a laborer in the soap factory of Lamont and Coate. He left the grocery trade because in Canada it lacked dignity, he later said. However, his real reason for the switch was the opportunity to earn a higher wage, which in that era meant one dollar a day.

Yet the family managed—even with self-respect. Nothing was wasted, ever. That this should be so was like a religion with James Joseph and Emma Couzens.[1] So their style of living was pinchedly narrow, but the boy developed into a sturdy, alert, good-looking youngster.

Very early, James Joseph, Junior, showed some positive characteristics. About the time he was learning to talk, his mother one day heard him making a great commotion in the backyard. Investigating, she learned that all the noise was his way of registering protest against a gust of wind that had blown down his alphabet blocks.[2]

2

A few years more and he made a decision about his name. He would not be known any longer as James Joseph Couzens, Junior. He insisted on being known simply as James Couzens.

It was not in him then, or ever, to be a junior to anyone. In his personal creed, indeed, this was to be a primary tenet—something to be remembered for future reference. To be sure, this decision about his name was a reflection of his attitude toward his father, an early declaration of independence from him.

For such a declaration, the elder Couzens gave him sufficient reasons. The townfolk considered his father a man who was amiable and cheerful enough, although highly dogmatic on religious matters pertaining to his Scotch Presbyterian affiliation. He was also known as the "soul of deference" toward his wife, perhaps because she "bowed to him in everything." Yet toward his first son, the father was strangely tyrannical and given to curious displays of the most violent temper, slapping and whipping the boy frequently. His son recalled later, "I have been panned ever since I was two years old." It was his father's conduct toward him that he had in mind.[3]

3

For such conduct on his father's part, there seldom was any realistic reason. For by no standard was the boy a delinquent. On the contrary, he was respectful to a fault and almost always obeyed to the letter any instructions given to him by either parent, even though he once said that all his life he felt an "unjustifiable resistance to people making me do things." [4] He thought he kept this "resistance" concealed, but apparently not so well concealed that his father did not suspect and resent this streak in him.

He was also tidier than most boys. He did willingly and well all the household chores assigned to him. Even his father took pride in "the punctiliousness" with which he performed the task of keeping the wood boxes clean. "He would pick out every piece of wood, each shaving, every bit of bark—that's the way he did everything," his father once said.[5]

4

Yet there is the record—the angry beatings, slappings, and endless emotional scolding from the dignified man whom the townfolk considered so amiable and polite.

It is clear that there was involved here an unusually strong case of tension between father and son. No doubt the elder Couzens never understood the cause of his flare-ups (significantly confined to his firstborn son). Nor was he able to restrain them. No doubt, too, just as lacking in understanding about the anxiety produced in him by his father, the boy often provoked the outbursts of "tyranny" without realizing that he had done so. But whatever the cause, the disturbance was certainly there, with all its consequent conflict. Inevitably it was to produce a defensive as well as aggressive youth, one destined to be in an almost constant state of resistance to most forms of authority, real or fancied. This side of his nature once came clearly into the open at school when, on very slight provocation, he yanked at the beard of the principal, getting himself suspended for the offense. He himself later said that he "guessed" he did that because the principal's beard represented "authority" to him.[6]

Yet, significantly, during his youth, he never rebelled openly against his father. Rather, he accepted, even courted, a great deal more punishment from his father than was necessary. As a sister, Alice, once recalled: "On many occasions, I tried to protect him from punishment by denying that he had committed little mis-demeanors, such as running across the garden. But he would always contradict me, and would have nothing but the truth—and take his punishment." [7]

To Alice, these incidents denoted a penchant for telling the truth, even if the truth hurt. This was true, for he certainly had a penchant for truth-telling that hurt. But his sister's comments also reflected an aspect of his character that was more significant than his insistence on telling the truth. This was a tendency to court conflict and also, it seems, punishment, as if these were necessary to his existence. As would be said of him later, "He seemed always to need to wear the hair-shirt." [8] If so, the reasons for this must remain obscure. He himself often pondered his nature, but could not explain it. Probably much of the answer would be found in his attitudes toward his mother, as well as toward his father. But, except that he loved her, little is known for certain of his feelings toward the mild-mannered mother "who bowed in everything" to his father. He talked freely about other members of his family. But he reminisced very seldom of the blue-eyed Emma Couzens, his mother.

CHAPTER III

THE MONEY-MAKING MACHINE, I

BY THE time young James was seven or eight, his father's job at the Lamont and Coate soap establishment had become twofold. He manufactured the soap by the primitive, grimy process of steam-mixing wood ashes with discarded animal fats and he also acted as salesman. Once in a while, young James went along with his father on the selling expeditions. Chathamites remembered the sight. The erect, clean-faced, good-looking little boy sat pridefully, they thought, beside his bearded, incongruously dignified father on a one-horse wagon, taking in with intent eyes his first impressions of the world beyond the shabby area of Elizabeth and Grand streets.

On these trips, the boy naturally learned something about the customs and ethics of commerce. One custom called for housewives to save the wood ashes from their own stoves and fireplaces in order to trade them for free bars of soap if other bars were purchased. Some women tried thriftily to get more free bars than were coming to them. Young James Couzens listened with sharp and alert interest to the bargaining that resulted—his first bit of education on how to become a businessman; and he noted especially his father's satisfaction in not permitting a customer to get the better of him.

He learned also that people could be gullible. For example, some of his father's customers insisted upon buying the soap according to brand names on the wrappers, preferring his "Electric" soap to his "Gladstone" soap, or vice versa. They were sure the one was much better than the other. But James knew that both brands came out of the same odoriferous batch.

2

When the boy was nine, a great event happened to his father. The elder Couzens became a soapmaker on his own, establishing the "Chatham Steam Soap Works, James J. Couzens, Prop.," helped in this by an inheritance of about fifteen hundred dollars that unexpectedly fell to his wife on the death of her father.

Young James was well aware of the marked elation his father showed on becoming his own man, an independent entrepreneur, no less, in the great world of commerce and industry, a world in which the little "Chatham Steam Soap Works" was a substantial unit —at least in the eyes of its "prop."

Bearded James Joseph Couzens, Senior, the new independent man, began to walk with greater dignity than before. But so also did young James Couzens, *sans* the "Joseph" and *sans* also the "Junior," with ideas percolating in his well-shaped head, it may be assumed, of one day also becoming an independent man and heading some enterprise bigger and better even than his father's "Chatham Steam Soap Works."

This sudden economic rise in the world for the Couzenses of Chatham was accompanied by an appropriate growth in the size of the family. Two girls, Alice and Rosetta, were born. Later came two more boys, first Albert, then Homer. The fact of their existence naturally had an influence upon James, for a big-brother role now fell to him. Looked up to by four awed youngsters, he was now of lordlike stature in the family circle, his only rival for eminence being his father. Boyhood friends recalled, "He carried himself like a young lord." [1]

3

When this "young lord" was going on thirteen, the elder Couzens became a dealer in coal and ice, along with soap. He also began to manufacture cement paving blocks—some of which were still in use in Chatham seventy years later. Indeed, James' father had in fact become a real entrepreneur in Chatham, a status confirmed by his election as an elder of St. Andrew's Presbyterian Church.

Quite early, James concluded that making money was synonymous with growing into manhood, an idea that his parents and the general cultural climate in Canada, as in the United States, encouraged. Before he was nine, he was earning money on his own—ten cents a week for pumping the organ at St. Andrew's. When he wanted a saddle for the horse that pulled the soap wagon, his father told him to earn it. He should go out and sell soap, his father declared. This he did.[2] When gas street-lamps were at last installed in the neighborhood, James scurried to get the job of lamp-tender. He obtained the plum and was paid one dollar a month from the town treasury for turning on four lamps each night and for keeping them clean.[3] Of him, a town chronicler wrote: "In school, if a football or baseball were wanted, he organized the drive, persuaded the youngsters to chip in their dimes, nickels, and cents, and he made the ultimate thrifty dicker with the storekeeper." [4]

4

His young mind obviously was much occupied with the power that went with money. To impress his sisters and brothers, he did an interesting and prophetic thing one day with his mother's "Nightingale trunk." Secretly he placed some coins inside it, then called the youngsters together, waved his hand, and cried, "Presto!"— revealing the coins. The trunk, he announced grandiosely to the astonished audience, had been converted by him into a "Money-making Machine." Its secret was known only to him.[5]

5

He had, said his mother, "big dreams."

Once he scolded her quite earnestly because he had been born in Canada: "I can never be King of England, but if I had been born in the United States, I could be President." [6]

From another boy such a remark might have been set down as idle chatter. But his mother knew that he was serious.

She was often puzzled as to the source of such thoughts, and she would become hurt when such things occurred as a neighbor complaining that James "deliberately snubbed" her daughter. The girl had called hello to him from across the street, and he had ignored her. But he had an explanation. "If a girl wishes to speak to me, she should come across the street and do it properly." [7]

One of his schoolmates recalled most vividly his conduct on the day that the pupils of his school, Central, were invited to attend an entertainment program at the McKeough School. "In came the Central pupils with Jim Couzens in the lead, and he proceeded to jump from one desk to another. His idea was to get for himself the choice of seats—and he took *the most direct way*." [8]

This, too, was prophecy.

6

For a time, he worked in his father's soap factory. But the smell and mess of the place offended him. Then too, working there meant working for his *father*, which he detested. Already he wanted to be on his own—especially in relation to James Couzens, Senior.

One day, during the summer after he had completed primary school, when he was only twelve, he saw a want ad for a book-keeper, placed in the local newspaper, the *Chatham Planet*, by a flour mill. A job like that would get him out of the soap works. So he applied for it, although, as he later admitted, he knew nothing about keeping books. Incredibly, he was given the position.

His father was not at all happy over this development. There was an emotional scene. But his father could give him no "good reason" why he should stay at the soap works if he could land the bookkeeping spot. So he took the job at the flour mill. He tackled it as though he really were qualified, and soon announced that bookkeeping was to be his career. Moreover, he said, he had no intention of going on to high school. He didn't need that—a waste of time, he said.[9]

But, as might have been expected, he was soon to sustain some severe blows to his ego. One came when he lost the bookkeeping job when his employers finally concluded that he was too young. Then, after he decided to enter high school after all, he failed to pass the entrance examination. His father was irate and heatedly ordered him to get back to the soap works. The "punishment" proved a spur for him to "bone up" for another try at the entrance examination. This time he passed.

At high school he was more studious and tensely so than he had ever been before. He spent less time than his fellows in idling with other boys in Market Square. Instead, he put in more time with his books.[10] He had not liked the taste of failure. It grated on his whole being. He "swore that it would never happen to him again." [11]

In his mind, too, was an anxious need for erasing the stigma he felt was attached to his failure on the bookkeeping job. So, after two years at the high school, he enrolled for a two-year course in bookkeeping at the Canada Business College in Chatham, to be properly prepared for "the next time." To pay his way while at this "college," he worked as a newsbutcher on the Erie and Huron. The railroad "never had a better one," recalled his superior, Bill Turtle. He was, said Turtle, a "hustler." [12]

7

It was inconceivable that such a "hustler," a youth whose anxious need for success gave him no rest, would long remain in the little town of Chatham.

He was bound to feel the lure of some bigger place—London, in Ontario; or Montreal, in Quebec; or even Detroit, only fifty miles away from Chatham. And just as inevitably, in view of his relationship with his father, he was destined to leave home as soon as he could. Only then could he—or his father and mother—have any real peace in the household: this was understood, though never expressed in so many words, by all three of them.

8

In 1889, when James Couzens was seventeen, a friend named Dickson went to Detroit, obtained a job with the Michigan Central Railroad, and wrote back that another job was to be had there. Young Couzens hurriedly packed up, and left at once to get it. But something went wrong. In a short time he found himself, unhappily, back home again.

A few months later—it was then 1890—he set off for Detroit again, and this time he stayed. On August 9, 1890, just as he was turning eighteen, he was hired as a car-checker by the Michigan Central in Detroit.

On the railroad his wage was forty dollars a month for a twelve-hour shift, seven days a week, and yet he was delighted. It was, he recalled, "great stuff" to be checking freight cars, even in weather so cold that the tacks which he carried in his mouth for affixing labels on the cars literally froze to his tongue. After each shift, he went to his room, in a place called the Amos House, feeling that he was "running the railroad." [13] Only when he had that kind of feeling was he ever content.

Most of all, however, he enjoyed the status of being on his own at last.

CHAPTER IV

THE NEW DETROITER

THE place called the Amos House was a ramshackle, weather-beaten lodging and boarding place, favored by railroad workers employed at the "Junction Yards." Then, though not later, it was on the outskirts of Detroit. Its main attraction: low-priced meals. For the next three years, young James Couzens lived there, his steel-blue eyes more intently than ever focused on his goal: success.

It was noticeable that he did not mix much with the other Amos House boarders. He stayed out of their bull sessions and only rarely joined in the beer drinking that went on. Nearly everyone else there was called by some nickname. But not Couzens. His deadly serious manner about almost everything discouraged such familiarity.

He did make some friends. But these had to overlook or discount a "don't-tread-on-me" attitude that often became quite explosive. It was accepted, or at least expected, that if one made a remark that young Couzens disliked, or with which he simply disagreed, he would blurt out a stinging comment or retort. This seemed almost an instinct with him.

In appearance alone, he stood out from most of his fellow railroad workers. Even in his work clothes, he had a buttoned-up look. Instead of a car-checker, he could have been taken for an English bank clerk or even a divinity student, especially after he began to wear thin-rimmed spectacles.

From his always impeccable clothes to his neatly clipped, carefully brushed, blond hair, everything about him except his temper proclaimed disciplined orderliness, precision, and restrained tension. And always, in the taut mold of his forceful, open face, there was a warning that here was a man who spoke his mind.

2

By then, he had become a clean-cut youth of exceptional handsomeness. He was, indeed, a perfect specimen of the Anglo-Saxon type—fair, well-built, with finely chiseled features. That girls would be interested in the young transplanted Canadian, if he gave them half a chance, could have been assumed. In Chatham, he had had one or two friendships with girls, but none that were "serious," no doubt because of his "don't-tread-on-me" attitude. In Detroit, he was in no greater hurry to make any such alliance. He was not, however, altogether aloof in this matter. He did have a number of casual dates. Some Saturday nights, he even unloosened the buttoned-up look enough to attend the public dances at the Detroit Armory. On one trip back to Chatham to see his family, he boasted to his brother Homer: "I have so many girls in Detroit that I can take out a different one every night and not get back to the first one for two weeks." But the brother gathered that this was mainly a boast.[1] Actually, his major concern was getting on at the Michigan Central, keeping his eyes open for all possible promotions.

3

He had come to Detroit at the proper time. In 1890, this city of two hundred thousand was already on the threshold of its destiny. Men in and near Detroit, at precisely this time, were beginning to conceive, and even to make, something that was to propel Detroit, in a span of ten years, to undreamed-of heights of activity and wealth: the horseless carriage. By 1890, young Ransom E. Olds was working at Lansing, Michigan, on just such a contraption, to be propelled by steam. In this same year, on a farm at Dearborn, near Detroit, another man, Henry Ford, was perfecting a two-cylinder gas engine, fascinated with the idea of applying mechanical power to farm chores.[2]

Not yet, to be sure, was the Detroit of the 1890's (more grim than gay) entitled to its later favorite nickname: "Dynamic City." On the contrary, in contrast to other cities of similar size, Detroit then seemed the opposite of dynamic. It was extraordinarily backward in (of all things) public transportation. After other American communities had been using electric trolleys for years, Detroit's streetcars were still horse-drawn.

Car-checker James Couzens had to walk three miles over dusty or

muddy unpaved streets from the Michigan Central yards to the nearest car lines. He was indignant about this—a fact to be remembered.

However, many of those factors destined to make Detroit truly
dynamic were already present. It was a city of marked manufacturing ability. Its location on the river connecting it with the Great
Lakes made the shipment of products and raw materials easy and
profitable. Its stoves, railroad cars, wheels, seeds, cigars, and other
manufactured items were known around the world. The Detroit
River was already alive with freighters, barges, and steamers.

4

Hazen S. Pingree, a well-to-do, successful, and ebullient manufacturer of shoes, was elected mayor of Detroit the very year young
Couzens became a Detroiter. Later this fact would be of special and
intriguing interest in respect to Couzens. For, although a wealthy
industrialist and also a Republican (in the same ranks as William
McKinley and Mark Hanna), this pugnacious Mr. Pingree conducted
himself in such a manner that he was scorned by his fellow industrialists as a "socialist." Indeed, it was in this same year that Pingree, at
times battling "special interests" alongside such progressives as Governor John Peter Altgeld, Illinois' "Eagle Forgotten," launched the
stormy Detroit and Michigan political career that would be credited
by one Michigan historian with helping to "lay the basis for the liberal movement in the Republican party which was carried forward
more successfully by some of his successors," [3]—including one successor named Couzens.

Pingree had burst upon the Detroit political scene just then as a
"People's Mayor," denouncing tax-dodging corporations and fighting
especially for improved public-utility service and lower rates for such
service. Critics said he was "utterly lacking in tact and diplomatic
gifts." [4] Nevertheless he became one of the *two* outstanding mayors
in Detroit history.

Worth recalling is the fact that in 1890 Pingree started a movement
for municipal ownership of public transportation, for which action
he suffered social ostracism from his clubs and his church. During the
panic of '93, Pingree increased the conviction of other businessmen
that he was a socialist, or another kind of radical, by his insistence
that unemployment relief was a function of government. He arbi-
trarily allowed unemployed laborers to take over vacant lots for raising food, mainly potatoes, and "Pingree's Potato Patches" became a

national phrase, along with "Coxey's Army"—fighting words in the ideological disputes of that day.

5

The furor stirred up by Pingree's "radical" ideas, and especially the heated denunciation of them by leaders of his own party, made a strong and lasting impression upon young Couzens. What's more, even in the 1890's, though more from temperament than from any studied conclusions, Couzens harbored certain inchoate Pingree-like ideas of his own.

For example, he barked some uncomplimentary remarks to fellow railroaders about the low wages paid to stevedores on the river-front. And he stopped to listen when Single-Tax orators lectured groups of workingmen on Woodward Avenue. Later, he called himself a Single Taxer—"in principle." [5] During a streetcar strike in 1891, a stormy episode linked with Pingree's municipal-ownership program, he sympathized impulsively with a group of strikers he saw tossing bricks at a streetcar. Young Couzens hurled a few bricks himself.

In 1894 there occurred a national railroad strike, the one that resulted from conflict between Eugene V. Debs' "one big union" and the Pullman Sleeping Car Company. This brought the "social conflict," as editorialists then described labor-capital tension, quite close to Couzens of the Michigan Central R.R. Company, in the "Junction Yards."

He was not at all taken in by the overheated propaganda that pictured the Pullman workers and their striking railroad-worker sympathizers under mild-mannered Debs as "anarchists," "communists," or some other brand of revolutionists bent upon destroying America. Nor was he taken in by the same kind of clamor that churned around Altgeld in Illinois for protesting on constitutional grounds President Grover Cleveland's use of federal troops to break the strike—a clamor that soon also churned in Detroit around Mayor Pingree, who supported Governor Altgeld. Young Couzens assessed the outcries of "anarchy" for what they were. Remembering his own slim pay-envelope at the Michigan Central, he made up his mind that the strikers were just railroad men, like himself and his fellows, who merely wanted what he also wanted—somewhat fatter pay envelopes.

His unit of the railroad escaped direct involvement in the Pullman strike. But, in his talks with others at the yards, he did not make it a secret that his sympathies were with Debs' men. He was aware that if his attitude were "reported" it might cost his job, but his feeling was: If he thought so, why shouldn't he say so? Nobody was going to take that right from *him*.[6] This attitude he never changed.

6

Actually, he was neutral on the "union question," so far as he himself was concerned, for he was sure that the state of being a "worker" was only temporary for him. So the union question as such was not really a personal matter with James Couzens. Although at times he growled about the Michigan Central that "this road doesn't appreciate what we workers do," he worked faithfully for the railroad. And he worked superlatively well. "He was always on the job, worked his head off, never did any fooling around," a fellow worker at the railroad recalled.[7]

True, his record at the railroad was marred by a "letter of reprimand" on July 20, 1891. This made him "sore as Hell"—and the roar of angry protest that broke from him that day was considered memorable at the "Junction Yards." The fault, he felt, belonged to a fellow worker for having failed to awaken him, as he had requested, when he was taking a nap toward the end of a long shift. But there was no other black mark against him.[8] "I was," he boasted in after years, "the best God-damned car-checker on the line!" [9]

7

As if to point up the fact that he was a "man," after he became twenty-one in 1893, he went to his superintendent and asked for promotion. The job he wanted was that of boss of the freight office in the yards.

Before long the position was his, although this meant passing over a number of men who had been car-checkers long before he had begun working for the railroad. For the first time, he now had the responsibility of directing the work of other men, including some much older than he. He had no lack of assurance in the way he assumed that responsibility. He was not a popular boss and made no effort to be popular. Already he was a strict disciplinarian. Yet, though he did not win affection, he did win respect. "He never tried to shift responsibility upon others to shield himself; if he made a mistake, he would own up regardless of what the result might be," one of his men recalled.[10]

Nor did he pick on subordinates while kowtowing to superiors. "He was just as assertive with those above him." A superintendent, one Buchanan, once gave him a "calling down." Couzens talked back.

"You're fired!" said Buchanan.

"You can't fire me!" retorted Couzens.

He wasn't fired.[11]

8

At the freight office, for the first time he came into contact with patrons of the railroad, something he had in mind when he asked for the promotion. For he had concluded that it would take too long to realize his ambitions if he stayed in the railroad business. He hoped to get into something with a better and quicker future by meeting the businessmen who used the railroad.

Yet, of all the clerks in the freight office, he was most notorious for treating patrons "rough," especially when it fell to him to advise them about demurrage charges, a new tariff which had just been established by the Michigan Central and which was bitterly resented by most of the patrons. "The way Jim Couzens talked with these patrons on the telephone, giving them holy hell, was just astounding," recalled an associate at the freight house.[12]

With Alex Y. Malcomson, a coal dealer, he had had some of his more heroic rows over demurrage charges. But rather than resenting Couzens' blistering way of laying down the law to him, Malcomson admired it. Malcomson obviously concluded that here was an employee who really looked after an employer's interests. To the amazement of nearly everyone, Malcomson one day offered a job to Couzens.

In October 1895 Couzens went to work for the Malcomson Fuel Company as assistant bookkeeper, private car-checker, and all-around general factotum, for which he was to receive seventy-five dollars a month.[13]

CHAPTER V

THE COAL CLERK

In 1895, Alex Y. Malcomson was a restless, energetic Scot with a lean, though well-built, body and a long nose framed by mutton-chop whiskers that gave him the look of a successful merchant going full-steam ahead. And this was true—fortunately true, in a material sense, for the new office factotum, James Couzens.

Because of what the future then had in store, Malcomson was a figure who deserves to be remembered in the history of Detroit, for his own major role as well as for his influence upon the careers of some important and better-known Detroiters. Yet, curiously, so industrious a gatherer of facts as John Gunther, in 1947, wrote in his book *Inside U.S.A.:* "I would like very much to know what happened to a man named Alex Y. Malcomson. . . . It seems that he was a coal dealer, and Couzens was a clerk in his office. . . . I was unable to find anybody in Detroit who knew . . . about Mr. Malcomson." [1] In 1895, however, and for at least two decades afterwards, few Detroit businessmen were much better known in the city's commercial circles.[2]

2

Malcomson in the 1890's typified in many respects the enterprising American businessman more accurately than the Goulds, Wanamakers, or Vanderbilts. Lacking their capital, he, too, as one of his sons recalled, was "the plunger type, a man who did not hesitate to take chances." And he was constantly looking for chances to take.[3] Starting with a small grocery in Detroit, he switched to coal, soon bought out several competitors, merged them into his business, and laid plans to make his mark in higher reaches of Detroit business.

About two years before Couzens went to work for him, Malcomson, during a coal strike, had staged a business *coup* that was the talk of the trade. Most other dealers had no coal to sell and he had very little. But he learned that the Detroit gas company had a surplus and arranged to distribute the gas company's coal to consumers, on commission, at somewhat inflated prices. "He made a handsome profit," admiringly reported the *Detroit Free Press* a little later in a "puff piece" on Malcomson.[4]

3

Between Couzens and Malcomson there developed something more than an ordinary relationship. They were in emotional ways like father and son. At times, this was uncomfortable for Couzens, as well as for Malcomson, since it turned out that Malcomson had certain character traits that were strikingly similar to those of Couzens' own father. "He had a fiery temper and would blow up fiercely when anyone did something he considered wrong or stupid." [5] So one of Malcomson's sons recalled.

Couzens was often on the receiving end of Malcomson's outbursts. Once Malcomson called him a liar. Red-necked, then redfaced, Couzens flung his office keys at Malcomson and announced that he had "quit." Not until Malcomson had humbled himself by sending him a note asking him to return, did Couzens go back.[6]

There were other such incidents, enough to justify the comment, "How Malcomson and Couzens managed to remain affiliated is one of the mysteries of destiny." [7]

But they did remain together at the coal company for nearly eight years.

It could not have escaped Malcomson, who seemed himself to receive more gratification from the "game" of business than from the monetary rewards, that in trim, bespectacled James Couzens he had an employe who really did not work for pay, but from the love of work. He had what to any employer would have been a "find," what some would call a "jewel," a man to be kept at almost any cost.

True, young James Couzens, his eyes still firmly set on his old goal, one measured by monetary rewards, wanted what compensation was coming to him. It is also true that he intended to ask for and to get much more than he was then making. But it was clear that this transplanted Canadian, so fully trained in the philosophy of work by his Chatham parents, did his work because work was then his basic philosophy. And Malcomson, of course, liked that.

CHAPTER VI

THE FAMILY MAN

EVEN before leaving the Michigan Central, Couzens had found the girl he had been looking for. She was Margaret Manning, a widow's daughter, from a family fairly well known in Detroit. Her uncle was Aaron A. Parker, a banker and head of the White Star shipping line, which operated ships on the Great Lakes from Detroit. A nephew of hers, John C. Manning, later became one of the city's best-known newspapermen, the editor of the *Detroit Times*.

A good-looking young woman, possessed of a lively nature, Margaret Manning also had a practical outlook on life that suggested strength of character. Thus, this blue-eyed Margaret was good company, without being giddy—the only kind of girl in whom young Couzens, so serious for all his handsome appearance, could possibly have become interested. Probably more than he realized, she reminded him of his own mother, both physically and because of her serene manner—a factor that undoubtedly drew him strongly to her.

They had met through another girl, Margaret's cousin, whom he had been squiring casually on his days off. But soon after meeting Margaret, he stopped seeing her cousin. His bicycle, a prized new possession, began to be parked in front of the Manning residence with noticeable regularity.[1]

2

Not long afterward, he took a room in Margaret's home, for her mother had adopted the custom followed then by many families of renting extra rooms in their oversized houses to "suitable persons." Young Mr. Couzens certainly was recommended by Margaret as "suitable."

He began taking Margaret bicycling on Belle Isle—the way many romances started in the Detroit of that day. Sometimes wearing a derby, sometimes a cap, he talked to her earnestly of his hopes for rising in the world. He found Margaret a good, as well as a willing, listener. A few more months and it was understood that Mrs. Manning's lodger was Margaret's "young man." Finally, one afternoon in the winter of 1897, on the last visit of the season to Belle Isle, he proposed to her. As he expected, Margaret said yes.[2]

3

There was one problem: the Mannings were devout Roman Catholics. Actually, so far as Couzens was concerned, this was only an opportunity that he welcomed to deliver to his father another and quite final declaration of independence. For, although his mother accepted the religious situation calmly, his father, the Presbyterian elder in Chatham, was horrified by the idea that his son intended to marry a "Papist." He said he would never permit it. But Couzens firmly and coldly replied that he intended to go ahead with the marriage.

As for Margaret and her family, they, too, had a similar religious problem. For Couzens, although not a churchgoer (too much of that in Chatham, under the lash of his father, had cured him, he once said), had no intention of embracing Catholicism.

Bishop John F. Foley of the Catholic diocese of Detroit was a friend of the Manning family. He was consulted and suggested that Margaret's "Presbyterian young man" call on him. "The Bishop took a liking to him, and gave his approval to the marriage," [3] with Couzens agreeing, of course, that any children of the marriage were to be brought up in the faith of the Roman Catholic Church.

On August 31, 1898, when Couzens had just turned twenty-six, Bishop Foley celebrated the marriage sacrament at the Manning home.

They took the conventional trip to Niagara Falls for their honeymoon, after which they made their home with Margaret's mother. Couzens did not like staying on at the Manning home. But his income, still seventy-five dollars a month, made it the prudent thing to do. However, in agreeing to stay, he made a family rule: Margaret, for her part, had to agree that they would live within *his* income, no matter what it was. She was not to receive any money from her family. "He simply would not stand for it." [4]

4

A few months before his marriage he had gone to the federal building in downtown Detroit to attend to another matter of personal importance. This was to give up his status as a subject of Great Britain, by renouncing his allegiance to Queen Victoria, to become a naturalized citizen of the United States. He had intended to do this for some time, for he clearly never considered going back to Canada to live.

5

The War with Spain was then on. Though a puny affair, it nonetheless was a shot in the arm for business generally. The new prosperity directly affected Couzens, for in one of his periodic spurts of optimism, this time produced by the war activity, Malcomson had acquired a coal business in Toledo, the Crescent Fuel Company. Deciding that Couzens should be his manager in Toledo, he sent him there and raised his pay to one hundred dollars a month. For Couzens, this change held the promise of prosperity and even of some independence. But the bright prospect soon was overshadowed. Margaret became ill shortly after they had established themselves in Toledo, and Couzens was forced to ask Malcomson to let him resume the old job in Detroit so Margaret could be near her mother. Again they went to live with Mrs. Manning.

Then came a sadder occurrence. As part of their preparation for a child, they had arranged for a home of their own, renting, at twenty-one dollars a month, a "terrace" on West Grand Boulevard, just off Fourteenth Avenue. The child, a son, was born in the spring of 1899, but it died almost at once.

In the following year, Margaret gave birth to a second child, another boy, who turned out to be an extraordinarily healthy, bright youngster. They called him Homer. Then began for Couzens "the happiest period" of his life, as he himself described it. He became, in fact, almost a different man—at home. Whereas, to the outside world, he still displayed, like a trade-mark, his don't-tread-on-me manner, at home he relaxed almost completely, romped with the boy, and enjoyed being called "Daddy Jim." [5]

Margaret Couzens proved a perfect companion for him. He seemed, literally, to worship her.[6] With her he was the soul of affability and deference, just as his father had been to his mother. With nearly everyone else he still, constantly, asserted his spirit of belligerent independence. "He had a direct, blunt way of speaking to fellow employees and to customers. He expected to be obeyed without any question," said a stenographer at the Malcomson Fuel Company.[7] He was not much different in that job than he had been at the Michigan Central before his marriage, when "no one could tell him what to do." But he actually encouraged Mrs. Couzens to boss him, something that would have amazed his old railroad co-workers. He appeared to derive a kind of serenity from being bossed by Margaret. She even communicated to him, when she was with him, some of her own serenity. He was, recalled an intimate, "The perfect family man." [8]

6

In 1902 another son, Frank, was born. By then, he was much more than just a clerk at Malcomson's. Though without the title, he was really the manager, as everyone understood. Despite all his single-minded devotion to work, however, his income was then only eighteen hundred dollars a year. This was neither enough for his family's needs nor for his ego. The turn of the century seemed a time of prosperity for the nation generally, but little of it had drifted his way. Detroit was growing. Skyscrapers were going up. A new, although still quite infant industry, automobile manufacturing, had developed. Yet he seemed to be standing still. He considered taking up law and began reading law books at night. A lawyer's career appealed to him as one way of increasing his earning capacity, and also of meeting his greatest need—to be on his own.[9]

CHAPTER VII

THE FORD MOTOR COMPANY

SIMILARLY driven by ambition, Malcomson also was restless. He had lately invested some money in an icebox scheme, only to suffer a failure that cost him several thousand dollars. Couzens lost in the venture too, having put in $100.

In 1902 Malcomson eyed a new business, in connection with which he was seeing much of the spare, angular man named Henry Ford.

Malcomson had known Ford from the days when Ford had been employed as an engineer by the Detroit electric light company and had bought coal for the light company from Malcomson. After resigning that job in 1899, Ford continued to buy coal from Malcomson for his home.

By 1902 Ford had already been in and out of two automobile ventures. His first was the Detroit Automobile Company, formed by a group of Detroit businessmen to produce automobiles from a model that Ford had developed. Later Ford referred to his backers in this company as "a group of men of speculative turn of mind," whose "main idea seemed to be to get the money." [1] They had an agreement with him to build at least ten automobiles on a budget of $10,000, yet this sum "didn't pay for one." [2]

The main trouble apparently was that Ford was "a perfectionist." He could not bring himself to the point of letting the company go into production, for he kept wanting to make changes.[3] An illustration of this trait of Ford's occurred when Henry B. Joy, who later formed the Packard Motor Company, wanted to buy a car and was discouraged from doing so by Ford himself, who said his car was not yet good enough. Little wonder that the "men of speculative turn of mind" became impatient. They gave Ford, as it was put, "an opportunity to resign." [4] As some of these men went on to form the company which became the Cadillac Motor Company, the first Cadillac was, in a sense, really a Ford.[5]

In November 1901 the Henry Ford Company was incorporated, organized around still another car designed by Ford and including some of the men who had been in the Detroit Automobile Company. A company which most histories of Ford ignore, the Henry Ford Company apparently turned out only one or two racing machines; then, as stated in a newspaper article, it died of inanition.[6]

So in 1902 Ford was at loose ends, but still hopeful. He had won some fame as an automobile racer. But many called him a "nut," while some persons derided him as "Crazy Ford."[7]

Malcomson had about the same esteem for Ford the man as other businessmen in Detroit at this time—that is to say, he did not esteem him highly. The general attitude can be illustrated by an incident which occurred when Ford was working on his first car. He had to buy parts from Strelinger's hardware store, where his credit was strictly limited to fifteen dollars. He wanted to make a larger purchase. "Fifteen is the limit," the storekeeper said.[8]

But Malcomson had made some careful inquiries about the kind of automobile Ford had designed, a runabout with an opposed-type two-cylinder motor in the rear. What he learned impressed him. He began thinking about financing Ford's car. Ford was more than willing. After many cautious talks, Malcomson decided in August 1902 to give Ford a third whirl at the automobile "game." But it was Malcomson's idea to "promote" Ford's car by himself—no other financial backers were to be in the scheme—and this appealed to Ford.

Ford had calculated that it would take $3,000 for him to complete a new model. Malcomson agreed to put up this amount, and also to arrange for any further financing that might be necessary. Malcomson was to have a half interest in the car, and he and Ford "were to share the emoluments and the profits of their joint venture equally." There was to be no "Ford Motor Company"—only a Malcomson-Ford partnership.[9]

That was the way the agreement was drawn up on the hot Saturday afternoon of August 16, 1902, in the law offices of John Wendell Anderson and Horace Rackham, two young members of the Detroit Bar whose main client was Malcomson's coal company, for which they handled, principally, the "bad accounts."[10]

2

And what about Malcomson's chief clerk? Couzens did not share his employer's enthusiasm for automobiles. Several times he had noticed Ford, then wearing a mustache, in the Malcomson office, and he knew that Ford was a customer. But he paid very little attention to him, not finding him then a man worth much attention. Back about 1892, when Couzens was still living at the Amos House, his path had crossed Ford's, for Couzens used to visit the gym of the Railroad Y.M.C.A. and, for a time, Ford taught a class in mechanics there to earn some extra money.[11] It is certain that Couzens would have paid no attention to Ford's class at the "Y," for he had not the slightest mechanical bent. "Malcomson used to take me out in his car sometimes and frequently he turned something on the dash board, explaining to me that he was changing the mixture," he once said. "I thought that he meant he was mixing water with the gasoline, and I continued to think so for a long time." [12]

But Couzens was greatly interested in Malcomson's new plans. They were bound to affect him, for he understood that Malcomson was prepared to pledge all his credit to get this automobile venture going. And if the automobile business failed, the coal business would go under too. But if the automobile venture succeeded, Couzens might find himself running the coal company, for Malcomson had already hinted that he planned to devote nearly all his time to the exciting new business. He had told Couzens that he would give him more responsibility at the coal office, a raise in pay, and a bonus of $1,000, if the coal office did a business of a certain amount in the next twelve months.[13]

3

There was another factor that brought Couzens directly into the picture. Malcomson wanted his dealings with Ford kept secret. He was afraid his credit with the banks would be injured if it were publicly known that he was backing anything "so risky" as an automobile venture.[14]

So Malcomson's money for the Ford project was placed in a bank in Couzens' name.

Malcomson also assigned to Couzens the duty of "checking up" on Ford's expenditures. "As Ford's bills piled up and finally went over the $3,000 limit, I warned Malcomson many a time," [15] he said.

Before long, Couzens was so much a part of the project that Malcomson brought him into most of the negotiations for getting cars produced.

He was no passive onlooker. This came out explosively at a meeting with John and Horace Dodge. These brothers, later to be famous as motorcar makers in their own right, owned a machine shop and were brought in to make the chassis for the Ford cars, as they already were doing for Ransom E. Olds.[16] At a session with Malcomson, Ford, and Couzens, John Dodge asked for certain provisions in the contemplated contract.

"I won't stand for that!" Couzens declared.

Not many persons had ever dared to talk that bluntly to muscular, brusque John Dodge.

"Who in hell are you?" demanded Dodge.

"That's all right," Malcomson said, "Couzens is my adviser in this." [17]

4

When finally signed, the contract called for the Dodge brothers to produce, within a year, 650 chassis at $250 each—a commitment, in this one instance, of $162,500. Other parts, such as bodies, wheels, and tires, plus costs for promotion, brought the total of Malcomson's obligations to about $350,000.[18]

No such sum was in Malcomson's possession. He even lacked, in ready cash, the $10,000 which he had agreed to pay the Dodges, on account, once they started actual production.

Malcomson counted on "a perfect craze" for automobiles on the part of the public to carry him through safely.[19] He expected to sell the completed cars as soon as they were assembled, and then pay off his suppliers out of sales. He determined—a crucial decision—that a factory would not be needed, only a place for assembling the various parts, work for which even a barn would do. Everything would be made outside the assembly plant. *Thus no investment in machinery would be required.* By selling the cars for $850 (the price of the Cadillac) he figured on a profit of at least $95,000 on the first lot.[20]

On paper Malcomson's optimism seemed wholly justified. Soon, however, trouble developed. Couzens advised him that "Ford's bills" totaled $7,000, or $4,000 above the agreed limit. Then the Dodge brothers began demanding the $10,000 payment. Malcomson succeeded in stalling them for a time. But as the Dodge brothers grew more insistent, Malcomson decided to trim his sails somewhat. In November 1902 he moved to enlist some outside financial support after all. His plan was to sell some shares in his half of the partnership. He had new articles of partnership drawn up; these provided for a company to be called "The Malcomson-Ford Company, Ltd." [21]

"But everybody shied off from his stock," so Couzens said later,[22] and the original precarious arrangement had to stand—at least for a while.

5

In February 1903 Malcomson persuaded the Dodges to wait for their $10,000 until they had delivered some chassis. He boldly inserted large advertisements in trade papers concerning what he called "The Fordmobile," advertisements signed "The Fordmobile Company, Ltd." There was no such car and no such company. Both were merely reflections of Malcomson's desperate hope that this advertising would bring some advance orders for the car—and perhaps some cash in advance.[23]

He did get orders—but no cash.

As the date neared for the Dodge brothers to deliver the first chassis, Malcomson lost some of his nerve. He talked with the owners of the Daisy Air Rifle Company about having them take over his commitments, with the view of making the Ford car in their air-rifle plant at Plymouth, Michigan. He offered to give them half his interest.

There was some earnest talk of the car being called "The Daisy." But Ford objected and told Malcomson his car had to be called a "Ford." The plan fell through anyway, when the Daisy people decided against taking the chance. The whole business of making automobiles seemed too risky. Besides, one of the air-rifle company principals was interested in putting money in some land in one of the Southern states. Mississippi land seemed to him a much better bet than the Ford-Malcomson automobile deal.[24]

Then the Dodges issued an ultimatum. If Malcomson could not live up to his contract with them, they would produce and market the car themselves.[25]

Facing this threat, Malcomson decided he had to abandon the partnership idea entirely. He would have to make a clean breast of things to his bankers and organize a stock company after all. He called on John S. Gray, president of the German-American Bank of Detroit, who was related to him and whose bank did most of Malcomson's coal-business financing. Malcomson wanted two things from banker Gray. He wanted money—enough to pay the Dodge brothers —and he wanted Gray himself to join the company, for he believed that Gray's name would serve to attract other investors.

6

John Gray was aghast. Only a short time before, Malcomson had obtained considerable credit from Gray's bank for another merger, consolidation of the Malcomson Fuel Company with Jewett, Bigelow and Brooks.[26] Gray now suspected that he had cause to be worried about that loan.

"I want you to go out to the Dodge place this afternoon and see what is being done," Malcomson urged.

Gray went, but when Malcomson urged him to join in the venture, the banker refused.[27] "Invest in a horseless carriage?" he snorted. "Asinine folly!" Now it was Malcomson who seemed "crazy."

"Put up some money and I'll guarantee it to you any time within a year," Malcomson said.

"You mean if I am dissatisfied, at any time, I can call on you for the money?" Gray asked.

"Yes," said Malcomson.[28]

Under this arrangement, what did Gray have to lose? He agreed to put up $10,000 personally, but he still had profound misgivings despite Malcomson's "guarantee," never dreaming that what would later be known as "the fabulous Gray estate" was being founded by him that day.

7

On the strength of Gray's interest, Albert Strelow, who ran a carpenter shop, was persuaded by Malcomson to put up $5,000, and also to provide the shack in which the automobiles were to be assembled. Vernon Fry, a dry-goods merchant whom Malcomson knew as a fellow church member, was taken for a ride in Ford's runabout in an effort to interest him. He "was scared to death," but finally told Malcomson to put him down for $5,000 too. Charles T. Bennett of the Daisy Air Rifle Company then agreed to invest $5,000 as a personal matter, and the two lawyers, Anderson and Rackham, agreed to pledge $5,000 each.

To get his $5,000, young Anderson, who had studied at Cornell and graduated from the University of Michigan Law School—a spare, well-dressed barrister who parted his hair stylishly in the middle—wrote a glowing letter to his father, a physician in LaCrosse, Wisconsin. Dr. Wendell Anderson was "somewhat skeptical." But having a strong affection for his lawyer-son, he could not bear to turn down the touch.[29] Rackham, who always looked like something of a farmer, raised his $5,000 by selling a piece of Detroit land he had acquired. "What finally decided me," Rackham recalled, "was a bundle of letters, most of them bona fide orders for cars, which Malcomson and Couzens showed me." [30] C. J. Woodall, a junior clerk at Malcomson's, put up $1,000. And the Dodges finally said that, in lieu of the $10,000 owed them, they would take $10,000 worth of shares.[31]

8

And Couzens? In his and Margaret's bank account, he had just $400.

He told John Anderson that he intended to "beg, borrow, or steal" all the money he could, to be well represented in the venture.[32] But from whom?

His wife's mother had a nest egg of $15,000. He talked with her about a loan of a size that would have made him one of the biggest investors of all. There was a family meeting on the question. Mrs. Manning hesitated, for she recalled "Jim's icebox failure," the venture with Malcomson.

In the end, however, she agreed to a loan of some figure, but suddenly, at that moment, he decided that he could not bring himself to borrow from his mother-in-law after all. He simply could not be beholden to her in that way.[33]

9

There was his father in Chatham, but to borrow from him struck Couzens as being almost as distasteful. Yet he swallowed his pride and made the trip across the river to Chatham. He knew that, like his mother-in-law, his father had a nest egg, though not as much as $15,000. The elder Couzens had come a fairly long way from the time when he was a dollar-a-day laborer at a soap works. But he quickly and tartly demonstrated that he had no intention of parting with any of his funds, not even on a loan, for any such foolish enterprise as his son described to him.

"You should not even invest your own money!" the elder Couzens exclaimed.[34]

Rosetta Couzens had $300, saved from her earnings as a public-school teacher in Chatham. She was willing to lend that to her brother. But again, the father raised heated objections. Finally, Rosetta compromised and offered $150. "But he wanted it in even hundreds, so I gave him $100." [35]

Couzens returned to Detroit with the disappointing conviction that all he could invest was $500—his $400 and his sister's $100. Luckily, he found Malcomson in one of his expansive moods. Malcomson agreed to advance him $500 on his expected bonus, and also arranged for acceptance of a promissory note of $1,500. Thus, among the twelve shareholders—Alex Y. Malcomson and eleven disciples, so to speak—Couzens finally was recorded as a holder of $2,500 worth of stock.[36] In Couzens' view, there actually should have been thirteen shareholders, counting his sister Rosetta. But Ford objected strenuously to a woman being allowed in the enterprise— any woman—so Couzens carried Rosetta's one share in his own name.[37]

It irked Couzens that, except for the junior clerk, Woodall, he was low man on the shareholders' list, and it is probable that he suspected Woodall's interest was really a "blind" for Malcomson— a way for Malcomson to have a bigger interest than Ford. But there was no way for Couzens to improve his position at the time, and so he made the best of it, while making a mental note to correct this matter some time in the future.

10

On June 16, 1903, the Ford Motor Company was incorporated. Two days later, the twelve stockholders held an organizational meeting at the Russel House, a Detroit hotel.

Malcomson had expected to be chosen president. But that office went to banker Gray—an irony, in view of Ford's later attitude toward bankers—and Malcomson was named treasurer.

Ford was not even considered for president. Everyone concerned, even Ford, agreed that to have Ford as president would probably have been fatal to the financial rating of the new company. Instead, he was given the title of vice-president and general manager in charge of mechanics and production.[38]

The posts of business manager, in active charge of all business affairs of the new company, as well as of secretary, went to Couzens.[39] This was another disappointment for Malcomson, who had intended to be the business manager himself. His plan was to have Couzens run the coal office, but John S. Gray, still worrying about his bank's loans to the Malcomson Fuel Company, decided matters otherwise. "I am putting up my money because you are a good coal man," Gray told Malcomson. "You must stay in the coal business."

Malcomson argued that the coal business would be safe with Couzens in charge. He praised Couzens' extraordinary ability. "If Couzens is so good," said Gray, "then you can send him to the automobile business. He can watch that for you." [40]

Malcomson had no answer to this, and the decision that was finally made was in line with John Anderson's report on June 4, 1903, to his father in LaCrosse:

"Mr. Couzens . . . is going to leave the coal business, for the present at least, and devote his entire time to the office and management of the automobile business. And he is a crackerjack." [41]

CHAPTER VIII

THE BUSINESS MANAGER

As THOUGH by instinct the "crackerjack" paired off with Ford after the organizational meeting. Ford volunteered to take Couzens home in his odd-looking, tiller-steered runabout, and Couzens accepted the invitation. For the Ford Motor Company, this was the real beginning—and also for the two "partners," as, in due time, they would be called.

Up to that moment they had not had much to do with each other. "In the beginning, I did not esteem Couzens highly," Ford recalled.[1] As for Couzens, it has already been noted that he had no better opinion of Ford. Now things between them were different.

Ford had special reasons for seeking to cultivate Couzens. It obviously bothered him that his associates in the company were strong men who could out-talk him and, so long as he owned only a fraction more than a quarter of the stock, out-vote him. He felt the need of support, as he would often in the future. Only then could he function.[2] And Couzens seemed to be his man, for he would feel much less like a lamb among lions if Couzens were lined up with him. "He does his own thinking, no one could tell him what to do," Ford later said, and he appreciated that quality in Couzens—then.

For his part Couzens also was looking to the future. He seemed to recognize almost at once that his future lay more with Ford than with Malcomson. With Malcomson he would always have had to maintain a junior relationship, or leave him. But with Ford, he could expect a more equal relationship, even an equal one. Or so he thought. Besides, whether he realized it or not, he was psychologically attracted by Ford's apparent meekness, the easygoing ways that made him appear so different from Malcomson, the side of his personality that Ford usually showed at this time.[3]

44

2

As they bounced along that evening in Ford's car, both wearing derbies—Ford's somewhat at an angle over his birdlike face, Couzens' square, firm, and level on his solid head—they talked of their plans. Among other matters, they discussed the salary each might expect from the new company. Couzens suggested $3,000 a year for Ford, $2,400 for himself. Ford, the mechanic, wondered if $3,000 were not too much.

"No," said Couzens, the businessman. "This could be an important project." [4]

Ford's way of introducing to Couzens the matter of salaries was especially interesting: "What do you think we ought to ask from *those fellows?*" Couzens of course caught on to Ford's meaning. On one side there was to be Ford and Couzens; on the other, "those fellows." Already there was a division in the new company, and Ford also made some vague remarks, that June night, which caused Couzens later to believe he had said as well: "If this succeeds, I will go fifty-fifty with you." [5]

3

The next day the two managers began working together. The place was Strelow's barnlike carpenter shop on Mack Avenue, on which was painted a sign that read: FORD MOTOR COMPANY.

There were as yet no cars. There were only space and some un-assembled parts. The motors and chassis were in a state of "being," at the Dodge brothers' machine shop. This, of course, was by design, for Malcomson's original idea was adhered to. The company was to make no pretense of being a manufacturing concern. It was to be only an assembling and selling organization. This was agreeable to Ford as well as to the others. "If the automobile craze goes to smash, I don't want my money tied up in walls and machinery," [6] Ford said.

But the "craze" did not "go to smash." The new business "moved along almost as by magic," as Ford remembered it.[7] The "magic" lay, in the main, in the public demand for automobiles—any kind of automobiles. It was a demand that no automobile manufacturer up to then had been able to satisfy.

Specifically, for the new company the magic lay in those advance orders Malcomson had obtained from his desperate advertising. "One dealer from Buffalo was here last week and ordered twenty-five. Three were ordered today, and other orders have begun to come in every day," Anderson reported.[8]

To assist in assembling the cars, C. Harold Wills, of the defunct "Henry Ford Company," a tall, dynamic, and resourceful man, was brought in to serve as a sort of foreman over about half a dozen hastily recruited mechanics.[9] Both Ford and Wills maintained a heroic pace in the assembly work to keep pace with the production activity of the Dodge brothers.

4

Speed was essential. In those days cars were sold mostly during the summer months, and it was already past the middle of June. Moreover, the new company's total working capital was only $28,000 to take care of payrolls, advertising, and the like, for others besides Couzens were represented in the final accounting only by promissory notes.[10] If the first season was muffed, this $28,000 would not be nearly enough.

Yet in "the factory" Ford and Wills labored no harder than did Couzens in "the business office." Most of the time he was on the job in the office and sales room of the plant from seven in the morning until after eleven at night.[11]

Couzens also played an important role in the production phase, for Ford's old perfectionism came close to endangering his third venture before it was even under way. Because he felt "they were not yet as good as he could make them," Ford held up shipment of the first cars. Couzens put his foot down—his first, but not his last, crucial act in the company. He insisted that the cars must go out so that money would come in.[12] He was not going to let Ford do to this company what he apparently had done to the Detroit Automobile Company. For a long time, the point has been made by automobile, and other, historians that Ford was very different in 1903 from the way he had been in 1902 in the matter of getting the cars out. In 1950, one such historian, Milo M. Quaife, commented: "How to account for this sudden change of attitude on the part of Mr. Ford is still a subject of speculation. As good a guess as any would be that he was now subject to the influence of such aggressive action as Couzens and John and Horace Dodge." [13]

5

To make doubly certain that there was no slip, Couzens even joined Ford and Wills in the manual task of getting the first cars to the railroad freight station. He helped to crate them and to nail the doors of the freight car. Then, putting back on his black, four-button jacket, he went to the bank to draw sight drafts on purchasers in Indianapolis, Minneapolis, and St. Paul, to whom those first cars were shipped on July 23, 1903.[14]

At last the new Ford company was on its way.

But once again, Ford's perfectionism threatened the venture. Shortly after the first cars had been delivered, complaints began coming in. Some of the cars would not climb even modest hills. Couzens knew by personal experience the validity of these complaints. When John Anderson's father came up from LaCrosse to visit the plant, Couzens volunteered to drive him to the railroad station. "On the way, he attempted to drive through a small park, but the car stalled at a little hill and after frequent attempts to cross the hill, Mr. Couzens was forced to detour around the block," said Dr. Anderson.[15] Ford was mortified and said that all shipments must be halted immediately.

Again Couzens took a firm stand. If necessary, mechanics should be sent to the customers to work on their cars, but he insisted that the cars must go out. "Stop shipping and we go brankrupt."

Couzens' judgment again prevailed,[16] and re-orders came in from the dealers.

6

The company's first "annual statement" was prepared by Couzens as of October 1, 1903. Sales from July 23 to September 30 totaled $142,481.72. Profits were estimated at $36,957.64.

In November 1903, on the basis of this showing, the directors voted for a dividend of 10 per cent. Couzens was given a new title, "Sales Manager," and his salary was increased from $2,400 to $3,000 a year. He was also authorized to employ a stenographer.

Another dividend, this time of 20 per cent, was voted at the first directors' meeting held in 1904. On the company's first anniversary, by which time a thousand cars had been sold, the directors celebrated with a dividend of 68 per cent.[17] Everyone in the enterprise had by that time taken out nearly 100 per cent. "Ford and I then declared our independence," Couzens commented later. They felt that they now had rights above the others. They were the producers; the others were "coupon clippers," and they intended that the distinction should be recognized.[18]

7

As the year 1904 was closing, the company moved to its own four-story building at Piquette and Beaubien Streets. For the first time, the company began to manufacture its own small parts.[19]

On June 16, 1905, a cash dividend of 100 per cent was declared. This was followed by another of the same size only one month later. Two hundred per cent in one year, nearly 300 per cent since the company had been organized only two years before! [20]

Perhaps "magic" was a factor, but it was not only magic. As put by one informed Ford Company employee: "Everyone worked like dogs, early and late, without regard to the hours of service or where they had to go to do it." [21] And Couzens was the pace setter. "In those days," said the *Ford Times,* "J.C. was the entire office management— he hired and fired—he kept the books, collected, spent, and saved the cash, established agencies, and dictated policy."

The company paper added that what Couzens did was too much "for most men but he did it." [22] Garet Garrett, a specialist in writing about business, who for many years paid great attention to the Ford Company, perhaps told the whole story best and most pungently when, in 1952, in his book *The Wild Wheel,* he summarized Couzens' role: "From the beginning . . . James Couzens had been the great he-person in the Ford organization. His gifts were four—a genius for the role of ringmaster in the arena of business, an immense store of energy, a terrible temper and leonine roaring pouches." [23]

CHAPTER IX

THE CLOUD

BY 1903, at least 145 other automobile firms had been founded in the United States. Already, despite the public's continued interest in motoring, most of them had disappeared. "Look at the constantly lengthening list of 'dead ones' in the automobile trade," the *Automobile Magazine* warned in December 1903. At that time the Ford car was not priced lower than a number of other cars—indeed, it cost more than some. Then what did the Ford Motor Company have that kept it alive?

In 1908, the *Ford Times* itself gave one answer: "While Henry Ford had the right car and inexhaustible confidence, push, and fight, it has been Mr. Couzens who has had to meet and solve those problems which daily confront every business enterprise and ruin or make it, according to the way they are met." [1]

How carefully Couzens looked after details is shown by some entries in a notebook he kept: "Boston says March telephone bill not paid, $6.69." "Mail Robbins check." "Get one bond for Block." "Philadelphia needs trouble-locater." "Radiator leaking." "Nuts on lamps hurt in cranking." "Cushion on rear seat not fastened." "Battery box off." "Wood-screws on fenders don't hold." "The gears on Buffalo K absolutely abominable." [2]

The production men heard about such things from him.

2

With dealers, if not with the public, he turned out to be a kind of supersalesman. Charles T. Bennett saw him in operation at the plant. "A man came in from a West Coast city to inquire about being a dealer. He had in mind ordering one car. Mr. Couzens asked him for the population of his town and when he learned the answer, said, 'For a town that size you ought to order 100 cars!' He talked the man into doing just that, and what's more, collected in advance for the ordered cars." [3]

He also demonstrated a keen sense for picking dealers and salesmen who would be hustlers like himself—men like urbane Gaston Plantiff in New York, knowing Louis Block in Philadelphia, hustling Tom Hay in Chicago, and ubiquitous Guy Herring in Des Moines, pillars of the Ford sales hierarchy for years. He personally selected all the Ford dealers and salesmen.

Couzens also made several innovations in organizing his sales force. Key sales points were manned by salaried employes rather than by independent agents. He called them branch managers, and they took instructions directly from him. William C. Durant of the Buick Company (later founder of General Motors) told him that such a plan would not work. "You cannot get a man to work for you as hard as he will work for himself." Couzens said: "We will pay him more than he could possibly earn for himself." [4] And for him, and the Ford Company, this plan worked superbly.

Other departures marked his management. He developed an incentive system. On top of their salaries, the managers received bonuses when sales topped certain figures. This was new for those days.

"If the Ford Company had begun with traditions, no one would know of that company today," Couzens said in 1921. "It made its success by striking out for itself and I imagine if we had only had more experience, we might have gone about our work differently. Certainly we should not have known that many of our most successful innovations could not possibly succeed!" [5]

3

Yet he was a cautious financial administrator. Extensions had to be paid for out of profits, not borrowed money. "It is easy to spend too much when money can be freely borrowed," he said.[6] He learned early not to speculate on materials.

"When we started business we were informed," he recalled, "that it was a safe rule to buy liberally on a rising market and to go slow on a falling market. . . . Time and again we tried it, and time and again we found that in the end we were no better off in price than if we had bought right along as we needed and at the market price. . . . The material speculator is as certain to be hit as the stock speculator." [7]

He set the company's credit policy. As stated in the *Ford Times*, it was:

"The Ford Motor Company never cuts a price, is never a party to a trade deal, does not consider anything but real money in selling cars, quotes no discounts or special allowances and would carry a thousand cars over rather than discount the price." [8]

4

He knew precisely how he wanted company affairs handled. Correspondence had to be taken care of on the dot. Accounts had to be kept precisely. Instructions had to be followed out to the letter. Contracts had to be fulfilled to the last comma. Infractions of such rules brought from him rebukes that made such infractions rare.

He was still a hard man to work for. Success did not soften him. He would remain as he was from now on by deliberate intention as much as by temperament. Like John D. Rockefeller, who once told members of a Bible class not to be "good fellows" because "good fellows end up in the poor houses," he earnestly believed that being a good fellow was incompatible with being a good businessman—perhaps a rationalization of his own temperament. "I am one of those who hold that it is not worthwhile to attempt to be popular. I should prefer to be a hard taskmaster—but a fair one," he once said.[9] "A floor walker in a big department store gets twenty-five or fifty dollars a week because he knows how to be pleasant and shake hands with the trade. But the man in the back room, who buys the goods and runs the business, gets $50,000 to $100,000 a year because *he* knows how *to run* the business." [10]

He prided himself on his fairness to an extreme—a fact that once cost a branch manager a tidy sum. About the time that bonuses were given out, this man wrote to Couzens to tell him what a good manager he was, with the bonus in mind, as Couzens understood. He wrote back: "I had put you down for $21,000 before I received your letter. Your letter has cost you $5,000, because it showed me that you did not trust me to treat you fairly. I have now put you down for $16,000." [11]

5

Indeed, he had become a businessman. He looked the part, too. He had filled out since the days when he had been a slender coal clerk, sitting on a high stool in the window of the Malcomson company. That rather tight look that had characterized his eyes before had now become one of firm assurance.

His face was rounder. He wore his hair, which was carefully parted down the middle, less closely clipped than before. There was about him now not so much the "don't-tread-on-me" manner as "be-careful-or-I-may-tread-on-you."

Milton A. McRae, the Scripps-McRae newspapers executive, met him about this time and made a mental note that "here was a comer," a man with leadership ability.[12] Others were puzzled by his aloof, outwardly cold manner. "In spite of all our meetings, I feel that I really do not know him . . . that there is something in reserve that I do not get at," said James Wilkie, the pharmaceutical merchant and Detroit civic leader.[13] But Ida M. Tarbell, the biographer and industrial historian, who saw him a little later, was not perplexed by his aloof manner. She catalogued him as a man who would leave a mark.[14]

He moved his family into a somewhat better residence on middle-class Frederick Street. In 1904 a daughter, Madeleine, was born. That same year, after paying off his promissory notes in the company, he prudently invested his Ford dividends in a house at 80 Chandler Avenue, for which he paid $7,500. Owner of his own home, father of three children, a key figure in a new industry, he was now, at last, beginning to fulfill the promise of the resourceful, independent boy of Chatham.

6

Yet there remained a cloud.

The company had been born under this cloud, for as early as July 1900 the owners of a certain patent had begun filing suits for infringement against various automobile manufacturers. Moreover, the validity of the patent had been conceded by Alexander Winton, then the leader in the industry. In March 1903 there was formed "The Association of Licensed Automobile Manufacturers," with the avowed purpose of forcing out of business anyone not licensed under the patent.

Not everyone would be licensed, either; the Association intended to practice discrimination.

Malcomson had gone about organizing the Ford Motor Company in ignorance of this patent, as well as of the existence of the Association of Licensed Automobile Manufacturers. In their own excitement, John Anderson and Horace Rackham, his lawyers, had not checked very well the patent status of the automobile, although Anderson later said that he had "made a very careful investigation,

as careful as I thought a man could make, before I ventured my
money in the Ford Motor Company." [15] Had they checked, it is
most probable that they would have held back, and would have
discouraged the others. So this, too, may have been part of the
"magic." Not until a week or so after the Ford Motor Company
was organized did any of the Ford promoters hear about the matter
of the patent.

7

But then, this is what they learned: Back in the early 1870's,
George B. Selden of Rochester, a lawyer with a mechanical turn
of mind, a member of a prominent up-state New York family, had
begun studying horseless locomotion. According to his son, he
was inspired to do this by "some disagreeable experiences" with
horses while serving with the United States cavalry during the Civil
War.[16] His idea was to "construct a light-weight self-propelled vehicle with a large cruising radius, which could be operated by one
man, not a skilled engineer." [17]

Selden at first experimented with a steam engine. Then he turned
to the internal-combustion type. By 1879, he had progressed far
enough to apply for a patent on this latter engine.[18] He had interested
six financial sponsors, but "one of these men died suddenly; another
went into bankruptcy; another became ill; still another met with
an accident. The remainder changed their minds." [19]

Selden then determined to wait for the world to catch up with
him. He contrived to postpone the issuance of a patent, but kept
his application alive through a long series of "amendments." The
patent was issued on March 5, 1899, after he had entered into an
assignment of it to the Columbia and Electric Vehicle Company.

The owners of the Columbia and Electric Vehicle Company were
a group of Wall Street financiers, including William C. Whitney,
who were backing electric automobiles. Apparently they had no
serious intention of producing cars themselves, but they intended to
extract royalties from those who did—at the rate of 5 per cent.

Under the leadership of the Olds Motor Company, a group of
Detroit manufacturers then formed a protective committee. They
had a showdown with Whitney and the others of the Wall Street
group. But instead of challenging the royalty principle, they merely
took it over, after forcing Whitney and his associates to agree to
reduce the royalty from 5 per cent to 1¼ per cent, of which only

three-fifths would go to the patent holders. Two-fifths would go to their committee, which then would undertake to fight infringements and to police the industry.

Among the admitted, even boasted, aims of this committee was a restriction of production. Only manufacturers granted a license could produce cars, and these had to agree to limit the number of cars produced to a figure set by the committee. It was this committee that became "The Association of Licensed Automobile Manufacturers." [20]

Couzens first heard about all this a few days after the Ford Company was established, when John Anderson gloomily reported a conversation he had had with Frederic L. Smith, then head of the Olds organization and later president of the Association of Licensed Automobile Manufacturers. John Anderson, whose middle name of Wendell was an inheritance from the Wendell clan that included Oliver Wendell Holmes, Senior, may have then recalled that he was a descendant of the New Englander who owned the "Wonderful One-Hoss Shay" which Holmes immortalized for having gone to pieces all at once. He may have wondered if the Ford Company, with his investment and its prospects, might not go the same way.[21] For Anderson was convinced by his talk with Smith that he had invested "in a man's size lawsuit, instead of in an automobile company." He suffered "a feeling of gone-ness in his stomach." [22]

The seriousness of the situation became more apparent on July 26, 1903, when an advertisement appeared in the *Detroit Free Press* as follows:

NOTICE

To Manufacturers, Dealers, Importers, Agents and Users of

GASOLINE AUTOMOBILES

United States Patent No. 549, 160 granted to George B. Selden, November 5th, 1895, controls broadly all gasoline automobiles which are accepted as commercially practical. Licenses under this patent have been secured from the owners by the following named manufacturers and importers. . . .

No other manufacturers are authorized to make or sell gasoline automobiles, and any person making, selling, or using such machines made or sold by any unlicensed manufacturers or importers will be liable to prosecution for infringement.

ASSOCIATION OF LICENSED AUTOMOBILE MANUFACTURERS
No. 7 East 42nd Street, New York.[23]

A conference between Smith and the officers of the Ford Motor Company was held at the Russel House. In after years, Smith wrote: "By what miracle that flimsy patent was ever sustained . . . I know not." [24] But at this meeting, he politely, but firmly, repeated: the Ford Company could not stay in business unless licensed. For the Ford organization, he had only one kind of advice: they should go out of business. The Ford people were only assemblers, not manufacturers. Assemblers were not wanted.[25]

Nobody among Smith's listeners said anything for awhile. They had been told that a legal fight for carrying the matter to the highest court would cost at least $40,000, nearly as much as the total investment in the company. And there was no assurance that such a fight could be won. The patent lawyer in Detroit with the best reputation, Ralzemond A. Parker, whom they had consulted, had guessed that the chances of *losing* were high. Some of the Ford stockholders were for yielding to what appeared to be the inevitable. Others, Malcomson included, hoped for some kind of a compromise.

Banker Gray talked moodily. He lamented that now he could not even unload his stock on others because he could not "conscientiously" recommend the shares as being a good investment.[26]

Couzens broke the indecision and gloom. Following the pattern he had established as a boy in Chatham, as a freight clerk at the Michigan Central, and as assistant to Malcomson, he told Smith: "Selden can take his patent and go to Hell with it!"

"Couzens has answered you," said Ford.[27]

CHAPTER X

THE REALIGNMENT

AT THE next directors' meeting it was voted unanimously "to throw down the gauntlet, come what may." [1] Space in newspapers was purchased for denunciations of the Selden patent. These Ford advertisements assured prospective car buyers, "We will protect you." Then, to offset the Licensed Association, the Ford Company took the lead among independent firms in organizing a rival association, "The American Motor Car Manufacturers' Association." Formed at a meeting in New York, this association, for years afterwards a major factor in the industry, picked Couzens for its first president. [2] Thus he became the official voice of the opponents of the "monopoly manufacturers."

In the meantime, he dusted off his old law books and acquired others with which to begin reading law once more—patent law. Before long, he was able to talk on almost equal terms with the patent lawyers and often, at conferences, advised them on procedures and pleadings. [3]

When a trade publication asked the Ford Company for a public statement on its strategy, the answer was abrupt and to the point:

> We regard the claims made under the Selden patent as . . . entirely unwarranted and without foundation in fact. We do not, therefore, propose to respect any such claims, and, if the issue is forced upon us, shall defend not only ourselves but our agents and customers to the fullest extent . . .
>
> Yours Truly,
> J. COUZENS, Secretary [4]

Up to that time the Licensed Association had taken no legal action against the Ford Motor Company. But after the appearance of this letter, it acted. In the U.S. Circuit Court, Southern District of New York, two suits were filed at the same time: one against the

Ford Motor Company, another against its New York agent, C. A. Duerr & Co. A week later another suit was filed against a Ford customer, the O. J. Gude Company, to restrain it from even using a Ford car it had purchased.[5] So the legal issues were joined.

2

The ensuing battle was fought on the propaganda front as well as in court. New advertising barrages that specifically warned the public against the sale, purchase, or use of Fords were set off by the Licensed Association. Any "infraction" would lead to prosecution, these ads said. Fords were barred from the automobile shows held at Madison Square Garden. In reply, the Ford Company then advertised that it would put up surety bonds "to protect dealers, importers, agents and users from any attempt on the part of the TRUST to prevent you from buying the 'car of satisfaction.' " The American Motor Car Association, under Couzens' leadership, held its own annual shows—events that soon rivaled, at least in ballyhoo, the exhibits in Madison Square Garden.

The word "trust" was featured in much of the Ford advertising—shrewd exploitation of what was then becoming a popular political issue, thanks to President Theodore Roosevelt's "trust-busting" program.

On this issue of "monopoly," the Ford Company soon acquired an interesting and powerful ally, John Wanamaker. The great Philadephia and New York merchant, John Wanamaker, had fought a patent war with the so-called bicycle "trust." Now he looked forward to another and similar fight. Already handling Fords in his stores, Wanamaker began to feature them in his advertising. In January 1904 the Licensed Association filed suit against Wanamaker, and he hit back with full-page advertisements saying:

"Get a Ford car and enjoy it. We'll take care of the tomtoms. Don't give $600 to the Bogey man." [6]

3

All this uproar had an unanticipated result—perhaps the most important single thing that happened in the early days of the company. As Couzens said later, "The Selden suit was probably better advertising than anything we could put out." [7]

All the attention given to the controversy made the Ford car the best-known make in the land. Many persons bought Fords because they were the only automobile they had heard about. Others bought Fords because they hated "monopoly," or just to be contrary; still others because "Honest John" Wanamaker said they were good cars.

There was at least one other important result. Both Couzens and Ford came to feel great admiration for Wanamaker, who was then plumping a novel concept of business—that the purpose of business was to render "service to the public," that it was a duty of merchants to distribute products *at the lowest price possible.*

Both Couzens and Ford began to think and talk the same way. The influence of Wanamaker, indeed, may have been the central inspiration for the later, and world-celebrated, concept of the Ford Motor Company—that of producing and selling cars at low cost: the foundation of the mass-production system in heavy industry.

Undoubtedly, too, Couzens' attitude toward "big business" in general, as well as Ford's, was shaped in part by the Wanamaker influence, just as Pingree earlier had left an impression upon Couzens with respect to the labor problem.

Immediately, the fight engendered a crusading spirit on the part of the company and its dealers and salesmen. Ford advertisements reflected a spirit of pugnaciousness that was pure Couzens. A typical Ford announcement in *Harper's* said:

> We hear a lot these days about "hand-made" motor cars. It's funny, but these same concerns who, a year ago, prated of "quality, not quantity," as if the two were incompatible, now build 1,000 to 2,000 cars per year and still expect you to believe it is "hand work," "personal supervision," *and all that sort of rot. . . .*[8]

One day an Ohio Ford dealer telegraphed to Couzens: "My competitor wants to bet $500 that their machine will make a trip to Columbus and return quicker than the Ford Model S. Is it safe to bet?" Couzens answered: "Is it any credit for the United States to whip Venezuela? Take a bet like that with any car selling between $1,500 and $2,500." [9] This spirit paid off in sales, of course.

Yet the Selden cloud was to remain as a vexation and a threat until the courts finally decided the issue. As Horace Rackham observed, "The company could not determine what the future would be." [10]

Gray streaks showed up at Couzens' temples. He began to be tormented for the first time by massively painful migraine headaches. He consumed enormous quantities of aspirin. But he continued to push Ford sales just as if Selden really had gone to Hell with his patent.

And the company kept growing.

4

And Malcomson? In the light of his dominant importance in the formation of the company, it is a curious thing how little he figured in its affairs after the company was launched. This is not to be explained simply by saying that Malcomson was "too busy" at the coal office, nor by the assumption that he was content to let his former assistant take over completely. Nor is it to be explained by the fact that Couzens had demonstrated his ability to take over— true though this was. The fact is that in the genesis of the Ford Motor Company, Malcomson was doomed to play the role of a Moses, with Couzens his Joshua.

Like some of its cars, the Ford Motor Company very early developed "internal trouble." Ford's "those fellows" comment had borne strange fruit. There had come to the surface almost immediately a bad case of temperamental incompatibility. This arose not only between Malcomson and Ford, but also between Malcomson and John and Horace Dodge, and to an extent between Malcomson and Gray.

But it was most acute between Malcomson and Ford. After the first year, neither could abide the other. In the words of Rackham, "Both wanted to be boss." [11] And Ford, as soon would be apparent, was not at all the timid or lackadaisical man he had given the impression of being.

5

So long as the company appeared to be struggling, both Ford and Malcomson suppressed their true feelings, but the first appearance of prosperity brought a change. Directors' meetings became marked by explosive bickering. "There was much pounding on the table, and at times Ford's directors would get up and leave and refuse to come back." [12]

Couzens, not surprisingly, touched off some of these explosions. When Malcomson took an order for an automobile to be delivered to a friend at a discount, it was Couzens who insisted that there should be no discounts to anyone, not even to a friend of Malcomson. "He protested so vigorously that the other stockholders voted to compel Malcomson to pay the difference." [13] Malcomson considered this a personal affront.

In arguments between Ford and Malcomson, Couzens invariably stood with Ford, in accord with the understanding the two of them had reached on that June evening in 1903. Indeed, it became clear that Couzens was Ford's spokesman on all business matters, that if Ford kept silent, but Couzens spoke, it was really Ford, as well as Couzens, speaking. They began to seem like one person, and Malcomson resented this.

Couzens had begun to develop a deeper affection for Ford than he had ever had for Malcomson. Ford seemed to reciprocate that affection, although he did maintain a conscious line beyond which he would not let friendship carry him. Once, early in their relationship, he said to Couzens, "It is a mistake to make or have too strong attachments, because it weakens your will and your character." [14] Few persons ever heard them address each other in any way except "Mr. Ford" and "Mr. Couzens." Yet, T. J. Hay, the Chicago dealer, felt "they were like brothers."

Couzens saw that eventually either Ford or Malcomson would have to leave the company. If he himself wanted to stay, he had to choose sides. Actually, he had no choice, for Malcomson forced matters by his authoritarian and antagonistic attitude toward his protégé. Not long after the business was well under way, Malcomson flatly demanded that Couzens voluntarily return to the coal company.

Couzens refused.[15] At a directors' meeting later, Malcomson moved that Couzens be discharged as business manager.[16] The antagonism was out in the open.

6

There were five directors, each with an equal vote regardless of the amount of stock owned: Malcomson, Ford, John Dodge, John S. Gray, and John Anderson. If he could get two other directors to side with him, Malcomson would win his point about firing Couzens and establish his own supremacy in the company—even over Ford. Ford, of course, stood by Couzens. "I told Malcomson that I did not want him, but that I wanted his man Couzens," he later said.[17] And banker Gray stood by Couzens too.

John Dodge might not have cared too much for Couzens at that time. But, as he once said in court, he "really did not like Malcomson," [18] perhaps because, when the contract with the Dodge brothers had come up for renewal in 1904, Malcomson argued that the Dodges should reduce their price since their risk was less. Couzens had sided with the Dodges in that controversy,[19] and now John Dodge sided with Couzens.

Only John Anderson, Malcomson's lawyer, sided with Malcomson.[20] So Couzens remained as manager.

7

In September 1905 Malcomson raised another row at a directors' meeting because Couzens' salary was raised to $8,000.[21] Obviously, his objection was emotional. That year, the company had earned a net profit of $285,231.94.[22] The other directors voted Malcomson down. After that, even Malcomson had to concede that his own former clerk had supplanted him completely as the dominant businessman of the Ford Motor Company.

Which way the wind was blowing, how firmly the Ford-Couzens alliance had already jelled, was made evident even before this, when the Ford Motor Company of Canada was organized in 1904. In this corporation, Ford was president and Couzens was vice-president. But Malcomson was left out.[23]

In the parent company Malcomson was still treasurer, as well as a principal stockholder. But he really had little to say about policies. Ford and Couzens already had attained, substantially, their planned goal—independence from "those fellows."

Malcomson then did an astonishing thing. He formed another automobile company, the Aero, with himself as president, and set up a plant for turning out air-cooled "Aeros" not far from the Ford factory. Apparently his plan was to use his dividends from the Ford Motor Company for financing his own company, not only to add to his income, but also to show Ford, Couzens, and the others how an automobile company should be operated. Unquestionably, Malcomson took this step in anticipation of his complete separation from the Ford Motor Company, either voluntarily, or by being frozen out despite his large interest.

8

A procedure for freezing, or squeezing, Malcomson, as well as some of the others, out of the company already had been devised in the fall of 1905. This consisted of an interesting plan for organizing another corporation, "The Ford Manufacturing Company."

Ostensibly this second corporation was to make motors and other parts for the Ford Motor Company. Ostensibly, too, its creation was desirable for efficiency, as well as to make any expansion of facilities by the Dodge brothers unnecessary.[24] It was to be wholly controlled by the Ford Motor Company. But there was one important catch. Not all the stockholders in the parent company were to have an interest in the subsidiary. Malcomson, for one, was not to be included. Moreover, matters could be so arranged—for example, by the prices that the Ford Motor Company might pay the Ford Manufacturing Company for motors and parts—that the profits of the original company could be drained off into the subsidiary. Indeed, the subsidiary could swallow up the parent company.

The real purpose of the Ford Manufacturing Company was underlined by a comment made by Banker Gray. Vernon Fry had voiced to him his worries about the possible effect of the subsidiary on the parent company. "I have Mr. Ford's promise," said Gray, "that when they get things straightened out with Mr. Malcomson, the Ford Manufacturing Company is to be taken into the Ford Motor Company, just as if it had never existed." [25]

9

Not long after this plan had been devised, a resolution that formally requested Malcomson to resign as treasurer and as director was adopted by the board of the Ford Motor Company. "Moved by Mr. Rackham and seconded by Mr. Ford," this request was justified, for the record, on the ground that Malcomson's formation of another automobile company was "inimical to the best interest of the company." [26]

In the following week, The Ford Manufacturing Company was officially incorporated.[27] Later, a contract was entered into between it and the Ford Motor Company for it to supply ten thousand engines at a *price not stipulated.* And a building was fitted up for the subsidiary. Besides Ford and Couzens, the incorporators were the Dodge brothers, Rackham, Anderson, Bennett, and Wills.[28] Left out of the subsidiary were Gray, Fry, Strelow, Woodall, and, of course, Malcomson.

The morality of this procedure could be discussed and debated endlessly. Both Ford and Couzens unquestionably owed much to Malcomson. He was the real founder of the Ford Motor Company; he had given both men their start. However, it is doubtful if any of the principals in this drama looked at the matter at the time from the viewpoint of gratitude or loyalty—not even Malcomson. These were businessmen engaged in the game of business, playing the game according to the accepted rules. All played the game the same way and had the same objectives.

10

Malcomson put up a fight. In a letter to the board of directors, he indignantly refused to resign as treasurer and director. He denounced "such occurrences as the recent precipitate action of the board in doubling the manager's [Couzens'] salary, despite protest and without waiting for a full board meeting." Then he criticized bitterly the organization of the Ford Manufacturing Company. It was a scheme, he said, for causing "injury to those stockholders of the motor company that are left on the outside." He threatened a lawsuit to block the manufacturing company plan.[29]

His letter was ordered "placed on file." [30] It appeared that Malcomson had won a victory, for he did not resign as treasurer.

However, when the year 1906 opened, Malcomson was for all practical purposes, except for his ownership of stock, out of the Ford Motor Company. He was concentrating on his own company. And he issued an optimistic statement to the trade press: "We start in 1906, put up a factory and turn out 500 cars in one year. I believe that is a record." [31] It was better than the Ford Motor Company had done. He advertised his product as "The Car of Today, Tomorrow, and for Years to Come." [32]

In that optimistic mood, in May 1906, Malcomson made what later proved one of the great blunders in business history: he sold his one-fourth ownership of the Ford Motor Company to Ford. Couzens handled this deal for Ford.[33] His trump card in the negotiations was the existence of the Ford Manufacturing Company. Malcomson, of course, knew what that meant—that the profits of the Ford Motor Company could be siphoned out of it into the manufacturing company, to the point where Malcomson's one-fourth interest in the parent company could be made worthless.[34] Besides, Malcomson was fearful of the outcome of the Selden case.

He finally agreed to sell his one-fourth interest to Ford for $175,-000. Thus Malcomson, the real founder, in the phraseology of the principal Ford historian, was "jettisoned" from the company. Thus, too, for the first time, Henry Ford won a dominating interest in the company that bore his name. John Gray died in the following

July, and then Ford, also for the first time, received the title of president.

II

Later Malcomson made an effort to re-enter the picture. His two friends, Fry and Bennett, were indignant over the fact that the Ford Manufacturing Company was sold soon afterwards to the Ford Motor Company for $450,000. They decided to pull out, and it was Malcomson who bought their shares.[35] As a legal matter, it was highly questionable if these shares were salable to Malcomson, for each share bore the provision that if it were sold, it had to be offered to another shareholder—the provision that kept the Ford Motor Company a "closed corporation" for decades.[36] And Malcomson was not then a shareholder.

Ford and Couzens took the position that Bennett's and Fry's shares should have been offered to them, or to other shareholders, and that the sale to Malcomson was void. A new controversy with Malcomson ensued.

Couzens in the meantime had gone to Europe to set up agencies in England, France, Holland, Spain, Italy, Denmark, Germany, and Russia. In Denmark, he received a jubilant cablegram from Ford: Malcomson had conceded that the Fry and Bennett stock had to be sold to Ford and Couzens, at five dollars a share for the thousand shares.[37] The Malcomson "trouble" was over, forever.

A little later Couzens bought all of Strelow's shares for $25,000. He succeeded Malcomson as a director and treasurer, and then also assumed the title of general manager. The recorded ownership of the company stood:

Henry Ford	585 shares
James Couzens	110
Gray estate	105
John Dodge	50
Horace E. Dodge	50
J. W. Anderson	50
Horace Rackham	50

At last Couzens had attained his goal of moving up from the bottom of the list of shareholders.

12

After this the *Ford Times* contained as many references to "Mr. Couzens" as it did to "Mr. Ford." It seldom mentioned anyone else.

Everyone close to the company understood that they were the only ones who counted. Not a few understood something else. ". . . They used to tell it around the automobile shows and so forth that Couzens is the brains of the organization. Couzens is the front door. If you want anything you will have to see Couzens. This went on and on, without any inspiration from me. . . ." So Couzens himself said.[38]

Actually, that was how Ford wanted things. If anyone came to Ford about a business matter, he said: "See Mr. Couzens." [39]

Board meetings became perfunctory affairs. "I would not work for a company where the board did much interfering with actions or policies," Couzens said later.[40] In particular, he had in mind the Dodge brothers, and even Ford. The fact was, if the Ford Company then had a boss, the boss was Couzens.[41]

CHAPTER XI

THE MONEY-MAKING MACHINE, II

IN 1907, business in America was generally in a bad way. Mark Twain said this was because Theodore Roosevelt, the President, was a "crazy man." Others said it was because of the financial manipulations by the "trusts." Whatever the cause, the country was gripped by economic panic. The stock ticker even reported that Wanamaker had failed, which, if true, would have been to many businessmen like doom itself. It wasn't true, but Wanamaker's store was in trouble and the bold merchant-king himself wrote in his diary: "Many people think the world is coming to an end so far as money and business are concerned." [1]

Detroit was not spared. Among others, Malcomson's Aero automobile company folded up, although not his coal business. To save Detroit's supposedly strong Union Trust Company (an institution to be recalled later) the hat was passed among Detroit capitalists.[2]

But the Ford Company was not fazed. Indeed, as other automobile companies went bankrupt, the Ford Company in 1907 chalked up its first million-dollar-profit year. In his private notebook, General Manager Couzens made a pleasant entry.

"Net earnings for 1907, $1,331,371.68. Total sales, $5,773,851.38. Percentage of commercial expenses to sales, 3⅗ per cent."

In the next year, Couzens called in the press to make a sensational announcement. The Ford Motor Company's capitalization was to be increased from $100,000 to $2,000,000, or twenty times, to finance its Model T.[3]

2

The Model T was an instantaneous, colossal success. Just why, nobody could explain. Ugly, noisy, often unpredictable, it had defects enough almost to outweigh its draconic virtues. In the beginning, it was not even cheaper than several other cars. For example, when first introduced, it cost as much as the Cadillac. Yet it caught on as had no other car. In all probability, the answer was that it came just at the right moment, when Americans suddenly decided that the automobile was really here to stay. The people wanted cars, and the Ford Company was able to produce them in undreamed-of quantities.[4]

"The first 'ad' appeared on Friday," related the Ford Times. "Saturday's mail brought nearly a thousand inquiries. Monday's response swamped our mail clerks, and by Tuesday night, the office was well-nigh inundated." [5]

As a consequence, Couzens directed that the first Model T's could be distributed only on a restricted basis. Before a dealer could get a Model T, he had to sell all previous models on hand.[6] Even then, only one Model T would be shipped to a dealer until all dealers had been so supplied, and then only if they could show bona fide sales in advance.[7] Nothing like this kind of "rationing" had ever been known before.

Quite as astonishing was the announcement of a new production policy. No longer were customers to have their choice in sizes, styles, or motors. The Ford Motor Company, henceforth, would make only Model T's, and only black Model T's. A famous quip attributed to Ford was: "The customer can have any color he wants, just so it's black!"

3

The true meaning of this development was explained by Couzens more clearly than by anyone else. "We standardized the customer. It was formerly thought that selling started with the customer, and worked back to the factory. We reversed the process." [8]

And the "standardized customers" responded with a deluge of orders. Within six months, agents had to be asked to stop sending orders, for the company's facilities were swamped.[9]

Back in April 1907 a fifty-seven-acre site in Highland Park, then a remote suburb of Detroit, had been purchased against a possible need for a larger factory. With the demand for the Model T straining production facilities at the Piquette Street plant, that day had come. What would previously have been a full year's production was being turned out and sold in one month.

Profits for 1909 totaled $4,452,602; sales, more than seventeen thousand cars. Plans were rushed for building in Highland Park "the largest factory in the state under one roof," where, for the first time in the history of the Ford Company, manufacturing was to be done on a large scale.[10]

Only a short time before, when the American automobile editor Fred H. Colvin, while in England, mentioned that the Ford factory was turning out as many as ten thousand cars annually, a British newspaper scoffed: "No manufacturer can possibly build that many cars in one year; and even if he could, he wouldn't be able to sell half of them." [11]

But in fact the Ford Company was already producing and selling, under Couzens' direction, almost twice that number.

4

There was, however, one flaw in the almost bewilderingly dazzling picture: the Selden patent matter. In 1909, this patent was sweepingly sustained in the Federal District Court at New York, where Judge Charles M. Hough ruled that it was "so fundamental and far reaching as to cover every modern car driven by any form of petroleum vapor." [12] It made no difference, the judge said, that Selden had contrived a delay of sixteen years in the issuance of his patent, from 1879 to 1895. "He did delay," wrote the judge. "He was not in a hurry. . . . Doubtless he appreciated that, if he was ahead of the times, it was wise not to let his patent get ahead too." But, the judge continued, "Selden did not overstep the law . . . the inventor may use his discovery, or he may not; but no one else can use it for seventeen years." [13]

This meant that the Ford Motor Company was liable to an accounting for its profits, and to being enjoined from producing any more automobiles.

However, in 1911, the Federal Circuit Court of Appeals, also at New York, decided that *while Selden had a valid patent,* Ford and other manufacturers were using an *"entirely different motor principle."* To the layman, this is confusing language, but it meant the Ford Company had not infringed Selden's patent after all.[14] And at last, the cloud over the Ford Company disappeared forever.

That year, the company produced thirty-four thousand cars and made net profits of more than $6,000,000.[15] Some years later, these figures might seem ordinary, but at the time they were colossal.

5

The Ford plant really went on a "production" basis. Approximately half of all the automobiles produced in America were being made there.[16] "Watch the Fords Go By" became a slogan that was familiar everywhere. In 1913, the Ford production schedule called for 200,000 cars. By then the assembly-line technique was perfected. And the money rolled in. Whereas profits had been $13,000,000 for 1912, for 1913 they had built up to more than $26,000,000 for the one year.[17]

Husbanding these great sums became a major responsibility for Couzens, along with his pushing of the sales force. He saw to it that the company's surplus was put out properly to earn interest. He initiated a financial plan that probably had no equal then in the business world: *Ford* monies would be desposited in banks for the specific purpose of being loaned to *Ford* dealers for buying more *Ford* cars. The banks charged the dealers regular rates of interest, and shared the earnings with the Ford Motor Company, to the enrichment of everyone concerned.[18] It was like a magic circle.

On just the replacement parts for old Fords, huge profits were made—$800,000 on parts alone in 1912, $5,000,000 in 1913. By 1915, parts accounted for nearly $10,000,000 in profits.

It is little wonder that John D. Rockefeller himself was astonished, or that a leading economist referred to the Ford Company as a "seventh wonder of the world." [19]

As Roger Burlingame has noted, Couzens and Ford (aided of course by some others, like Wills, Walter Flanders, and Hawkins, as well as Charles E. Sorensen, who then was still far down the ladder) had ushered the Industrial Revolution into a new stage of maturity, although neither of them realized it at the time, for they did little thinking in such terms. Because of them a whole new economic world had dawned.[20] In this era, the impact of what they had achieved was not unlike the impact of atomic energy in a later day.

6

Both Couzens and Ford, of course, became millionaires, and it happened to them before either was truly aware of it.

Naturally, their living arrangements had changed. Ford had long since left behind the modest house at 82 Bagley Avenue. By 1913 he and Mrs. Ford and their one child, Edsel, had moved into a massive, forty-five-room, castle-like residence called Fairlane, on a thirteen-hundred-acre estate at Dearborn.

In the meantime, Couzens had Albert Kahn, the industrial architect who had designed the Highland Park plant, build him a fine brick house at 92 (later 610) Longfellow Avenue. He also acquired a farm near Pontiac, Michigan, in the Bloomfield Hills section, and erected there a large white frame house for a summer home. He called the farm "Wabeek." It was an Indian word he found in the *Saturday Evening Post,* and it meant "the best place." "My favorite relaxation," he said, "is to go to Wabeek farm. I go about looking like a farmer, with no one to bother me. My cows don't talk to me, don't ask me questions, nor criticize my way of doing things." [21]

7

He did not forget his family in Chatham. In particular, he wanted to do something to make his mother's closing years more pleasant. He persuaded his father for her sake, if not for his own, to retire from the coal and ice business and come with his mother to Detroit to live. He presented them with a comfortable house in Highland Park, and otherwise saw that they lived pleasantly. Both of his brothers, Albert and Homer, and his sister, Alice, received "nest eggs" from him to help them toward financial independence. Rosetta, of course, needed no such help. That one share in the Ford Company —her one-hundred-dollar loan—had made her wealthy in her own right.

By then, his own family included four children, for in 1910 a second girl, Margo, had arrived. Later, the two sons, Homer and Frank, and two daughters, Madeleine and Margo, were joined by another girl, Edith Valerie, called Betty.

The youngsters formed an interesting group, all wholesome and apparently unspoiled by Couzens' sudden wealth. It was a long time before any of the youngsters suspected that "Daddy Jim" was of that breed, often discussed so admiringly in the newspapers of the period, called "millionaire."

8

Nor were his business interests limited to the Ford Company, vast as it had become. In 1908 he was elected a director of the National Bank of Commerce of Detroit. Before long, he was also on the directorate of the Old Detroit National Bank and of the Detroit

Trust Company. In February 1909 he became a banker in his own right, organizing the Highland Park State Bank, a banking subsidiary of the Ford Motor Company. He was its president. "I ran it from across the street, in my office of the Ford plant," he said.[22]

To the annoyance of other Detroit banks, he used his influence as general manager of the Ford Company to persuade other companies to keep deposits in "his" bank. If a company had money coming to it from Ford supplies, it would be told that the amount due had been deposited in the company's name in an account in the Highland Park Bank, whether the supplier wanted it that way or not. The suppliers usually acquiesced.

He accepted two more directorates in 1909: one in the Scotten Tobacco Company, and another in a new railroad, the Kansas City, Mexico and Orient—a variation of an old dream of John C. Fremont's, in which he became interested, because its promoter, A. E. Stilwell, was trying to create a new transcontinental railroad "without kneeling to Wall Street." [23] That appealed to Couzens' "Single Tax" and John Wanamaker-like ideas.

In 1911, he became a director of the Detroit Salt Company. He also went into the real-estate business, through the Highland Park Land Company. He invested in downtown Detroit real estate, and erected the Couzens Building on Woodward Avenue. He even entered the retail shoe business, as president of the Rogers Shoe Company, though this mainly was to help preserve the estate left by a brother of Mrs. Couzens.

As suited his status, he joined the Detroit Club and the Detroit Athletic Club. He contributed, although moderately, to the Republican party. The press played up the fact that he endorsed a Republican candidate for the Michigan Supreme Court. His comments on women's suffrage were solicited. He became active in the Detroit Board of Commerce and, in 1913, was its president. In short, he emerged as one of the biggest business names in Detroit, so outstanding indeed that a Canadian newspaper-writer soon would describe him as "this square-jawed, successful, masterful son of Chatham, Ontario." [24]

Definitely, he had arrived. The promise of the caul had been realized.

CHAPTER XII

THE CRISIS

YET the Midas touch left something to be desired for both Couzens and Ford. In spite of the riches that flowed in on them, in spite of all the doors thrown open to them, neither was really a happy man. Both illustrated a fact—that success often is harder to endure than failure, that it frequently carries with it the greater pitfalls for mind and soul.

Ford, who was a man of moods anyway, was often listless or dejected in the period between 1908 and 1913. He constantly talked about retiring and becoming a farmer. He spent little time at the plant. "He would come in maybe once or twice a week, and then just roam around," said an associate.[1] At one time, in 1913, Ford suggested that Couzens take his title—president of the company. "He said that he did not want to come to the office at all," Couzens recalled, adding, "I told him that we were getting along all right as we were." [2]

2

On two occasions, Ford even seriously contemplated selling the Ford Motor Company, once in 1908 and again in 1909.[3]

The first occasion was in connection with a merger plan set in motion by Ben Briscoe and William C. Durant, whose idea was to establish one big company, through consolidation of Ford, Buick, Reo, and Maxwell—then the leading producers. They had sounded out Couzens on that proposal before 1908. In his 1907 notebook, he had set down an interesting item:

Sell	$5,000,000 preferred 6% common?		Ford	$7,125,000
Bonus	2,500,000 common		Buick	7,125,000
Reo	7,125,000		Maxwell	6,125,000
		$35,500,000		

3

This tabulation summarized a tentative agreement: A $35,000,000 corporation was to be organized, shares to be distributed in proportion to the value set on each company in accord with Couzens' notation. Extra stock was to be distributed "mostly to the men who were doing the trade, as a consideration for keeping out of business and not lending their name to any other automobile." [4] This, specifically, included Ford.

Throughout the first six months in 1908, Couzens and Ford were in frequent conferences on the proposed merger, both in Detroit and in New York. An initial meeting was held at the old Hotel Pontchartrain in Detroit, where the principals discussed such questions as: "How was the (new) company to be managed?" "Who was to be the 'boss'?" "How were the different companies to be represented?" [5] Other meetings were held in the Wall Street law offices of Herbert L. Satterlee, attorney for Briscoe, and a brother-in-law of J. P Morgan. "We expected to get the capital to buy out Ford and to acquire other property and start the consolidation going from J. P. Morgan & Company," Satterlee recalled. "Fords and Olds were planning to get out of the business." George W. Perkins, a Morgan partner, selected a name for the new company—"The International." [6]

But these negotiations reached an impasse after Briscoe unexpectedly took the position that his company, Maxwell, was being undervalued. Ford then insisted that he had to have at least $3,000,-000 "in cash," in addition to stock. This set off Ransom E. Olds, who declared that if Ford was to get cash, he wanted an equal amount.[7] Then Ford presented another problem. He would not, he said, agree to subscribe to stock in the International above his merger holdings. Durant summarized the development:

> This was a great surprise and the bankers who were expecting a large subscription from Mr. Ford were quite disappointed . . . Mr. Satterlee was quite put out and, after giving the matter a few moments thought, went back into the other room and very diplomatically stated that there had been a misunderstanding, that the matter of finance was entirely up to the bankers and when they had perfected their plan, another meeting would be called.[8]

The bankers never called another meeting. Durant went ahead to form a merger of his own, which became the General Motors Corporation.[9] And Ford and Couzens returned to Detroit to preside over the birth of the Model T.

4

Then, in September 1909, Ford heard about the adverse Selden patent decision and reacted gloomily. "He was in a very serious frame of mind," said Horace Rackham. Coincidentally, Durant was having trouble with his General Motors Corporation. Acquisition of a "going" property such as the Ford Motor Company would be "a way of getting out of a bad hole." [10] Could the Ford Company be purchased despite the Model T's success? Theodore McManus, the financial writer, told Durant that because of the Selden case it was possible. Later Couzens confirmed this, saying to Durant:

> Mr. Ford is very much concerned about the Selden patent suit and its outcome. The prospects of winning or losing the case are equal. To lose, means the payment of a very large sum of money. He is not a member of the license agreement and, on general principles, has opposed the right of any man to control this patent situation. General Motors, with its several companies holding licenses, would probably be able to make a very satisfactory adjustment with Selden if it owned the Ford Company.[11]

Durant had another talk with Couzens just before Couzens and Ford went to New York to discuss with lawyers the adverse Selden decision. "I told him frankly that the General Motors would like to acquire the Ford Motor Company and asked him if he would talk the matter over with Mr. Ford," said Durant.[12]

It was arranged that Couzens and Durant would see each other again in New York. They did so at the Hotel Belmont on October 5, 1909.[13] Ford did not meet with Durant this time, for he was "sick in body and disturbed in mind," as Couzens later recalled,[14] and he told Couzens to carry on the negotiations. When Couzens and Durant were talking, Ford was lying on the floor of his hotel room, suffering from lumbago.[15]

5

Part of the new proposal was that Couzens would increase his holdings in the Ford Motor Company from 11 to 25 per cent, so that he would own a porportionate share in the new General Motors. For the most part, this was to be Couzens' compensation. Ford was to have his payment in cash. He was to retire entirely from the automobile business, although with the right to engage in making tractors.[16]

Couzens told Durant:

> Mr. Ford will sell the Ford Motor Company for $8,000,000 giving me the privilege of purchasing 25 per cent of the company's stock, which I am prepared to take over, as part compensation for service rendered. The balance of the purchase price, the remaining three-quarters interest of $6,000,000 to be paid for as follows: $2,000,000 cash at the time of the sale, the remaining $4,000,000 at 5 per cent interest due on or before three years. Mr. Ford to have his proportion of the annual profits on the stock which he carries until paid for and delivered.[17]

Couzens then returned to the hotel room and reported on this proposal to Ford. "Tell him he can have it, if the money's all cash!" Ford shouted from the bathroom. "Tell him also, I'll throw in my lumbago!"

"He's gone. He's coming back tomorrow for an answer," said Couzens, adding the question: "You want to let it go for that?" meaning $8,000,000.

"What do you think?" asked Ford.

"I'd say yes," said Couzens.

"If we get cash," Ford said.

"Cash, or the answer is 'no,'" agreed Couzens.[18]

But later a part-cash, part-notes proposal was agreed upon.[19] Durant received a written option for the Ford Company.[20] On Sunday, October 24, 1909, both Ford and Couzens met Durant secretly at the Ford plant to check the inventory.[21] Two days later the General Motors board of directors formally ratified the purchase agreement.[22] All that remained was for Durant to raise $2,000,000. Frank A. Vanderlip, president of the National City Bank, agreed to get the money for him. But when the loan committee of the bank vetoed Vanderlip's plan, Durant failed to act upon the option.[23] And the Ford Motor Company was again saved by bankers, although somewhat obliquely.

6

The question may be asked: Aside from his concern over the Selden matter, what was troubling Ford so profoundly that he would have abdicated? Undoubtedly some of the explanation is to be found in the peculiar status Ford then held in his own company.

Until the success of the Model T, the Ford Motor Company was really more Couzens than Ford. The important aspects of the company were business, sales, and financial matters. Not until after the Model T came out did production matters begin to come to the fore. It was no wonder that Ford spent little time in the office that went with his title of "president." There was little for him to do there. One executive of those days remembered only one occasion when Ford spent many hours in his office. Ford was toying with the idea of preparing a book, and was dictating his ideas to a stenographer. The subject was birds.[24]

7

Couzens was no better satisfied with his own role in the company. His association with the Ford Company, rich as it had made him, had become a source of frustration, for the Ford Company would always be just that—"the Ford Company" and not "the Couzens Company"—no matter how important he was within it.

In view of Couzens' whole temperament it is plain that this was becoming emotionally intolerable. His frustration was apparent in his resistance to letting himself mellow in disposition. He was still much the way he had been as a boy in Chatham and as the young freight clerk at the Michigan Central—assertive, often testy, and aloof. When some acquaintances from Chatham came to visit him at the Ford plant and greeted him as "Jim," he turned a cold stare upon them. "They call me Mr. Couzens around here," he said.

When Cyril Arthur Player, then a Seattle newspaperman, approached him at a hotel to get material for a story that would help publicize the Ford Company, Couzens snubbed him: "Newspapermen! Nothing to say!" In the Ford office one night with T. J. Hay of Chicago, he embarrassed a clerk by saying: "See that gentleman there—the only man in the organization who can't get his work done when it should be done, in the daytime!" [25]

A dealer in Denver, thinking Couzens would be pleased, wrote that he was preparing a certain report at night, and in longhand, in order to get it in on time. His response was a curt note: "You should get your work done on time and have your letters typed. We haven't time to read letters written in longhand." [26]

No wonder that nearly everyone in the organization trembled at the message: "Mr. Couzens wants to see you." [27]

His testiness, especially with representatives of suppliers who called on him to sell goods to the Ford Company—and invariably failed to get orders by the conventional salesman's flattery and "good-fellowship"—became proverbial and gave rise to numerous stories, some true, some apocryphal. One of the more famous of these tales concerned his reaction to jokes about the Model T. It was said that when the *Detroit News* devoted an article to these jokes, Couzens sent the editor a letter saying: "Sir: I hereby forbid you ever again to mention the name of the Ford Motor Company in your publication" and withdrew all advertising from the paper, an order which Henry Ford later cancelled.[28] This story, circulated for years, was generally accepted as a true reflection of Couzens' temperament, though it never happened.

Clearly, Couzens was not a happy man. On the contrary, he was a profoundly discontented man—an unhappy multimillionaire.

8

On top of whatever ailed him temperamentally, he began to be concerned about the possible bad effect of his wealth, a worry resulting as much as anything from a reawakening of a social conscience, although he had not revealed this much since the days of Pingree. Except for his admiration of Wanamaker, he seemed to have suppressed this conscience while engaged in making a success of the Ford Company. Now it was coming to the surface.

There was a revealing occasion in this connection when his daughter Madeleine happened to read an article in a newspaper about his and Ford's suddenly developed fortunes. "Whew, that's a lot of money we have!" He answered her solemnly: "But it doesn't belong to us. . . . It's a trust. It's a responsibility, and a tough one." [29] He really believed this, though the idea would have shocked a good many of his business friends.

He kept his children on modest allowances. Both he and Mrs. Couzens deliberately conditioned them to avoid any conspicuous display of wealth. "I am always annoyed at any sort of display and have fought against that for years," he told them.

He took seriously, more than ever, the duties of fatherhood. "It does not pay to waive all discipline because then no character is developed. Resistance to temptation is developed by discipline." [30] Hewing to that line, he was more stern as the children approached their 'teens than he really wished to be, even with the handsome older boy, Homer, whom he doted upon particularly. He once apologized for this. "I am not very demonstrative," he wrote, "but

I think and keep on thinking of you, and I am perhaps more concerned or interested than a parent who is more demonstrative. . . ." [31]

He strove to build in his children a large measure of emotional self-discipline. To Madeleine he once wrote a revealing letter:

> The measure of your happiness will depend largely on how you show yourself outwardly. To surrender to every trial or disappointment only weakens your resistance and drives friends and sympathizers to the position of unconsciously hindering your recovery rather than aiding it. Your outward cheerfulness will help you and help your friends to help you. So buck up, and be my dear little Pal and chum again. . . .[32]

But he himself found it hard to "buck up" under the discontent that gnawed at him. He was able to deaden his discontent somewhat by continuing to drive himself almost savagely in work. Work was both a medicine to him and a drug. "I am never happier," he once said, "than when I am working at top notch, and the only reason I let down at all is to be able to work at top notch the majority of the year." [33] However, by 1913 he faced a crisis in his discontent so acute that even this medicine failed. To a large extent, this crisis was precipitated by a drastic change in his relationship with Ford.

9

In the earlier years, he and Ford had been inseparable companions. Not only had they worked together harmoniously, but there was also a certain display of friendship between their families. "Henry Ford submitted to me in everything as far as the business, sales, and finances were concerned. . . . He was the most perfect working companion I have ever known," Couzens once recalled.[34] But after the golden flood of profits had set in, Ford was no longer "the perfect working companion."

No longer did the two "partners" see as much of each other as they had in the past. As early as October 1912 Couzens informed a dealer in England, who had inquired about Ford, "I have not been able to visit with Mr. Ford very much . . . but I hope and believe he had a most excellent time this summer." [35] In view of their former close companionship, this comment and the almost impersonal manner in which it was made certainly struck a new note. The fact is, the "partners" did not wish to see much of each other any more.

They were beginning to rub each other the wrong way.[36] The same thing was happening that had happened with Malcomson.

Couzens' temperament, notably his desire for independence and achievement, was, of course, one root cause. But in the main, what had happened was that Ford no longer "submitted" to Couzens in everything. Ford had worked through his own discontent by determining to be more aggressive in the company. He shoved aside thoughts of retiring. To Garet Garrett, Ford made a significant remark: "I own fifty-eight per cent of the stock, and I can do with the company what I like, can't I?" [37]

Also, there was the impact on Ford of the success of the Model T. In view of the way the company had leaped ahead once the Model T took hold, Ford could hardly be blamed if he believed that it was his Model T alone that had made the company. In the words of Allan Nevins, "Success had given him a feeling that he was almost infallible." [38] Besides, Ford was never as disinterested in business affairs as he had let on. He had his own ideas about how a business should be operated, as he had demonstrated back in the days of the Detroit Automobile Company.

Of course, many of Ford's ideas could not be put into practice unless plenty of money were available. By 1913 the company had more money than it knew what to do with. There was no longer any reason for Ford to hold back in expressing his ideas or insisting that they be put into effect. He now encroached at times even on Couzens' domain. With increasing frequency there now occurred such incidents as this: The manufacturer who supplied many of the wheels for Ford cars came to Couzens for renewal of his contract. Couzens declined to renew unless the price were lowered. Ordinarily that would have ended the matter, but the manufacturer went to Ford, and Ford signed the contract himself.[39] Couzens was angered. The period of "See Mr. Couzens" obviously was over.

Ford also had shed the apparent meekness that had attracted Couzens in their earlier association. He was now almost as symbolically authoritarian, in Couzens' eyes, as had been the bearded school principal in Chatham, and as had been both his father and Malcomson. When this would become absolutely clear to Couzens, the outcome could be predicted.

There was as well another force at work. Mrs. Ford, "The Great Believer," as Ford called his wife, had begun to dislike Couzens. Possibly this was merely the reflection of a loyal wife's defense of her husband's good qualities. In any event, there is evidence that Mrs. Ford began to resent Couzens' assumed influence over her husband and also the general publicity to the effect that Couzens was the "man behind Ford." Couzens said that he knew of the talk against him at the Ford home.[40]

In short, many cars had flowed from the Ford plant since that June evening both had ridden home in Ford's tiller-steered runabout and talked of what salaries they would get from "those fellows."

10

Still another change in their relationship occurred. Ford had taken to scoffing at the importance of the financial and sales end of the business. All that was necessary, Ford felt, was to keep lowering the price of the car, and sales and management would take care of themselves. He began vetoing carefully worked-out sales and promotion campaigns that Couzens had approved. In talks with associates, he even belittled Couzens' contribution.[41]

Once Ford became indignant when he was asked by an employee to sign a printed form as a receipt for some item he had requested. The form was part of a system that had been installed with Couzens' approval. Ford asked to be shown all of the forms on hand, took them into the yard of the plant, poured gasoline on them, and burned them.[42] Whether Ford realized it or not, this act bespoke contempt for much of Couzens' role in the company.

For his part, Couzens began to lose much of the respect that he had had for some of Ford's mental processes. He continued to recognize Ford's indisputable shrewdness and the validity of Ford's "common sense" judgments on many things, especially on mass production. But he found himself shocked by certain points of view taken by Ford, like Ford's anti-Semitism and such absurd statements as: "If you will study the history of almost any criminal, you will find he is an inveterate cigarette smoker."

One of Couzens' first real jolts came over the way Ford reacted when Walter Flanders resigned as production superintendent to join the competing E-M-F Automobile Company across the street and subsequently "raided" the Ford Company for personnel.

"If you say the word, I will have his head knocked off," said Ford.

"What do you mean?"

"Oh, I have a couple of fellows who will beat him up."

"Oh, no," said the shocked Couzens. "We will stand this without *that*." [43]

This incident set Couzens to "thinking" about Ford. He concluded: "Mr. Ford was not one man, but two men." [44]

As early as 1907, Couzens had received a jolt of another kind, as later he had reason to recall. He had told Ford of the trouble the company had obtaining sufficient currency because of the business panic that year. A few days later, Ford announced a solution: "I am going to build a vault and take our money out of the banks and put it in the vault, so that we can pay our men in cash without having all this trouble with currency." Couzens said to him, "But this money is not in the banks! You can not think that money is in the banks?"

"Certainly it is there," replied Ford.

Even after Couzens gave Ford a painstaking explanation of the credit system, he felt that Ford still wanted to try out his scheme "even if it would wreck the country if everyone followed suit." [45]

On at least one occasion, Couzens delivered a lecture to Ford for certain of his public utterances: "Look here! You are in a very prominent position. You should think over some of these things before saying them!" Ford did not like that.

"Mr. Ford does not want to be influenced or argued with. He wants to tell people what to do and have them do it," Couzens later said.[46]

II

Something even more important happened to Couzens in 1913. He had passed forty, and apparently had come to a kind of climacteric in his life, a change for which, as yet, he possessed no adequate philosophy. All of a sudden, the foundations of his very existence seemed to drop out from under him. Until now, his existence had meant the struggle to establish himself economically. By 1913 he suddenly realized that this struggle was over. Psychologically, nothing could be more devastating to the ambitious man. It was like going blind—or suddenly seeing for the first time. Like many another businessman, he had measured the worth of the struggle by money, and now it dawned on him that he had all the money that he wanted.

"You know," he said later, "there comes a time when the fun of making money is all gone. Say what you will, every man deep in his heart must acknowledge that. . . . The battle is won; the goal is achieved; it is time for something else." [47]

The idea of continuing to devote himself merely to making more money began to produce in Couzens "a kind of nausea." [48] The recognition struck him with shattering force that there could be something more important in the world than producing Ford cars—or dollars.

12

If not more money, what, then, did he want? He wanted—indeed, he needed—the constant sense of achievement. This was central with him, and it was being denied him.

The conviction tormented him that everything ahead for him in the Ford Company would be repetitious. Ironically, he, the general manager, was in the same position as the mechanic in the plant who spent his days endlessly turning "Bolt No. 2" on the monotonous assembly line.

The years of climbing had been stimulating. The Selden fight had been a challenge. The establishment of agencies all over the world had been exciting and broadening. But from the way the company was going in 1913, he found himself believing that almost anyone could direct it without anything serious going wrong. In this, of course, he was right. The framework of the Ford Motor Company had been solidly built.[49] As its later history was to demonstrate, only a major catastrophe could wreck it, or keep it from growing still larger, if only from its own momentum. The Ford Company could even climb back to first place in production and sales, as in the 1950's, after having slipped far down in the 1930's, and do this despite the great resources of the giant that General Motors had become after Durant lost it.

As Couzens pondered the solidity of the company, he concluded that for him to stay on would mean accentuation of the trouble between himself and Ford, which he would regret. It would also mean something just as unpleasant—a coasting on past achievement, which could only heighten his feelings of frustration. "I seemed to have no interest in life for awhile," he said. "I had achieved what I started out to do." [50]

CHAPTER XIII

THE FIVE-DOLLAR-A-DAY PLAN

REALIZATION that he faced a crisis in his life plunged him into a state of self-examination, doubt, discontent, and indecision. He was at a dead end. He had to give his life a new purpose, or throw the balance of it away in dissipation, in absorption in trivialities, or in activity that bored him. He suffered from sleepless nights, and complained of not feeling well. His doctor recommended that he go away for a rest.[1] He knew, however, that his trouble was not merely physical. "Be assured," he wrote to a friend, "that when you see me you will think there is nothing on earth the matter with me, that I am only four-flushing." [2]

His trouble was really a result of inner conflict which could be cured only by making a decision. In July 1913 he took the first tentative step:

"Notified Mr. Ford of my desire to resign, have office downtown, or have year's absence." [3]

Thus did he record in his little notebook the fact that a new James Couzens was ready to emerge. His money-making period was nearly over. No longer could he tolerate a career that was in such contradiction to his primary personality trait—a desire for independence. He had to be James Couzens—not merely Couzens of the Ford Motor Company.

2

He certainly felt, although often tentatively, that he had to separate himself from Ford, especially since Ford, who was also apparently going through some kind of climacteric, continued to conduct himself in ways that depressed Couzens. For example, in 1912 Ford had reacted violently on his return from Europe to finding that C. Harold Wills and others in the plant had put together an improved Model T. They had worked up a model with longer and lower lines—almost streamlined—apparently thinking that Ford would be pleased. Instead, Ford went into a rage, ordered the car taken outside, and he "himself helped knock it to pieces." [4]

Among other things, this incident showed that Ford's *real* trouble was that he could not bear having anyone beside himself play a part in the design of the car that bore his name—not even when they improved it. The Ford had to be *his* and his alone, and so must the company—an attitude that inevitably led to antagonism, if still largely suppressed, toward Couzens.

Couzens sensed Ford's personal problem and there were times when he went far out of his way to cater to him. Thus, not long after Ford had gone into his rage over the improved Model T, Couzens became involved, for Ford's sake, in a heated controversy with young Roy D. Chapin, president of the Hudson Motor Car Company. In the September 28, 1912, issue of the *Saturday Evening Post,* the Hudson company had published a double-page advertisement which stated, among other things, that its Howard E. Coffin was "the foremost engineer in the industry." This was certainly a harmless puff, the sort of claim Couzens would ordinarily have ignored. But instead of ignoring it, Couzens sent Chapin one of his characteristically blunt letters, demanding "to know" how Hudson could claim Coffin to be "America's foremost automobile designer" whereas "I have learned from many sources which are considered reliable, and which I think you will admit are reliable, that Mr. Ford is considered 'America's foremost automobile designer.' " [5] This led to an acidulous exchange of letters that merely added to Couzens' reputation for cantankerousness. But, obviously, his real motive had been to please Henry Ford.

At times Ford was appeased, but not permanently.

3

Two events made Couzens postpone action on his decision. First, the Dodges, also distressed by Ford, had served notice that they planned to bring out their own car, the Dodge, and that they would cease making parts for the Ford Motor Company. This produced a crisis for the Ford Company. Out of loyalty, Couzens decided he should stay on. Then, while he was talking this matter over with Ford, Couzens was offered an interesting assignment. At the suggestion of John Dodge, Mayor Oscar B. Marx of Detroit asked him to accept the chairmanship of the Detroit Street Railway Commission, only recently created by the city to attain, at last, Hazen

Pingree's goal of municipal ownership of the streetcar lines.[6] Couzens jumped at this opportunity, and soon became so engrossed in the municipal streetcar problem that he began to feel that he could solve his discontent without leaving the Ford Motor Company.

By sheer aggressiveness, he scored a dramatic victory over the streetcar corporation. When the corporation refused to settle a dispute with the city over fares, he issued an ultimatum: "If you do not take this proposition, we will stop your cars and I will supply one thousand Ford automobiles to replace the service." The corporation gave in.[7]

As a result, when the year 1914 opened, Couzens seemed more settled in the Ford Company than ever before, for he had also become vice-president, the post that John Dodge had given up.

4

He was not, however, the same Couzens. As he groped for a way to give his life a new direction, he began obviously to look at the Ford Motor Company from a different perspective. Up to then, the company had been merely a money-making machine. In Calvin Coolidge's phrase, its "business was business," and nothing more. Now Couzens began to view the company as a possible social instrument, particularly in regard to "the labor problem." Not for some years had he given much thought to his youthful ideas about wages and the general position of the workingman. Now those ideas occupied much of his thinking.

At his clubs, he began to get the reputation of an "argumentive fellow" on economic subjects, for he questioned the ideas then common among successful businessmen. In part, he was bent on deflating some swollen egos. It pleased him to tell other wealthy manufacturers bluntly that they were "successful," not because of "superior brains," but because of a direct, or indirect, government subsidy, or because their labor was "sweated." [8]

In May 1911 as a member of a committee of the Detroit Board of Commerce, he went to Washington to testify on the effects of the Payne-Aldrich Tariff Act. He was for revising it downward. So unorthodox was his testimony that Oswald Garrison Villard, editor of the liberal *Nation*, hunted him up at the New York automobile show shortly afterwards "to see what kind of a freak he was." [9] Couzens, co-head of the great Ford enterprise, had taken a position on a great and controversial public issue that, surprisingly, was the same one taken by Senator Robert M. La Follette of Wisconsin,

Louis D. Brandeis and other outstanding progressives and liberals of the period.[10]

5

In one major respect, however, Couzens was not yet unorthodox at all. Wage rates were no higher at the Ford plant than at any other automobile plant. Indeed, for certain skills, they were even lower at Ford's, where janitors were paid as little as seventeen cents an hour.

In 1911 he did not question the prevailing idea at the Ford plant that workers should be obtained for the lowest possible wage rates. But by 1913 he began to examine the concept—in this way responding to the temper of the times.

Woodrow Wilson, who had just been elected President, talked of "the new freedom" and "industrial democracy." William Jennings Bryan, still a symbol of revolt for "radical" Democrats in the 'nineties, was in Wilson's cabinet. Many businessmen were dismayed. On the inauguration of Wilson, John Wanamaker gloomily wrote in his diary: "The first entry under the reign of a Democratic president . . . I am unpatriotic enough to want a habitation in Sicily or Italy for the next four years!" [11]

But Couzens was interested in the Wilsonian reforms, even sympathetic. He had not voted for Wilson; he had supported the Bull Moose candidacies of Theodore Roosevelt and Hiram Johnson. Now, as president of the Board of Commerce, he invited Bryan to make an address to the board on "The New Era." Through him, too, Miss Jane Addams, of Chicago's Hull House, appeared as a Board of Commerce speaker.[12]

He read crusading, or "muckraking," magazines like *Everybody's* and *Collier's,* which exposed the methods of the "trusts," and while he read them, he remembered the Selden patent fight, a personal symbol of his opposition to monopoly. He began subjecting all businessmen, especially the most publicized, like Rockefeller, to critical scrutiny.

6

His real awakening was emotional. During the winter of 1913 the Ford Company ordered some temporary layoffs of factory workers. He knew that the vast majority of laid-off men could not have any savings. "All winter," he recalled, "I sat in my office on the second floor of the Ford Building and every time I looked out the window,

I saw a sea of faces looking up. There were men shivering in the cold with their coat collars turned up." This sight haunted him, he later said.

Another incident occurred that especially distressed him. A crowd of jobless men had stormed the Ford employment office, and the police had turned a fire hose on them although they were already shivering from the cold.[13] He was upset for several days afterwards. In addition, I.W.W. organizers, seeking to unionize the Ford workers, were saying things about the Ford management that troubled him, albeit he "wanted no truck" at this time either with the I.W.W. or even with milder forms of unionism.[14]

He discussed with Ford the idea of instituting a pension plan. He later said that this occurred to him because of a sentimental interest in an old man to whom he had given a job in the stationery-supplies office a few years back. This man, named Bruce, once a schoolteacher in Chatham, had begged for the job at the Ford plant after having been forced to retire as a teacher. Now, in 1913, Bruce was hobbling around as a watchman, but really was too infirm to work at any job. Couzens was on the point of ordering a pension for the former teacher. Then he rejected the whole idea as being contrary to his own concept of independence.[15]

Ida Tarbell came to the plant at just this time to gather material for a book. Couzens discussed his notion of Bruce's pension with her. "He says that he thinks it degrading . . . but he also said that something had to be done," Miss Tarbell wrote. "His idea was that the solution should be something which would enable the man to take care of himself. He said: 'We have no right in this country to allow conditions that make pensions necessary. I hate the word.' " [16]

If not a pension, what then? Profit-sharing, or higher wages, or both? He did not know. But he was sure that employers, including himself, owed a greater duty to their workers than they had accepted. In his conversations, he dwelt especially upon the influence of luck in the economic fate of individuals. He felt keenly that "time and chance" had been important in his own case, that it was accident that brought him into contact with Malcomson, and also with Ford. He recalled his married life, his wife's illness, and the death of their first child, and found himself identifying himself with workers in economic trouble. People who considered him "cold" and "unfeeling" would have found this hard to believe, but this is the sort of man he was becoming.[17]

7

At the Ford factory, meanwhile, certain practical, economic facts were being explored. The most acute problem of the company was how to increase productivity without increasing unit costs. The famous assembly line had been installed, but this by itself failed to provide a complete solution.[18] It dawned on certain Ford executives that something had to be done to "improve" labor, as well. They observed that the workers resisted the speed-up. All too often, Ford workers quit for other jobs, just after they had been well broken-in. Quite a large number were discharged by foremen. The result was an enormous—and costly—turnover in the labor force.[19]

This turnover was first spotlighted by a lawyer who had been told to "look around and see what he could do" about improving efficiency. After noticing how often men were being hired and fired, the lawyer began studying the factory payrolls. In telling of his findings, Ida Tarbell recorded:

> At the end of three months he had some figures. The manager of the factory said they couldn't be true. One day, Mr. Couzens asked the lawyer what he was doing, and he showed him the figures. They were alarming enough to startle even a stand-pat manufacturer—to a man like Mr. Couzens . . . , they were a shock and a condemnation. They showed that to keep a force of 12,000 men, Ford's was hiring 60,000 a year. What did it mean? How could it be corrected? . . .[20]

Couzens issued a revolutionary order as a result of the report. Foremen were to be stripped of their authority to fire. No employee anywhere in the company was to be discharged unless Couzens or Ford approved. Even then, no employee was to be fired until he was tried out in some other department, since it had been discovered that many men applied for jobs for which they had no training. "They, of course, say they can do anything. . . . Anyone of us would do the same if we were out of a job," Couzens told Miss Tarbell.[21] Wage studies were then made to "classify" labor according to various skills, with varying rates. As a result, wages were raised 15 per cent. More studies were made and another revolutionary step was taken. The working day was reduced from ten hours to nine.

Conditions improved—but not enough.

8

One evening near Christmas in 1913, Couzens was at home reading a magazine "of socialist tendencies," as he described it—probably it

was *Everybody's*. He came across an editorial item that seemed to
have a bearing on the labor problem at the Ford plant. The editor
was commenting on a letter from a reader who had asked why, "if
it believed in socialism, the magazine did not practice what it
preached in its own affairs." The editor answered that progress
had to be universal, that until everyone changed, a single person or
company could not change and survive. "That," said Couzens, in
telling Miss Tarbell about it, "was an asinine answer!" [22]

To B. C. Forbes, Couzens himself told what followed. Forbes
wrote:

> An idea flashed through his head. Why shouldn't the Ford Motor
> Company take a decided lead in paying the highest wages to its
> workers, thus enabling them to enjoy better living conditions? The
> company was making money hand over fist and could, therefore,
> afford to do something worthwhile.[23]

The next morning Couzens told Henry Ford that the basic minimum wage at the Ford plant should be five dollars a day. He decided
on five dollars because "it's a good round number," he told Ida
Tarbell.[24]

9

Ford raised objections. "We pay as much as anyone pays," he said.

"But we're responsible for those men," Couzens said, pointing
to the men outside looking for jobs, "because we don't pay them
enough to live on. . . . We should give our people wages that permit
them to save against the time when we have no work for them." [25]

Couzens mentioned to Ford the incident of the fire hose. "Do you
know that a Russian woman, an anarchist, has been talking to those
unemployed men and advocating that you be assassinated?" [26] He
also pointed out to Ford that the I.W.W. had been making efforts to
"organize" the Ford plant. "Do we want a union to tell us what to
do?" he asked.

He recalled to Ford their talks about pensions and the difficulty
workers had in surviving periods of unemployment. The solution, he
said, was to pay the workers enough so that they could "accumulate
something for hard times." [27] "We should raise the minimum for
all employees to five dollars a day and charge the difference to our
profit account." [28]

10

Ford continued to object, but Couzens renewed his arguments.
Then he put the whole matter to Ford in the form of a dare. Ford

answered that he did not take dares.[29] But Ford did consult his production assistants, including Peter Martin, the general superintendent. They could not see the point of an increase as large as Couzens proposed. Rather, they thought of increases in terms of "twenty-five cents" or "fifty cents." [30] In this connection, Theodore McManus, in his authoritative *Men, Money and Motors* [31] wrote that Ford came back to Couzens with the following argument: "Martin says he is willing to pay three dollars a day. That five dollars a day will cause trouble. That other firms . . ."

"I know how Martin thinks," interrupted Couzens. "He thinks if we pay five dollars a day it will cause a general disturbance in the labor market. That we will be flooded with requests for jobs. What if it does? And, what if we are? We'll get the pick of the workmen and you know, as well as I do, that a good workman is worth five dollars a day.

"You and I have talked this over enough—not this plan, exactly, but some similar plan—and each of us realizes that the division of our earnings between capital and labor is unequal and that we ought to do something in the way of relief that is suitable for others. You, yourself, have often said that is what we should do."

"Well," Ford said, "I'll go back and talk with Martin."

Couzens pressed for a decision. He knew, he said later, that if he didn't get Ford to consent at that time, he would probably never be able to get the plan through. "If we talk of anything more than forty-eight hours, we never do it." [32]

Ford came back next with the suggestion that minimum wages for everyone be increased to three dollars and fifty cents a day.

"No, it's five or nothing," said Couzens.

"Then make it four," said Ford, adding that Martin would agree to that.

"No," insisted Couzens, "five or nothing." [33]

And then, Couzens added: "A straight five-dollar wage will be the greatest advertisement any automobile concern ever had."

As E. G. Pipp (to whom Ford told this) stated: "Couzens did not have to say that twice to Ford." [34]

II

At just this juncture, Horace Rackham came into the office. "The three of us make a quorum," Couzens said. "Let us consider this a meeting." [35]

The results are in the Ford Company minutes:

Present: Henry Ford, H. H. Rackham, James Couzens. It was stated by the officers that a plan of better equalizing the company's earnings between the stockholders and the labor of the company be inaugurated. The plan was gone over at considerable length, but briefly it carried with it, in addition to wages, sums to make the minimum income of all men over 22 years of age $5.00 for eight hours work, and that other increases were to be made to men getting above the minimum wage, to maintain the same rate between the minimum, intermediate, and maximum wages.

After considerable discussion, it was moved by Director Rackham, and supported by Director Couzens, that such a plan be put into force as of January 12, 1914, which plan, it was distinctly understood, would approximate an additional expenditure for the same volume of business of $10,000,000 for the year 1914. Carried unanimously.[36]

12

It was Couzens, about this time described by a visiting writer as a man with "the keen, 'unwinking' blue eyes of the old gladiator," [37] who made the announcement to the press. The following April, in *Everybody's* magazine, Garet Garrett put down his version of the scene: "Henry Ford was there, with an air of restless detachment from the business at hand, and stood silently by a window [in Couzens' office], while Mr. Couzens read the statement he wished the reporters to publish." [38]

The statement was an oddity because of the way it reflected an obvious effort to divide credit for the plan evenly between Couzens and Ford.

It was also the best description ever made of the famous wage plan, which, because it doubled wage rates at one stroke in a great factory, was indisputably one of the major events of the era, both in its immediate and in its later impact upon the economic structure of America. His statement was:

The Ford Motor Company, the greatest and most successful automobile manufacturing company in the world, will, on January 12, inaugurate the greatest revolution in the matter of rewards for its workers ever known to the industrial world.

At one stroke it will reduce the hours of labor from nine to eight, and add to every man's pay a share of the profits of the house. The smallest amount to be received by any man 22 years old and upwards will be $5.00 per day. The minimum wage is now $2.34 per day of nine hours.

All but 10 per cent of the employees will at once share in the profits. Only 10 per cent of the men now employed are under 22, and even every one of those under 22 will have a chance of showing himself entitled to $5.00 per day.

Instead of waiting until the end of the year to make a distribution of profits among their employees in one lump bonus sum, Mr. Ford and Mr. Couzens have estimated the year's prospective business and have decided upon what they feel will be a safe amount to award the workers. This will be spread over the whole year and paid on the regular semi-monthly pay days.

The factory is now working two shifts of nine hours each. This will be changed to three shifts of eight hours each. The number employed is now about 15,000 and this will be increased by 4,000 or 5,000. The men who now earn $2.34 per day of nine hours will get at least $5.00 per day of eight hours.

This will apply to every man of 22 years of age or upward without regard to the nature of his employment. In order that the young man, from 18 to 22 years of age, may be entitled to a share in the profits he must show himself sober, saving, steady, industrious, and must satisfy the superintendent and staff that his money will not be wasted in riotous living.

Young men who are supporting families, widowed mothers, younger brothers and sisters, will be treated like those over 22.

It is estimated that over $10,000,000 will be thus distributed over and above the regular wages of the men.

"The commonest laborer, who sweeps the floor, shall receive his $5.00 per day," said Henry Ford.

"It is our belief," said James Couzens, "that social justice begins at home. We want those who have helped us to produce this great institution and who are helping to maintain it to share our prosperity. We want them to have present profits and future prospects. Thrift and good service and sobriety all will be encouraged and recognized."

"If we are obliged," said Mr. Ford, "to lay off men for want of sufficient work at any season, we propose to so plan our year's work that the lay-off shall be in the harvest time; July, August, and September, not in the winter. We hope, in such case, to induce our men to respond to the calls of the farmers for harvest hands and not to lie idle and dissipate their savings. We shall make it our business to get in touch with the farmers and to induce our employees to answer calls for harvest help.

"No man will be discharged if we can help it, except for unfaithfulness or inefficiency. No foreman in the company has the power to discharge a man. He may send them out of his department if they do not make good. The man is then sent to our clearing house, covering all the departments, and is again repeatedly tried in other work until we find the job he is suited for, provided he is honestly trying to render good service."

"We shall still pay," Mr. Couzens said, "we are quite sure, good, handsome dividends to our stockholders, and will set aside reasonable amounts for additions and improvements and assembling plants in other parts of the country. And after that it is our hope to be able to do still better by our employees. We want them to be in reality partners in our enterprise.

"Believing as we do, that a division of our earnings between capital and labor is unequal, we have sought a plan of relief suitable to our business. We do not feel sure that it is the best, but we have felt impelled to make a start and make it now. We do not agree with those employers who declare, as did a recent writer in a magazine, in excusing himself for not practicing what he preached, that the movement toward the bettering of society must be universal. We think that one concern can make a start and create an example for others. And that is our chief object.

"The public need have no fear that this action of ours will result in any increase in prices of our products. On the contrary we hope to keep up our past record of reducing prices each year.

"We may have to make changes in our plan. If hard times should befall us we may have to reduce or modify our distribution of profits. But the outlook now is such as to justify this distribution for the present year."

"We believe," said Mr. Ford, "in making 20,000 men prosperous and contented rather than follow the plan of making a few slave drivers in our establishment multi-millionaires."

13

The appeal of the plan to workers—not to mention social reformers—was instantaneous. Mechanics from all over America streamed to the Ford factory for jobs. The employment office was swamped.

It developed later that the wage plan included some naive, although well-intentioned, interference in the lives of the Ford workers, such as the following:

Employees should use plenty of soap and water in the home, and upon their children, bathing frequently. Nothing makes for right living and health so much as cleanliness. Notice that the most advanced people are the cleanest. . . .

Improved garbage cans, of which there are several good types available, should be used. The can should be covered at all times, especially during the summer time. . . .

From 12 years of age to 18 is especially a time when (children) should be guarded well, and not allowed to contract habits and vices injurious to their welfare and health. . . .

Do not spit on the floor in the home. . . .

A double purpose is served under the profit-sharing plan. First, to provide money for future needs; second, to foster self-control. The second is the more important of the two, because, having that, the first is quite assured. . . .

> Avoid, as much as possible, making purchases upon the install-
> ment plan. . . .
> A good understanding should be had between husband and wife
> as to expenditures and savings. . . .
> Cases have been brought to the company's attention indicating
> that some young men, in order to qualify as profit-sharers, have
> hastily married without giving serious thought to such an impor-
> tant step in their lives. Seldom does such a marriage prove a happy
> one. If they would give more thought to the uncertainty of business
> affairs and the certainty of the obligations and responsibilities as-
> sumed in the marriage vows, there would be less work for the divorce
> courts. . . .[39]

The company sent investigators to the homes of the workers to see
how their beds were made, check their bank accounts, and advise
them on their most intimate affairs. This, of course, was paternal-
ism.[40] Couzens deplored this later, although at the time he defended it as "simply an effort to show our people how to take care of
their money, how to live and how to get the best out of the increase." [41] He knew the plan "paid off" for the company. He quoted
with approval a Ford worker: "I work for what I get. When I get
three dollars a day and work ten hours, I make 300 bolts. Now, when
I get five dollars a day and work eight hours, I make 900 bolts." [42]

14

Ford at the time received all the credit. The reason for this was
explained by Couzens himself:

> It was quite natural that Mr. Ford should be credited with this
> project because he was the head of the company, a majority stock-
> holder, and it was to the benefit of the Ford Motor Company that
> he should be credited with it; because it gave it a personal touch
> which was greatly beneficial in an advertising way and kept the
> name Ford much more before the public, and this is great adver-
> tising. . . .[43]

In 1915, he bluntly wrote: "When you get down to the wage
scheme which we started at the Ford Motor Company, I will say that
I, personally, am responsible for it." [44]

It is significant that Ford never claimed, over his signature, that
the wage idea was his. He certainly played his part. As Couzens
frequently said, the wage plan could not have gone into effect without Ford's approval, but Couzens was its sponsor.[45]

CHAPTER XIV

THE FINAL BREAK

THE wage plan proved a good temporary palliative for the tension between Couzens and Ford. Ford enjoyed being interviewed for magazines, newspapers, even books. Both Couzens and he obtained pleasurable excitement from watching how the paternalistic side of the plan worked, and eagerly followed reports on what was being done to make certain that the workers "deserved the big envelope."

While Couzens was in California, a glowing report on this aspect of the plan was sent to him by Klingensmith, now his assistant. "I wish you could be here [Klingensmith wrote] just to see the enthusiasm among the investigators on this welfare work. . . . You need have no fear that this branch of this work which you started will have the very best of attention. . . . Mr. Ford has been at the office practically every day . . . and is very enthusiastic over the work and puts a lot of enthusiasm into the people in realization of the possibilities of this profit-sharing plan." [1]

Especially was Couzens pleased because his predictions as to the advertising value of the plan were justified. Sales leaped upward. As a consequence, he pushed expansion plans, particularly those for Ford assembly plants in other cities. "The plans for Atlanta are practically completed. The many questions re Pittsburgh are being worked out. Indianapolis goes out for bids today. They have started the plans for Cincinnati and have gotten out a preliminary sketch for Cleveland." So Klingensmith summarized progress. [2]

Once again, Couzens became the busy, absorbed executive. The attitude of other businessmen had a stimulating effect on him, for nearly all other American industrialists and financiers denounced the plan. [3] Garet Garrett recalled:

> The Board of Commerce was in a panic. Smaller manufacturers, outside the motor car industry, had been serving notice that they

were leaving Detroit, and several of them did. The owner of the barber shop at the hotel told me that he would have to go out of business; even barbers would be wanting five dollars a day. . . .[4]

"Consternation" was the word Alfred P. Sloan of General Motors used to describe the reaction of industrialists generally.[5] The program at Ford, they said, was bound to "disaffect the working class." [6] The Ford management was described as being in the hands of men who had lost their minds.[7] Bankers issued instructions to their loan officers "to watch the credit of 'any customers doing business with Ford.' " [8]

Couzens became even more interested in seeing it through. "This is the most interesting subject in the world to me. It is one I can spend more time and more thought on than any other thing I ever came in contact with," he told a friend.[9] Indeed, he became a veritable crusader for a fairer distribution of the profits of industry.

To E. D. Stair, then publisher of the *Detroit Free Press*, he wrote: "It is my sincere judgment that even if a company made only six per cent, it should divide three among its employees. This would follow out to the betterment of all concerned." [10]

2

In the following winter, despite the prosperity at the Ford Company, Detroit was gripped by a severe depression, as a result of the war abroad. Thousands of men tramped the streets in a vain search for employment. So serious was the situation that the Board of Commerce organized a committee on unemployment.

Couzens, who a short time before had been president of the board, watched this committee with increasing skepticism. Its main purpose, it seemed to him, was not to find jobs for the men but to direct them to charity. Three days before Christmas, Couzens strode into a Board of Commerce meeting to speak his mind—

> You fellows sit back, smug and complacent, and don't give a damn what becomes of your workmen.
> You go down to the Board of Estimates and ask for high-pressure systems to preserve your plants from fire; you ask for more patrolmen to guard your property; but what do you do for your workmen? . . . You kick them into the street, and that's all there is to it. . . .
> The situation is up to the employers of Detroit. These unemployed are sent to charity for assistance, when they want work. . . .

It is not the man's fault he has not had enough wages to carry him over a period like this. Many absolutely refuse to line up with those seeking charity. They are a part of commerce just as much as we are. Then what in hell have they to do with charity?

They are just as human as you and I, but they are not as well taken care of. You can't give these men work during the summer and then discharge them in the winter while you take your golf sticks and go to California, and do your full duty. . . .[11]

He incurred the lasting enmity of a good number of Detroit businessmen as a result of that outburst, one that anticipated by forty years the acceptance by the automobile industry, and particularly by the Ford Company under Henry Ford II, of a form of guaranteed annual wage system. The *Detroit Journal* referred to his as a "commercial Savonarola," and what many Detroit businessmen called him was unprintable. But his outburst did provoke the formation of a new committee that obtained jobs for hundreds of unemployed workers.[12]

3

All this eased his relations with Ford. But, again, the easing was only temporary. True, in the fall of 1914, he told newspaper reporters that "perfect harmony" existed in the company. "Sometimes Mr. Ford will drop into my office, as he did this morning, and we will discuss things for an hour or two. Again, we may not see each other for a month. But all of the time every part of the immense organization is running smoothly in its own groove." [13] However, within six months after the wage plan had been put into effect, the old trouble between him and Ford came to the surface again. As put by one Ford biographer, "Relations between Mr. Ford and his general manager became more and more strained." [14] Plainly, all that was needed for a final break to occur was some appropriate "incident."

In August 1914, it appeared that such an incident had occurred. The war in Europe had caused runs on banks and Ford began talking of withdrawing his personal funds from the Highland Park State Bank—Couzens' bank. Couzens assured Ford that his money was safe where it was. Ford seemed to accept that assurance. He agreed not to make a transfer. But he ordered the withdrawal anyway.[15] Couzens flared up, and sent the following telegram:

August 5, 1914

HENRY FORD,

HARBOR BEACH, MICHIGAN

IN THESE STRENUOUS TIMES MEN INVARIABLY SHOW THE KIND OF STUFF
THEY ARE MADE OF. WE ARE MAKING ARRANGEMENTS TO TRANSFER YOUR
MONEY TO THE DIME BANK.

JAMES COUZENS [16]

To his secretary, Henry S. Morgan, Couzens talked about resigning
right then. "You may have to choose soon between continuing with
the Ford Motor Company and staying on with me," he told Morgan.[17]

4

Still the break did not come—this time because of a profound
personal tragedy. On the afternoon of August 8, 1914, he had cut
short a golf game at the Bloomfield Hills Country Club—later he felt
that it was a kind of premonition that caused him to forego the full
eighteen holes—and thus he was at his Wabeek residence in time to
receive a telephone call that sent a chill through him. An automobile
listed as belonging to the Couzens family had overturned on a road
near a small lake close to Wabeek. The driver, a boy, had been
pinned in the water beneath the car. With Margaret, Couzens rushed
to the scene. They found their worst fears confirmed. Their elder
son, Homer, was dead in the Model T Ford they had given to him
on his fourteenth birthday.[18]

That evening, although obviously near the breaking point, Couzens
insisted that the family sit at the dinner table as usual. "We must not
give in to our feelings," he said. Klingensmith called at the house,
and Couzens took him in to see the body. "Wasn't he a fine big boy?
Wasn't he a fine big boy?" he kept repeating. But there were no tears.
He simply refused to let them come.[19]

Yet he was a man distraught, and he remained so for months.
He thought a motor trip would help, and set out on one with the
family, but he soon turned back. Work, endless work, was all that
made any sense to him. So he clung to the Ford Motor Company, regardless of how things stood between himself and Ford.

5

But the break was not to be avoided. Ford had begun issuing various pronouncements on the war and its meaning for the United
States, statements that increasingly irritated Couzens. He would never
permit his factory to produce war material, not even if the United

States was involved, Ford said in one statement. In another: "To my mind, the word 'murderer' should be embroidered in red letters across the breast of every soldier." [20]

Now, Couzens then was also, in a sense, a "peace advocate." In a newspaper interview in October 1915, he said: "Mr. Ford and I are one in our desire for peace. . . . I was born in Canada, but I am absolutely neutral." [21] When William Howard Taft, Hamilton Holt, Alton B. Parker, and others formed a "League to Enforce Peace" Couzens joined and contributed $5,000.[22] So something deeper than just Ford's Peace views was involved.

6

Milton McRae, who was a friend of both men, tried to patch things up. He suggested to Ford that he employ "a public relations counselor," hoping that such a counselor would steer Ford along a different path. Instead, Ford engaged a "peace secretary," a newspaperman, who, with Madame Rosicka Schwimmer, later came up with the plan for his famous "peace ship," the *Oscar II*.[23] On October 11, 1915, there occurred the conversation between Couzens and Brownell about the *Ford Times*. It was followed the next morning by the decisive meeting between Couzens and Ford.

7

Klingensmith described the incident as he saw it develop:

> On the day that Couzens quit, I saw Ford go into Couzens' office, and then come out, and walk down the corridor. A minute later, Couzens called me into his office. "I've just resigned from the Ford Motor Company. There's my resignation, right there."
>
> His face was red, from anger and agitation. He pointed to a sheet of paper on which he had written his resignation from the Ford Motor Company, to take effect immediately.
>
> He had written it out in longhand, and given it to Ford, but Ford had left it on Couzens' desk.
>
> "I decided," said Couzens to me, "that I had had enough of his God damn persecution."
>
> Then Couzens put on his hat, and walked out of the office. He went downtown and notified a newspaper friend.[24]

The newspaper friend was Jay G. Hayden, then secretary of the Street Railway Commission (later chief of the Washington Bureau of the *Detroit News*.) "About eleven o'clock in the morning," recalled Hayden, "he came busting into the board room. I thought *I* was to be fired. 'I've just resigned from the Ford Company and I want your help,' he said to me.

" 'On what?'

" 'I want to give the story to the papers before Ford does, but I don't want to give it out myself.' "

Hayden then went over to the Book-Cadillac Hotel and called the various newspaper offices.[25]

To Louis B. Block, Ford dealer in Philadelphia, Couzens made an observation that largely explained the whole matter. "A man sometimes gets to the point where his freedom of thought and independence is greater than all else." [26]

8

Years later Couzens learned that Ford had come into his office that morning to provoke his resignation. As Ford himself said to E. P. Pipp, a managing editor of the *Detroit News:*

> It's like this. I have had a check kept on him, and he has been at the plant only 184 days during the past year. He has been in California and now plans to go to Asheville. I don't believe in absentee control. If Jim is on the job, I'd rather have his judgment than anybody else's judgment, but Jim's judgment off the job isn't as good as somebody else's on the job. If a man has a job with us, he must stick to it. . . . I got to thinking about it, stayed home two or three days to figure it out, and came over to the plant to make an issue of it. Jim sprang the thing about the article in the little magazine. Fine, I thought, that's a dandy way out of it, so I stood pat.[27]

All this was merely a rationalization on Ford's part. There never could have been any valid criticism of Couzens on the ground that he was not on the job. If anything, he had worked too hard at it. The truth was that Ford had determined to take over, to deal with Couzens as he had with Alex Malcomson, and the determination had coincided with Couzens' own inevitable decision to be on his own.

BOOK TWO

The New Public Man

CHAPTER XV

THE JOB-SEEKER AGAIN

EVEN after his break with Ford, Couzens remained a director in the company, and continued to take an interest in the "social experiment" in the Ford organization. He continued to make crusading speeches to other businessmen. Before the Windsor (Ontario) Board of Trade, he denounced businessmen who paid low wages to girls and then headed "committees to save women from prostitution." "I have no use," he said, "for the man who works a lot of girls at $3.50 and $4.00 a week, and then puts on a frock coat on Sunday." [1] He had in mind a millionaire merchant who was known for paying low wages to female employees and whom he ordered out of his house when this merchant called on him for a contribution to a home for wayward girls.

He also retained the presidency of the Highland Park State Bank. That activity, his Wabeek farm, his investments, and his post as head of the Detroit Street Railway Commission should have been sufficient to keep him contentedly occupied. Instead, he became restless and fidgety.

It seemed for a time that the Street Railway Commission by itself would provide a cure for what he considered his idleness. During the previous year, in August 1915, he had stirred up the old Pingree municipal ownership issue, informing Jere C. Hutchins, the president of the Detroit Union Railways, that the city should buy the D.U.R. lines. Hutchins had been astounded when Couzens called him on the telephone to make the suggestion. "It has seemed to me that the people are satisfied with conditions as they are!" Hutchins said.

"Not at all!" Couzens said. "What is wanted is municipal ownership. What do you want for the lines?" [2] So he forced the issue—and a municipal election on the question.

2

A referendum on the question was set for the following November. Couzens threw himself into the campaign to get Detroiters to vote in favor of the proposal. Victory would mean a satisfying and ready-made job for him, for he would be the manager of the city-operated streetcar system if the referendum proposal carried. With his own funds he financed the printing of literature that supported the purchase of the system. He directed the lawyers in a fight against an effort to have the referendum barred by a court injunction, one asked for by Clarence Burton, the Detroit historian. "I don't care about the merits of this or any other plan," said Burton. "I want the courts to say that municipal ownership of street railways is illegal and can never be had in this city." [3]

The injunction suit was killed, and the issue went to the voters as scheduled, with Couzens the principal speaker at mass meetings organized behind the proposal. On the whole, his speeches were effective. The spectacle of a multimillionaire arguing for municipal ownership caught the imagination of the city and it seemed the answer to the main argument of the D.U.R., that the plan was "socialistic."

But he had naively committed one serious political error. Shrewd Jere C. Hutchins had refused to set a price on the D.U.R properties. Couzens determined to go ahead with the referendum anyway. If the people voted to buy the lines, the price was to be set later by the judges of the County Court.

Coached by Hutchins, the opposition immediately raised a powerful cry: "Couzens is asking the city to buy a pig in a poke!"

Couzens tried to counter this move by announcing that if the price eventually set by the court was not satisfactory, he, personally, would re-purchase the lines for $40,000,000, higher than any figure the company had ever set on its property. But the "pig in a poke" cry deterred even old-time followers of Pingree from actively supporting him.

Another handicap was a matter with which Couzens himself was not involved—at least not yet. The city administration then admittedly was corrupt. The police department, especially, was notoriously graft-ridden. "Do you want such an administration to run the streetcar lines?" the opposition demanded. Couzens had what sounded like an effective answer. "The opposition tries to befog the issue by talking of graft. Well, speaking of graft, how about private business?

There is more favoritism, more politics, and more graft in private business—and I should know—than in any city government in America. If you can't run your lines and keep out graft, you are a poor lot of citizens. What does the D.U.R. care about you? All they care about is your fares. The streetcar line is by nature a monopoly, and you should own it." [4]

But this argument was not enough. The referendum lost by three thousand votes.[5]

"I'm in a mess," Couzens told Jay Hayden that night. "Now I have to get a job." [6]

The following spring, out of sheer desperation, he organized another bank, the Highland Park State Bank of Detroit (later the Bank of Detroit), and became its president. At first, he was delighted with the new bank. "I never experienced such joy in my life as I did the day of the opening," he told John W. Anderson. But soon he was forced to recognize the bank for what it was—just another money-making machine. He was still looking for a "job," a new career.

3

The streetcar question apart, it seemed inevitable that he would find his career in public affairs. Milton McRae had been urging him for some time to go into politics. Indeed, in 1913 he had advised Couzens to accept the Board of Commerce presidency with that in view.[7] And Couzens clearly was interested even before leaving Ford.

He had set his sights high—on national politics. Thus, after the failure of the streetcar referendum, he "considered" becoming a candidate for United States Senator, and some of the newspapers began printing items to the effect that his wealth made him a natural contender against Senator Charles E. Townsend in 1916.

But he dropped the idea when it became obvious that he could not hope to unseat Townsend. Instead, he served as treasurer of Townsend's re-election campaign.[8] He believed, naively, that this was the way to break into politics.

In that same year, 1916, he dabbled in the preliminaries of the Presidential campaign that developed into the contest between Woodrow Wilson and Charles Evans Hughes. To Charles B. Warren, the Republican National Committeeman, he wrote: "I am keenly interested in the success of the Republican Party this fall." To prove his interest, he sent Warren a four-thousand-dollar check for the party campaign fund.[9] Out of gratitude for this contribution, the party designated him as a Hughes elector, even though he had been active in an unsuccessful boom on behalf of Theodore Roosevelt and had sat conspicuously on the platform at a Detroit meeting for "T.R." He was a delegate to both the state and national Republican conventions, in opposition, incidentally, to a group from Michigan that was booming Henry Ford for the Republican nomination for President.[10]

4

Before voting time, however, it was a local election that became more important to him. Mayor Marx, a Republican, was seeking re-election, and was handicapped by his lax police department. Marx's secretary, Edward T. Fitzgerald, called on Couzens to ask him if he would be interested in becoming commissioner of police.[11] The political strategy was obvious: If Couzens became Commissioner of Police, the Marx regime could be salvaged.

"It came to me like a flash," Couzens later recalled, "that here was my opportunity." He said he was interested, but on a condition. He had to have a "free hand without political interference of any kind." [12] There followed talks with Marx and John Dodge. On September 28, 1916, Marx announced that Commissioner John Gillespie had resigned and that Couzens had taken his place, a substitution that saved the election for Mayor Marx—and launched Couzens upon his new career.[13]

CHAPTER XVI

THE POLICE COMMISSIONER

IN THE words of Detroit's semi-official historian, George B. Catlin, he "immediately began making history" as Commissioner of Police.[1] Owing to that penchant of his for saying what he thought, he started off with a storm. During an interview with the newspapers he was asked to give his policy on law enforcement, particularly in regard to the state law forbidding the sale of alcoholic beverages on Sunday. Instead of repeating what every other police commissioner had said —that, of course, he would enforce all laws—he was frank. He said that he had not "made up his mind," and added:

> Certain laws are debatable. It is debatable whether it is right for a man to have a glass of beer on Sunday. It is not debatable that when a rich man may have his glass of beer in his club or elsewhere, the poor man is entitled to the same privilege. Whether either should be permitted is the question. There are in statute books and among city ordinances so many obsolete and absurd laws that it would be foolish for an official to announce that he intended to enforce the law strictly.[2]

He soon learned that it was more foolish for a police commissioner to be so forthright. "Can Detroit hope for much from a man who, even before he takes the required oath of office, announces in the public press that the enforcement of the public law in some regards is to him a debatable matter?" inquired Judge William Connolly, the Democratic candidate for mayor.[3]

"Is Couzens going to enforce the law passed by the people in Lansing, or just a little of it here and there, as it appeals to him personally?" asked one newspaper.[4]

A newspaper in Grand Rapids commented: "It would seem as though it is about time for the state authority to take Mr. Couzens and the whole Detroit outfit by the ear." [5]

Ministers denounced him from their pulpits.

2

For once, he was indecisive, as a statement he issued showed. "Neither wets, drys, ministers, politicians, nor the public have any reason to become panicky because I have not determined what policies are to be enforced as yet. I do not intend to be driven into a panicky condition. I know I shall not be." Which of course meant that he really was "panicky"—for him.

Then he made a wise decision—to conduct a personal survey of police conditions in Detroit. Emulating Police Commissioner Theodore Roosevelt of New York some twenty years before, he prowled around the city, night and day. Without revealing his identity, he talked to policemen, to saloonkeepers, to streetwalkers, and to ordinary citizens. He later recalled:

"I found conditions far worse than the public dreamed they were. The real inside conditions were never known to the public. . . . The town was wide open . . . gamblers ran as they pleased; hundreds of houses of prostitution were scattered around, and 1,400 saloons ran all day and all night and on Sundays." [6]

He then made the only decision possible for him: *All laws would be enforced.*

To Police Superintendent Ernst Marquardt he sent the kind of order he might have issued as general manager of the Ford Motor Company:

> Effective at once, I want every man in the department instructed to absolutely enforce all laws twenty-four hours of the day, whether on or off duty. . . . From now on, I want every law and ordinance complied with, and this includes specifically the prevention of crime of all kinds, and the proper regulation of laws, ordinances, rules, and regulations governing traffic, saloons, pool rooms, and every other thing that will bring about a clean and decent city. . . . No excuses will be accepted.[7]

3

There was first amazement, then amusement over this order. It was considered by the "wise ones" ludicrous as well as fantastic. A police commissioner of a metropolitian city issuing a command actually calling for complete enforcement of all laws!

To be sure, it was fantastic, in a sense. And of course the Couzens order was not fully obeyed, for the city was not the Ford Company. Yet it did bring some results, enough to cause "wise ones" to hold their breath. For example, his order called for the enforcement of the ordinance against saloons being open on Sundays.

People had said that nobody could enforce the Sunday law, that the politicians would not permit it. But Couzens enforced the law.

He soon learned, however, that types of lawbreaking other than violation of the Sunday rules were not so easily uprooted, not even by the strongest, most Couzens-like general order. "I discovered," he said, "that there was a vast difference between running a government department and manufacturing automobiles. . . . When they asked me to clean up Detroit, they didn't mean it. They wanted me *to* clean it up and *not* clean it up. They wanted me to make it nice enough for the reformers and let it stay rotten enough to appease the bums." [8]

4

His goal, he now said, was "a disciplined city." [9] No one before him had ever seriously tried to discipline Detroit, not even Pingree. The temperament of the city had never encouraged such efforts. The city's nonconformism was shown even in the way Detroiters operated their automobiles, for at that time practically no traffic regulations were enforced. Perhaps symbolically, during Couzens' first month as police commissioner, his own automobile was stolen, to the great delight of his ill-wishers, whose number by then had greatly increased.

The politicians formed an almost solid opposition. Most of the city's forty aldermen were openly hostile. "Why give Commissioner Couzens everything he wants?" an alderman cried at a council budget meeting. "To let him hang himself!" jeered a colleague.[10]

5

On one occasion, Mayor Marx openly tried to frustrate him. When Couzens wanted certain legislation at Lansing to strengthen the police department, the mayor had a representative at the capital to lobby on the other side—against his own police commissioner.[11] "I learned all the emotions of public service when I was commissioner of police," Couzens wrote later to Arthur H. Vandenberg, then editor of the *Grand Rapids Herald*. He had in mind such headlines as these:

"COUZENS FAILS EVEN TO REGULATE MOTORISTS" . . . "POLICE KEEP RIGHT ON WITH THEIR BUNGLING"

. . . "VICE DENS FLOURISH IN HEART OF DETROIT" . . .
"COMMISSIONER COUZENS HASN'T MADE GOOD."
This hurt. But he concluded: "Nearly all public men who did
their duty had to endure about the same sort of stuff. A man can't
set himself up as a target if he doesn't want to be hit." [12] So he held
to his goal doggedly. "He made life miserable for everybody in
Detroit who violated any statute, ordinance, order, edict, enactment,
provision, rule, regulation, or section thereof," said the writer
William Hard.[13]

6

He announced that he was determined to abolish the so-called
red-light districts. This caused a group of reputable citizens to
descend on him to argue that his policy would lead to worse evils.
He answered that they should go to the state legislature and get
prostitution legalized; until then, he intended to enforce the law.
"But our families!" protested the citizens. "They would misunderstand our motives!" "Well," he replied, "if you think you can convince me that prostitution is all right, you should have no trouble
with your families." [14]

Still another group of citizens visited him to save the red-light
areas. They said they were interested "only in Detroit's welfare."
To these Couzens displayed a little black book and read off some
automobile license numbers. "Are those your license numbers?"
he asked. Some of the callers admitted that they were. "Well," said
Couzens, "I have a mind to publish these numbers!" Then he told
his dismayed callers that the numbers had been taken down by investigators from cars found parked in front of some of the more
flashy brothels in the city! [15]

In dealing with traffic regulation, he succeeded in stirring up an
even bigger storm than he did by his frankness on the red-light
districts. After becoming convinced that elimination of all parking
in the busiest downtown streets was necessary, he issued an order
to that effect, although warned by the city's law department that
his order exceeded his authority. Business leaders assailed him as
a "czar." Former Mayor Philip Breitmeyer counseled open rebellion.[16]

The stir was such that the order had to be rescinded. But the very
impulsiveness of his action so dramatized Detroit's need for some
traffic control that shortly afterward the city council enacted legisla-

tion along the lines that he had intended to establish. Thus he became the father of the city's modern traffic code.

7

His biggest storm—actually a serio-comic episode worthy of Gilbert and Sullivan—began in March 1917, when he decided to bring into the open a half-secret scandal involving a municipal judge. "Judge Albert Sellers," he announced to the press, "is giving blanket releases to professional bondsmen with the names of prisoners to be filled in as the occasion arises." [17] The judge sneered at him. "Police Commissioner Couzens should quit his job and go home."

Couzens then issued an order that henceforth the police department would ignore Judge Sellers' releases unless they had been issued in a regular court session.[18] Then the city settled back to await the inevitable collision. It came very soon afterward when Couzens' order was enforced in the case of two women arrested as streetwalkers. Judge Sellers had issued the pair his usual prearranged releases. Couzens' police officers refused to honor the releases. So the judge issued a contempt citation against Couzens.

Haled into court, Couzens was given the choice of paying a fine of $100 or serving a thirty-day sentence in jail. He refused to pay the fine and was taken to jail.[19] Of course the city howled, either in indignation or with delight. The city's multimillionaire police head locked up in his own jail! Not even Teddy Roosevelt had endured such an experience in his similar efforts to clean up a crime-ridden city.

Couzens did not remain long in his own jail. But the incident did win for him the favorable public opinion that a bad press had denied him. He carried this fight with the judge to the State Supreme Court, and won a decision that outlawed the practice of giving blanket releases.[20]

8

For a time this civic comedy made him a hero. But his troubles were not over. That spring the United States entered the European war. The city filled up with "floaters." Crimes increased—and Couzens was blamed. The *Detroit News*, usually his supporter, said: "The present condition cannot continue. If Mr. Couzens is responsible even in part, it is preposterous that he be kept in his place. . . . Certainly the stubborn pride of any one man or any group of men cannot be permitted to result in perpetuation of this reign of terror." [21]

The situation really was impossible. There was one face-saving avenue of escape open to him—to take a war job in Washington, and thus get out of the police "mess." Just at this time, General George W. Goethals, then Acting Quartermaster General of the Army, invited him to Washington to talk over a proposal that he become head of a new motor-truck division of the war department.[22] This was the result of a recommendation Milton McRae had made to the Secretary of War, Newton D. Baker, that Couzens be brought into the national picture in some wartime capacity. He and Goethals got along very well. Goethals' greeting to him was: "So! You are Couzens! They tell me you are a hell of a hard man to get along with. Well, I am too!" [23]

But while Couzens was negotiating with Goethals, the politicians at home had the City Council pass a resolution requesting his removal. The resolution said that the crime wave was a result of his "incompetency," and directed Mayor Marx to remove him, "in order to restore confidence in our city and for the protection of our homes and our loved ones." [24] Couzens immediately returned to Detroit to face his opponents. "The politicians want me to quit because I will not grant them special privileges. They can't remove me," he announced.[25] He was not removed.

CHAPTER XVII

THE ODD CANDIDATE

"THE first thing you know, Jim, you will be a national character. Remember that Theodore Roosevelt started his career as police commissioner of New York City. Incidentally and confidentially, let me tell you that William Alden Smith will not be a candidate for United States Senator again two years hence. What's the matter with Jim Couzens for his job?" [1] So Milton McRae had written him in November 1916.

Couzens was skeptical then. "It is one thing to receive an appointment to a public office, and another thing to get elected. I make such a poor public showing that I doubt if I could be elected." [2] By 1918, however, on the basis of his eventful record as police commissioner, he began to believe he might be a successful candidate after all.[3]

In April 1918 the *Detroit News* reported "a real Couzens boom for the Senate" was "getting definite," but that there was an odd fact about it. The Couzens "boom" was being openly promoted by John Gillespie, the discredited former police commissioner. The *News* commented: "The boys think that Mr. Couzens as a police commissioner would make a wonderful United States Senator. They have taken him to their bosoms to get him off their backs." [4]

2

To Couzens patriarchal Senator Smith then gave some "candid" advice. He would make "a good senator," but he would "find great difficulty in being nominated and elected." For he had never done anything to get the party obligated to him. "And that was a hard handicap." [5]

Deciding this was sound, Couzens withdrew his name from the senatorial race, in which the contenders by then included Commodore Truman H. Newberry, Governor Chase S. Osborn, Editor Arthur H. Vandenberg—and Henry Ford. "I have been advised by counsel," Couzens said, "that my continued ownership of Ford Motor Company stock disqualified me for the Senate because the Ford Company is engaged in making war materials for the government." [6] Of course, this reasoning also applied, as Couzens well knew, to Ford, though Ford ignored the thrust and became an active candidate for the senatorial nomination, not only as a Republican but also as a Democrat.

That same year, Detroit had adopted a new charter, mainly in order to get a strong chief executive—something previous charters had prevented.[7] Shortly after the "strong mayor charter" was adopted, Couzens made an announcement—he would stand for mayor. His aim, he said, was to be the first of a new line of powerful mayors who would give Detroit the kind of government it needed.

3

At first his announcement provoked amusement among the political experts, even those who were friendly toward him. They said about him exactly what had been said of Hazen S. Pingree: one so lacking in political tact and diplomacy could not be elected mayor of Detroit. John Dodge assured him that he could not be "dog catcher or coroner." E. Roy Pelletier, a former Ford Company advertising manager, laughed when Couzens asked him to handle his campaign publicity. Pelletier did not think it possible to "sell" a man so lacking in "good fellowship." [8] Mayor Marx thought "nothing was funnier," was certain his police commissioner would make one of "the oddest" candidates in political history.[9]

The *Detroit News* said:

> They say he is arrogant, bull-headed, uncompromising. They say he has no consideration for other people's feelings. They say he would rather refuse a favor than grant one. According to their lights, they are right. Toward the special-favor seeking politicians, Mr. Couzens looks that way because he feels just that way.[10]

The *News* then suggested that Detroit ought to have precisely that kind of man as mayor.

4

He started his campaign by making a curiously candid admission. He was not a candidate by "overwhelming requests of my friends, or anything of that sort." He was a candidate solely because he "personally" believed that he would make "a good mayor." The new charter said the mayor was to be "the chief executive officer of the city." He would be precisely that "without the assistance of any political boss."

He drafted a lengthy platform, its most important plank being a statement on the old Pingree issue of municipal ownership of the streetcar system. "My plan," he said, "will be to proceed to condemn the property of the street railway company so the city may get possession as soon as possible." [11]

5

Unintentionally, the streetcar company gave him a tremendous political assist. For the D.U.R. picked just this time to raise fares on the so-called "Pingree lines" from a nickel to six cents. According to the company, wartime inflationary costs forced them to do this, and probably the increase was justified. But in a political sense, it was ill-timed—for the D.U.R.

Taking advantage of this blunder, Couzens immediately announced that he would institute court action to block the increase in fares. Then Edward T. Fitzgerald, Mayor Marx's secretary, who was working for Couzens, came up with an even better idea. He recalled that in a similar situation in 1895, Mayor Pingree had boarded a streetcar, offered the old rate of fare, and had been thrown off the car. Detroiters had rallied to Pingree's support.[12]

Fitzgerald persuaded Couzens to copy Pingree. So in the morning on August 7, 1918, three weeks before the primary, Couzens boarded a Fort Street streetcar, dropped only a nickel in the fare box and proceeded to a seat. "Just a minute!" called the conductor. "The fare is six cents."

"I won't pay it," said Couzens.

"You'll pay six cents or you will have to leave the car," said the conductor, following the instructions issued by the corporation.

"I'll do no such thing!" said Couzens. "I insist on my rights."

The conductor stopped the car and announced it would not proceed unless Couzens got off. Other cars piled up behind and traffic was blocked, but Couzens refused to get off voluntarily. The conductor pushed him off while newspaper reporters and photographers stood by to record it all.[13]

6

The stunt was eminently successful. Indeed, it was too successful. Hundreds of other Detroiters followed his example. The streetcar company met the rebellion by stopping all cars, with the result that there was rioting all over Detroit. Of course, many citizens were outraged. And among them was John Dodge, Couzens' successor as president of the Street Railway Commission. Dodge accused Couzens of "encouraging the thousands of Bolsheviki and Anarchists in the city." "He ought to be put in jail!" Dodge cried.[14]

Although Couzens too was dismayed, he shrewdly said nothing, counting on the rioting to subside. When it did subside, most citizens decided that he had won a victory for the car riders, for the company abandoned the increase in fares.

In the primary, Couzens led all the other candidates, running ahead of Judge Connolly, who had Democratic party backing, ahead of Ex-Commissioner Gillespie of the Marx-Republican machine, and ahead of Divie B. Duffield, a respected lawyer who had drafted the new city charter.

The following November a runoff between Couzens and Connolly was held. Again he defeated Connolly, and became Detroit's new mayor. Of considerable additional interest to him then—and of great importance to him later—was the fact that the same night's election returns showed that Ford, running as a Democrat, in the senatorial election, had lost a bitter contest with Commodore Newberry, the Republican candidate.

CHAPTER XVIII

THE STRONG MAYOR

"I AM by nature somewhat more destructive than constructive," Couzens had said back in 1915 in a burst of self-analysis.[1] What he really meant was that he received pleasure out of challenging accepted patterns of conduct that did not jibe with his own strictly disciplined moral code. This is the way he had performed his job as police commissioner, and as mayor he followed the same course. "I will conduct myself so that I have my own self-respect, regardless of whether people like me," he announced.[2]

He was aware of what some people said about him, that he "had ice water" in his veins, as he once put it.[3] He was caricatured as "King James." He felt that he was "probably the loneliest Mayor any big city ever had," because he did not "grant favors." [4]

But he proved to be the answer to Detroit's wish for a strong executive. Actually, even in the opinion of some who had professed a desire for a non-political mayor, he was too strong—stronger than Pingree, stronger even than big-fisted old Zach Chandler, mayor of Detroit in the 1850's and later a boss of the national Republican party in the time of U. S. Grant and Rutherford B. Hayes.

2

He did not share the view that a man in public office must, if possible, act in an ingratiating manner toward everybody. Rather he conducted himself in accord with his own code. He might have ingratiated himself, for example, with Senator William Alden Smith. President of the Grand Rapids Savings Bank as well as owner of the influential *Grand Rapids Herald.* Senator Smith had asked him, as "a great compliment to me," to place a deposit in the Smith bank. This would have been a nice gesture on Couzens' part, especially since he wanted Smith's good will, as well as that of Vandenberg,

Smith's editor. But Couzens bluntly turned down the request. "I cannot afford to carry any money on deposit," he wrote Smith, citing local taxes.[5] The incident was but one of many that caused his friends to bemoan his "political dumbness."

Just as typical was his response when an employer telephoned him one day for a police squad to "chase away some strikers," complaining that the pickets were calling him names.

"What are they calling you?" asked Couzens. When the man told him, he replied: "Oh, I've heard you call your workers the same names!"

He refused the request.[6]

3

He began almost every day by handing over to his secretary a list of automobile license numbers to be sent to the police department—license numbers on cars which he himself had observed breaking traffic laws as he drove to City Hall.[7]

He did not even hesitate to lay down the law to newspapers, as in the following letter:

November 1, 1921

Detroit Journal
Detroit, Michigan

Gentlemen:
One of your delivery wagons deliberately parked double just west of Wayne on Congress this morning. The car was left unattended, blocking traffic. This kind of disregard for law must be discontinued, otherwise the driver will be arrested.

Very truly yours,
JAMES COUZENS, Mayor.[8]

4

Because he always said forcefully just what he thought, regardless of diplomacy, he stirred up even more tempests as Mayor than he had as Police Commissioner. When the Detroit Board of Commerce opposed his plan for improving a municipal hospital, objecting to the expense, he let fly the statement that the Board leaders were a "pack of curs." [9]

He threw the City Council into an uproar by shouting "Liar!" at the president of the Edison Company during a discussion of utility-company profits, and found himself "banished" from the council chambers because of the outburst. In answer, he announced that he would seek the impeachment of the respected and venerable presiding councilman, James Vernor, the ginger-ale magnate, who had ordered Couzens to "mind his manners." [10]

He even provoked a near fist-fight with an old friend in the council, John C. Lodge, being too quick, as he himself later admitted, to voice the charge of "sell-out." [11]

He antagonized nearly all of the medical profession in Detroit and Michigan when, over the protests of the medical societies, he invited Dr. Adolf Lorenz of Vienna to Detroit to use the Lorenz treatment on children with infantile paralysis. When the doctors refused Dr. Lorenz the facilities of the private hospitals, Couzens opened the municipal hospitals to him, the while denouncing the doctors for "un-American intolerance." [12]

5

Well-wishers urged him to exercise greater restraint, to be more affable, even with his critics. His old hero, Pingree, had not been affable, he answered. "I recognize the desirability of composure . . . but sometimes it takes an explosion to cause action to be taken to prevent a repetition of what causes the explosion." [13]

But while his temperament provoked a great deal of controversy, it produced much positive good for the city of Detroit. He completely transformed the shabby atmosphere that had prevailed in the municipal offices. After his first ten months in office, an unfriendly newspaper had to concede that he had brought into the City Hall "business dispatch, confidence, and decorum. . . . Since the first floor front of the City Hall became his home, scandal has become a lost word in the municipal lexicon. Not a hint of bossism, bargaining, political debt-paying."

The Board of Commerce, with which he was almost continually at loggerheads, also had praise for his non-political administration. "Couzens' favorite campaign phrase was 'I'll reward no friends and I'll punish no enemies.' He kept his word. His appointments were made on merit—he paid no political debts," said its official publication.[14]

City functionaries of long standing who had never before seen any mayor in their particular bailiwick, now saw Couzens frequently. The first person to enter the City Hall and the last to leave, he almost literally wore out stenographers with the amount of correspondence that he insisted on handling.[15]

Veteran officeholders were astonished to discover that when he called something to their attention, he expected to hear that the business had been transacted immediately. "If he did not get a report promptly, we got a request for a report; that had never happened before in the City Hall." [16]

On a holiday, a subordinate found him at his desk as usual, and asked, "Why do you work when everyone else is out playing?" "I have to make good on this job," he said.[17]

6

From the time he had come from Chatham twenty-eight years before, Detroit by then had grown fivefold in population. It was then a city of nearly a million persons, the fourth city in America. Since 1915, it had doubled in area, mainly under the pressure of the automobile industry he had helped to build. Yet only slight efforts had been made to keep even the basic municipal services in line with the city's growth. In 1919 the city still had the same sewer and water installations that had been insufficient when Detroit was half the size. Schools were overcrowded, with thirteen thousand children on half-time schedules. Public hospital facilities, parks, and playgrounds were lacking. The main thoroughfares were narrow, traffic-choked, and studded with bottlenecks and deathtraps.[18]

Most glaring of all was the city's continuing deficiency in streetcar transportation. Always a source of annoyance to Detroiters, as Couzens well knew from his own first days in the city, the streetcar system was then abominable, and even the streetcar corporation admitted as much.

7

To change this, Detroit had long needed bold, energetic leadership that would be able to win the people's confidence. Couzens did not hesitate to recommend the expenditure of millions of dollars for the needed schools, sewers, hospitals, and street improvements. Convinced of his honesty and ability, the people followed his guidance, and it was his good fortune that within a week after his election, the Armistice came, bringing an end to wartime restrictions on materials needed for rehabilitating and extending the city's services.

In his first three years as mayor, Couzens directed planning for the expenditure of approximately $243,000,000—an astounding figure in that period.[19]

Under his leadership, Detroit became, in government as well as in industry, the "city dynamic." [20] Indeed, it would be years (in fact, not until Fiorello H. LaGuardia, a strikingly similar sort of man, became mayor of New York) before all America was to know another such aggressively constructive mayor of any city in the land.

He eschewed all partisan politics, except when he secretly tried to play a part in the 1920 Republican Presidential nominations. He favored the nomination of the old Bull Mooser, Senator Hiram Johnson of California, then still reputed an insurgent. Couzens personally paid all of the expense, about five thousand dollars, for establishing a Hiram Johnson campaign headquarters in New York.[21] The nomination went to another senator, Warren G. Harding, who soon invited Couzens to visit him at his home in Marion, Ohio, to "discuss the coming campaign." Couzens declined. He was too busy, he said. But his real reason was that Harding, darling of the Old Guard, was not his kind of man.

CHAPTER XIX

THE PEOPLE'S MAN

IT WAS not merely because Couzens was a "builder mayor," nor even because he was so conspicuously honest and aggressively non-political, that he became one of the few outstanding mayors in American history. In all probability, his "disgraceful contemporary," as he called Mayor "Big Bill" Thompson of Chicago, outdid him in the field of public improvements.[1] And, even in those days, there were other mayors who were honest and non-political. But Couzens was outstanding primarily because he stood for liberalism and intelligence during a period—the aftermath of World War I—that was characterized by reaction.[2]

He frankly favored not less government action, but more government action whenever he was convinced of the social need—and this was a full decade before Franklin D. Roosevelt's "New Deal." Indeed, when there was a nationwide coal strike in 1922, he went so far as to advocate government ownership of coal mines.[3] When an acute shortage of homes in Detroit developed at the beginning of his term, he announced that he favored having the city government appropriate funds for home building, an early suggestion that there should be "public housing." "I do not believe private initiative and capital are able to cope with this situation," he announced. "Meanwhile, Detroit cannot wait. We must have accommodations for these people. . . . I do not see why we cannot float a $5,000,000 bond issue of five-year bonds to aid workers in getting homes. . . . Workers would get their homes nearly at cost, and the city would get the money cheaper than private interests could get it." [4]

He did not drop the idea until lawyers had convinced him that the city could not go into the home-loan business without changing the state constitution.

2

In 1919 and again in 1921, Detroit was hit especially hard by severe postwar unemployment. Like Pingree, Couzens insisted that the city assume responsibility for relieving distress, and also for providing jobs on public works. So many jobless men were put to work in the streets department, he once said "the streets were almost disgracefully clean." Just as openly, he dispensed doles from the city treasury to needy workingmen's families.[5]

Also like Pingree, of the "potato patches" of the 1890's, he was called a "socialist." His answer was: "Human beings cannot be permitted to starve because of political theory."

3

Significantly—and oddly, perhaps, to some—only one other man in the nation received as much attention in the field of unemployment relief as did Couzens. This was Herbert Hoover, the Secretary of Commerce in Harding's administration. Then a symbol of liberalism in Washington, Secretary Hoover caused President Harding to call a White House conference on unemployment in September 1921, to which Couzens was invited.[6] As chairman of this conference, Hoover declared: "There is no economic failure so terrible in its import as that of a country possessing a surplus of every necessity of life in which numbers willing and anxious to work, are deprived of these necessities. It simply cannot be if our moral and economic system is to survive." [7] Couzens was delighted with Hoover's viewpoint, especially since Hoover specifically endorsed the program for which Couzens had been called a socialist in Detroit. Later, Hoover visited Detroit and was an overnight guest at the Couzens home on Longfellow Avenue. Couzens found Hoover to be "a hard man to entertain socially." [8] But there then began, if not a friendship, an association that seemingly foretold harmonious relations in the future, if their paths should happen to cross again.

4

As an advocate of freedom of speech in America, Couzens was even more commanding on the municipal scene. In New York City, Mayor John Hylan announced a ban on "unlawful assemblages" which his police took to mean all meetings of radicals. Emma Goldman, the anarchist, was hounded from city jail to city jail. There was a demand for rough treatment of strikers and all "labor agitators." In most cities, the police complied with enthusiasm. But not in Detroit. Despite all the postwar hysteria about "Bolshevism," Couzens determined to uphold democratic procedures.

A test came in the winter of 1919. "Big Bill" Haywood, then the most publicized radical in America, was billed for a meeting in Detroit. A statement authorized by the state headquarters of the American Legion declared: "If Mayor Couzens and the police department do not intend to prevent Haywood from speaking here, the American Legion will." [9]

Couzens' own police commissioner, Dr. James Inches, urged that the Haywood meeting be suppressed. Dr. Inches argued that if the Legion intended to break up the meeting, in his opinion the only solution was to keep the meeting from taking place.

But Couzens said this was cowardice. "As long as Haywood conducts himself within the law he can speak." [10] The Legion backed down; Haywood made his speech. And Couzens himself was there to see that he did.

5

Not long after this, A. Mitchell Palmer, Wilson's Attorney General and also a candidate for President to succeed Wilson, staged his so-called "red raids" all over America.[11] In later years, even conservatives came to view this activity as a shameful, unnecessary "witch hunt." In 1930, before the Harvard Law School alumni, Chief Justice Charles Evans Hughes spoke "with deep concern about inflammatory appeals to prejudice made by district attorneys and about the browbeating of witnesses . . . in every part of the country." [12] Yet, at the time, with the exception of a few senators like La Follette, almost the only official voice to be raised in America against the Attorney General was that of Mayor Couzens. When he learned that his own Detroit police department had cooperated with Palmer's agents, and with an assistant U. S. district attorney in Detroit named Frank Murphy in seizing and jailing supposed, or even real, "reds," Couzens ordered the practice ended.[13] "I am not sure that there is any reason for these raids," he said. "I won't be stampeded by federal officials." [14] He wasn't, and, at least officially, Detroit resisted the general hysteria.

6

Just before Palmer began his movement to "stamp out Bolshevism," Couzens prepared a noteworthy statement for the Newspaper

Enterprise Association. He branded propaganda about "Bolshevism" a disguised effort to halt social progress, the same position vigorously taken in Kansas by another enlightened Republican, William Allen White of the Emporia *Gazette*.[15] Couzens went on:

> The makers of dictionaries in the future are likely to have a hard time defining the term "Bolshevism" as it is being applied in America today.
>
> The word is a vague definition applied to almost anything that disturbs our social viewpoint.
>
> In the typical American metropolis of Detroit, we are confronted with every phase of the [war] reconstruction problem. But we have not found it necessary to throttle free speech nor to interfere with the lawful expression of radical ideas. Criticism of government is absolutely needful. I am convinced that to attempt to bottle it up is highly dangerous. Are we to stifle every symptom of thinking by shouting Bolshevism? . . .[16]

Published in newspapers throughout the country under the heading "Don't Bottle Free Thinking!" this statement indicated a further step in his maturing as a public man, one who, often without realizing it himself, had become a people's man. Like Pingree of his own city, like Altgeld of Illinois, like La Follette of Wisconsin, like Tom Johnson and Brand Whitlock of Ohio, like Brandeis of Massachusetts, and others, Republicans and Democrats, who fought for people's rights, he was following a long-standing American tradition of progressivism and freedom.

CHAPTER XX

THE BATTLE FOR M.O.

IRONICALLY, no one in the Detroit of that period was more often called a "Bolshevist" than Couzens himself—mainly because of his battle to establish municipal ownership of the city's streetcar lines.

He had flatly declared in his inaugural message that Detroit needed to run its own public transportation system. His blue eyes never looked more like steel than when he said: "Unless the Detroit United Railway agrees to reasonable terms by which the city takes over its city lines, I will be ready to adopt war measures." If necessary, he added, he would submit a purchase plan "every six months, until one was adopted." [1] For his one idea was to put over municipal ownership, no matter what it cost him.[2]

Even so, against his deepest personal inclination, he began with a compromise. He had concluded long before that the best procedure would be for the city to build competing lines, "start small like the Ford Company did," deny any more franchises to the D.U.R. while letting the old franchises expire, and then sit back to watch the municipal lines crush out the company lines. But he let the members of his Street Railway Commission, three amiable businessmen, persuade him that such a course meant a fight which, they said, would be "bad for Detroit." They induced him to go to the voters in a referendum in April 1918 with another purchase plan—to buy the D.U.R. lines for $31,500,000, a price to which the D.U.R. had agreed. They also persuaded him to conduct only a mild campaign, keeping himself in the background. His commissioners argued: why stir up the people when the company had agreed to sell and all the Detroit papers were in favor of the purchase? [3]

2

The compromise turned out badly. For one thing, the D.U.R., which had ostensibly agreed to the sale, had in fact prepared reams of literature against the proposal and distributed this material at the last minute.[4]

But more serious opposition came from Henry Ford. In 1915 Henry Ford had unqualifiedly endorsed Couzens' M.O. plan in a front-page interview in the *Detroit News*, saying: "It is one of the safest business propositions I have ever heard of. I will gladly work under James Couzens in the street railway matter." [5]

True, Ford's newspaper, the *Dearborn Independent*, had carried an item, just after Couzens' election, that had belittled Couzens' streetcar program. But Ford personally had sent a copy of the paper to Couzens accompanied by this message:

"While I have bought this paper, I am not taking active management until January 1st, 1919. I do not agree with this article in any way. My sentiments are to help you in every way." [6]

But despite this, during the last week of the streetcar campaign, Ford, acting through Charles E. Sorensen, then general manager of the Henry Ford and Son Tractor Plant, let loose a resounding blast against the Couzens plan. Everyone understood that while the statement ripping into Couzens' plan (which soon was posted all over Detroit in handbills and printed in full-page advertisements) bore Sorensen's signature, it was really Ford's. Indeed, Ford had admitted to E. G. Pipp that he intended "to keep Couzens from getting his way." "He seemed to feel unusually peevish toward Couzens that day," recalled Pipp. Pipp reminded Ford that previously he had supported Couzens' efforts toward municipal ownership. "I have a right to change my mind," snapped Ford.[7]

3

The Ford statement injected a wholly new argument into the streetcar controversy: electric streetcars are out of date; the "coming thing" is gasoline-propelled cars; Henry Ford is developing the new type of car; hence the city of Detroit would be paying $31,500,000 to the D.U.R. for "junk." [8]

Of course, the Ford gasoline streetcar was pure fiction, or little more than just an idea. In the words of Jay G. Hayden, "The announcement was plainly designed to scuttle the purchase proposal." [9]

Couzens boiled with anger. "What Mr. Couzens said regarding Mr. Ford could not be presented in these polite columns," the *Detroit Saturday Night* recalled later.[10] Ford came back with a barbed statement filled with sarcastic references to Couzens' "lack of mechanical knowledge." [11]

Had this exchange continued, it would doubtless have dawned on the majority of Detroiters that the "Sorensen statement" was really an expression of personal feeling and had nothing to do with the merits of Couzens' streetcar plan. As it was, the time was too short for the public to catch on.

As a result, thousands of Detroiters, who otherwise were for M.O., voted against Couzens' plan because they were taken in by the Sorensen statement. So Couzens lost his second M.O. referendum. [12]

4

The *Detroit News* analyzed the defeat as having resulted from Couzens having been, for once, too soft. The people were fed up with inadequate transportation and wanted the D.U.R. treated roughly. "What they want is to hang the D.U.R.'s hide on the fence." [13]

Couzens agreed, and bided his time for another occasion when he could again raise the M.O. issue. It came when a strike, two months later, halted all streetcar service. He decided that the strike, ostensibly for higher wages, was really a collusive affair between the D.U.R. management and the unions to get further rate increases. [14] On the second day of the stoppage, he issued a decisive statement:

> The moment has arrived to finish up our dealings with the D.U.R. I reached that conclusion last night. That conclusion was confirmed when I left my farm at 5:55 this morning and came to town and saw how comfortably we were getting along without the D.U.R. . . . We will order the company off the non-franchise lines and put our own equipment on the tracks. . . . By fall, we can have cars sufficient to have a fair-sized system of our own running, or to have forced the D.U.R. to turn over its property at junk prices.
>
> If the Council will cooperate, I am willing to let this end all relationship with the D.U.R. once and for all. We have been grasped by this lying corporation until it seems to me that they have made their final grasp. [15]

And to this he appended—as if in answer to critics of his "impulsiveness"—a personal note:

"I have reached this conclusion under no pressure and after no moments of excitement, but after thirty-six hours of quiet thought."

An ominous postscript, that—for the D.U.R.

5

Then the D.U.R. knew it was in for a battle to the finish. It promptly settled the strike, after Couzens had directed his city attorneys to seek a court order placing the company in receivership for failure to render transportation service.[16] Then, suddenly, the company discovered that it wanted to build numerous extensions that it had previously refused to consider. Just as suddenly, it discovered that it could increase wages without charging for transfers.[17] It started a discussion of subways, and even offered to surrender its city lines to another company, keeping only its interurban properties. Or it would deal with the city on a service-at-cost basis —anything, in fact, to keep the people from accepting the Couzens proposal for a rival municipal line.[18]

Most of the members of the City Council backed away from a showdown, saying that it would be better to try to get improved service and, perhaps, a subway, than to start another fight. Couzens' own street-railway commissioners, all personal friends who had been appointed because they supposedly favored his program, also backed away. They said that instead of municipal ownership, Detroit should adopt the so-called Taylor Plan, a service-at-cost scheme under private ownership which was being tried in Cleveland.

"Well, gentlemen," Couzens said to them, "if that's your conviction, I'll have to ask for your resignations." [19]

He then announced a referendum for April 1920 on a bond issue of $15,000,000 for the establishment of a competing independent, city-owned streetcar system.[20]

Against this plan, the D.U.R. enlisted an army of orators and sundry propagandists. The Board of Commerce and a special group of business leaders, led by Alvan Macauley and Henry B. Joy, both of the Packard Motor Car Company, joined the D.U.R. in its fight.

Even the three friends who had been Couzens' streetcar commissioners openly opposed the proposal.[21] Aided by utility companies in other cities, the D.U.R. let loose a flood of literature that literally clogged the Detroit post office. It was estimated that the company spent $500,000 to defeat the plan.[22] Joining in the attack were not only those interests opposed to "socialism," but also those eager to see a personal setback for Couzens. As Jay Hayden has recalled: "For years, he had been stepping on sacred toes. If he won this battle, it was clear that he would be even more firmly entrenched. The myriad of interests that he had thwarted moved as one in a supreme effort to stop this man." [23]

But, luckily for Couzens, just at this time Ford had set his heart on buying out all of the minority stockholders in the Ford Motor Company. There had been a good deal of jockeying on Ford's part to get the other stockholders, including Couzens, to sell out without knowing who wanted to buy. Couzens had held out until he could discover who was behind mysterious offers being made by various brokers. He found out that the buyer was Ford himself when Edsel Ford, in September 1919, came to his home and put all the Ford cards on the table.[24] Unless Couzens agreed to sell, some of the others would hold back. Couzens was the key to the whole transaction.

At the session with Edsel, Couzens agreed to sell, although he insisted on getting a higher price for his stock than the others in recognition of his part in the creation of the company. John Anderson, for one, endorsed this proposal, saying to Stuart Webb, one of the negotiators: "If there is anybody in that organization who is entitled to a little bit more than anyone else . . . it is Mayor Couzens. It was due to his efforts that the company became a success." [25]

The deal was closed for $30,000,000 for his stock, of which $29,-308,857.90 was for himself, and $691,142.10 for his sister Rosetta.

Apparently out of gratitude, Ford then made a truce with Couzens that culminated in a curious letter which Ford had his secretary release to the *Detroit Saturday Night*—to correct some "rumors":

> The relations between Mr. Ford and Mr. Couzens during his association with the Ford Motor Company, or afterward, have at no time been strained. Both men have ideals wherein they are desirous of serving the people in the best and most beneficial way, and each has chosen his method of doing so. I believe as well that neither one of these men would hesitate to cooperate with the other if the resulting benefit was for the best of the people.
>
> Very truly yours,
> E. G. LIEBOLD,
> General Secretary to Henry Ford.[26]

Ford now forgot the Sorensen's "gasoline car" and came out for the M.O. plan. This time more than 63 per cent of the voters approved Couzens' program for municipally owned and operated streetcars. Couzens immediately gave the order to begin excavation work for the new M.O. lines—thus starting, at last, to carry out the program first proclaimed as far back as the 1890's.[27]

CHAPTER XXI

THE "DAMNABLE OUTRAGE"

PROBLEMS remained, however. The D.U.R. launched nine different lawsuits to try to invalidate the referendum. One suit was even based on the point that the paper used for the ballots was too thin.[1]

Steel for the rails was needed, and no major steel company would submit bids. The bonds voted in the referendum had to be sold, and investment brokers boycotted them.

Couzens arranged for the steel by making a personal plea to James A. Farrell, president of the U.S. Steel Corporation. He met the boycott of the brokers by buying many of the bonds himself, and by using certain municipal funds for buying others. Lawyers argued that the procedure was illegal,[2] but he went ahead—and was sustained by the courts. Meanwhile, construction went on.

The tracks of the new municipal lines had to cross D.U.R. tracks at several points. As the law was then understood, the D.U.R. had the right to prevent this. Consequently, there occurred another of those civic comedies with Couzens as script writer.

At midnight on Saturday, January 8, 1921, some two hundred city workers, under secret orders, converged at the intersection of St. Jean and Mack Streets. Policemen ringed the intersection to keep out "intruders," and under their protection, the workers proceeded to saw and hack the D.U.R. rails in two. As expected, the D.U.R. general manager arrived with a court order commanding that the city work be halted. He was arrested and taken to a police station on Belle Isle, where the drawbridge to the island was lifted, so that no one could get to the park to serve legal orders for his release. By the time the manager was freed, the crossing had been achieved and city streetcars began running across the D.U.R. lines.[3]

There was an appeal to the courts. D.U.R. attorneys said that the midnight crossing was "an abominable, damnable outrage." [4] The

lower courts agreed and ordered the city not to use the crossing, but
—and this was the important thing—the city was not ordered to tear
up its tracks. The case was appealed to the Supreme Court of the
United States. The D.U.R. retained as its counsel none other than
Charles Evans Hughes, then marking time between two terms in
the highest court, but even he was not able to save the D.U.R.
In effect, the Supreme Court rendered a decision which supported
fully the "damnable outrage." [5]

2

One more effort was made by the D.U.R. to destroy the municipal
lines. It submitted to the voters a proposal that the city lines be
merged with those of the D.U.R. in a new private company to operate on the service-at-cost principle. This plan offered a number of
attractive concessions to the public. But Couzens presented a counter
proposal—for the city to take over certain D.U.R. lines on which
there was no franchise and which the D.U.R. had no choice but to
sell. In the campaign that followed, the D.U.R. issued a threat. If
its proposal were not accepted, it would take all its cars off the streets.

"We will not be intimidated," [6] said Couzens, and the voters
supported him in sufficient numbers to kill the D.U.R. proposal
while they approved his own proposal.[7]

However, unless the city system could operate on certain D.U.R.
routes—notably those on such main thoroughfares as Woodward
Avenue and Fort Street—the city's position still was not yet satisfactory. Couzens then asked the D.U.R. to sell its lines on those two
main streets, but, as usual, the D.U.R. refused.

Then it was Couzens who made a threat: He would tear up the
D.U.R. tracks—a weapon that no other mayor of Detroit had ever
seriously considered using—if the voters approved. In an election
of November 1921 the people again stood by Couzens, voting the
ouster authority, at the same time re-electing him mayor for a
second term.

3

Couzens then prepared for the kill, forcing the company to permit
city cars to operate over its lines, with an interchange of transfers.
In effect, he achieved by this a unified car system for the city.[8]

Knowing it was licked, the D.U.R. then presented him with the
proposal that the city lease its lines.[9] He refused; his goal was to

purchase, not to lease, and he knew he had the corporation in his power. A meeting of the D.U.R. stockholders was called. Having purchased a share of stock to qualify as a shareholder, Couzens himself occupied a front seat. He listened to the discussion, and then stood up. Unless the D.U.R. agreed to sell to the city *all* its municipal lines at the price he had already specified, he would carry out his threat to tear up the tracks on Woodward Avenue and Fort Street. "This issue must be settled now, in February," he added.[10]

4

On the last day of February 1922 the D.U.R. surrendered.

That April, Couzens presented the voters with an agreement by which the city would acquire the D.U.R. city lines for $19,850,000. It was approved—and a month later the D.U.R. lines became a part of the municipal railway.[11] The long battle for municipal ownership in Detroit was won at last. Probably no one but Couzens could have won it. Considering the stakes, the obstacles, and the bitterness of the opposition, he had, by his "bull-headedness," scored a victory that was unique in the annals of American politics in his or even later eras.[12]

CHAPTER XXII

THE REWARD

COUZENS' satisfaction at having established the nation's largest mu nicipally owned railway was "sweeter," he said, than anything he had ever achieved in business.[1] Best of all, he had demonstrated beyond any question that he was his own man. The *Detroit News* commented:

> The only way to dictate successfully to Mr. Couzens about anything would be first of all to throw him into a deep well and then to fill up the well with scrap iron and paving bricks. After that, it is assumed that if you told him to stay there, he might do it.[2]

This was precisely the reputation he wanted.

2

Would he now be content to rest on his laurels? Would he be satisfied to continue as Mayor of Detroit, to run for that office again, and then call matters quits? No one who really knew him could have thought so. Close to fifty then, he was still subject to the drive of ambition that had always marked him.

The truth was that he had never given up the idea of being United States Senator from Michigan, the highest office to which he could aspire in view of his Canadian birth, and he seldom forgot that this was his ultimate goal. In November 1922 there would be another senatorial election.

Henry Ford had unexpectedly precipitated a political issue that made it altogether reasonable for Couzens to expect to capture the Republican nomination from Senator Charles E. Townsend. For Ford had placed with the Department of Justice evidence that Senator Truman H. Newberry had expended large sums of money in the 1918 campaign. On the basis of this, Newberry had been convicted of violating the federal corrupt-practice act in a lower court. The

United States Supreme Court had overruled the conviction,[3] but the issue had been kept alive.

In January 1922 the Senate took up a resolution to expel Newberry. On one side were the Old Guard Republican senators; on the other, insurgent Republicans, led by La Follette of Wisconsin, and, of course, the Democrats. Senator George W. Norris of Nebraska made a powerful, sarcastic speech against Newberry, which began, "Mr. President, they had a public sale up in Michigan . . ." [4] This resolution was defeated, but this did not end the matter. Instead, in the 1922 elections, "Newberryism" became an issue against every senator up for re-election who had supported Newberry.[5] This was particularly true in Michigan, for Senator Townsend had defended Newberry.

3

Here was a situation that seemed made to order for Couzens. No other nominal Republican in the state so definitely represented the antithesis of "Newberryism." Besides, when he had stood for re-election in the mayoralty campaign the previous year, 1921, he had demonstrated that he was a political force of the first magnitude in Michigan on his own, regardless of party machinery. If his first election as mayor could have been passed off as a freak, this was not so in 1921, for all of his shortcomings, real and alleged, had been fully aired, and all the people he had offended by refusing to be a "good fellow" had opposed him. "You are too mean to people to be re-elected," his friend Jay Hayden had told him.[6]

The business elements generally had been against him. "They opposed my activities at every turn," Couzens himself said.[7] Yet he was handsomely returned to office. "He hasn't a soul with him— except the city of Detroit," said one observer.[8]

4

His health, however, finally determined that he would not enter that senatorial race after all. From the first year of his mayoralty, his physical condition had become a cause for concern. Just after his initial municipal-ownership victory, marked by the heavy speaking program that had clearly overtaxed him, he began to be conscious of a stiffening in his left knee. Severe rheumatic pains attacked him. His leg was placed in a cast and he was forced to hobble about with a cane.

Then his tonsils, considered a possible cause of his trouble, were removed. For a man of his hitherto perfect health—except for headaches—he was remarkably slow in recovering from the tonsilectomy. The stiffness in his leg and the pain persisted. Later, he began to suffer from severe abdominal pain.

He was operated on again, this time for the removal of a gallstone. After spending two months in Florida, he seemed to have recovered his health. But soon he was again operated on, this time for bladder trouble. His condition became so desperate that it was reported he was dying.[9] He staged a comeback, only to be subjected to still another operation two months later, this time for an infection resulting from the previous operation.

When he finally did get back on his feet, he was by no means an invalid. Back at his desk in City Hall, he took on even more activities, adding the active managership of the street railway lines to his general duties as mayor. He was proud of the way he could still drive himself. "I get up at 6:30 every morning and hustle to get out of the house at 8 o'clock. I make straight for my office at the street railway headquarters and stick on the job there until noon. Then I change from being general manager of the traction system . . . and get on the job as Mayor. . . . I have never worked so hard in my life." [10] But the made-to-order opportunity to be a United States Senator had slipped by—so he thought.

5

Actually, the "Couzens luck" was running with him again.

Almost as soon as he had reconciled himself to a long wait before he could have another chance at the senatorship, the news came that Commodore Newberry intended to resign from the Senate. His colleague, Senator Townsend, had been defeated by a Democrat, Woodbridge N. Ferris. Very correctly, Newberry interpreted Townsend's defeat as a rebuke to himself. He also foresaw that when a new resolution for his expulsion came up in the Senate, it would certainly pass. Therefore, on November 18, 1922, he prudently resigned—"lashed from the Senate," in the words of Mississippi's Senator Pat Harrison.[11]

Governor Alex J. Groesbeck, known as a progressive Republican, then described the kind of man he would appoint to the vacancy. He would be "aggressive, and capable of taking care of himself on the floor of the Senate . . . something besides a mere dispenser of patronage," one who would be against "so-called standpatism" and "have the capacity and courage to do things that will advance the state and national welfare, regardless of personal and political considerations." This seemed to fit Couzens to a T, except for one thing. The appointee naturally had to be a Republican. Couzens professed to be a Republican, but was he?

6

It was widely known that he placed an individual's stand on public questions ahead of party regularity. Back in 1918, in response to a request for a campaign contribution on behalf of Republican Congressional candidates, he had told Fred W. Upham of Chicago, treasurer of the Republican National Committee:

> I must confess that I am not so much a party man as I am for individuals, and, in declining contributions to their campaigns, I have stated that I would have to know for whom the campaign was being conducted. . . . There are Democrats that I would rather vote for than some Republicans, though I am a Republican.[12]

Governor Groesbeck was warned against the Couzens "temperament." The Detroit Times, then owned jointly by William Randolph Hearst and Arthur Brisbane, commented: "The principal objection to Mr. Couzens seems to be that he is temperamentally unfitted to work on a job where he is surrounded by men equal to him in authority. He is a lone hand player." [13]

On Saturday, November 25, 1922, Governor Groesbeck called on Couzens at his home, obviously for a confidential "feeling out" sort of conversation. Couzens reiterated that he was a Republican, but he frankly said there was not much about the party's program at that time that he approved. The Governor really felt the same way, and so this was not against Couzens in Groesbeck's view. As for patronage, Couzens said: "I hate the very sound of the word." Couzens made one concession that Groesbeck accepted as satisfactory: he did "believe" in "party government." [14]

7

Groesbeck had said that he would definitely announce his choice on the 27th. The 27th passed and Groesbeck was silent. The press began to mention other available men. Among them were E. D. Stair of the Free Press, Ralph Booth of the Booth newspapers, and Marion L. Burton, president of the University of Michigan.

As for Couzens, he went about his affairs as usual. He had planned to spend Thanksgiving Day in New York City with Madeleine, who was at school there. Besides, Frank Couzens had married Margaret Lang of Kitchener, Ontario, the previous October 22nd; the newly-weds would also be in New York, and Couzens wanted to see them. He did not see fit to change his plans.[15]

Only a few hours after he and Mrs. Couzens and Madeleine had settled themselves in the Hotel Belmont on November 29, 1922, there was a telephone call from Governor Groesbeck. He had been appointed to the Senate as Newberry's successor.

BOOK THREE

The Senator

CHAPTER XXIII

THE ONE-MAN BLOC

He was a marked man in the Senate from the very beginning. His career in industry as well as in municipal government, plus his wealth and his reputation as a fighter formed a combination that caught the public fancy.

One news service, unaware of his Canadian birth, sent out during his first month a story to the effect that he was "a natural candidate for President in 1924." "If the Democrats pick Ford, the Republicans are sure to seize upon Couzens as the only man who has a chance to beat him," said the story.[1]

Indeed, he rivaled in public attention, quite successfully, that distinctive feature of the year 1922—the "flapper." [2]

2

The Washington newspaper writers as a group immediately liked him, in particular such journalists as Thomas L. Stokes, Paul Y. Anderson, and Ray Tucker. Many senators were cautious in permitting the press to quote them, but not Couzens. Consequently, he was often good for a "story." The journalists, especially those of a liberal bent, flocked to his office. On the basis of one such meeting in his first week, William Hard wrote: "He is a perfectly non-political type of person . . . comes close to being the perfect independent." [3] This was sound prophecy.

3

He never mastered the art of oratory. For the most part, parliamentary procedure was a complete mystery to him. But he worked hard at his new career, attended every committee meeting, unless ill. He naively attempted in the beginning to function in the Senate as an executive, and never fully reconciled himself to the fact that this was impossible. Indeed, quite early in his career he remarked to a colleague: "This senator thing is not my line, and I probably won't be here long. There is too much talk, talk, talk." [4]

"He goes for the point like a bullet. He's a man of strong likes and dislikes. He's far from patient. Riled, he manifests it with plenty of vigor and urgency. Called to order, he effervesces like a shaken-up bottle of soda water. If you have business with Senator Couzens, make it snappy. He's there to transact it, and he's very accessible, but he doesn't want a conversation to drool along. . . . Efficiency, efficiency. That's Senator Couzens." So one observer wrote.[5]

In those first weeks, he spent considerable time searching in books to try to learn what a senator should do and be.[6] Finally, he gave up the study—and decided to be himself.

4

When he was sworn in by Vice President Calvin Coolidge on December 7, 1922, to become "a real live senator," as he wrote Madeleine, Harding was still President. The Secretary of the Treasury was Andrew W. Mellon. Many believed he functioned as the real power of the Harding administration. Charles Evans Hughes was Secretary of State. Herbert Hoover still headed Commerce. William Howard Taft was Chief Justice.

In the Senate itself, there was still Henry Cabot Lodge of Massachusetts, a link with an era long past. The venerable Mr. Lodge's celebrated whiskers were fading somewhat, but he remained the grandee of the Old Guard, symbolizing a strong hold on the government by old line conservatives. As faithful lieutenants in the Senate, Lodge had James Watson of Indiana, Reed Smoot of Utah, David Reed of Pennsylvania, George Moses of New Hampshire, and Simeon Fess of Ohio, all fervently devoted to the policies that President Harding had termed "normalcy." [7]

With Wilson's party largely in a state of coma after the defeat of James Cox and Franklin D. Roosevelt for President and Vice President in the 1920 election,[8] the Old Guard leaders, for all practical purposes, were the Senate of the United States throughout the first half of the Harding era.[9]

5

It is true, however, that by 1922, the Republican stalwarts found themselves confronted with a challenging force, even so. In the Senate then were men, mainly Republicans from the West, who appeared to have been infected with the virus of Populism which many believed had been annihilated in the first Bryan campaign of 1896. These included Senators Robert M. La Follette, Sr., of Wisconsin, George W. Norris of Nebraska, Hiram Johnson of California, William E. Borah of Idaho, and, to some extent, Albert Cummins of Iowa, Arthur W. Capper of Kansas, and Charles L. McNary of Oregon. As the result of a kind of political dust storm in Iowa, the 1922 elections had even turned up a supposedly peculiar Republican who was pictured as a cross between John Peter Altgeld of Illinois and Nicolai Lenin—Senator Smith Brookhart, whose middle name was "Wildman."

Under Old Bob La Follette's magnetic personal leadership, these men had formed a Progressive bloc to make war on the clique around Harding, the "curious crew," as Senator Norris called them.[10] Senator Moses called this progressive group "Sons of the Wild Jackass," with Couzens to be included in the epithet.[11]

This group contrived at times to stir up heated controversy. They inveighed against domination of government by big business and flayed Wall Street and the power trust. They championed the cause of the western agricultural areas, which somehow did not share fully in the blessings of Harding's "normalcy." They opposed the administration tax policies. And finally, they turned the spotlight on evidence of corruption that made the Harding regime comparable to that of President Grant, uncovering a scandal, in the Teapot Dome oil leases, that rivaled any governmental venality the nation had known before.[12]

William Allen White thought he saw in this Progressive bloc, mainly Republican, a movement "that portends revolution—not noisy, bloody and disorderly . . . but a nice, decent, and dangerous revolution that will take a long forward trek toward economic justice for those who have been hankering to see something smash something."[13] This was optimism, for the basic calmness of the over-all political scene was really little disturbed just then. It would be ten years before the "nice and decent revolution"—that of Franklin D. Roosevelt—was to come.

6

Couzens himself was anxious for action. He gave a hint of this by his behavior when he was sworn in by Coolidge. When his name was called, he loped down the aisle so swiftly that retiring Senator Townsend, supposedly his escort, had to hurry to catch up.[14]

But the general listlessness of these early 1920's was a definite handicap to him. His nature demanded that he strive to be outstanding, to leave his mark. The criticism which had been voiced to Governor Groesbeck that Couzens was a "lone handed player" was accurate, and therefore he could not wholly identify himself with any group in the Senate and gain satisfaction from the activities of the group—much less his party. He had to be on his own. He was at his best when tackling major problems, as in the case of the streetcar issue in Detroit. But the Senate as a whole was slow then in facing up to major problems.

7

As might be expected, he became an almost constant thorn in the side of his own party. His enemies never said anything more accurate about him than that he was a Republican "in name only." He himself later summed up his partisanship: "I am a Republican, but not like Harding, Coolidge, and Hoover!" Inasmuch as these three were the titular heads of his party throughout his senatorship, a fair question would have been: "Republican? What kind?" A newspaper headline of the period came closest to pegging him properly:

JAMES COUZENS—ONE-MAN BLOC [15]

Curiously enough, despite his progressive record as Detroit's mayor, he did not immediately commit himself as to which group he would line up with. But which group *could* he line up with? The Old Guard, under Lodge? The Progressives, under La Follette?

One of the first things he did was deliberately to insult Senator Jim Watson of Indiana by pretending to him that he had never heard of him before and asking him what party he belonged to. A Republican organ in St. Louis reflected Watson's reaction by observing: "Evidently, this new specimen of the political fauna from the wilds of Detroit intends to make it plain that he was formerly associated with Ford by trying to out-Ford himself in arrogance. It is safe to predict that he will fade away from Washington just about the same way as Multimillionaire Senator H. A. W. Tabor of Colorado." [16]

8

Couzens' first vote as Senator was in opposition to a ship-subsidy bill, which the Harding clique supported with great fervor. This bill was an outgrowth of World War I, during which the government had acquired a great merchant fleet operated by the U. S. Shipping Board. The Ship Subsidy Bill of 1922 provided that the vessels "be turned over to private companies on generous terms and that substantial appropriations be voted to help them operate on a comfortable margin." [17]

Although it is debatable how well this jibed with the popular idea that the government should get out of business, it certainly was good business for the companies that were to get the ships and the generous subsidies, estimated at $850,000,000.

Along with Brookhart, Couzens caused this bill to be shelved in the Senate just when its passage appeared near. For he and Brookhart obtained enough signatures to a round robin to get the subsidy measure taken off the calendar in favor of a farm-relief measure.

This ship-subsidy issue had been prominent in the 1922 Congressional elections, a number of members having been defeated primarily, it was said, because they had favored it. Now the Lame Duck Congress was given its orders to pass the bill before the new members took their seats—a maneuver that inspired Senator Norris later to begin his long and finally successful fight for the so-called "Lame Duck Amendment" to the Constitution.[18]

Harding made a personal appearance before Congress on behalf of the subsidy.

It was no wonder that the Couzens-Brookhart action produced a sensation. As stated by the *Baltimore Sun:*

> This was the most novel experience the Senate has had in many years. Here were two senators who had hardly acquainted themselves with the methods of getting in and out of the Senate chambers and yet they had become leaders in fact in the subsidy fight, if not in name.[19]

The staunchly Republican *Philadelphia Public Ledger* headlined the incident:

POLITICAL CHAOS NOW
REIGNS IN WASHINGTON [20]

9

That Couzens in his first week had helped to incite all this seemed to mean that he, too, was an insurgent Progressive. Additional evidence along this line appeared when the Senate began considering an offer by Henry Ford to buy the Muscle Shoals, Alabama, facilities (later the basis for the Tennessee Valley Authority). This offer, which had enormous popular support, was almost accepted by Congress.[21] Couzens asserted bluntly that neither Ford nor any other private individual ought to have the government-owned nitrate and power development, but it should be held by the government for the benefit of the public.

In this, of course, he shared the view of Senator Norris, "father of TVA", who at just this time issued a report that called Ford's offer "the most wonderful real estate speculation since Adam and Eve lost title to the Garden of Eden." [22]

Couzens felt so strongly on this issue that he gave it as one reason for giving up his interest in the Bank of Detroit just before he took the oath as senator. "I am going to fight Mr. Ford on Muscle Shoals and I don't want my stand to embarrass the bank," he told the directors of the bank.[23]

His attitude helped to bring about a sharp decline in Congressional sentiment for the Ford offer, and helped to save Muscle Shoals for the later T.V.A. As the *Detroit Free Press* put it: "That Senator Couzens, former business partner to Ford, is opposed to the offer . . . has convinced Republican leaders that it would be a mistake to put the Ford offer before the Congress." [24]

Even so, Couzens' vote on the Ship Subsidy Bill, his outcry against the Ford offer, was not yet a safe indication of his political thinking. He had acted against the subsidy bill merely upon impulse. Later, he said, "If it is the business of the United States to see that we have a Merchant Marine, then we ought to assume the responsibility and not transfer it to private interests, augmented by taxes." [25] But in December 1922 he had merely been annoyed that the business of the Senate had come to a stop while senators orated for days on the shipping bill.[26]

10

Political success is often corrosive of political principles. When the rebel, the iconoclast, the independent, finds himself in a position of high influence, there is a tendency to retract the horns, to prove that, after all, he is "safe" and "sound"; a kind of self-reformation of the reformer occurs. With some, this change lasts only a short time; with others, the weak ones or the opportunists, it becomes permanent.

Couzens experienced this change temporarily. He demonstrated at the outset an unwonted sensitivity to the charge that he was not a "regular Republican." It was commented upon that his social companions, at lunch and at golf, were all of the Old Guard, men like

Frederick Hale of Maine or the steel millionaire Lawrence C. Phipps of Colorado.

When he was in the company of Progressives like Norris, "he developed streaks of orthodoxy," one observer noted.[27] Another, in talking with him, suggested that he would naturally be classified as a Progressive, citing his record as mayor of Detroit, but Couzens on this occasion was evasive. "I don't want to be classified at all," he said. "If this bloc you call progressive is for something I believe in, then I'll be with them, but I'll not commit myself to any group. The standpatters are not always wrong." [28]

II

Early in his Senate service, he cast a vote that was odd for a man considered a "Bolshevik" back home.

Senator J. Thomas Heflin of Alabama, a lesser figure of the species of "Pitchfork" Ben Tillman and Tom Watson, had made a remark, during debate on an agricultural credit bill, which the Old Guard took as a special slur. He was in the Senate, Heflin said, to "represent the people . . . not the bond sharks, the big financiers of Wall Street." [29] Senator Lodge especially was outraged, asserted that Heflin had violated the Senate rules against impugning the motives of colleagues, and demanded that Heflin be refused further use of the floor. Vice President Coolidge so ruled. A vote was taken—and Couzens voted for suppression of Heflin.[30]

In one respect, this vote could have been deemed praiseworthy, even for a Progressive. For Senator Heflin could by no means represent personally a cause worth a Progressive's martyrdom. In the words of a quite moderate observer: "Congress had its quota of strong men, weak men, and fools, and foremost of the fools was . . . Heflin . . . the national idol of the Ku Klux Klan." [31]

Yet, in a larger view, the silencing of Heflin was an attack on free and open debate, a principle Couzens always championed.

12

Heflin turned on Couzens. He said sarcastically that he knew the explanation for Couzens' vote. It was his money. He had heard it said that, though Couzens was a multimillionaire, he was progressive. "I said, 'Say that to me again and say it slow.' . . . Mark what I tell you. . . . When the big interests are attacked, you will see him go over and take his place with the bellwethers of the standpat party.

"I saw him do it this morning—my good friend Couzens of Michigan, parading himself down here as a Progressive, and this morning he walked right over and sat right down under the whiskers of the Senator of Massachusetts." [32]

Although another man might have laughed, Couzens characteristically lost his temper. He stood up in the aisle to answer Heflin, "his posture that of a bulldog." In angry tones he made a demand that startled everyone. The Senate reporter should be instructed to read the record of the remarks just made by Heflin, because, he explained, Wadsworth of New York had advised the Senate at an earlier time that Heflin had edited certain remarks he had made about Wadsworth.

"I do not propose to give him the opportunity to go in the night time, in the dark, and change the references he has made to myself. If Senators are free to get up here and tell the galleries and the American people that the motives of a senator of any state are to be questioned, we might as well stand up here and call everybody thieves and liars!" [33]

There ensued a scene which was, according to the *New York Herald,* "reminiscent of Socialist outbreaks in the Reichstag, the French Chamber of Deputies, soap-box events in Union Square and Hyde Park, London." [34] Undoubtedly, this was an exaggeration, but by dropping the pose of a dignified Roman Senator as soon as he was attacked, Couzens certainly had transformed the Senate into something resembling the rowdy Detroit city-council meetings when he was mayor.

Nine senators were on their feet at once, all clamoring for recognition and arguing loudly one way or another about Couzens' request. The upshot of all the furor was that both Couzens and Heflin withdrew their remarks. Couzens found himself praised by a group whose praise he would not appreciate for long—the clique around Harding, to whom Big Tom Heflin was especially obnoxious. The Old-Guard press hailed him as "a hero." Couzens was all right after all, they decided.

13

But at just this time he also gave Harding and the Old Guard newspapers cause to regret his presence in the Senate. For he had deliberately attacked Harding's leadership on the subject of government ownership versus private ownership of the railroads.

In a special message to Congress, Harding had referred to the government's administration of the railroads during the war as "folly." For the railroad brotherhood's newspaper, *Labor*, Couzens prepared a sharply critical statement on the President's message.[35] He also carried on the attack in an address before the Philadelphia Real Estate Board.[36]

He did not commit himself definitely in favor of government ownership, but he made it plain that he resented the idea that government ownership was evil *per se*. In this same address, to make the point that private business could be worse than government, he ripped into the Lincoln Motor Car Company for the profit it made on its contracts to produce Liberty airplane motors during World War I.[37]

He strongly refuted the propaganda line put forward by *The Railway Review*, that those who even considered government ownership of the railroads were subversives, in league with "the most dangerous organizations of radicals in the country." But, as the Kansas City *Star* said:

"Couzens has the background of many years of successful business experience and . . . is the wealthiest man in the Senate. It will be difficult for foes to brand any plan he puts forward as coming from a 'wild-eyed radical.' " [38]

The Progressives were exultant. "Jim Couzens is one of the greatest men in Washington!" Senator Brookhart exclaimed.[39] La Follette and Norris paid him an unprecedented compliment, for a first-termer. They backed him, though unsuccessfully, for chairman of the Senate Committee on Interstate Commerce.[40]

14

It was inevitable that Couzens and Harding should eventually be at loggerheads. They were antithetical figures: Harding, the prince of good fellows, had, in the words of William Allen White (who liked him), "the harlot's virtues";[41] Couzens was the epitome of the rigidly ethical. Indeed, at their first meeting there was an air of suppressed hostility.[42]

Just at this time, Harding appointed James G. McNary, a Texas banker, to the office of Comptroller of the Currency. Couzens, as chairman of a subcommittee of the Senate Committee on Banking and Currency, had the duty of investigating McNary's background. When a banker himself, he had adhered to certain rules which he considered basic: A banker must not borrow from his own bank, nor must he permit associates in his bank to make loans to themselves.[43] To his amazement, Couzens came upon evidence which indicated

that Harding's choice for Comptroller had violated these rules in an
extravagant fashion as president of his bank in Texas. Couzens was
advised for example, that "for a period of more than five years, Mc-
Nary was a continuous borrower from the bank of which he was
president. . . . At one time 88 per cent of the capital and surplus
funds . . . was loaned directly to the officers and directors." Couzens
immediately went to the White House to tell Harding to withdraw
the McNary appointment.[44]

Harding, however, adopted the position that McNary's background,
instead of disqualifying him, proved him "a very practical man,"
the kind "needed as Comptroller of Currency."[45] Couzens stood
firm. "I agree with you that Mr. McNary is a very practical man.
I am afraid he is too practical to be the kind of disciplinarian that
the Comptroller of the Currency should be."[46]

Despite Couzens' opposition, Harding insisted that the Senate confirm McNary. He was angry that Couzens had made public the Senate
committee's findings on McNary, evidence obtained in "executive
session." To have made it public was "in violation of the long-
established conception of wise procedure," he wrote Couzens.[47]

The strongest possible pressure was brought on the Republican
leaders in the Senate to push the nomination through, for McNary
was an important cog in the Republican organization of the South-
west, described by William Allen White as the party's "field agent"
in Texas and New Mexico.[48]

On the last day of the session, Couzens, carrying on a singlehanded
fight, threatened to filibuster unless the McNary appointment were
withdrawn. He so informed "Jim" Watson, Harding's floor leader.[49]
Rather than see other legislation lost, Harding yielded, and the appointment was withdrawn. Daniel R. Crissinger of Marion, Ohio,
Harding's home town, who later became Governor of the Federal
Reserve Board, was named instead.

15

That a Republican senator could be responsible for such an affront
to a Republican President revived a familiar question. Was Couzens
a Republican? He himself raised the point in a talk at Bay City,
Michigan. "I would like to be considered a member of the Republican party. . . . But, if being a Republican means kow-towing
to the President, I do not care to be a Republican."[50]

From then on, he was the old Couzens. No one would ever again be able to say that he sat under the whiskers of Senator Lodge or any other standpatter. He dropped the pose of not knowing the difference between the Progressives and the Old Guard. To a reporter for *Nation's Business,* who inquired about statements that he was a radical, Couzens said, "Yes, I'm radical as hell when I see an evil that ought to be ended." [51]

To the *Saturday Evening Post* he became "The Scab Millionaire." [52]

CHAPTER XXIV

THE PLAIN-SPEAKING STATESMAN

IN THE summer of 1923, a full-fledged boom was under way to nominate Henry Ford for President of the United States. Ford was set to run on either major party ticket, but preferably the Republican, judged the most likely to win. To a later generation, one nursed on the picture of Ford as a man above politics, or even against politics, this movement would seem unbelievable. Ford himself later denied that he had Presidential ambitions.

But it is indisputable that the boom had his approval.[1]

An article signed by Ford entitled "If I Were President," appeared in *Collier's* magazine August 8, 1923. Allen Benson, prominent in the Socialist Party, wrote a laudatory biography of Ford as part of the boom. Besides, Ford as much as admitted to Couzens that he was a receptive candidate. On one occasion, at a wedding, "with just the inflection of seriousness to make me realize that he meant every word," he even discussed with him the possibility of having him in his cabinet.[2]

A good deal of joking went on in the press about the Ford-for-President movement. But the reality of the Ford boom was no joke. Even Senator Norris, the Nebraska liberal, greatly admired Ford at the time, and perhaps would have suggested him for President.[3]

That summer there was also much discussion, pro and con, of the desirability of modifying the national laws, adopted during World War I, prohibiting sale of intoxicating beverages. Both subjects—the Ford boom and prohibition—were too hot for most public officials to discuss openly with any forthrightness. The passions they generated were too strong. But Couzens, though he hadn't planned it that way, was soon doing precisely that.

2

That June he was visiting in Ottawa, while on a motor trip with his family. A newspaper reporter there asked him to comment on the liberal Quebec liquor laws, "I think they are fine," he said. "I think the United States might with good grace adopt some of them. If our constitution were easier to amend, I believe the Volstead act would be repealed." [4] Somewhat embroidered, these comments were telegraphed to newspapers in the United States—on the same day that President Harding, on a "voyage of understanding," spoke in Denver in spirited defense of prohibition. "I am convinced," Harding had said, "they are a small and a greatly mistaken minority who believe that the Eighteenth Amendment will ever be repealed."

The result of this divergence of views between Harding and Couzens was a newspaper sensation:

HARDING DEFENDS DRY LAW:
COUZENS ASKS O.K. ON BEER

The results could have been foreseen.[5] Couzens was denounced by the prohibitionists all over the land, but especially in Michigan. The Anti-Saloon League, the most powerful pressure bloc of the day, went after him in full cry. He was called a "traitor to America," a "betrayer" of his party, his state, and his nation, and of all decent people. The Anti-Saloon League served notice it would seek his defeat in 1924 if he had "the gall" to become a candidate to succeed himself.[6]

He hit back at the Anti-Saloon League. It was, he said, an organization that sought "to dictate" who should hold public office on the basis of one issue, "disregarding all other problems." "They are out to elect a man who will go to Congress and do what they want, no matter whether he is a bum, an anarchist, or what not." [7] These were fighting words, and other politicians shuddered at his daring—or folly.

To the amazement of other politicians, he gave a half dozen speeches in this vein. *Time,* a new magazine, ran his picture on its front cover as if to cheer him on. But for the few who praised him, hundreds denounced him.[8] "Mr. Couzens Destroys Himself," the *Christian Science Monitor* headlined. "It is a pity. There were possibilities in Couzens as a public man that now may never be tested, for his political future is, alas, behind him." [9]

With this din in his ears, Couzens took himself and his family off to Europe for the balance of the recess between Congressional sessions, wiser perhaps, but not chastened in spirit.

On his return from Europe he made some interesting comments about European conditions. La Follette, Borah, Norris, Johnson, and Wheeler, on foreign affairs, were largely "isolationist," to use a term which became current only in the 1940's. It was then almost a hallmark of a Progressive to turn one's back on Europe and Asia. But with remarkable insight, Couzens warned:

> Germany is decidedly unhappy, with sixty-five or seventy millions of people, the majority of whom are in great distress. . . . The extreme isolationists [in America] have forbidden or intimidated the United States from having a voice in world affairs. We cannot go on that way. We have got to stand up and be counted, for or against these various proposals for settling the economic conditions in Europe.[10]

He also advanced a program. The United States with other powers should establish "a receivership for Germany," to put its affairs in order. Ultimately, he hoped, there would develop a "United States of Europe."

While in Paris, he copied into his notebook a statement by Victor Hugo. "I belong to a party not yet born, but which will be born in the Twentieth Century. This party will have its principle in a United States of Europe." He read this to newspaper reporters, pronouncing it a "sound idea." [11]

3

While Couzens was on the ocean, Harding's death had occurred. Promptly on his return, Couzens wrote a letter of advice, based on his observations in Europe, to the new President, Calvin Coolidge. Coolidge should abandon "the Harding isolationism," he said. He hoped, he wrote, that Coolidge in his first message to Congress, would "express a very strong, energetic, forward position on foreign relations."

At that time, the principal "isolationist" in the Senate was Hiram Johnson. Johnson was and remained Couzens' friend. Nevertheless, Couzens now bluntly told Coolidge: "I do not think that we are going to get anywhere in any way by trying to placate Senator Hiram Johnson." [12]

4

Couzens also made a number of public comments at this time that caused some observers to suggest that he had gone over completely to the camp of "noisy radicals," notably La Follette, who was being accused of wanting "to undermine the Constitution and the Supreme Court." For he was outraged just then by a decision of the court against federal regulation of child labor, a decision which set off a revival of the movement Theodore Roosevelt and Albert J. Beveridge had sponsored a decade earlier for permitting Congress to overrule the court.[13] La Follette sounded anew a call for "curbing the court" and Couzens was instinctively in agreement. To the press, he said: "I am for bringing about a change which will not permit the Supreme Court to declare acts of Congress unconstitutional by a majority of one. I would have at least a favorable vote of two-thirds of the court necessary." [14]

To Editor Arthur H. Vandenberg in Grand Rapids, who was alarmed by his comments, he wrote:

"The point I want to raise . . . is that the interpretation of the Constitution is made by human minds, and I do not believe the opinions of five human minds should offset the interpretation of the Constitution of the United States made by hundreds of Congressmen and four members of the Supreme Court. . . ." [15]

Vandenberg attempted, by long letters, to change Couzens' views, arguing that Supreme Court decisions ought to be considered sacred. Any proposal to let Congress "nullify" a court decision would "emasculate" the court and turn Congress into a "despotism," he said.[16] He sent Couzens copies of editorials he had written in the *Grand Rapids Herald,* including one that bitterly denounced the Scripps-Howard newspapers, as well as the *Detroit News,* for supporting the La Follette proposal to permit Congress to overrule the Supreme Court.

It was all very well, Couzens came back at Vandenberg, to be "theoretical" about such matters. But he could not see how "a decent man" could defend a Supreme Court decision that condemned children to labor in factories and mines. "I am not out looking to stir up trouble, where trouble does not exist," he wrote. "I cannot help, however, before concluding, raising the question of how many thousands of children may be suffering because of the Supreme

Court. . . . May it not be that we are prone to let these things go, rather than risk a change? Does not the doctrine of 'leaving well enough alone' sometimes impose a lot of hardship, which we do not truly visualize?" [17]

5

As for Ford, who had been granting some interviews to Dr. William L. Stidger, a Methodist minister later associated with Boston University, for publication in newspapers and in a book on Ford's Presidential aspirations, the *Detroit Times* on October 25, 1923, published this:

DR. STIDGER: What do you think of the stand that your friend Senator Couzens is taking on the prohibition laws? He is in favor of going back to five per cent beer and light wines.

FORD: He knows he is wrong about it. Mr. Couzens knows better. He knows that in the Ford motor plant booze never did anybody any good, and he is taking a backward step when he stands for five per cent beer and light wines. *Jim Couzens knows better than that.* Maybe he feels he is striking a popular chord.

Couzens considered Ford's remarks about him an attack on his integrity.[18] A week later, Couzens, for the first time in his career, publicly gave vent to his anger at Ford.

He began a speech before the Republican Club at the Hotel Statler in Detroit with an apparently general discussion of the need for truthfulness in public affairs. "Parties and public men have not always been truthful," he said. Then he said he was "forced" to discuss a man who "exemplified" this. "The example is our chief Democratic politician, Henry Ford, who recently gave a newspaper interview, so it is reported, and he has not denied it, differing with me on the amendment I suggested on the Volstead act." He denounced Ford in particular for ascribing political motives to Couzens' suggestion that the Volstead Act be modified. He went on:

It comes from poor taste from a man who is so politically ambitious as Mr. Ford and who has never gotten over his peevishness because of his defeat for United States senator on the Democratic ticket. A man who has perhaps made more unfulfilled promises than any man in America should be more guarded in challenging the motives of other people. . . .

If Mr. Ford wants to be president—and it is quite evident he does —because he has filed his name, or at least permitted it to be filed, in the Nebraska primaries—why does he refrain from announcing himself as a candidate? The reason, it appears to me, is that he is afraid, realizing that the probable outcome would be as great a fiasco as his "Peace Ship" . . .

Mr. Ford for president? It is ridiculous. . . . If the American people ever stop to analyze Mr. Ford's experience and his qualifications for the presidency of the United States, he will never even get started. It is my hope that they will stop and think.

I say this not only because I want to save Mr. Ford from the greatest humiliation that could befall him. But I want equally to save the United States from the humiliation it would suffer.[19]

A good many persons had been saying precisely these things privately. Republican leaders generally were pleased that Couzens did so publicly. In his syndicated column from Washington, Mark Foote wrote: "Republican politicians howled with delight. President Coolidge is said to have pulled a wry Puritanical smile. . . . Politicians who had never been able to discern any good points in James Couzens now declared him a great man." There also was some comment on the fact that just before leaving Washington for Detroit to make his speech on Ford, Couzens and his wife dined with the Coolidges.[20]

6

He did not return to the subject of Ford's Presidential ambitions. He had not really relished attacking his former associate openly. Moreover, the Ford boom suddenly petered out, after Ford and Coolidge had a meeting at which Coolidge seemed to agree to support Ford's ideas for Muscle Shoals.[21] After this meeting, Ford said to reporters: "Muscle Shoals? Where is Muscle Shoals?" [22]

Ford did not answer Couzens. And before long, curiously enough, he and Couzens seemed better friends than they had acted for a long time.

Besides, Couzens was soon involved in an heroic controversy with Secretary of the Treasury Andrew W. Mellon, who more than any other individual embodied the dominant philosophy of the Republican party in this era.

CHAPTER XXV

THE MILLIONAIRES' WAR

EARLY in November 1923 the *New York Times* sent a telegram to Couzens in Detroit: "We will appreciate it if you wire us collect your views on Secretary Mellon's propositions to reduce income taxes." [1] Quite innocently, this telegram directed him on a course that touched off one of the most explosive political controversies of his generation.

Couzens had not planned things this way. Indeed, he answered the *Times* noncommittally. "It would not be wise," he said, "for a Senator to commit himself in advance to a proposal of this kind. The matter will naturally go to the Finance Committee and no Senator should commit himself until he hears the arguments and recommendations of the Committee." [2]

Only a few days earlier, in a speech before the Detroit North End Republican Club, he had mentioned the Mellon proposals in passing. He seemed to favor them. In any event, he did not denounce them. "There is going to be a suggestion before Congress," he said, "that the surtax be reduced from fifty to twenty-five per cent, and a hurrah goes up that it is all in favor of the rich. Well it does not make much difference who it is in favor of, so long as the Government gets its proper taxes from each and every individual." [3]

But what were "proper taxes?" The *New York Times* telegram set him to thinking about this in specific terms. He was aware, of course, that Mellon's proposals, widely acclaimed in the press, were close to being canonized doctrine of the Republican party. For this was the era in which Andrew Mellon was hailed as "the greatest Secretary of the Treasury since Alexander Hamilton." In the words of one observer: "Anyone who disagreed with Andrew Mellon on taxation was a menace to constitutional government." [4]

Promptly on returning to Washington the following December, Couzens summoned a stenographer and dictated a letter to Secretary

Mellon. By asking Mellon some pointed questions—his habitual manner—he hoped to clarify his own thinking. He set down the claims made for Mellon's proposals—that the current high wartime surtax rates were retarding business; that the government would get more revenue, not less, from lowered rates; that high surtaxes were driving vast sums of capital into tax-exempt securities and thus retarding industrial investment, etc.—and after each argument, he asked for "proof."

Now, Mellon, a multimillionaire financier and industrialist in his own right, was a man of mild appearance. He was "self-deprecating, gentle and smiling," William Allen White said.[5] But this appearance was deceptive. Actually he was as self-assured and nearly as aggressive as Couzens himself.[6] He was used to being treated with the utmost respect, even by those who did not like him, even by Democrats. Yet here was Couzens, a Republican, challenging his views on taxation, views considered to be his great contribution to public service, or so Mellon interpreted Couzens' letter.

2

Mellon responded with a letter that displeased Couzens violently.[7] As he afterward told Vandenberg, "Whatever has been the outcome of my first correspondence with Mr. Mellon, has been due entirely to Mellon's own arrogant desire to 'lord it' over all of us who dared to question him." [8]

He was not alone in that opinion. David Lawrence, an admirer of Mellon, conceded that "Mr. Mellon rubbed the Michigan senator the wrong way." [9] Even Mark Sullivan said, "Although Secretary Mellon is one of the gentlest of men, and Senator Couzens one of the most truculent, I think the former is a little more responsible than the latter for the beginning of the row." [10]

What Mellon ought to have done, said Sullivan, was to "dump a couple of barrels of figures on Mr. Couzens." Instead, he wrote Couzens a letter "that sounded a little resentful." [11] In effect, Mellon told Couzens that he ought to leave such matters in the hands of a man who understood them.

3

Couzens replied caustically. He accused Mellon of seeking to impose his views on the nation to the exclusion of everyone else. "I dissent," he wrote, "from permitting one individual doing the diagnosing and prescribing the remedy. I propose to engage in this diagnosis myself and perhaps have some voice in the decision." [12]

Mellon sent back a reply, but not one calculated to placate Couzens:

> It is reported in the newspapers that all your capital is now in tax exempt securities, and I have not seen any denial from you. This means, if it means anything, that you pay no income tax. . . . Must a system of taxation which permits a man with an income of over $1,000,000 a year to pay not one cent to the support of his Government remain unaltered? [13]

This was a jab at Couzens in a sensitive political spot. It was a fact that the bulk of Couzens' money was in government bonds. He never denied it. His usual reply to critics on this was: "In reality, I prepaid my tax by investing my money in municipal, state, and government securities at a very much less return than I would receive if I had invested in mortgages, railroads or industries." [14] Then, too, he had switched his investments from private securities to government bonds because, as he once explained, he wanted to insulate himself against pressures that might be exerted through ownership of stock in companies or banks. But he could never get people to understand these considerations, as he himself conceded some years later in urging that tax exemptions on government securities be abolished.[15]

To Mellon, Couzens rejoined: "So long as you have entered into the record of my securities, will you please tell what your securities are, how much you own of them, and how much you will benefit by the reduction of surtaxes as proposed by you?" He followed with barbed references to a well-known fact: much Mellon money was invested in the distillery business. Is money used for making whiskey more "useful" than money invested in public improvements? he demanded.[16]

Ordinarily, cautious men in politics might have dropped matters there—assuming they had let things proceed this far. But neither Couzens nor Mellon was cautious. They kept up the exchange, sending each other a sufficient number of letters to make a good-sized book, and each contrived that much of this correspondence should become public.

In one letter, Couzens cited his own experience as evidence that Mellon's proposals would "help the rich." It was ironic, in view of what was to come, that he recalled that when he sold his Ford Company stock to Henry Ford, he paid an income tax of $7,229,161.75 for the year 1920. "If your proposal had been law, I would have saved nearly four million dollars; so I do not see where the country gains by creating these enormous savings for those well able to pay."

He wound up by urging that Mellon engage in a public debate on the matter, "where both of us will be forced to rely upon our knowledge, rather than upon statisticians who can make figures tell any kind of a story, or upon lawyers who can argue from any side." [17]

Couzens soon found himself thrust into the role of the nation's leading opponent of "Mellonism." Though he had not intended this, he accepted the role, while the public enjoyed a dramatic spectacle: two multimillionaire public officials at war.

Couzens cleared his decks for action by abruptly accepting the resignation of his secretary, Walter Dorsey, whom he had inherited from Senator Newberry. Trained in the old school, Dorsey felt that Couzens "ought not have criticized Mellon." [18] Then, at the suggestion of Jay Hayden, Couzens took on a new secretary—John Carson, a Scripps-Howard reporter with a flair for fact-finding and crusading who, years later, was appointed to the Federal Trade Commission by President Harry S. Truman. With Carson's help, Couzens prepared for a real assault on Mellon.[19]

4

On February 21, 1924, he struck at Mellon in a way that startled everyone. He introduced a Senate resolution calling for an investigation of the Bureau of Internal Revenue.[20]

This bureau had never before been subjected to investigation, though its financial and political powers were obviously enormous, a fact that Couzens was to point up when he said: "Give me control of the Bureau of Internal Revenue and I will run the politics of the country." [21]

Almost before Mellon and the Old Guard were aware of what had happened, the Progressive bloc, joined by some Democrats, had lined up behind Couzens' bold resolution, and it had passed.[22]

With the aid of John Carson, Couzens was soon making public some interesting material. Over the protests of Senator Watson, chairman of the committee, and Senator Richard Ernst of Kentucky (a personal friend of Mellon), Couzens had obtained from the Bureau of Internal Revenue its files on thirty-eight corporations in which Mellon was at that time, or had been previously, financially interested.

These files revealed that certain of the firms had received large tax rebates. They also revealed, through various memoranda, that the Bureau had gone out of its way to treat these corporations with special deference, if not with favoritism.[23]

Mellon denounced the revelations as "nonsense." The rebates were merely routine. The companies in question were entitled to what they had received. He professed to be unconcerned. But Mellon was obviously fuming, and began to look for a politically safe way to bring the Couzens "nonsense" to an end.

One way to stop the investigation was to get Couzens out of the Senate. Couzens soon found himself a guest at the White House, where an attractive offer was made to him by President Coolidge— the ambassadorship to the Court of St. James. But Couzens' answer was, "I won't be kicked upstairs."[24]

5

Governor Gifford Pinchot of Pennsylvania, the old Bull Moose Progressive, then entered the picture. An ardent "dry" and an equally ardent political enemy of Mellon's, he gave Couzens some material which suggested a scandalous situation in the Bureau of Internal Revenue with regard to prohibition enforcement.[25] But it would be useless, Pinchot said, to go into this, or even into income-tax matters, unless the committee had the services of a lawyer experienced in investigations. He had a name ready—Francis J. Heney of California, a La Follette follower who had handled the public-lands scandal investigation during the Theodore Roosevelt administration.

Indeed, Pinchot had already consulted Heney by telephone.

Heney was interested, but there was a stumbling block—Heney had to be compensated. Was Couzens aware that his resolution for the investigation had omitted any mention of retaining and paying for counsel?

For the first time, Couzens realized that he had omitted such a provision. But he quickly came up with a solution. "I will pay Heney out of my own pocket!" he told Pinchot.[26]

At the next meeting of his committee, Senator Watson raised vigorous objections. For a Senator to use his own funds for such a purpose was highly irregular, he maintained. But the two Democratic members of the committee sided with Couzens, and Heney was retained.[27]

Watson immediately communicated with Mellon and also with President Coolidge, as he later told the Senate.[28]

A conference of administration leaders was hastily summoned.

For months, these leaders had been disturbed over Senate investigations in general. The Teapot Dome investigation was then in
progress. There was also an investigation of the Department of
Justice and one of the Veterans' Bureau under way. Ahead was the
1924 election. The thought of Heney being set loose on prohibition
enforcement, as well as tax administration, was appalling to the Old
Guard. Watson was surprisingly candid about this. With Heney
conducting an investigation, backed by Couzens and by Pinchot,
Mellon's old enemy, there would result, said Watson, "a saturnalia
of vituperation and aspersion unequaled hitherto in the political
annals of America!" [29]

6

On the heels of the leaders' conference, Mellon sent Coolidge a
solemn communication. The Couzens investigation, it said, was
merely an effort to "vent some personal grievance," but its effect
would "threaten the institution of government itself." "A private
individual is authorized to investigate generally an executive department of the government. . . . If the interposition of private
resources be permitted to interfere with the executive administration of government, the machinery of government will cease to function." [30]

Coolidge then promptly dispatched Mellon's letter to the Senate,
incorporating it in a special message of his own:

> It seems incredible that the Senate of the United States would
> knowingly approve the past and proposed conduct of one of its
> committees which this letter reveals. . . .
> Under a procedure of this kind, the Constitutional guarantees
> against unwarranted search and seizure breaks down, the prohibi-
> tion against what amounts to a Government charge of criminal
> action without the formal presentment of a grand jury is evaded,
> the rules of evidence which have been adopted for the protection of
> the innocent are ignored, the department becomes the victim of
> vague, unformulated and indefinite charges; instead of a Govern-
> ment of law, we have a Government of lawlessness.
> Against the continuance of such condition, I enter my solemn
> protests and give notice that in my opinion the departments ought
> not to be required to participate in it. . . . It is time that we re-
> turn to a Government under and in accord with the usual forms
> of law of the land.
>   CALVIN COOLIDGE [31]

7

Obviously, this was not a Presidential message calculated to please senators. Even regular Republicans in the Senate were angered. Only a short time before this, Coolidge, in a confidential chat with Chief Justice Taft, had referred to senators as "cowards," [32] but he was to learn now that some senators could strike back, even at him. Tom Walsh of Montana, in charge of the Teapot Dome inquiry, called the Coolidge message "the most arrogant sent by an executive to a parliamentary body since the days of the Stuarts and Tudors." Reed of Missouri called it "such an insult as one branch of the government could not accept from another." He presented a resolution to have it expunged from the records. [33]

Carter Glass, who had been Wilson's Secretary of the Treasury, declared that Coolidge had "impeached the probity of the Senate . . . charging it with subterfuge and insincerity." Glass added: "This message, this letter of the President and of the Secretary, constitute the most extraordinary breach of official etiquette that has ever occurred in the history of the Republic." [34]

8

Clearly, Couzens had found himself with ardent allies, but he himself was not among the senators who replied to Coolidge from the floor of the Senate. For several weeks before this, he had been suffering from intense abdominal pains. [35] On the very day of the Coolidge blast, he was laid so low that once again his family feared he was dying. His son Frank and Dr. Hugo Freund were called from Detroit. Soon he was at Johns Hopkins Medical School Hospital in Baltimore for another operation, his fifth in four years. Mark Foote published an appropriate comment: "It was an irony of fate that just as Senator Couzens was cited by the President for 'throwing the government into disorder,' he should be sorely stricken and taken to a hospital. . . . Thus the Michigan senator, whose worst enemy would not accuse him of running away from a fight, is not able to fight back. . . ." [36]

Just before he was placed on the operating table, good news was brought to him. The Senate had defeated a resolution by Jim Watson for squelching the investigation. It was to proceed, this time with authority to employ counsel at Senate expense. Couzens had to make one concession. Heney could not be retained, but was to be replaced by another lawyer acceptable to all members of the investigating committee.[37] But he had the satisfaction of knowing that he had scored a smashing victory over both Coolidge and Mellon.

9

After his recovery, he returned to the investigation. Senator Watson had in the meantime had the good grace to resign as chairman of the committee, and Couzens succeeded to that post, which, according to all precedent should have been his from the outset.

Beginning in December 1925, Couzens issued a series of reports that were revealing documents, particularly with regard to tax allowances permitted corporations that had engaged in military production during World War I.[38] They showed that such companies had obtained "refunds" running into many millions, on the basis of Treasury interpretation of tax and defense acts. One such report, issued in December 1924, listed refunds, among others, of $4,590,585 to the Gulf Oil Company (a Mellon concern); $3,378,000 to the Standard Oil Company of California; $5,000,000 to the Sinclair Consolidated Oil Company; $1,638,375.87 to the Kennedy and Springer Corporation.[39]

The following January, Couzens' committee issued a report which estimated that "improper amortizations" on World War I production facilities, between July 1, 1921, and April 30, 1924, had cost the federal treasury nearly $460,000,000. Among the firms cited were the Aluminum Corporation of America (Mellon), $15,589,614; the United States Steel Corporation, $55,063,312; the Bethlehem Steel Company, $22,103,942; the E. I. DuPont de Nemours Company, $15,369,123; the Federal Shipbuilding Company, $10,849,786; the Midvale Steel and Ordnance Company, $9,336,440; and the National Aniline Chemical Company, $9,912,140.[40] Among other beneficiaries of Treasury rulings, the report showed, were various persons prominent in Republican affairs, and publisher W. R. Hearst.[41]

These refunds were all legal. But this was Couzens' main point. His purpose was to show what loopholes existed in the tax laws, and with what leniency the Bureau of Internal Revenue had secretly been interpreting the laws, often without the general public having any inkling of what was going on.

It was said at the time, and later, that "nothing came" of Couzens' revelations. In a sense, this was largely true. His reports did not completely reform the Bureau of Internal Revenue. In World War

II, large "amortizations" on war production were again permitted, and in many cases they were probably no more justified than those revealed by Couzens' committee.

But his inquiry did end the secrecy. In 1929, in consequence of his reports, an executive order issued by President Hoover provided for publicity on all Treasury refunds of more than $20,000.[42]

In addition, his inquiry resulted in the creation of the Joint Committee on Taxation of the Senate and House, which, for the first time, placed at the disposal of Congress a continuing staff of experts on a legislative subject—a major reform in Congressional history.[43] In Ray Tucker's phrase, this was Couzens' personal "monument."

10

There was, however, a surprising, even shocking, sequel. On March 7, 1925, Mellon brought a tax action, in the name of the Treasury, against Couzens.[44] It charged that Couzens had underpaid approximately $10,000,000 in taxes due from his profits on the sale of his Ford Motor Company stock back in 1919. All of the other former Ford stockholders were also sued. But Couzens was the real target of the action.

Later it developed that this incredibly vindictive counterattack was an indirect outgrowth of both the Newberry case and Henry Ford's lawsuit against the *Chicago Tribune* in 1916. In connection with the Ford suit, a *Tribune* reporter, in 1922, had suggested to Senator Watson that an investigation be made of the income-tax payments made on the Ford stock sold to Ford. A memorandum purporting to prove that not enough taxes were collected was handed to Watson, who in turn handed it to the Bureau of Internal Revenue. The memorandum was checked by the Bureau and found unsubstantiated. When Senator Newberry was being prosecuted by Ford, the same information was produced by Senator Watson.[45] Again the Government rejected the matter.

Now, in connection with Couzens, this old and discredited memorandum was remembered by someone, who called it to Secretary Mellon's attention. And it was on the basis of this that Mellon took action against Couzens.[46]

11

There followed a legal battle before the United States Board of Tax Appeals that lasted three years. Joseph E. Davies (later the

United States ambassador to Moscow) joined Arthur J. Lacy, Clarence E. Wilcox, and C. J. Huddleston, Couzens' personal attorneys in Detroit, in the defense battery. Perhaps no other tax action by the federal government was ever so vigorously prosecuted—or defended. In taxation history, it was a *cause célèbre*.

The upshot was a complete vindication of Couzens. For it was brought out that in the government's own files were documents that cleared him of the least suspicion of tax evasion. They showed, in fact, that his tax return on the Ford stock sale had been subjected to investigation on various occasions and that each time it had been decided there was no basis for reopening the matter. The action was flagrantly political.[47]

The decision was that he had paid not too little tax on the Ford stock sale, but too much—that instead of owing the government $10,000,000, he was entitled to a refund from the government of more than $900,000 as overpayment.[48] Indeed, not only the financial angle, but the whole matter redounded to Couzens' advantage. For the proceedings exposed to the public, for the first time in an official way, much of the inner history of the Ford Motor Company, and this history revealed what few realized—that Couzens was as much responsible for the fabulous Ford Company success as Henry Ford. A typical newspaper headline throughout the world read:

COUZENS THE MAN BEHIND FORD SUCCESS

Politically, this was all to the good for Couzens. Moreover, as one journalist noted, "this denouement was crushing for Mellon," for it placed the High Priest of the Administration Temple in "the role of a shyster prosecutor." [49]

CHAPTER XXVI

"THE LA FOLLETTEITE!"

BY THEN, Couzens' political creed had matured. It was not conscious Progressivism, in the La Follette sense, though most of the time he did stand close to La Follette. Nor was it simon-pure insurgency, in the style of Brookhart or Magnus Johnson, the Minnesota whirlwind, though much of the time, certainly, he was an "insurgent" in the Republican ranks. His political principle was almost purely and simply the principle of Independence—the old-fashioned American habit of dissent. "I can't help it," he once exclaimed, "that the Progressives generally are in agreement with me!" [1]

The closest he ever came to formulating any definitive political philosophy was in a letter to a newspaper editor:

> I want to do what I can to see that life is not made a burden for the many and a holiday for the few. I want to do that which will contribute the greatest good to the greatest number. That has been and will be the basis for my work in public life. [2]

In practical political terms, his position of independence always presented him with a problem. It naturally cut him off from any political organization, in particular the old-line Republican cliques in Michigan, headed by such leaders as Charles B. Warren. These never wanted him on any terms. Because, almost as a matter of honor, he scrupulously avoided building a personal organization, as La Follette and others had done, it was asking for an apparent miracle to expect him to get elected to remain in the Senate. "Bullheadedly," Couzens did not believe this. In 1924, when his appointed term was finished, he set out to prove he was right.

The 1924 election was the crucial one in his Senate career. In the primary, he was opposed by the Anti-Saloon League, as could have been expected. But he was also opposed by the chambers of commerce, the manufacturers' associations, and (because Mrs. Couzens was a Catholic) by the Ku Klux Klan, then at its peak of influence. The various state Republican factions put up candidates against him, notably Hal H. Smith, an attorney for the Michigan Manufacturers Association, and Federal Judge Arthur J. Tuttle, who declined, thriftily, to resign as judge to join the race.

Former Congressman Joseph W. Fordney undoubtedly expressed the sentiment of the dominant party leadership:

"Senator Couzens is a wolf in sheep's clothing. He is not a Republican. He is a Socialist. Anyone who is for President Coolidge should not be for Senator Couzens." [3]

2

The major 1924 campaign issue centered on Senator La Follette. When La Follette, following Coolidge's nomination, announced he would run for President on a Progressive platform, the big question in the Republican primary in Michigan became loyalty to Coolidge and the Republican party. The Republican leaders, and the party press, attempted to submerge every other question, especially after Senator La Follette, together with the railroad brotherhoods, issued strong endorsements of Couzens.

The partisan press set up a statewide commotion. If Couzens were not a "La Folletteite," it was up to him to denounce La Follette, the editors said.

This Couzens refused to do. He insisted that he, and La Follette too, had as much right to the Republican label as Coolidge or Andrew Mellon. Besides, he admired La Follette's courage, unquestioned integrity, keen analytical mind, and great oratorical ability.[4]

In May 1924 the Old Guard tried to smoke him out. Burt D. Cady, chairman of the Republican State Central Committee, sent Couzens a letter which asked him to sign a pledge that he stood for "the principles of the Republican party" and that he would support any candidates nominated by the party. Couzens rejected any such pledges. He was "always prepared" to tell how he stood on any principle. He would do so, but it would have to be "in my own way" and "at the proper time," not by the signing of a partisan "pledge." [5]

3

In Grand Rapids, Editor Arthur Vandenberg was worried. He admired Couzens' independence, he said, but feared his defiance of the party leaders would cost him the nomination. If Couzens would only come out strongly against La Follette, Couzens would be all right. The situation certainly seemed critical, for the Republican state convention had just then handed Couzens an unprecedented snub, convening without even extending him an invitation to attend. In effect, he had been read out of the party, in so far as this could be done.

Vandenberg met with Couzens and they had what both described as "a delightful talk." [6] But Vandenberg got nowhere with his attempts to persuade Couzens to disavow La Follette and at the same time declare himself for Coolidge for President and Charles G. Dawes for Vice President in any statement he planned to make of his own candidacy. Instead, when he announced his candidacy, appropriately enough on Independence Day, Couzens took the occasion to denounce what he considered an effort by the state political organization to dictate to him. He would not be controlled "by party bosses," said his statement. It included no statement at all on the Presidential election.

As for pledging himself to support the party's principles, he asserted that he could be a Republican without approving the state and national platforms. Platforms, he said, too often are designed "to fool the people." To which he added:

> I claim to be a Republican as much as though I abjectly said I will follow President Coolidge. Nothing in the Constitution requires that I say "yes" to everything that the President, whoever he may be, proposes. I consider the fact that Congress refused to be dictated to and controlled by the President as a strong element in the safety of our Republic.[7]

4

Vandenberg and other conservatives were, of course, saddened and dismayed, though Progressives generally hailed his defiance of the state machine. La Follette was delighted, and immediately offered to come to Michigan to help Couzens campaign for the nomination.[8] Hiram Johnson, equally jubilant, telegraphed to Couzens that he had demonstrated "independence and courage . . . the two qualities most feared by those who would exploit government for selfish purposes." [9] Taking note of reports that Coolidge and Mellon were working for Couzens' defeat, Johnson said:

> The fact of the matter is your offense, like that of some of the rest of us, was your position on the Mellon Tax Plan. . . . Mr. Mellon and his Tax Plan were the test of progressivism, and also the acid test of our conservative brethren. The gentlemen who be-believe that government is for the few . . . could forgive any other action than opposition to Mr. Mellon and his tax scheme.[10]

The *Detroit News* carried an amusing comment:

> The political situation is somewhat confusing. . . . President Coolidge is for Senator Couzens, provided Mr. Couzens is for President Coolidge. Mr. Mellon is not particularly for Mr. Couzens. Senator Couzens is somewhat against President Coolidge and somewhat against Senator La Follette, but not enough against either one to be for the other.[11]

5

Vandenberg kept peppering Couzens with arguments against La Follette, most of which amounted to the allegations that La Follette was either a "radical" or a "hypocrite."

Couzens did not pretend to possess Vandenberg's ability for full-blown rhetoric. But he certainly held his own in their exchange. "What I do not understand," he told Vandenberg, "is the intolerance such a finely-educated and clear-thinking gentleman as yourself has for Mr. La Follette." "Even Christ was a radical," he reminded Vandenberg, and enclosed an editorial from the *Detroit News,* which said, "It is idle to pretend that La Follette or the Conference for Progressive Political Action are opposed to American institutions in any particular. Even those who disagree most strongly with La Follette admit his honesty, his loyalty and his courage."

"This *Detroit News* piece," said Couzens, "comes much nearer meeting my views than the editorial which you wrote." [12]

In August, Vandenberg did wring a concession from Couzens. He personally would vote for Coolidge for President. He reasoned that he might as well, since there was no chance that La Follette would win. There certainly was no difference, in his view, between Coolidge and the Democratic candidate, John W. Davis. But Couzens refused to call for a Coolidge victory or to repudiate La Follette. Vandenberg and his newspaper had to be content with endorsing Couzens' nomination on the basis of his unenthusiastic commitment to cast his personal vote for Coolidge.

6

Hysteria in the Republican ranks over the La Follette uprising reached a climax in September. The Republican campaign managers expressed a fear that La Follette would get enough electoral votes to result in a draw, necessitating a decision by Congress as in the case of President Rutherford B. Hayes in 1876.

This, they said, might conceivably lead to the selection of Governor Charles W. Bryan of Nebraska, brother of William Jennings Bryan, the Democratic candidate for Vice President, as "Acting President." In the words of a careful scholar of the campaign, the prospect of "Brother Charlie" becoming President "was an anomalous situation carefully nurtured by Republicans to frighten voters away from the La Follette candidacy." [13]

In Michigan, Couzens' opponent, Hal Smith, of the manufacturers' association, immediately raised the cry: "How does Couzens stand?" He demanded that Couzens state whether he would vote for "Hell and Maria" Dawes for Vice President, or for "Brother Charlie," should the issue reach Congress. In Grand Rapids, Vandenberg professed great alarm. To Couzens, the whole matter was "fantastically silly." Besides, he had no intention of committing himself in advance to a "standpatter" like General Dawes.

He conferred with Governor Groesbeck. So far as he knew at the present time, he told the governor, he "probably" would vote for Dawes. But "whether I would be of that mind next December is another question." How could he say in advance? He did not think the matter was a real issue. He would not make any statement, and he telephoned Vandenberg to that effect.[14] Vandenberg was beside himself. All might be lost if Couzens persisted in his attitude, he insisted.[15] But Couzens stuck to his position. In a letter to Vandenberg he wrote: "It would be perfectly stupid to promise something today and then next December find that to carry it out would be the height of folly. . . . For example, suppose Mr. Dawes went crazy or became unbalanced in any way between now and December; certainly then he should not be put in the office of President." [16]

Afterward, he explained that he "resented" being "hounded" on the Dawes-Bryan matter, whereas nobody raised that question with his primary opponents. "It makes it seem as though I were some outcast and begging to be taken in," he told Vandenberg. "I assume you understand how I feel about that. So long as I feel that way, the office would never induce me to surrender."

To which he added:

I have seen a number of editorials that the country is going to the bow-wows if any one of the three candidates for President is elected. We go through all these tortures and excitements, each side claiming if the other side gets into control, the country is done for. Yet we go on, decade after decade, no matter who is in the White House. . . . In other words, I cannot get excited over this question.[17]

7

Couzens turned out to be right in saying there was "nothing to get excited about." Despite his "irregularity," sentiment ran so strong for him that Hal Smith retired from the race at the last moment. Smith urged his supporters to vote for Judge Tuttle in the primary. But Couzens had a counter in that game, for it was apparent that many Democrats planned to cross over into the Republican primary to vote for him. In August, William A. Comstock, the Democratic state chairman, declared: "Couzens is really a Democrat, only he doesn't know it!" [18]—something that would be said of President Dwight D. Eisenhower a generation later by newspapers like the *Chicago Tribune*. E. D. Stair's *Detroit Free Press* set up a constant barrage against Couzens on one theme: He was a "Socialist . . . La Folletteite." It called for all Republicans to rally behind safe and sound Judge Tuttle. But the primary resulted in a resounding Couzens victory. The best part, Couzens wrote to Vandenberg, was that the result "freed me of any obligation to serve the organization Republicans or to be with them." [19]

In the election itself he was supported by La Follette Progressives, by Socialists, and by many Democrats, as well as regular Republicans who had no other place to go. He was returned to the Senate for his first full term by a majority of enormous proportions, a victory all the more remarkable in that, although his independence had alienated him from the regular political organizations of his party, he had refrained from building any real personal organization. This would have meant making use of patronage in one way or another, and this he never would do. So his senatorial destiny, as he wished it, was to stand or fall on his record alone.

CHAPTER XXVII

THE CRITIC OF COOLIDGE

"WHAT I hope for is that there will be enough aggressive Republican representatives in the next Congress to make the party stand for something better than it has in the past," Couzens had told Vandenberg during the campaign.[1] His hope was ill-founded. For the landslide that kept Coolidge in the White House had crushed not only the Democratic party—forever, some mistakenly said—but also the La Follette movement. In Charles A. Beard's phrase, the era of the "golden glow," was on. Less than a year later, Senator La Follette died.

Couzens, in addressing the Brotherhood of Locomotive Firemen and Enginemen the following day, paid La Follette's memory one of the finest of tributes.

> Yesterday we lost, I think, the greatest American of our age. No man stood up for so many years against the abuse, the misrepresentation, and the lies of the big press and of capital more fearlessly or more unflinchingly than did Senator La Follette. We may not always have agreed—any of us—with all he did or said, but none there are, who, having a proper appreciation of his noble attributes of mind and heart, could fail to admire him. . . . The few who dare, must speak, and speak again, to right the wrongs of many. I think Senator La Follette typified that thought more than any man who has ever been in public office.[2]

The Old Guard under Coolidge and Mellon had conspired to deprive La Follette of his committee chairmanships as punishment for his third-party heresy, and now they looked askance at Couzens for his praise of La Follette. Some charged it to his "idiosyncracy." But as often happens history provided a sequel. In 1955, on the one hundredth anniversary of Old Bob's birth, at an observance arranged by the Wisconsin State Historical Society, Chief Justice Earl Warren of the Supreme Court of the United States, a Republican appointed to the Court by a Republican President, Eisenhower, stood alongside one of La Follette's surviving colleagues, Editor William T. Evjue of the liberal *Madison Capital-Times,* and paid tribute to La Follette in almost the same phrases used by Couzens in 1925.[3] Had he lived, even Vandenberg would probably have been there—thirty years later.

In 1957, a bipartisan committee of the United States Senate included La Follette among five Senators—along with Clay, Webster, Calhoun, and Robert A. Taft—to be considered as "immortals" of the Senate.

2

No one emerged to take La Follette's place in the Senate during the 1920's. Neither Couzens nor Norris had his precise qualities. La Follette's son, Robert, Jr., who succeeded him and with whom Couzens always had a kind of father-son relationship, carried on his policies, but he was too young.

Besides, for many of the old farm bloc, the attraction of insurgency had begun to wane. Hiram Johnson, for example, began to reflect the views of Hearst more and more and to make a narrow isolationism, rather than progressivism, his standard. William Allen White commented: "The country is in a Coolidge mind." [4] And Senator Norris recalled: "Those were dark days and years, when America seemed lulled into indifference." [5] No wonder; prosperity seemed to be everywhere. The political atmosphere was becalmed.

When squalls did develop, Couzens was usually at their center— or nearby.

There was, for example, the controversy at the beginning of Coolidge's new term over the nomination of Charles B. Warren of Detroit as Attorney General. Stone had been appointed to the Supreme Court, "kicked upstairs," some said, for his embarrassing integrity. This was the same Warren whose Detroit Board of Commerce committee on unemployment relief Couzens had so severely criticized in the hard winter of 1914–1915—and whom he had "buttered up" with a $4,000 contribution to the Republican party in 1916, when he considered himself a "regular" Republican. But now Couzens had different ideas about Republican leadership, and joined progressives of both parties in opposing confirmation of Warren.

3

Ample reason certainly existed for Couzens' opposition to Charles Warren. As Couzens knew from personal experience, Warren had long been associated with the so-called "Sugar Trust," as attorney and also as principal owner of sugar-corporation shares. In 1911, when a Congressional committee investigated the trust, he was one of the figures called and later even placed under indictment. Indeed, this case was still pending in March 1925 when Coolidge sent his name to the Senate. As Couzens, along with Senator Tom Walsh of Montana, emphasized in Senate debate, this meant that as head of the Department of Justice, Charles B. Warren, if confirmed, would be in a position to dispose of his own anti-trust case.[6]

To Couzens, this appointment by Coolidge was another McNary case. Just as he had opposed Harding in that appointment, he now opposed Coolidge. As the Republican senator from Warren's home state, Couzens' stand was crucial. When the Judiciary Committee, following custom, requested his expected approval of Warren's nomination, he declined to give it. "Mr. Warren is an able and shrewd lawyer," was all he would say.[7]

Tremendous pressure was exerted to win him over to Warren. For by then Warren had become an important contributor of Republican campaign funds. Harding had sent him to Tokyo as United States Ambassador, and he had served Coolidge well as a floor leader in the Republican convention of 1924.[8] Warren himself made a personal appeal to Couzens, on the basis of "old days" and local patriotism. The Michigan and Detroit bar associations flooded Couzens' office with telegrams in Warren's behalf. Coolidge himself exerted all possible White House influence.[9] In the judgment of William Allen White, Coolidge, who had all the facts about Warren, "was stubborn to his own hurt and without much principle involved."[10]

To his face Couzens told Coolidge that he simply "could not stomach" Warren as Attorney General. There was no use in pressuring or cajoling him.

On the original Senate vote, there was a tie. Vice President Dawes might have broken the tie in Warren's favor, but he was absent, supposedly taking a nap in the Hotel Willard. By the time Dawes was summoned, the confirmation was rejected.

Then, obtusely, Coolidge re-submitted Warren's nomination. This appalled even Chief Justice Taft, who wrote to his son, Robert, in complaint about Warren's "subterranean methods."[11]

Couzens was subjected to another barrage. More appeals to his "loyalty to Michigan" were made. The *Michigan Manufacturer and Financial Record* snapped: "No emotion or joy over the promotion of any citizen of Michigan seems to enter his mind." [12]

But he remained adamant. He frankly told Warren that he might support him for some other post, but not for Attorney General. The public had a right to an Attorney General "above any kind of suspicion," he said.[13] On the second vote, Warren was rejected 46 to 39, and Coolidge had to admit a galling defeat.[14]

During the debate over Warren, the Senate also had been the scene of considerable acrimony when the Republican caucus determined to discipline Senator La Follette and Senators Brookhart, Frazier, and Ladd, who had supported La Follette's candidacy for President. The penalty was refusal to recognize them in committee assignments as Republicans, hence cause them to lose all committee memberships.[15] Couzens was on the point of entering into that debate, on the side of La Follette, when he found that he himself was the object of "discipline." For this was the moment Secretary Mellon selected to file against him the $10,000,000 tax case. It was a safe guess that Mellon had obtained the President's permission for the action as retaliation for Couzens' stand against Warren.

4

Couzens himself broke this news on the Senate floor. "Mr. President, I want to point out that all party discipline is not administered in the Senate. Party discipline is administered throughout the states and party discipline is administered in the Departments of the Government here. . . ."

Whereupon he told his colleagues of the tax suit, and read into the record the complaint filed against him. The action, he said, was taken because "the senior senator from Michigan has not been regular, and because he has persisted in endeavoring to eliminate rottenness in governmental departments, no matter under what administration it may occur." [16]

Immediately there was a new furor, one that almost overshadowed even the Warren controversy, as various senators rose to denounce the action against Couzens, and others as stoutly went to the defense of Secretary Mellon.

Senator Ernst was among those who went to Mellon's defense, and brought against himself from Couzens the charge that he had played a part in filching certain papers from the committee's files.

This accusation caused Senator Ernst to make an outburst destined for parliamentary anthologies. "I want the chair to tell me," he cried, "whether there is any way under the rules that I can call a fellow senator a willful, malicious and wicked liar!"

Carter Glass had just taken the floor, and thought Ernst was referring to him. "I want to know whom he is calling a liar!" Glass cried.

"That's just what he can't do; he can't call anybody a liar here," ruled the presiding officer, Joseph T. Robinson, to the amusement of the whole chamber.[17]

Couzens told the Senate that he considered the Mellon action an effort to intimidate him in the investigation.

"Will it have any effect upon the further investigation of the Bureau of Internal Revenue?" asked Kenneth McKellar of Tennessee. "It will have a most vital effect," answered Couzens. "The Senator from Michigan will be more energetic than ever in prosecuting the investigation!"[18] It did not displease him that a few months later Kentucky voters unseated Senator Ernst in favor of Democrat Alben W. Barkley, later Vice President under President Harry S. Truman.

5

Another squall developed when Coolidge disapproved of legislation for raising salaries of postal employees. Couzens fought for the legislation. Economy at the expense of human beings was false economy, he maintained.

Coolidge called Couzens to the White House. The result was an encounter that left the President sputtering with anger.

"A postman cannot raise a family on $1,500 a year," said Couzens.

"In Northampton, Massachusetts, you can have a first-rate house to live in for $30 a month," answered Coolidge.

"That's no argument!" snapped Couzens. "All of our postal employees can't live in Northampton, Massachusetts!"

"I had an uncle in Northampton," continued the President. "He sent his children through high school and college and he never made more than $1,500 a year in his life."

Couzens banged his fist on Coolidge's desk. "That's the trouble with you, Mr. President!" he roared. "You have a Northampton viewpoint, instead of a national viewpoint!"

The interview came to an abrupt end. Couzens had gone to the White House in the first place mainly to urge the appointment of

Governor Groesbeck for Attorney General, but never even got to that.[19] A conservative Vermonter, John Garibaldi Sargent, was appointed to succeed Harlan Stone.[20]

6

Couzens also bitterly criticized the administration for its treatment of General William "Billy" Mitchell, who was ousted from the Army in 1924 because of his advanced views on aviation power.[21]

He was openly contemptuous of the U.S. State Department then headed by former Senator Frank Kellogg, whom some called "Nervous Nellie," for its refusal to permit a member of the British Parliament, Shapurji Sakatvala, a Communist, to enter the United States to attend a conference of the Inter-Parliamentary Union, an early instance of what, in a later era, would be called lowering an "iron curtain." "The idea that this great United States is afraid to let one man come into this country just because he believes in a form of government different from ours is the greatest joke imaginable. Are we afraid of one man among our one hundred million?" Couzens asked.[22]

In 1926, he stirred a storm in Detroit over a similar issue. The industrial department of the Detroit Y.M.C.A. had invited William Green, president of the American Federation of Labor, to talk there. The board of directors of the "Y" ordered that Green's appearance be cancelled. Couzens was so indignant that he advised the Detroit Community Fund, to which he was a leading contributor and which helped support the "Y," that unless the ban on Green were withdrawn, he would not make his annual contribution. At the same time, he resigned in protest as honorary chairman of the Community Fund.[23]

All along, in the meanwhile, he kept up a constant fight with Secretary Mellon. In March 1928 he introduced a resolution calling upon Mellon to resign from the cabinet, charging him with "contempt for the law." [24] Mellon did not resign, but there was another fine fight.[25]

7

But by and large, these actions did little to disturb the national calm. The Bull Market was on in earnest. "Don't sell America short!" Arthur Brisbane wrote day in and day out in the most widely syndicated newspaper column of the period. Though some economists (later) would conclude that precisely in the period 1925–1927 things happened in the economy in America, and abroad, which assured disaster ahead, almost everyone was in an euphoric state. In the phrase of John Kenneth Galbraith of Harvard, in looking back at 1925 through 1929, from the vantage of 1955, the Coolidge Bull Market was a "remarkable phenomenon." [26]

True, there were some happenings which even to the layman did not seem to blend wholly with assurances of good times without end. In England there had been general strikes. In Italy there had occurred the Fascist march on Rome. In Germany the Weimar Republic was tottering, despite a Dawes Plan and a Young Plan. Even in the United States, there had occurred the Sacco and Vanzetti case, revealing that, seemingly, down underneath, there was not the confidence in the social order that most of the nation's leaders professed to have. Yet, the over-all atmosphere was one of satisfaction on the part of nearly everyone.

The independent man in politics does not flourish in such an atmosphere. Nor does the man of action in public life. There was not much business of importance before the Senate. So when his committee for investigating the Bureau of Internal Revenue had finished its work, Couzens found time hanging heavy on his hands. He began to suffer acutely from ennui. In this mood, he wrote self-analytically, and with considerable insight, to his daughter Madeleine:

"With no physical disabilities for twelve whole days, I still am not contented. What a queer character. . . . Strange incongruities to exist in one human being." [27]

CHAPTER XXVIII

THE RESTLESS STATESMAN

He knew what was missing. Back in the time when he was mayor, a group of newspapermen one day asked him for a definition of success in life. "Contentment and peace of mind, something that comes from within you," he said. "I sometimes think that I will never find them for myself."

He certainly tried to find them. His whole career, in one sense, was a monument to that search. But aside from the material results, what he had attained was not contentment, he said, but "the forgetfulness that comes from work." [1]

Now in the slow pace of his senatorial duties, in the Coolidge period of the "Golden Glow" even this balm was denied him and he was often wretched about this.

2

There was, of course, the outlet of Washington social life. He did participate in this social whirl, and with enjoyment—much more than he cared to admit. "Invitations" naturally poured in on him and Mrs. Couzens, because of themselves, but of course also because of their wealth—and the lovely daughters.

On their part, they did considerable entertaining in the various handsome residences they occupied while in Washington. First, they lived in the former Newberry house on Massachusetts Avenue. Then they moved to the former Senator Freylinghuysen place on Sixteenth Street (later the site of the Hotel Statler). But Couzens was so sensitive to even slight traffic noises at night that, in spite of all those rooms, he had to fix up a bedroom for himself—in a clothes closet. So they moved to still another Washington residence in the gladed Rock Creek area.

They were frequently at the White House on social calls—remarkably frequently, considering Couzens' status as an insurgent. But there, too, he found that wealth was a door-opener, as he had discovered in Detroit in the early days of the Ford success. Besides, perhaps oddly, Calvin Coolidge liked the Couzens society if not the Couzens politics. It would be stated that Coolidge was so impressed with business success—"The business of America is business," he had said about this time—that he could forgive Senator Couzens' political irregularities, even against himself, in view of the Couzens wealth. And the Couzenses, as did everyone, enjoyed having easy entree to 1600 Pennsylvania Avenue.

Besides, while he never came to like Coolidge's political and social views any more than Coolidge came to agree with his, Couzens also developed a certain real affection for Coolidge, the man, enjoying especially his unostentatious, even homely, ways. They got so that they could discuss divergent views frankly, without a blowup. "I admire Coolidge," Couzens wrote to Vandenberg. "I do not believe he admires the sycophant who bows, scrapes and dances to please him. There are men of that kind, but I do not think he is, and certainly I could not be that kind of a fellow even if I were told I had to be to enter the Kingdom of Heaven." [2]

3

He found pleasure, too, in his daughters, observing with fatherly pride their maturing. He and Madeleine developed an especially tender relationship that was wonderfully satisfying. After having finished her course at the Bronson school in New York, she delighted him especially by undertaking to do what he himself once had wanted to do—study law.

As a student at Washington College of Law, she followed closely the legislation in which he was interested, and frequently was to be found in the visitors' gallery of the Senate listening to the proceedings. Madeleine and he, walking to and from the Capitol, became a familiar sight, and their walks together were among his most cherished activities.

When Madeleine was away, he wrote to her in a warm, affectionate way that probably surprised even himself, considering his reputation for being cold-blooded. He once told a friend that he had trouble all his life "to say what I feel in my heart." [3] But this was not true between himself and Madeleine.

In one letter he wrote:

You are well and happy, so I am pleased, although no one but myself knows how much I miss you. Something keeps you in mind every hour of the day and in many of my dreams. I miss seeing you in the Senate gallery and I miss your cheery welcome when I come home. All this even though I have a loving wife and two sweet and loving daughters still with me. . . .[4]

At this time he joined the Burning Tree Country Club and became one of the most avid and best-known golfers in Washington.[5] He also developed intimate friendships with other senators, most of all with Charles L. McNary of Oregon (the 1940 Republican candidate for Vice President with Wendell L. Willkie), and with Pat Harrison of Mississippi, Frederick Hale of Maine, and Hiram Johnson.[6] This camaraderie was something he had never permitted himself in his earlier years.

However, in none of this outwardly pleasant life did he find the complete cure for his restlessness. He simply had developed no philosophy that permitted him to accept, let alone welcome, a calm existence. He did much thinking and reading—the *Nation* and the *New Republic* being his favorites among magazines. But actually the contemplative life was foreign to him.

He kept religion at arm's length, perhaps, as he once said, because "there was so much religion at home in Chatham." So nearly all he had to fall back upon, since he could not indulge in just pleasure, was his old formula, "making good."

4

Twice he came close to returning to the business world. Just after his election in 1924, Joseph P. Tumulty, who had been Woodrow Wilson's secretary, informed him that the *Washington Post* could be purchased from E. B. McLean for $6,000,000. To own a newspaper in the capital appealed to Couzens. He became seriously interested, and Tumulty was eager to act as broker.

However, McLean's well-known eccentric ways—oddities that finally caused him to be committed to a sanitarium—were a stumbling block. He refused, for example, to submit any kind of financial statement. Nor would he answer a series of specific questions concerning the property that had been drawn up for Couzens by Jay Hayden. He stubbornly took the attitude that if Couzens wanted the *Post,* he should buy it without asking questions. The farthest he would go was to give a "warranty" that the newspaper was "profit-

able." Couzens then refused to have any further dealings with Mc-
Lean and gave up entirely the idea of acquiring the *Post*.[7]

In 1926, he actually launched another commercial enterprise of
his own—the Couzens Ice Machine Company, which he capitalized
at $1,000,000 for the purpose of producing mechanical refrigerators.
His principal motive, he said, was to assure a fitting career for Frank,
then in the house-building business in Detroit with John P. Frazer.
There was an impulsiveness about this whole matter which indicated
how desperate he was to be in "something active." When Wilcox, his
lawyer, warned him that it might be wise to check the status of patents
on mechanical refrigerators, he brushed the warning aside.

"Nonsense. We'll go ahead and fight out the patent trouble later,
as we did in the Selden case."

It was also suggested to him that there be more testing done, but
he vetoed this too.

"If we did that in the beginning of the Ford Motor Company,
we never would have gotten any place. The thing to do is to start
production and make improvements later."

Two factory sites were purchased, one in Detroit, and another in
Wapokeneta, Ohio. Dealers were signed up. Literature was printed.
Sample machines were displayed in stores. Then, just as the company
was preparing to go into production, he suddenly called the whole
thing off, at an enormous loss.[8]

5

He had been studying the installment purchase system. Installment
buying and selling were bad for people morally, encouraging them
to live beyond their means, and even worse for the nation economically, he concluded. He became something of a crusader on this
view, made several speeches about it, and also contributed several
magazine articles in which he warned that the system was bound to
lead to a crash [9]—one of the few warning signals sent up during
this era of euphoria. And he had been advised that it would be impossible to market the Couzens refrigerator except on the installment
plan. Rather than do that, he determined to kill the enterprise entirely. At least, this was his excuse.[10]

It was just as well. Frank, himself now a father, with one of his
sons named James Couzens II, did not need to have his career
mapped for him. He was already shaping a future quite satisfactorily,
incidentally moving along a path paralleling his father's, for in 1928,

Frank became a member of the Detroit Plan Commission. Later he became a commissioner of the municipally owned Detroit Street Railway.

By 1929, Frank was to be a figure of status in his own right in municipal politics. A statement issued by him on the mayoralty campaign that year attracted wide attention. "You see, I have competition in the family already," Couzens told Madeleine.[11]

6

Having decided against re-entry into business, Couzens turned to personal projects. It had been logical for some time that he should erect a permanent, year-round residence at Wabeek. Soon after he called off the refrigerator project, he became engrossed in building a new Wabeek residence, completed in time for it to be the scene of Madeleine's marriage in January 1928 to William R. Yaw. He undertook still another construction project, an office building in the town of Birmingham, Michigan. There he established his personal office (and, a few years later, the Wabeek State Bank, created mainly for handling his own financial affairs). It was no longer necessary, he said, for him to keep an office in Detroit. By having his headquarters at Birmingham, he would not be disturbed by people "wanting favors or to sell him something." [12]

In the country-squire existence that he began to lead at Wabeek, there were gratifications in abundance for him. He took to spending a great deal of his time in the outdoors. He enjoyed puttering around the estate and superintending farming operations at Wabeek, although it exasperated him constantly that he could not make the farming side of it pay. The feeling of being a great landowner—Wabeek by then was expanded to some 800 acres—pleased him. Then in 1929, he launched a project that filled some of the more basic requirements of his restless nature and won for him a measure of peace that had come from nothing else. This was his creation of, for the era, one of the nation's most important philanthropies, the Children's Fund of Michigan.

CHAPTER XXIX

THE MAGNIFICENT GIFT

BACK in 1915, Couzens had written to a friend: "You are quite right, I have more money than I am entitled to. I am just commencing to take time to learn how to separate myself from some of it." [1] That year Henry Morgan, his secretary, persuaded him to visit a small home for crippled children in Detroit maintained by a Blanche Leuven Brown, herself a cripple. He could not get the sight of these children out of his mind. Almost before he knew it, he became the principal financial backer of the Brown home, giving it $10,000 in 1915. And from then on, he began to become a "giver."

In 1918, he made an interesting alliance. A young man named Byers H. Gitchell, later a figure in department-store merchandising, had been talking to him about certain social improvements needed in Detroit. Gitchell had been secretary of the Board of Commerce at the time Couzens was its president. Like Couzens, he had resigned because he felt this commercial group was not "getting behind the real things that should be done for the city." [2]

To Couzens, Gitchell now sketched an almost pioneer concept of city planning—better homes for workers, more parks, improved educational opportunities, better hospital facilities, and more integration of various organized charities. If he could afford it, Gitchell added, he would like to devote his energies to developing such a program—this at the time Couzens was thinking of standing for Mayor.

"All right," said Couzens. "Go ahead. I'll pay your salary!" [3]

One result of this was the creation in 1918 of "The Detroit Patriotic Fund," forerunner of the Detroit Community Fund and Community Chest. Couzens was its leading contributor, his gifts averaging $150,000 a year. For several years he served as president of the fund and was the dominant influence in its administration. [4] It was he, too, who was chiefly responsible for having brought to

Detroit, from the Cincinnati Council of Social Agencies, William J. Norton, a hardheaded yet progressive and liberal-minded Maine-born social worker, to serve as founding director of the Detroit Patriotic Fund—thus beginning for himself, as well as for Detroit and Michigan, an important relationship.

2

In 1919 Couzens gave a $650,000 nurses' residence to Harper Hospital of Detroit. In that same year, as a birthday present to Mrs. Couzens, he made a gift of $1,000,000 for the furtherance of what by then was his great hobby, the helping of crippled children. This donation was really an outgrowth of his interest in the Brown home. He had become a member of a committee (along with Alex Y. Malcomson) for converting the Brown home into a scientific institution.

Largely on his initiative, it was merged with the Michigan Hospital School.[5] Later, he was instrumental in effecting a merger of this Michigan Hospital School with the Children's Free Hospital of Detroit. When this was achieved, in 1922, and there came into being the Children's Hospital—the word "free" was eliminated as "distasteful," at his insistence—he donated an additional $1,000,000, which was used, among other purposes, to create the hospital's famous countryside branch at Farmington.

3

He liked to say that helping children was a matter of "absolute justice," not sentiment, as he once wrote to Norton.

But no man could have been more sentimental than he over the plight of deformed youngsters. He suffered actual pain at the sight of a crippled child, or even if he merely read about such a child. Morgan once sent him a pamphlet describing the work of an organization for helping cripples. Before returning it, Couzens wrote on it: "I'm glad you showed me this, but it has spoiled my day."[6] And this at a time when other leading Detroiters insisted he was "cold-blooded" and "unfeeling."

In 1924, he donated still another residence for nurses, this time to the University of Michigan, at a cost of $620,000. In this same year, he established a $100,000 fund for making loans to physically handicapped war veterans, primarily to help them "make a start in a self-supporting business in a manner which will enable them to maintain their self-respect."[7]

The idea for this came to him after a crippled war veteran had come into his office at the Senate and asked for a loan of fifty dollars. Couzens had abruptly turned down the veteran, saying a casual loan "would do no good." But after a sleepless night he set up the $100,000 fund.

4

His great philanthropy, however, was the Children's Fund of Michigan.

Over a long period, he had discussed his plans for this with Dr. Freund, his personal physician, with Norton, and with his lawyer, Judge Arthur J. Lacy, formerly of the Court of Domestic Relations, then with John Anderson's firm.[8] He reached his decision to act just after Madeleine's first child, Margot Yaw, was born. A letter to her gave a hint, but only a hint, of his decision. She had asked him to come to Detroit from Washington to see his new granddaughter sooner than he had planned.

"I want Frank to be there when I come to Detroit," he wrote. "I have something important to do and want Frank present." [9]

The "something important" was the Children's Fund.

Its purpose was told in the carefully selected words of the trust instrument:

"To promote the health, welfare, happiness, and development of the children of the State of Michigan primarily, and elsewhere in the world."

He started the Fund with an irrevocable gift of $10,000,000. Later, in November 1934, he added $1,880,700. Counting income as well as principal, the gift resulted in the expenditure, as of its final reporting date, May 1, 1954, of $18,038,656.36. In later years, after other wealthy men had seen the desirability of establishing welfare foundations (also after money values had become inflated) this sum perhaps would not seem extraordinarily remarkable. But at the time, his gift was sensational and amounted to one of the fifteen largest publicly listed charitable trusts.[10]

For him, the Children's Fund represented a broadening of his interest in the welfare of children. Though still greatly concerned with helping physically handicapped children, he now desired to do his part for the benefit of children generally. In 1935, he summed up his views:

> I know of no greater obligation resting upon the adults of a civilized nation than the application of their love for their children

in those practical, organized ways which guarantee that each generation . . . will have progressively greater opportunities of arriving at manhood and womanhood better equipped for life's contest than their predecessors had.

Science contributes year by year a constantly enlarging stream of knowledge of how to keep the body well, how to cure sickness, how to train the mind for more efficient performance, and how to mold the character for strong and resourceful struggle against odds. It is a major business of adult mankind so to organize this growing fund of knowledge and so to apply it that more and more children will be able to start the race of life without handicaps and on even terms.[11]

5

He stipulated that all of the money in the Children's Fund must be expended within twenty-five years after May 1, 1929, and that, on the average, at least $700,000 was to be distributed each year. Permanent foundations, while pleasing to the vanity of men who wanted their names remembered in perpetuity, tended to defeat their purpose, he felt.

He also made it clear that the least possible portion of the Fund was to be used for buildings of any kind. Not monuments to himself, but effective activity for children, was his goal.

Indeed, he leaned over backwards in this. When he donated the nurses' home to Harper Hospital, he refused to permit it to be called "The James Couzens Home," as was proposed by the hospital board. "He would not hear of it," related Dr. Stewart Hamilton, director of the hospital. He asked that the home be named after the then principal nurse of the hospital, Emily A. McLaughlin, in tribute to her service in France during World War I.[12]

He was positively indignant upon learning that the University of Michigan authorities had designated the nurses' home he had given that institution as "The Couzens Residence for Nurses." [13]

He held to this principle always. In the notes of Arthur J. Lacy, who, with Clarence Wilcox, handled the legal matters involved in setting up the Children's Fund, there appears this:

We tried to induce Senator Couzens to call this the Couzens Foundation, but he refused to have his name included. He said the fund belongs to the children. . . . He said it is not where it comes from, but where it is going that is important.

He insisted too, that there be no racial or creedal discrimination of any kind. "I have never felt justified in contributing to any particular creed, color, or race, and I am anxious to see that all are treated alike," he once said.[14]

He participated directly and actively in all that the Fund did so long as he lived. He had himself designated as chairman of the board that was formed to administer the Fund. No detail in planning or execution was too small to command his interest,. as the work of the Fund progressed. He wrote "voluminous letters from Washington" about it to its officers.[15]

6

The original board of trustees, of which Frank Couzens, as well as himself, was a member, was carefully chosen by him. All were men who knew his views, who were definitely interested in social welfare—Lacy and Wilcox, McPherson Browning, a Detroit banker, Dr. Freund, and Norton.

Dr. Freund, a physician of unusual social and psychological insight, was exceptionally well qualified to be Couzens' adviser in this field. Aside from the experience that came from a large medical practice, he was well grounded in public-health work, having been a member of the Detroit Board of Health for a number of years, under Couzens as well as other mayors. He was interested in research. Perhaps most of all, Dr. Freund concerned himself with the general problem of mental health, and he was a doctor interested in social conditions. He was named president of the Fund and much that the Fund accomplished bore the impress of his broad and informed interests.

Norton was well acquainted with Couzens' views because of their close association with the Community Fund. A true humanitarian, yet levelheaded and practical—outstandingly so among welfare workers—Norton was precisely the man for operating director. Couzens "drafted" Norton to serve as executive vice-president and secretary. At first this was on a part-time basis, with Norton continuing with the Community Fund. Then Norton made the Children's Fund his full-time career. He and Couzens made a superb team.

7

The Children's Fund adopted and followed two main policies from the beginning. It decided to support selected activities of already existing agencies in the children's field. It initiated activity of its own in more or less neglected fields, but always with the thought that this activity ultimately would be carried on by some other agency, preferably by state or local governments. Thus, the work of the Fund would go on, even though the Fund itself was to cease existence after twenty-five years. In this respect the Fund was a trail blazer.[16]

Michigan was a backward state with respect to public-health work in rural areas when the Fund was established. Numerous counties had no public-health facilities at all, not even the minimum services for inspecting water supply or controlling communicable diseases. To correct this lack became a major objective of the Children's Fund. Its approach was to offer financial support to selected counties, by which health officers, nurses, dentists, and sanitary inspectors would be employed, provided the counties established health districts.

The Fund constructed and undertook the operation of two children's clinics outside Detroit—the Northern Michigan Children's Clinic at Marquette, and the Central Michigan Children's Clinic at Traverse City. Serving large areas, these clinics made available medical services including orthopedic treatment of cripples, that previously were unknown to rural children. It also maintained a laboratory, mainly in the field of biological chemistry, where scientists launched studies in problems of nutrition and of growth, with the view to finding means of improving the physical well-being of children everywhere. This laboratory, in which the offices of the Fund were located, was constructed adjacent to the Children's Hospital, in accord with Couzens' plan that ultimately it should be a gift to that hospital, so that its work would continue after the Fund had expired. The executive headquarters and laboratory building were deeded to Children's Hospital when the fund was liquidated on April 30, 1954.

In Detroit there was established the Children's Center, staffed by psychiatrists, psychologists, and psychiatric social workers, who specialized in treating maladjusted children. With the cooperation of the state, a similar center was established at Lansing, Michigan, to bring the value of mental-hygiene work to the attention of the state at large. In addition, the Fund sponsored a program for acquainting teachers in the public schools with advances in the understanding of juvenile personality problems.

Some twelve years later, the Michigan legislature authorized the State Hospital Commission to establish three child-guidance clinics

—at Muskegon, Kalamazoo, and Saginaw. This meant that the Children's Fund had played a vital role in fostering acceptance of a progressive step in public health, and that its work in an important field would go on. Indeed, it had sparked many such activities and encouraged gifts in its field by other persons and foundations.

Couzens himself once summarized accurately its work:

> New services for health, new implements for self-discipline, and an enlargement of scientific knowledge have come into being with our assistance. And we have entered practically into the lives of hundreds of thousands of children to their happiness and advantage.[17]

8

Nothing that he had ever done—not his role in the building of the Ford Motor Company, nor the winning of public office—gave him more real pleasure. A tabulation of all his contributions—counting the Children's Fund—showed an interesting total, approximately $30,000,000, or precisely the sum he had received for his Ford Motor Company stock.[18]

The mail he received from all over the nation from persons pleased by his gift "has been terrific, like a cyclone," he told Madeleine. "I have taken the trouble to personally answer each letter." [19]

In the following June, while at his desk in the Senate, he wrote her an interesting personal letter.

> I just happened to observe that I was getting older and shrinking up. When I went shopping for some shoes and stockings the other day, my sizes had to be reduced. Socks for me for years were ten and a half, but now I have to have size ten. . . . Keep well and keep your temper and disposition sweet; it pays immensely, in spite of the fact that I have not practiced it! [20]

If he was getting old and "shrinking up," this by no means indicated an easier, more relaxed time ahead for him. Actually, one of his most active periods lay just ahead. For a vast change was to occur in the American scene—and there was work aplenty for a public man with a sensitive conscience.

CHAPTER XXX

THE "DANGEROUS MAN"

His Children's Fund gift was cited in many quarters as proof of the healthy working of the American economic system. By coincidence, however, the system was just then on the eve of a great spell of sickness, the first symptom of which was a pronounced rise in unemployment.

Nearly everyone dismissed this trend in the latter days of the Coolidge Bull Market as something that would pass. Secretary of Commerce Herbert Hoover had been elected President in the previous November. During his campaign he had said hopefully: "We in America today are nearer to the final triumph over poverty than ever before in the history of the land." [1]

Couzens was not so sure of this. Indeed, as early as 1924, he wrote:

> Notwithstanding the abundance of everything in this country, we never seem to have devised a way to create security for those "have nots" who are willing to work. . . . I have unbounded concern for the family man who has no security in a job. This is the one outstanding problem to be solved.[2]

In 1926, when he was studying the installment-buying question, he said, "I am sorry that so much publicity is given to universal prosperity that does not exist." [3] In February 1927 he told Frank Couzens, "Times are not too good and it is my impression that they will be worse before they are better." [4]

During Coolidge's last days in the White House, Couzens warned the President that danger existed in the widespread stock-market gambling, especially in banking securities.[5]

On the Senate floor he sharply criticized the Federal Reserve Board for encouraging "a great orgy of speculation." This, he said, was a "dumb" policy that could only end in disaster.[6]

2

Early in 1928 along with "Young Bob" La Follette, he persuaded the Senate to authorize an investigation into unemployment. As chairman of the Committee of Labor and Education, he took charge. The result was a Senate report that became a significant document, a kind of American "Beveridge Report," which called attention to the need for unemployment insurance and old-age pensions.[7]

In one respect this document was historic. It endorsed a principle that was not to become part of the doctrines of progressivism in the United States until after World War II—that, under democracy, men have a *right* to self-supporting employment. In the main, this doctrine was Couzens' personal contribution. His report said:

> No one will question that every man is entitled to the opportunity to provide for himself and his family. That is a fundamental right and society cannot consider itself successfully organized until every man is assured of the opportunity to preserve himself and his family from suffering and want.

The report also said:

> Cyclical unemployment has been like the plague; it has come and gone at regular intervals until it has been accepted as a necessary evil by some who should know otherwise. . . .
> We do not believe any more that it is necessary for the baby to have diphtheria and rickets and other "diseases of childhood." We have found and are finding methods of preventing these diseases. We should recognize also that there is an obligation on all society to attack, unceasingly, the problem of unemployment.[8]

His report included two recommendations of great significance later:

> The government should adopt legislation without delay which would provide a system of planning public works so that they would form a reserve against unemployment in times of depression. States and municipalities and other public agencies should do likewise.
> Future consideration might well be given to two questions, the effect had on unemployment by industrial developments such as consolidation of capital, and the necessity and advisability of providing, either through private industry, through the states, or through the federal government, a system of old-age pensions.[9]

And all this, of course, before the "New Deal" and the social security program that came with it. As a Senator, he was again the trail-blazing industrialist that he had been in 1914 when it was he who pushed through at the Ford Company the $5-a-day plan and also, as in 1915, had urged upon the Detroit Board of Commerce a policy which, in effect, meant a guaranteed annual wage.

He engaged in a good deal of correspondence with key industrialists throughout the nation upon these problems. To a businessman in Connecticut, who had objected that relief funds did not get at "fundamentals," Couzens wrote:

> That is true, but . . . relief has got to be had while we are attacking the fundamentals. I, for one, am unable to see the suffering that goes on while we are trying to find the basis of permanent relief.[10]

This was in May 1929—before "the Great Crash."

With George W. Johnson, the shoe manufacturer, he carried on a correspondence in which he championed a favorite idea. Industry must undertake payroll-stabilization plans for ending seasonal and cyclical unemployment. "That means," he said, "the arousing of the consciousness of the employer to the necessity of doing for his employees what he does for his plant and his stockholders." When Johnson argued that it was necessary to go slow, to learn by experience, Couzens agreed. "But we must not let too many people suffer while we are gaining this experience." [11]

It was then, in 1925, that he began to speak out strongly for a proposal which other progressives were not to espouse seriously until a quarter-century had passed: The guaranteed annual wage for industrial workers.

In short, he was for scrapping the old-style wage system entirely, and substituting the annual salary for all men and women in industrial employment. Especially did he recommend this for the great automobile industry, which he had helped to found.

3

The stock market collapsed in October 1929. The *Commercial & Financial Chronicle* called the result "the greatest stock market catastrophe of all ages." [12]

President Hoover, however, assured the country that all was really well. "The fundamental business of the country . . . is on a sound and prosperous basis," he said.[13] But this was whistling in the dark. The "great depression" was on,[14] though *The Literary Digest* called it a "prosperity panic." [15]

In the following December Couzens addressed the annual dinner of the Michigan Manufacturers Association at Detroit. By then the depression had unmistakably set in. Fifteen years almost to the day after his memorable address on unemployment before the Detroit Board of Commerce in 1914, he repeated almost word for word what he had said then about the irresponsibility of employers toward their workers. By failing to act, the manufacturers were, in large part, to blame for the unemployment, he said, adding that low wages had reduced the needed purchasing power of the people.

He chided the business leaders for opposing increased taxes for unemployment relief and for their slogan, "No government interference in business!"

> You can prevent these high taxes. You can prevent bureaucrats from interfering with progress and development of business. You can prevent officials from sending out forms by the bushel for you to fill out and return—if you will solve these problems yourselves. Government does not interfere with business until business itself has created the necessity.[16]

Now he was no longer bored. Once again he was the crusader, constantly plumping for what he saw was the only sound solution of the unemployment problem—adoption, by basic industries, of the annual wage for factory employment. And he was more realistic in assessing the causes and the extent of the "crash" than nearly everyone else in the land.[17]

4

In 1930 he stood again for re-election. Then it was not much of a handicap that he had not gone along with Coolidge. Indeed, by 1930, this was almost in his favor, even with Republicans.

A suggestion of the change in the land was personified in Vandenberg. Back in 1927 the quiet Senator Ferris had died, and Vandenberg was appointed to the vacancy. Now himself a senator, Vandenberg was not so completely Hamiltonian as he had been in 1924, when he was so certain that La Follette intended to undermine America. At first, he and Couzens did not get along well in the Senate. "I did not want you appointed. I think you are too conservative," Couzens frankly told Vandenberg just after he was sworn in.[18]

But by 1930 Vandenberg was more sympathetic toward even mild "La Folletteism," although he would never come to be styled a progressive himself.[19] Frank R. Kent said that Vandenberg took on "a progressive coloration . . . largely to keep Jim Couzens off his back." [20] If true, this was a straw in the wind indicating that even among orthodox Republicans the old order was giving ground. It had to, for this depression was vastly more severe than any the nation had known.

5

So it was no surprise that Couzens this time won renomination, easily defeating the highly popular former Bull Mooser and ex-Governor, Chase S. Osborn. The Democrats had no more heart to campaign against him now in 1930 than did the troubled Old Guard Republicans. They considered not even putting up a candidate against him. Thomas E. H. Weadcock, a former Congressman, who finally did consent to run as a Democrat, polled only 139,814 votes in the election. Couzens received 520,247.

This vote of confidence—with many of the regular party leaders backing him, at least passively—did not cause him to change his style as the Senate's gadfly. The *Baltimore Sun* in March 1931 carried an item that showed that he was still the old Couzens.

> He likes Hoover personally and politically [wrote Frank R. Kent, with tongue in cheek] and has consistently voted against him in the Senate only because Hoover happened not to think the way he thinks. Actually, Couzens thinks he has been helping Hoover. It would be interesting to know what Mr. Hoover thinks.

One of the early votes Couzens cast against Hoover was on the appointment of Charles Evans Hughes as Chief Justice, to succeed Taft. Back in 1916, Couzens had taken his first tentative step into the political arena as an elector pledged to Hughes. Now he joined organized labor in opposing Hughes for Chief Justice because, he concluded, "Hughes is too conservative." [21]

6

As unemployment continued to rise in the nation as a whole as well as in the Detroit area in particular, Couzens hammered consistently away at two ideas—the unemployed must be given relief; businessmen were to blame. What had happened, he felt, had remarkably confirmed his long-standing opinion that leaders of business were no supermen, and that the much-publicized superiority of the successful was largely myth. As noted by one Washington writer, he, the multimillionaire, talked more and more "in a way to make a conservative's blood curdle." [22]

More people listened now to Couzens, fewer to Andrew Mellon.

Indeed, by then Mellon, with his world apparently going to pieces, had become, as Thomas L. Stokes wrote, "an uncertain little man . . . lonely and tragic." [23]

Couzens' targets now were the leaders of big business, the bigger the better, in his view. One target became Albert H. Wiggin, chairman of the governing board of the Chase National Bank of New York. Wiggin had made the front pages by suggesting two principal "remedies" for the depression: scale down the war debts owed the United States by foreign nations, and reduce wage standards in the United States generally. Sympathetic toward the first suggestion, Couzens was wrathful concerning the second:

> When it comes to a cut in wages and calling upon labor to accept such reductions, it seems wholly unreasonable, in view of the fact that one of the difficulties that brought about this depression, and in my opinion the major one, has been unequal distribution of the earnings of industry between capital and labor. . . . This should not be considered, even though the suggestion comes from a great financial giant such as Mr. Wiggin.[24]

He challenged the Chamber of Commerce of the United States to present a program for relieving economic distress, issuing in 1931 a bitter statement which lambasted business leaders for opposing social-security legislation—they called it the "dole"—without offering a constructive substitute. He took the chamber to task for its propaganda against "government interference with business" and its scary pronouncements about the evils of "a dole."

> Congress is warned against a dole; it is warned against unemployment insurance and old age pensions. When capital is idle, it continues in many cases to receive dividends and interest, but I have heard no complaint registered that anybody has been offended because it was a dole. Why is a dole to men and women more offensive than a dole to capital? [25]

7

In 1928 he had supported Hoover's election. To be sure, he was not so active for Hoover as Vandenberg. But he had gone out of his way to make a few speeches for Hoover's election. Remembering Hoover's leadership in the Conference on Unemployment in 1922, Couzens believed that Hoover was something of a progressive, a view that many, even the liberal *New Republic* magazine, had shared. He considered Hoover a competent executive, a man of strength, the "Great Engineer," who knew how to act in time of crisis. Moreover, Hoover had once described himself as an "independent progressive" who objected "as much to the reactionary group in the Republican party as . . . to the radical group in the Democratic party." [26]

But Hoover was a disappointment to Couzens. The first glimmer came when Hoover failed to replace Mellon. Couzens had understood from Senators Brookhart and Borah that Hoover had promised not to reappoint Mellon. The promise was kept, technically. Hoover did not reappoint Mellon—he simply let him carry over.[27]

Then, Hoover asked Couzens for a memorandum on reforming the Bureau of Internal Revenue. Couzens prepared a lengthy one —and nothing happened, except the executive order on publicizing refunds of more than $20,000.[28]

His disappointment soon turned to disillusionment and, finally, into bitter antagonism.

It did not help matters that Hoover, as President, impressed Couzens as being ponderous and authoritative, the very kind of personality least palatable to him.[29]

8

Hoover did not conceal an antipathy on his part toward Couzens. He frequently went out of his way to single him out for criticism. Couzens was "a very dangerous man," Hoover once told a White House visitor, according to a report that Couzens himself received.[30]

This was sad, for Hoover, as well as for Couzens, and for the country too; for undeniably Hoover was a man of great ability, and the country would have benefited had he and Couzens been able, with others, to work harmoniously together toward meeting the problems of the depression. But between them, as the phrase "a very dangerous man" indicated, was a great gulf, not only temperamentally, but also in social outlook, and this was tragic for the nation in its larger implications, for it meant a policy of drift, or government by doctrinaire slogans, when obviously what was required was practical action along the lines that Couzens was urging, in broad policy if not in detail.

CHAPTER XXXI

THE CRUSADER AGAIN

THEIR first major clash was on the old question of Muscle Shoals. For Hoover held to the same view on Muscle Shoals that Coolidge had advocated, that it should not be operated as a government power project, but should be turned over to private power companies, if developed for power at all.[1] In his very first message to Congress, Hoover denounced the idea of government ownership of Muscle Shoals with a characteristically unfortunate phrase, calling it "degeneration." [2] This was galling to Couzens and he said so.

Early in the administration, he also broke with Hoover over another issue carried over from the Harding and Coolidge days— that of the railroads. Then chairman of the Senate Committee on Interstate Commerce, he had begun an intensive study of the railroad problem. In principle, he favored a program of consolidations, for getting rid of unnecessarily competing lines. But at the same time, he was against combinations which would mean "killings" on the part of speculators in railroad securities and the perpetuation of "watered" capitalizations. He was also on the alert against a program that would "solve" the railroad financial problem at the expense of the railroad workers.[3]

While Couzens' committee was engaged with this problem, Hoover came out with a proposal for consolidating all railroads east of the Mississippi into four systems.[4] Couzens criticized Hoover's program. It was solely "a proposal to help the railroads out of their financial difficulties," rather than a program that considered the railroad problem in its larger aspects, he said. He added that the Hoover program would result in fewer jobs for railroad workers at a time when unemployment was becoming a major problem.[5]

Hoover defended his program and, in doing so, attacked Couzens. "If Senator Couzens blocks it, that will add sensibly to our depression difficulties," he said.[6]

Supported by the railroad brotherhoods, Couzens made sure that the Senate did block the Hoover plan. "A victory very pleasing to me," he wrote to Madeleine.[7]

Reflecting Hoover's attitude was the observation made twenty years later by a friendly Hoover biographer:

> The radical bloc in Congress, led by Senator Couzens of Michigan and supported by the Democrats, defeated the proposal. Their evident purpose was to keep the railway industry demoralized in the hope that eventually the government would have to take them over. Socialism was in the air then, as it is today.

This, of course, proved nonsense of a type that would have been especially irritating to Couzens.

2

On the soldier's-bonus issue, Couzens again broke with Hoover. Normally, he was as opposed as anyone else to "veterans' raids" on the Treasury, for he had none of the politician's fear of the so-called veterans' vote. But he felt that with the government failing to provide adequate depression relief generally, prepayment of the Soldiers' Bonus, as provided by the bill in Congress, was a practical, if inefficient, way of getting funds to needy citizens who happened to be war veterans.[8] Hoover, however, took the position that this would seriously impair the federal credit. He cited Secretary Mellon as his authority on this.

Couzens was scornful. If the outlay for the bonus would bankrupt the nation, he asked, what was there to the earlier argument that Mr. Mellon was "a wizard" in his conduct of the finances of the country? He unburdened himself in the Senate of a sarcastic thrust at both Hoover and Mellon:

"In view of the great Secretary Mellon being alleged to have served under three Presidents, I desire to point out that the fact is that three Presidents have served under the Secretary of the Treasury." [9]

When Hoover vetoed the Bonus bill, Couzens was lined up with the senators who re-passed the bill over the veto.[10]

3

He was especially outraged when Hoover advocated a national manufacturers' sales tax on all commodities "except necessary food" and possibly "some grades of clothing," as a way to balance the budget.[11]

The sales tax was a "monstrosity," a levy that mainly hit the poor, Couzens declared. "When we scratch down below the surface of this question of a sales tax, we find an effort to get rid of the income tax." "Whenever anyone mentions a general sales tax I become irrational," he once wrote.[12]

He was a leader in the revolt in Congress that blocked enactment of the sales tax.[13]

To his personal lawyer, Arthur Lacy, who that year was unsuccessful Democratic candidate for governor of Michigan, Couzens commented acidly on senatorial colleagues who had voted against an amendment of his to forbid the sales tax and to substitute a 10 per cent increase in surtaxes on large incomes. "What I think of some of my colleagues who voted against my proposed amendment could hardly be dictated to a female stenographer. 'Wealth' certainly has an enormous number of friends, even among those who are not wealthy. It seems that practically every publisher, nearly every lawyer, nearly every public official and nearly everyone who has the public ear is on guard, in defense of 'wealth.' " [14]

4

But it was over unemployment relief that he found himself in sharpest division with Hoover. In principle, he believed, with Hoover, that the federal government should not undertake direct unemployment relief and that relief funds should be distributed by the state and local governments. But he parted from Hoover by vigorously taking the view that relief by whatever means, had to be made available even by federal handouts, if the need existed, precisely his position during the depression of 1921 as mayor of Detroit. The victims of the depression could not be fed and sheltered on political philosophy, he asserted.

To Couzens, the spectre of jobless men, the sight that had caused him to initiate the five-dollar-a-day plan at the Ford Company, still was a haunting thing. That his and Young Bob La Follette's 1928 report on unemployment, urging a social security program, was gathering dust did not surprise him. But he did expect Hoover, whose reputation as a public figure was built largely on his humanitarian zeal for getting food to the people of Europe during and after World War I, would come up with some imaginative program for relieving similar distress in America. Yet Hoover even opposed a proposal for appropriating $20,000,000 to the American Red Cross for assisting the poor in drought areas with food. The President took the position that it would violate the "American way" and desert the principle of "private charity" if the Red Cross received support from the government.[15] To Couzens, this was carrying "rugged individualism" to absurd lengths.

In August 1931 Couzens was one of several senators who urged Hoover to call a special session of Congress to enact legislation for federal funds to be distributed through municipal governments. He acted after Mayor Frank Murphy of Detroit advised him that the city was unable to raise funds to provide unemployment relief, that at least $10,000,000 was needed to tide Detroit over the winter.

"We have played ostrich enough," Couzens said. "Families cannot be allowed to starve." [16]

But Hoover refused to call the special session. In his view, the suggestion had come from "radicals." "We cannot legislate ourselves out of this depression," he said.[17]

Couzens was all the more angry over this because he had just had a personal experience with appeals to private relief. To meet the situation in Detroit, he advised Mayor Murphy that he personally would contribute $1,000,000, if other wealthy men of the city would contribute an additional $9,000,000. Not only was the $9,000,000 not forthcoming, but at a meeting called by Mayor Murphy, Couzens was criticized—for having made such an "embarrassing offer." [18]

In November 1931, over the radio, Couzens spoke out vigorously against Hoover's tendency to minimize the seriousness of the depression. "Conditions today seem to indicate the bankruptcy of business genius and leadership in this country," he said. He criticized leaders who "take refuge inside their storm cellars of wealth and tell those on the outside not to be alarmed, because the country has always pulled through and will do so again." [19]

5

By the time Congress convened in December 1931 conditions had become much worse. Even Hoover then admitted that extraordinary measures were needed and proposed the creation of the Reconstruction Finance Corporation, by which the government would make available millions of dollars to banks and other financial institutions. Although reluctantly, he went so far as to recommend that the RFC be empowered to loan up to $300,000,000 to states and municipalities for relief expenditures, if these local units were unable to sell bonds on their own account in the regular market.[20] Indeed, here was the real start of the later New Deal. But such concessions by Hoover came too late.

As 1932 moved forward, the worst fears of Couzens and others came to pass. Unemployment in the United States reached, according to some informed estimates, the unprecedented total of 17,000,000 persons. Banks by the hundreds failed. The Insull empire in Illinois collapsed.[21] Farmers in some instances threatened to hang judges who foreclosed mortgages, in others halted the shipment of farm products to the cities because of the ruinous prices.[22] In Chicago, the city police were alerted and held in stations to be prepared for rioting. To save the banks there, the RFC loaned $90,000,000 to Charles G. Dawes' bank, just after Dawes resigned as RFC president.[23]

6

Detroit in particular was shaken. For Couzens, this was doubly jolting. He had helped to make Detroit the great industrial center that it had become, one that had attracted thousands of workers. Now, it seemed, it had all added up to a social disaster.

Although only a few knew it, the banking structure of Detroit was in a state bordering on collapse. More obvious as to Detroit's distress was the fact that the Ford plant closed down.

With amazement, Couzens read the startling news. Ford had even abandoned the five-dollar-a-day plan! No longer was it true that "the commonest laborer who sweeps the floor shall receive his five dollars a day." Instead, the minimum rate for common labor was cut to fifty cents an hour, or four dollars a day.[24] In May 1932, 80,000 unemployed workers gathered in Cadillac Square, in front of the Detroit City Hall, for a demonstration to demand action by the government. Not long after this there occurred a riot at the Dearborn plant of the Ford Company in which four men were killed.[25]

A number of magazines and newspapers carried sober articles that discussed whether or not America was on the verge of revolution, and how a revolution might be staged.[26] Dwight P. Morrow, a House of Morgan partner turned United States Senator from New Jersey, wrote: "Most of my friends think the world is coming to an end." [27]

Couzens' reaction to all this was more indignation. In his view, many of the individuals who then talked of the "need" for a Mussolini, or who were fearful of a revolution, were the very ones who had produced the crisis.

7

His attitude in this respect was considerably reinforced by the results of an investigation, begun in December 1931 by the Senate Finance Committee, with his participation, which examined procedures used by American banking and investment firms in the floating of foreign loans. A legislative result was the Johnson Act of 1934, which barred the sale in the United States of the bonds or securities of any foreign government which had defaulted on the payment of its debts to the United States.[28]

Still another result, indirectly, was one of the most important reforms of the future New Deal, divorcement of investment affiliates from commercial banks. But what interested Couzens primarily was not the foreign-relations aspect of this branch of the securities field, but the morals and patriotism of the investment bankers. Thousands of Americans had their savings wiped out by defaults of the foreign governments whose bonds they had purchased on the endorsement of leading investment firms. By 1932, more than a billion dollars worth of foreign bonds, issued by Brazil, Bulgaria, Chile, Colombia, Ecuador, Greece, and El Salvador, among others, had become all but worthless. Couzens wanted to know if "world conditions" alone were responsible, or if, in truth, investors had been swindled.[29]

The investigation confirmed his suspicions, he felt. It brought out that the bankers in certain cases had literally forced loans on foreign countries, so eager were they for the profit from floating the resultant securities in the American market. In some cases, the bonds were sold to American investors after the State Department had warned that the issuing governments were shaky, politically as well as financially. Instances were uncovered showing that some of the most respectable banking houses of the nation were not above using peculiar, if not illegal, methods.[30]

Couzens was especially indignant when it came out that Charles E. Mitchell of the National City Company not only personally profited to the extent of $4,418,732 in bonuses for his operations during the years 1926–1929, but also managed, by the device of selling some bank stock to a member of his family, to avoid paying an income tax in 1929.[31] His National City Company, as said by Thomas L. Stokes, spurred on its stocks salesmen "by contests, just as if they had been selling soap or vacuum cleaners." [32] Also, to keep up the "morale" of its officers, as Mitchell testified, it maintained a "management fund," out of which the executives received extra compensation on the basis of the earnings of the company. Couzens wanted to know if this system of "splitting" earnings did not cause "a lack of care in the handling and sale of securities to the public."

"I do not recall seeing it operate that way," said Mitchell.

"You wouldn't," retorted Couzens scornfully.[33]

8

It was no wonder that Couzens was even more contemptuous than ever of the big financiers. He now regularly raised questions about RFC help to big banks, such as the Dawes bank in Chicago. To him, the RFC operations smacked of bailing out "banksters" and preserving their undeserved gains, at the expense, he feared, of the general taxpayers. In July 1932 he proposed a full-dress Senate investigation of the RFC, but was appeased by the establishment of a select committee with the authority to confer with RFC officials.[34]

The bankers, he felt, were the very men who, while aided by the RFC, opposed, with cries of "no dole," every proposal to help the little people of the land who were out of jobs through no fault of their own. The conviction grew upon him that millions were out of jobs actually, in large part, through the fault of these same financial giants. No wonder, too, that their talk of the need for a "dictator" irritated him.

He was naive in taking up temporarily with an economic fad called "Technocracy," and for this he was held up to ridicule.[35] But at least he did not make common cause with those who welcomed a dictatorship for America. Back in 1917, in a discussion with a Detroit lawyer, he had conceded that democracies were often inefficient, but said: "Democracy will never be efficient. . . . As long as we believe in democracy, we will have to pay the price, and I for one am willing to do it." [36] He had never changed. Not dictatorship, but more democracy was the answer, he felt, meaning not simply political democracy, but economic democracy, through more equal distribution of security and income. As he wrote a little later to the editor of the *United States News*, when asked to comment on an article by David Lawrence, that said the great need was a greater dissemination of knowledge among the people, "This dissemination of knowledge, I believe, has brought our people to the conclusion that there has to be something besides the dissemination of knowledge, and that is the wider dissemination of this world's goods, so that the masses may have some economic security." [37]

9

In the summer of 1931, he began to work in that direction himself. Recalling the recommendations in his 1928 "Report on Unemployment," he announced that he hoped to introduce legislation for a national unemployment-insurance law, one that also would provide for old-age pensions, despite frequently expressed opposition by President Hoover to any such government program. The *Detroit Times* commented editorially: "He means to work most of the summer with a view to urging immediate legislation in the next Congress. . . . With Couzens working for unemployment insurance and old age pensions, these two reforms appear less remote of realization than they once did." [38]

About this same time, Ray Tucker, the Scripps-Howard writer, dropped into his office. They fell to discussing Hoover's objections to spending large enough sums of government money to diminish unemployment. Couzens told Tucker that even if it meant tripling the federal debt, the government ought to "make work by building libraries, museums, highways, bridges, schools, and so forth, even if they returned no income."

Tucker was astonished by the boldness of the idea, and asked him if he, a businessman and millionaire, would stand for quotation.[39]

"Sure!" replied Couzens.

"So fantastic was the suggestion at that time," recalled Tucker, "that I got an eight-column banner in the New York *World-Telegram.*" He thought that Franklin D. Roosevelt, then Governor of New York, might have obtained from that story inspiration for his public-works program after he became President.[40]

Of course, Couzens got nowhere with his "fantastic notions." Such reforms, he knew, would have to wait for a new administration.

He had lost all vestige of hope in Hoover, though events were pushing Hoover also in the direction of federal action.

CHAPTER XXXII

THE END OF AN ERA

AHEAD was the 1932 election. Basically, this election among other things was a referendum on the Hoover policies on the depression in general, on unemployment relief in particular. Including many Republicans, the people plainly were angry with Hoover, rightly or wrongly. Even so stanch a regular Republican as Frank O. Lowden, the former Governor of Illinois who had come close to getting the Republican nomination for President in 1920, instead of Harding, deserted Hoover, though mainly on the farm issue. When he appeared in Detroit, Hoover was booed—something that rarely has happened to any President in office—and Secret Service men in Detroit feared for his life.[1] To Thomas L. Stokes, this experience was Hoover's "Calvary." [2]

The Democratic candidate was Governor Franklin Delano Roosevelt of New York, who in 1920 had been defeated for Vice President in the Harding landslide.

Couzens liked Roosevelt's speeches. Indeed, when Roosevelt made his famous "Forgotten Man" speech, and was attacked for it as a "demagogue" by former Governor Alfred E. Smith, it was Couzens who defended Roosevelt in the Senate. "I'm awfully tired of hearing men accused of demagoguery because they speak out for the little fellow," he said.[3] It did not escape him that Roosevelt's speeches were built largely around ideas which he had long championed in Detroit, as well as in Washington. Moreover, he sensed intuitively that he and Roosevelt held a similar view as to the causes of the depression. This was that the depression was in reality a moral, rather than economic, breakdown, that ethical conduct by the business leaders would have prevented the crash.

Neither Roosevelt nor Couzens was much of an economist. But both thought they knew what was "wrong" and "right" in the distribution of the good things of the world and they were for wider distribution.[4] Both would be assailed as socialists, or some other breed of anti-capitalist. But this was nonsense for political effect. If anything, both Couzens and Roosevelt were pure capitalists, concerned with preserving the individual-enterprise system. In the thesis of Louis M. Hacker,[5] Couzens was the "industrial" capitalist, who viewed the "finance" capitalist, moving toward monopoly, as an enemy bent upon destroying the very system by which he had built his own fortune. Roosevelt, in the last analysis, was on his side, he believed.

2

So, for this campaign, a Republican who could not go along with Hoover, Couzens kept silent. When Roosevelt won, he was pleased.

He was not even sorry that Michigan, rock-ribbed Republican since the days of "Zach" Chandler, had gone completely Democratic, electing for governor William A. Comstock, the Democratic chairman who had called him "really a Democrat."

Among the Old Guard Republicans, Jim Watson went down, as did David A. Reed of Pennsylvania, one of those who had infuriated Couzens by praising dictatorships. So did George Moses, "the master parliamentarian" and coiner of the phrase, "Sons of the Wild Jackass." Like Watson, Moses had felt more than once the lash of Couzens' temper, notably after he had accused him of "personal animus" when Couzens had introduced the resolution for Mellon's resignation in 1928.[6]

It amused Couzens to recall that Moses had apologized for this remark after Couzens told him that unless he did, he would hear a speech on the Senate floor about certain aspects of his political career that Moses would prefer, he said, not to have mentioned.[7]

In 1926, Smoot of Utah had insisted that Couzens be removed from the Senate Finance Committee. Smoot had taken this drastic step because Couzens so frequently objected to his high tariff proposals.[8] A famous feud had gone on between them ever since. "I'd like to drive a golf ball through your head!" Couzens once had snapped at him.[9] Now Smoot was also gone.

"The election pleased me from a national point of view," Couzens wrote to Madeleine. "The most joy I had, of course, was the defeat of Moses, Smoot and Watson—a mean streak in me, no doubt." [10]

But his "joy," if that were the correct word, was to be short-lived.

For the 1932 election marked more than the end of the Hoover administration. It also marked the end of a whole era of American political and economic policy, and such turning points are usually accompanied by considerable agony for the leading actors in the drama. This, as he soon was to discover, would be true for Couzens, as well as for numerous other Americans.

BOOK FOUR

The Independent Man

CHAPTER XXXIII

THE BANK CRISIS

ROOSEVELT was not to take office until the following March 4, 1933, and Couzens like nearly everyone else believed the period between the election and inauguration would be a quiet time. But this calculation was rudely upset. New tremors in the banking system of the country occurred in Nevada, Maryland, Ohio, Pennsylvania, and Louisiana.

Then, on February 14, 1933, less than three weeks before the new administration was to take over, there occurred in Michigan the worst jolt of all: At the request of the bankers, Governor Comstock ordered all the financial institutions of the state closed for a "moratorium," or "banking holiday," because of an acute emergency involving the leading banks of Detroit.

In the words of Charles A. and Mary Beard, "The news from Michigan jangled the American System from center to periphery." If anything, this judgment was understatement. For the Detroit bank crisis proved the time bomb that temporarily toppled the whole American banking structure, bringing the closing of all the financial institutions in the land.[1] Possibly, in view of general economic conditions, the national banking system might have gone down regardless of the Detroit situation. Perhaps there were no resources, not even in the federal treasury, adequate to have averted the collapse, once the situation had gotten out of hand. But in the event, it was the Detroit crisis that touched off the national crisis.

2

Couzens played a certain role in the Detroit bank crisis, though it was not the role that many accounts of the situation assigned to him.[2] Indeed, he really had less to do with it than almost any of the

213

other actors. Yet the Detroit situation resulted for him in the most violent controversy of his whole controversial career. He was blamed for having closed the Detroit, and hence the Michigan, banks. Yet his real involvement was in efforts to keep them open, and also, a little later, to reveal why they were closed in the first place. As will be seen, more than anyone else, his old partner, Henry Ford, touched off the explosion, although the conditions in the banks themselves were not of Henry Ford's doing.

In the larger sense, the Detroit banks crashed because they had epitomized the whole fantastic financial pattern of the era. As a Senate investigation demonstrated, one well summarized, it may be mentioned, by Federal Judge Ferdinand Pecora in his book *Wall Street Under Oath,* no weird financial practice of the period was omitted— from "window-dressing," pyramiding of resources for speculation and the voting of unearned dividends, to the use of bank funds for improper loans to officers and even minor employees.[3]

3

John T. Flynn, then a *New Republic* contributing editor, described the Michigan situation better than anyone else in an article in *Harper's* for December, 1933, under the title "Michigan Magic":

These Michigan magicians had invented something brand new in the way of banking. It was not so completely new, of course, as they supposed, for group banking has broken out in this country at intervals, and almost always with disastrous results. But this was group banking with more virulent tumescence and higher temperature and some new complications. It was a combination of unit banking and branch banking, security manufacture, real estate exploitation, and numerous other lines, including running a garage, and all brought together under the control of a holding company like a utility web or department store chain. There were, of course, holding companies running wild among banks in other places. But in Michigan two groups—two holding companies—set out to capture the entire banking resources of a whole state. . . .

In other cities one bank might fail and the others, somewhat strained, might continue. But in Detroit, failure of one meant the failure of all. And they did fail. Not just two banks, but 178 banks closed their doors. A great industrial city and a rich industrial and agricultural state were left for months almost without money. It was the most comprehensive bank failure in our history, and it marked the crash of the kind of banking which these magicians gave Michigan.

4

But it is necessary to get a good deal of background:

The two banking groups were the Guardian Detroit Union Group, Inc., and the Detroit Bankers Group, Inc. The former was known, if not wholly accurately, as "the Ford group." Prominent in its affairs were Edsel B. Ford and his wife's brother-in-law, Ernest Kanzler, who also headed the then Ford-controlled Universal Credit Corporation. In fact, the Universal Credit Corporation was organized as a joint enterprise of the Ford Company and of the Guardian Detroit Group.[4]

Ironically, among the units of this group, as a consequence of a series of consolidations, were the two banks that Couzens himself had founded, the Highland Park State Bank and the Bank of Detroit, by then merged into a giant called the Guardian Union National Bank of Commerce.[5] Indeed, because of stock in those old banks that his father had given to him, Frank Couzens was a director of the Guardian Group, although he resigned in 1931, "not liking the looks of things." [6]

The second group was composed of most of the old-line bankers of Detroit and included in its units the city's biggest bank, the First National-Detroit. Its nominal head—"nominal" should be stressed —was aging E. D. Stair, then publisher of the *Detroit Free Press.*

It was in the so-called Ford group that the trouble first developed —specifically in the Union Guardian Trust Company. This was a successor to the Union Trust Company, which had barely escaped the panic of 1907, and which since 1927 was housed, apparently quite solidly, in a $12,000,000 elaborately ornamented skyscraper surmounted by a tower—of gilded bricks. Charles B. Warren, whom Couzens had helped to keep out of Coolidge's cabinet as Attorney General, shared in the planning of this strikingly garish "Aztec temple of finance," as it has been called.

As a matter of fact, Warren was generally credited with having also been the originator of the legal basis of the Michigan banking-group idea as a whole.

This trust company, as the former Union Trust Company, had been having trouble since 1926, mainly because of overactivity in real estate loans [7]—trouble that was a prime reason for the merger of the Union Trust, first with the National Bank of Commerce, and then with the Guardian Trust Company, to form the Union Guardian Trust Company.

By December 1931, if not before, the trust company's condition was such as to make necessary an emergency loan of $15,000,000 from the Bankers Trust Company of New York and the Continental Illinois Bank of Chicago. Before making this loan, these banks obtained personal endorsements, and the pledging of securities, from both Charles S. Mott, another leader in the group and a General Motors Corporation executive, and Edsel Ford.

By January 1, 1932, the Guardian Group owed to Edsel Ford, personally, a total of $8,500,000 in advances and endorsements.[8]

At the end of that year the Ford Company itself went to the aid of the trust company, advancing it $3,500,000, under an agreement which made the company, for all practical purposes, a Ford Company subsidiary. For it could then transact no major business without Ford Company approval.[9] Later it was revealed that, at this time, the trust company could not meet even routine cash withdrawals, except for overdrafts honored by the Guardian National Bank of Commerce, its own affiliate, and its possession of the welfare funds of the City of Detroit on deposit with it.[10]

5

When the Reconstruction Finance Corporation was established, the Union Guardian Trust Company applied for a loan almost instantly. By putting up its best collateral the company borrowed, on May 24, 1932, $4,250,000 from the RFC. In July 1932 it obtained an additional $8,733,000 from it.

Yet even then, the company "was in imminent danger of suspension," its officers advised the RFC, unless the RFC were willing to loan an additional $15,000,000.[11]

A stumbling block was the requirement in the original RFC law —later amended—that *loans could be made only on the basis of sound collateral,* a legal provision important to bear in mind. Also, the RFC board of directors at this time took the position that enough assistance had been supplied by the government. The Fords, they said, should make up the difference, in view of their involvement.[12]

It was after this that Henry Ford approved the $3,500,000 loan from the Ford Motor Company.

6

But this Ford Company loan was only additional and inadequate shoring, for the trust company still tottered. "Disclosures of the true facts to the public on December 31, 1932 probably would have resulted in its immediate suspension," one analysis summed up its condition.[13]

In cold figures, the trust company then (its trust accounts aside) had no more than $6,000,000 in convertible assets, as values then stood, against deposit liabilities and borrowings of approximately $20,000,000, *a shortage of at least $14,000,000.*[14]

A plan was discussed for saving the situation—to take the trust company entirely out of banking and investment activity, which had caused its trouble, transfer its deposit liabilities to the Guardian National Bank of Commerce, and keep its trust business only.[15] But to do this meant covering, somehow, the $14,000,000 deficit.

There was the rub—and the nub—of the Detroit crisis, in its first stage.

7

Certain leaders of the Guardian Group gathered at Kanzler's offices in the Universal Credit Corporation, for a private conference, on Sunday, January 15, 1933. To this meeting had been invited A. P. Leyburn, the chief national bank examiner, with headquarters in Chicago. Only a few weeks before, Leyburn had appeared before the board of the Guardian National Bank of Commerce to warn that this bank was in bad shape.[16] Now Leyburn heard Kanzler say:

"The trust company cannot hold up much longer. We have to get considerably more money or the whole group is going to collapse!" [17]

As later it became plain, the purpose of the meeting was to get Leyburn's cooperation to persuade the RFC to change its attitude toward the trust company. A new approach had been determined upon. Instead of going to the RFC for additional loans to the trust company *alone,* an application on behalf of the *entire* group would be filed. On being consulted, Edsel Ford approved. As he later said, "The whole matter was gone over with me by Mr. Kanzler. . . . I concurred . . . and steps were taken to proceed." [18]

At this meeting Kanzler informed Leyburn that Edsel Ford had told him that the Ford Motor Company would agree to subordinate its deposits of $7,500,000 in the trust company. At least, this was

Kanzler's understanding. In that event, the deficit in the trust company could be considered as being no more than $6,500,000. Edsel Ford later corroborated Kanzler's statement concerning the possibility of the Ford Company's freezing its deposits. "It was understood that the subordination would take place," he said.[19]

Leyburn fell in with the plan, but suggested refining it. Congress, only a short time before, had passed a little-publicized amendment to the RFC law which permitted loans to be made to banks through special corporations set up to receive such loans. On the basis of this, Leyburn suggested that the Guardian Group form such a corporation and apply for an RFC loan in its name. The suggestion was adopted, the Wolverine Mortgage Corporation was formed.

To the Wolverine Corporation, the group then did transfer numerous assets, totaling, in face value, $88,000,000.[20] With these as security, Kanzler went to Washington with Leyburn and presented to the RFC on January 26, 1933, a request for a loan of $65,000,000 (counting the earlier advances by the RFC to the trust company). In the meantime, affairs at the trust company were going from bad to worse. Nor was this merely in the natural course of events. As would be said in court, "Throughout the month of January 1933, the Group continued to withdraw as much as possible from the Trust Company."[21]

8

The RFC began immediately to process the $65,000,000 application. Its chief appraiser, John K. McKee (afterwards a member of the Federal Reserve Board) was sent to Detroit to check the Wolverine collateral.

"The various officers of the banks came in with their collateral in pouches, and we attempted, working day and night there, to prepare a schedule," McKee recalled.[22] But he was not happy over what he discovered.

To the RFC, on February 6, McKee reported that the $88,000,000 Wolverine assets were worth, for loan purposes, only $37,720,000, including the assets on which the RFC had made its earlier loans.

But Kanzler pleaded for special treatment.

> Mr. Kanzler admitted [the minutes of the meeting of the RFC for February 6 read] that there was a considerable gap between the value of the collateral which could be pledged, and the amount of the loan desired, but said that the Guardian Group situation in-

volved the imminent danger of financial disaster of major proportions affecting the State of Michigan and the country at large, and
that he and his associates, feeling that if possible something should
be done to avert this, had decided to lay the circumstances before
the directors of this corporation.[23]

The board members of the RFC shook their heads. A new administration was coming in. There had been widespread criticism of the
Dawes bank loan. Moreover, earlier loans to the trust company had
received unsavory publicity, John T. Flynn having written them
up, with the implication that Roy D. Chapin, of the Hudson Motor
Company, by then Secretary of Commerce in Hoover's cabinet (and
another of the founders of the Guardian Group) had used his "influence" with RFC.[24]

Besides, the Detroiters were asking something that was clearly
illegal. To accede would mean leaving the RFC board members
personally liable for any loss.

The RFC board refused to take such a risk.

As a solution, the board pointed to the Fords.

In view of the previous help by Edsel Ford and the Ford Motor
Company, the Fords actually were the leading creditors of the trust
company. If the RFC did grant a new loan, even if it were legal, in
effect this would have meant transferring the load from the Fords
to the federal government. Concerning the RFC board members'
views, Leyburn later recalled:

> They figured there was not enough security there. And they asked
> all the time, "Well, what will Mr. Ford do?" . . .
> Their idea was all the way through, or their thought was—and
> they did not hesitate to say so—"Why should we bail out Mr. Ford?"
> They figured that he should come to the rescue up there.[25]

Kanzler reminded them of the understanding that the Fords would
freeze their $7,500,000 in the trust company. But he was dubious
about the Fords doing more. To get them to put up an additional $6,-
500,000 was probably out of the question, he said.[26]

In the meantime, McKee telegraphed to Detroit to see if his RFC
assistants there could not dig up more assets. Kanzler finally agreed
that the application should be scaled down from $65,000,000 to $50,-
000,000.

"We revamped the application," McKee later said, "but there was
still a hole." He added, "We had just gone the limit." [27]

The "hole" in the trust company amounted to $6,000,000—provided the Ford Company stood by Edsel Ford's commitment of subordinating its deposits. Otherwise, it would be larger.

Not emphasized at the time, but highly significant later in connection with Couzens, was one objection to the Wolverine Corporation plan in addition to its legal and political aspects. This was a moral objection. For the plan, in essence, called for using sound assets of *all* the units of the Guardian Group—banks outside as well as in Detroit—to bolster the shaky trust company. In short, innocent depositors in other banks were to have their funds jeopardized for the sake of the trust company, albeit the authors of the plan justified this, perhaps properly so, with the argument that failure of the trust company would also bring down the other banks.

In the event, the RFC flatly turned down the Wolverine scheme.[28] This should be noted in connection with allegations, repeated as late as 1952 by Herbert Hoover and reiterated still later by others, that it was Couzens who stopped the loan.[29] By design of the interested parties, as will be seen, he was not yet even in the picture.

CHAPTER XXXIV

THE WHITE HOUSE CONFERENCE

Two days later, February 8, 1933, Edsel Ford conferred in Washington on the situation with Ogden L. Mills, who had succeeded Mellon as Secretary of the Treasury. He also talked with Charles A. Miller of Utica, New York, who had succeeded Dawes as president of the RFC. Miller left a record of his conference with Edsel. "I . . . urged on him strongly the duty of himself and his father to come to the rescue of the situation [recalled Miller]. I gathered from him that he was entirely willing to do this, but that his father had other views and that influences other than his would have to be used to get his father to change his mind." [1]

There is no doubt that Edsel Ford was trying to be as helpful as possible, that he wished to avoid a disaster and wanted the Ford Company to help save the situation. But there also seems no doubt that he was meeting resistance from his father. As would be said by Roger Burlingame, Edsel's "life had always been more or less frustrated" [2] —mainly by Henry Ford, common knowledge in Detroit that Charles E. Sorensen amply confirmed in his memoirs published in 1956.

Edsel's remark about "influences other than his" suggested an idea to Miller. Why should not President Hoover personally request of Henry Ford himself that he save the situation? Miller's thought was that if the President invited Ford to the White House, Ford would not, could not, refuse.[3] Miller immediately called on Hoover and made that suggestion.

But Hoover, according to Miller, was reluctant to act on the proposal. "The President told me," Miller wrote, "that he was absolutely without influence so far as Mr. Ford was concerned, and to show that, he stated he had endeavored to obtain a contribution from Mr. Ford to the Republican campaign expense account, and had either been turned down entirely or had been offered some trivial amount, I've forgotten what, but I think about $500. Under these circumstances, he said he was entirely unwilling to ask any assistance in this matter from Mr. Ford." [4]

2

This was a strange attitude for Hoover to take, especially as Ford had spoken on the radio in behalf of his re-election, and in Ford Company plants all over America a pre-election notice had been posted, on October 17, which said:

> The Ford Motor Company is not interested in partisan politics. We do not seek to control any man's vote. [However] we are convinced that any break in [President Hoover's] program would hurt industry and employment. To prevent things from getting worse, and to help them to get better, President Hoover must be elected.[5]

Yet, apparently Hoover still did not feel he could appeal to Ford personally at this crucial time.

Of course, Hoover did honestly wish to save the situation. So in lieu of adopting Miller's suggestion, he decided to call a meeting at the White House for the evening of February 9th. To this conference he invited Secretary Mills, Miller, and Michigan's two senators—Couzens and Vandenberg.

It was this meeting that first brought Couzens directly into the picture.

3

Couzens had no idea as to the full nature of the Detroit banking situation until just two days before this White House conference. This had been because the representatives of the Guardian Group specifically had asked RFC officials not to let Couzens know of their application. Their later explanation was that they feared he would have "lectured them" on banking ethics.[6] Doubtless he would have. However, on February 7th, Jesse Jones and Harvey Couch, RFC directors, decided to tell Couzens. They did so, and also told him that there was no *legal* way for the RFC to accommodate the Guardian Group in the amount it had requested.[7]

Then, just before Senator Vandenberg advised Couzens that Hoover wanted both Michigan senators at the White House on the Detroit matter, Clifford Longley, a Ford attorney, and by then president of the Union Guardian Trust Company, and Colonel James Walsh, executive vice-president of the Guardian Group, called

Couzens to the anteroom of the Senate chambers, and gave him the details. At this same time they also requested his "support." (It was later testified that someone connected with the RFC had told them: "We want you to get Senator Couzens to recommend this loan to us.") [8]

Just then Couzens was a great deal more interested in some legislation he was sponsoring on the floor of the Senate than he was in any RFC matter. In the last weeks of the Hoover administration, his pet interest was to solve the problem of jobless, homeless boys and girls who, by the thousands, were roaming the highways of the nation in search of food and shelter. His solution, forerunner of the Citizens Civilian Conservation Corps (CCC camps of the Roosevelt administration), was to open Army forts in various parts of the country to homeless youths, who would work there on various projects, such as reforestation and flood control, for their board and shelter.[9]

The Senate was debating his proposal when a page boy advised him that two gentlemen from Detroit, Longley and Walsh, were waiting for him in the Senate anteroom. He went out to see them at once.

4

He did not give Longley and Walsh much of his time. When they began on the details of their application, he stopped them short. He knew all about the matter already, he said.[10] He commented acidly on the assets in the "Wolverine Corporation," asking pointedly if they included notes of a certain Detroiter, who, he said, he happened to know had been loaned a large sum and was notoriously unable to pay. The bankers ruefully admitted that these notes were included.[11]

There was some talk about the general problem of making RFC loans to banks. Finally he commented that as a matter of basic philosophy he was not at all certain that the RFC ought to save the banks. After the Dawes bank episode in Chicago, he had begun to have doubts about the soundness of the whole idea of the RFC, he said. In this, incidentally, he was not alone. Financiers as distinguished as Secretary of the Treasury Mills, Winthrop Aldrich of the Chase National Bank, and Melvin A. Traylor, president of Chicago's First National Bank, had voiced similar doubts as to whether unsound banks should be saved through government support.[12] Testimony about this interview was given later by Longley, in direct examination by Couzens himself.

> LONGLEY: You said you were in a quandary as to whether you should go one way in support of these institutions, or let things slide the other way and let them go. I have forgotten what your language was.
> COUZENS: I guess it was printable, was it not?
> LONGLEY: Oh yes, quite printable.

Longley and Walsh departed from the Senate feeling indignant.

5

Actually, this interview changed nothing. The decision was still up to the RFC, exclusively. No one as yet had devised any plan for meeting the objection that the Guardian collateral was not sufficient to permit a *legal* loan of more than $37,720,000, the McKee figure. This, as stated, was the nub.

That night Couzens went to the White House under a serious misapprehension as to the purpose Hoover had in mind. He believed that the conference was called to get approval of an *illegal* loan. If that were the case, he knew what he would do. He would voice opposition. He made this clear in a conversation with John Carson, his secretary, who drove him to the White House.

> Going to the White House that night [Carson recalled] I urged Couzens to take one position which might have been a cowardly one. I argued that the RFC had authority to make the loan, that he, as a senator, had no authority whatsoever in the matter, that if the RFC made the loan the RFC would divulge its action or keep it secret, that it was obvious the bankers and Hoover did not want to consult him until they felt compelled to do so, that therefore he would be justified in listening to the story and then saying that they had authority and responsibility and the facts and they should exercise their responsibility. His answer was that there was a critical situation and "you cannot run out on such situations." [13]

Actually, the White House conference was held, not for the purpose of putting through an RFC loan, certainly not in the case of the trust company, but to find a *substitute* for an RFC loan. As stated by Miller, later:

> Unless the directors of the RFC desired to take a really criminal responsibility, we could not have made the loan; and after we knew the facts and figures, none of us, I think, were in favor of making it, especially when Edsel Ford and the Ford Motor Company repre-

sented the large block of stock and held deposits there of an even larger amount.

The conference at the White House, therefore, was not held to discuss the possibility of the RFC making the loan as asked for, but was rather to find some feasible plan for coming to the assistance of this banking situation without violating our legal duty.[14]

President Hoover also made this clear—in 1933—in a communication to the later grand jury investigation of the crisis, saying:

> I was informed that the Guardian Trust Co. situation was such that, *even with the utmost of government assistance possible under the law, it would be insufficient without outside help* and reorganization internally. The request . . . was that I should endeavor to bring about cooperation from outside banks, private interests and leading depositors to reorganize the trust company and thus prevent a crisis. . . .[15]

6

The fateful conference was held in the Lincoln Room of the White House.

Unfortunately, it was opened by Miller in a way that contributed to Couzens' continued confusion as to its objective, as the RFC president realized later. For, instead of making clear at the outset, in his review of the situation, that the RFC could not make the requested loan, and had no intention of making it, Miller began the meeting by reading the *original* application for the $65,000,000 loan.

This convinced Couzens that the conferees were to be asked to give their approval to *that* application. His emotions began working when he heard Miller give his personal reasons why he, as RFC president, had rejected the loan—that the loan would be illegal and also immoral.

"Possibly I even overemphasized these reasons," Miller later recalled, "because my Washington experience had led me to expect that Senators and Representatives from a state where a loan was asked of the RFC were inclined to be very critical of any hesitation on our part to grant exactly the relief asked for, and were generally either ignorant or indifferent to the limitation of our powers under the act creating the RFC." [16]

If the RFC president expected the Michigan senators to act in accord with his "Washington experience"—that is, to insist that the loan be made—he got a surprise. "Senator Vandenberg made almost no comment on this occasion," wrote Miller.[17] As for Couzens,

Miller's use of the word "immoral" produced a predictable explosion.

If any such loan were made, he would "shout against it from the rooftops and on the floor of the Senate!" he said, a remark which, when lifted out of full context, was to get him into much trouble and also lead to much misrepresentation, unintentional or otherwise.[18]

7

But nobody else at the conference expressed any different views. Certainly no one expressed any disagreement with Couzens on his assertion.

President Hoover did not. It would have been strange if he had, inasmuch as in a speech in St. Louis, on the preceding November 4, he had gone out of his way to emphasize (concerning RFC loans) that "the law requires that they should be made on adequate security." [19]

In the words of Senator Vandenberg, all that Couzens had done was to be "particularly aggressive" in voicing his opinion.[20] It turned out later, however, that it would have been much better for Couzens had he not been so emphatic, for his explosion would be remembered and used against him.

After everyone had agreed that the RFC was estopped from helping the trust company, Hoover directed the conversation toward the real purpose of the conference. This, it turned out, was to induce Couzens personally to put up funds to help save the trust company.

As Hoover sketched the situation, the *status quo* in Detroit could be preserved if about $6,000,000 were raised privately. Hoover began this approach by saying that he had discussed the crisis with Alfred P. Sloan of General Motors and with Walter Chrysler, and that they had agreed to help, presumably assenting to advance $2,000,000 each. It should be noted that he did not then mention Ford. Hoover then asked Couzens if *he* would contribute $2,000,000.[21]

Still in an excited frame of mind, Couzens obviously was in no mood to have such a proposal made to him, especially not by Hoover. Also he resented hearing Hoover suggest to him his "duty" as a Detroiter. His reaction was told by Hoover: "He stormed that it was Ford's business." [22]

Hoover recalled:

I pointed out that Ford had previously put up $5,000,000 against assets of little value to help and was now proposing to take a further loss of $7,500,000.

The Senator showed great resentment to my pressing him, and I replied that if 5% of my fortune would save a panic in hundreds of banks with hundreds of thousands of small depositors and tens of thousands of people's jobs in my home town, they could have it tomorrow. He left in great heat.[23]

8

After Vandenberg, as well as Couzens, had departed from the White House conference, the decision was reached that someone ask Ford to put up additional cash. It was taken for granted, apparently, that the Ford Company would subordinate its deposits. Inasmuch as Hoover still elected not to talk with Ford personally, the discussion then came down to who would go to Detroit to get further Ford help. In view of Ford's personality, to select the right emissaries was all-important.

Here, if ever, was a case where the "personal equation" in a public matter needed to be reckoned with. If not Hoover, then Ogden L. Mills might have been a good choice. Ford might have been impressed by having the Secretary of the Treasury come to see him. But instead of Mills, Hoover suggested that Miller, hardly known outside of New York State, take the assignment. Miller begged off. He felt that he was needed in Washington to watch national developments. Besides, his wife was acutely ill.[24] So the suggestion was made that Secretary of Commerce Chapin and Arthur A. Ballantine, a Wall Street lawyer then serving as Undersecretary of the Treasury, go to Detroit on the errand.

This was to be the climax—and a worse-selected cast of characters could not have been imagined, if the play were to end happily.

CHAPTER XXXV

THE CLIMAX

CHAPIN and Ballantine arrived in Detroit on Saturday, February 11, 1933.[1] The date is important, for the next day, Sunday, February 12, was Lincoln's Birthday, making the following Monday a legal holiday; hence the banks would not be required to open. This meant that there was time until the following Tuesday morning, the fourteenth—an extra day—to make arrangements without the possibility of news of trouble in the trust company causing panic.

The interview with Ford was arranged for at Ford's estate at Dearborn. "Everything depended . . . on the result of the Ford interview," [2] recalled President Miller.

Chapin and Ballantine kept their appointment promptly, but Ford allowed them to wait for more than an hour. He was out inspecting his fields, they were told.

This was not a good omen as to Ford's mood. Chapin and Ballantine were worried anyway by reports in Detroit that Henry Ford might not even permit Edsel to go through with his pledge of subordinating the Ford deposits in the trust company, that Ford was displeased with the whole picture and angry with Edsel and also Kanzler, whom he blamed for Edsel's involvement.

"Word came to us," Ballantine later testified, "that Mr. Ford did not want to make that subordination." [3] When Ford finally appeared, he made it immediately plain that new trouble was definitely ahead.

2

Indeed, the Chapin-Ballantine mission turned out to be worse than a failure; it was a disaster.

When Ford was asked to put up more money, he not only angrily

228

refused this, but also then and there overruled the commitment that Edsel had made for subordinating the $7,500,000. He would not permit it, he said.

Ford delivered a "very vigorous diatribe against banks and bankers generally, and against the RFC in particular." He insisted that the RFC make a loan large enough to permit the trust company to pay off all deposits, including those of the Ford Motor Company.[4]

Ford said he was not impressed by the explanation that the RFC could not legally make such a loan. The RFC was organized to keep banks from closing. Therefore, it should save the Guardian institutions. His attitude was summed up later by one official biographer: "What was the RFC for, anyway, if not to assist in the stabilization of the banks?"[5]

3

Chapin and Ballantine attempted valiantly to get Ford to change his mind. They spoke of the possible consequences if the trust company failed. They "explained that the situation was so delicate throughout the whole country that the failure of the trust company, and with it a number of allied institutions, would almost certainly bring down the whole banking structure of the country and lead to distress and hardship, and even very likely to the failure of very many manufacturing and business institutions as well."

Ford said:

"Let them fail; let everybody fail! I made my fortune when I had nothing to start with, by myself and my own ideas. Let other people do the same thing. If I lose everything in the collapse of our financial structure, I will start in at the beginning and build it up again."

Chapin and Ballantine then appealed to Ford on the basis that "the country had benefited him and for him now to come to the assistance of the country and to save it was an opportunity that had never come to any businessman before." But this "only appeared to antagonize" Ford.

Ford then declared: "If the Reconstruction Finance Corporation does not make this loan promptly and immediately, I will have representatives at every Detroit bank the first thing Tuesday morning, when the banks open for business, and will draw my personal balances and the balances of the Ford Company from them without any further notice."[6]

4

This threat by Ford placed a wholly different complexion on the crisis. In addition to the $7,500,000 in the trust company, the Ford Company had deposits of nearly $32,000,000 in the Guardian National Bank of Commerce and more than $20,000,000 in the First National Bank-Detroit. Neither of those banks could have stood such a withdrawal. So now the crisis had spread from the trust company to the two leading banks of Detroit, the key institutions of both groups.

Whether or not Ford actually would have carried out his threat against all of the banks in Detroit—against the Detroit Bankers Group as well as the Guardian Group—cannot be known, of course. During the panic of 1907, it will be recalled, he had told Couzens that he believed he should withdraw all of his money from the banks then. Couzens commented years later, in 1927, that he believed Ford never gave up the idea of trying that. In 1914, Ford had withdrawn his funds from the Highland Park State Bank during the war panic—the incident that came close to causing Couzens to break with Ford at that time. In a book published in 1920, there is quoted this remark, seriously intended or not, by Ford: "I don't have to worry about banks—they have to worry about me." [7]

5

Worrying about Ford was precisely what banks were doing then. For in the meantime, an almost continuous meeting of bankers and other businessmen had been going on in the offices of the Union Guardian Trust Company. The original purpose was to raise what money the Fords might not supply. Kanzler had been zealously active in trying to get pledges. The most he could get totaled only $1,-582,000, which included $619,000 from General Motors and $274,000 from Chrysler. [8] But Kanzler certainly was trying to save the situation in every possible way, once it had gotten out of hand.

It was a curious scene. Nearly all the financial wealth of Detroit was represented at the gathering. New York and Chicago bankers, including such important ones as Melvin Traylor, Eugene M. Stevens, and S. Sloane Colt, also were there. Everyone was aware that the whole banking structure of Detroit was in danger, and with it, that of the nation.

As far as they knew then, however, only $6,000,000 was needed.

Yet nothing like this amount was forthcoming. "Everyone talked, yet no one said anything; the meeting was pitiable," recalled one who was there.[9]

When Chapin and Ballantine appeared at this meeting with the report of their interview with Ford, the meeting went into a real panic. The first consequence was that General Motors and Chrysler bowed out altogether from their earlier offer to help. If Ford would not help, neither would they.[10]

How to prevent Ford from carrying out his threat then became all that occupied the minds of most of the conferees. Only two proposals emerged—induce Ford, somehow, to change his stand, or close the banks to keep him from drawing out his money.

With the latter solution in mind—a holiday such as Huey P. Long had proclaimed in Louisiana—the governor in Lansing was asked to hasten to Detroit.

New appeals were made to Ford to change his mind. Ballantine telephoned to Liebold, Ford's secretary. Liebold answered: Ford felt as before.[11] Ballantine notified President Hoover, but if Hoover did anything at precisely this time, the results are not on record.

Wilson Mills, chairman of the board of the First National Bank, a son-in-law of Pingree, by now really alarmed, tried to reason with Ford that it would be unfair to punish the First National Bank for a situation involving only the Guardian Union Trust Company. But Ford repeated his threat.

> Ford stated to me [Mills later related] that unless the Guardian were permitted to open the following day, he would come down and take his money, every cent of his funds, from us and from any other Detroit bank that was open. . . .
> I said, "Why is that, Mr. Ford?" He said, "I think it is up to the government to save these institutions by making them loans. They saved the Dawes bank."
> I asked him to play ball, told him what the situation was, told him we were applying for a loan from the RFC . . . and we hoped to secure one. [But] Mr. Ford made the remark that I have testified to.[12]

6

Then, in Washington, Couzens re-entered the picture, to try his hand at reversing Ford's attitude.

Contrary to later assertions, his personal relations at this time with Ford were good. They had long since become reconciled after

Couzens' attack on Ford's Presidential ambitions in 1923. In 1926 they had jointly issued a statement opposing the restitution of the death penalty for capital crime in Michigan. In 1927 Ford had presented to Couzens, to the accompaniment of a good deal of publicity, one of the first new-model Ford cars, as a token of "fond remembrance" of the days when they were associated in the Ford Company. And Couzens was "thrilled," he told Ford.[13]

Nothing had happened since to mar their truce. Thus, when Couzens was told of Ford's ultimatum, he did not hesitate to telephone to Ford.

He did so from the office of the RFC, to which he and Vandenberg had been summoned by the distressed Miller and Secretary Mills. Miller recalled:

> I was present during this telephone interview, but of course, I did not hear what Mr. Ford said. I gathered, however, from Senator Couzens' talk to him that Mr. Ford claimed that the whole crisis was brought about by the machinations of his competitors and that he again expressed his determination to draw all his deposits from the Detroit banks unless we made arrangements to enable the Guardian Union Trust Company to pay its depositors by the opening hour on the morrow.
>
> I will say, parenthetically, that if there were any errors during all these negotiations in handling Mr. Ford diplomatically, Senator Couzens was not responsible for them on this telephone call. He had apparently been willing almost to tear Mr. Ford limb from limb when he put in the call, and I have never witnessed so complete a change in language and manner as his when the call came through. During his entire conversation with Mr. Ford, the Senator dropped sweetness into the phone at every word and never suggested even a mild criticism of Mr. Ford's position.[14]

When Ford had thus spoken to him against the RFC and refused to withdraw his threat against the Detroit banks, Couzens still did not give up. He determined upon another approach and toward the end of his talk with Ford he asked him to have Clifford Longley, Ford's lawyer, get in touch with him by telephone. "I think we can arrange this thing for the Union Guardian Trust Company," he told Ford.[15] There was no use trying to discuss details with Ford, Couzens explained later.

7

Couzens was at dinner with Mrs. Couzens when Longley telephoned from Detroit shortly after 8 P.M. Of all the numerous telephone calls between Detroit and Washington that evening, this one was easily the most important. It was the one outstanding effort made by anyone to save the situation in Detroit.

To Longley, Couzens now emphasized what he had tried to get Ford to realize, that the RFC could not make a loan to the Guardian Union Trust Company unless more and adequate collateral were put up, but that it could make a loan if such collateral were made available. He then asked Longley to get over to Ford a message:

He, Couzens, would go fifty-fifty with Ford in putting up the collateral that would make possible an RFC loan to the trust company. "I asked him to ask Mr. Ford if he would join me in making a joint note to guarantee the RFC against any loss." [16]

In effect, that meant that Couzens was willing to risk at least $6,900,000 of his personal fortune to keep the banks open, if Ford would do likewise. He was willing, now that he saw the certain result of Ford's position, to do more than three times what Hoover had asked him to do the previous Thursday.

Longley called back. He had put Couzens' offer up to Ford, and Ford's answer was "No." Ford in fact was "annoyed" at the suggestion.[17] So there now disappeared the last chance of averting the bank panic in Detroit, and also of averting the bank holiday.

8

Governor Comstock, by then in Detroit, was not at all anxious to accept the responsibility of so drastic a step as to order a bank holiday. He was not certain as to the legality of the move. C. J. Huddleston, of Lacy, Anderson and Wilcox, among other lawyers, finally convinced him that he did have the power to keep the banks closed, although conceding that how to get them open again might present a different problem.[18]

Then there developed some dissension among the bankers as to whether or not a holiday *should* be proclaimed. The Guardian bankers were all for it, but the Detroit Bankers Group, feeling that their institutions were not involved except indirectly, tended to oppose the action, until they discovered that an RFC loan for them could not possibly be arranged in time.

Later, directors of the First National Bank-Detroit were to discover something just as appalling—that the First National's condition, with respect to liquidity, was not much better than that of the Guardian banks.[19]

Comstock finally said that if all the bankers agreed to sign a document asking him to proclaim the holiday, he probably would agree. The bankers signed. The federal government representatives, including Undersecretary Ballantine, also gave their approval.[20] Comstock still hesitated, but agreed to make up his mind in time to advise the bankers and the public before the hour of opening the banks on Tuesday morning. About midnight he left the meeting with Arthur J. Lacy to get a "breather."

"It was a cold, misty night. We strolled twice around the two blocks around the Union Trust Company and the Hammond building," Lacy later recalled. "We talked the problem over as we walked and as we dropped into a hot dog stand for a hot dog. Comstock asked me what I would do in his position. I told him that everybody at the meeting was agreed that a bank holiday was imperative and that if we didn't have one it would cause a nation-wide banking collapse.

"So we went back and Governor Comstock told the bankers and government men that he would call a holiday. . . ."[21]

At 1:32 Tuesday morning, February 14, 1933, in the gilded tower of the Guardian Union Trust Company, Comstock affixed his signature to a proclamation that closed the banks.[22]

At 2:00 A.M., Herbert R. Wilkin (a name to be remembered), one of many vice-presidents of the Guardian Group, called Ernest Kanzler on the telephone and gave him a message: "The jig is up!"[23]

CHAPTER XXXVI

"A HELL OF A MESS"

THE holiday served its major purpose of keeping any depositors, including Ford, from making withdrawals. But getting the banks open again was another matter.

Originally the holiday was supposed to last only eight days. Governor Comstock, however, was forced to extend it indefinitely at the request of the bankers themselves. For the federal bank officials took the position that the Guardian National Bank of Commerce as well as the First National Bank-Detroit, the leading Detroit banks, each head of its group, could not be reopened unless they were reorganized and more capital put into them. Otherwise, the banks would simply collapse under new runs that were bound to develop, they said. Their condition had been perilous, anyway, for months. In fact, the federal officials said, both banks were actually insolvent.[1] Chief Bank Examiner Leyburn summed up the situation: "Gentlemen, we are in a hell of a mess!" [2]

With its nationwide repercussions, the "mess" was complicated by the attitude adopted by nearly everyone concerned. For the efforts of solving the humpty-dumpty situation that had developed were carried on against a background of the most bitter kind of recrimination and misrepresentation.

Everybody apparently tried to place the blame on everybody else.

President Hoover and those close to him, blamed, at first, Governor Comstock.[3] The proclamation of the holiday was unnecessary; Comstock had yielded to panic, they said. As Theodore G. Joslin, one of Hoover's secretaries, even said later:

"I have always felt that the governor lost his head; if he had not become panicky, that catastrophe would have been averted." [4]

2

A defense of Hoover in the banking crisis—a book, *Prelude to Panic,* by Lawrence Sullivan—contained an amazingly inaccurate version.

> Secretary Mills . . . had been informed that the Detroit bankers, now in alarmed confusion, had called Governor William A. Comstock into consultation. A few hours later all the RFC plans were brought to an end by the sudden determination of the governor to proclaim a ten-day banking holiday throughout the entire State! This proclamation . . . was issued without consultation between Governor Comstock and the RFC, Treasury, or White House. By this single stroke all the ground was instantly cut from under the Washington rescue plans.[5]

3

Hoover also blamed Roosevelt. Here the argument was that the bank crisis would not have occurred had not Roosevelt undermined "public confidence," first, by failing to commit himself to Hoover's economic policies, and second, by failing to disavow certain advisers who suggested that it might be a good thing for the country to go off the gold standard.[6]

As for many of the bankers, they at first placed the blame, generally speaking, on "general conditions," ignoring evidence that some of them had been making unwise investments or extending unwise loans on the basis of unsound security, or that some bankers also had been motivated by "manipulation, greed, and dishonesty" (Couzens' words later) as they helped themselves, in the form of loans, to depositors' money in their custody. Later many bankers also echoed Hoover: "Roosevelt was at fault."

The Reverend Charles E. Coughlin, the "radio priest" of the Church of the Little Flower at Royal Oak, Michigan, was blamed— because of speeches he had made attacking the banking system in general and the Detroit Bankers Group in particular.

The *Detroit Times* was blamed—because it had been devoting a good deal of its space to the Coughlin speeches.

The RFC was blamed. Communists were blamed.[7] The Senate Finance Committee inquiry into Wall Street was blamed.[8]

Henry Ford came in at the outset for some slight criticism, for Governor Comstock issued a statement telling in part, although in a garbled way, the connection Ford had with the holiday. Later

Governor Comstock issued a repudiation of his revelation about the Ford role. "I misunderstood the facts," he said.[9] Even Couzens elected not to emphasize the part played by Ford in the disaster, not even in his own defense.

4

But of all the scapegoats, Couzens himself became Number One.

"You do not and cannot realize how unanimous the belief is that you are to blame for this bank situation!" Thomas A. Payne, an attorney who had managed Couzens' 1930 re-election campaign, and one of his most loyal friends, wrote to him. This was all too true.

Instantaneously there grew up a legend:

The Detroit banks could have been saved by an RFC loan, but "Senator Couzens blocked the loan," first, because he "hated Henry Ford," and, second, "because he hated all rich men in Detroit."

Unwittingly, perhaps, Hoover was in large part responsible for starting this legend. In talks by telephone with various Detroiters at the beginning of the crisis, he had spoken bitterly of Couzens' "non-cooperation" and mentioned, without proper interpretation, Couzens' threat of "shouting from the rooftops." [10] Editor Malcolm Bingay, who admittedly disliked Couzens, obtained Hoover's version. On the second day of the holiday, he published in the *Free Press* on its front page a story that set the pattern. The headlines were:

FORD-COUZENS CONFLICT
REVEALED AS A FACTOR
IN FINANCIAL STALEMATE

Senator Opposed RFC Loan to
Trust Firm, Saying Collateral
Was Not Sufficient

Insisted That Motor King Keep $7,100,000
on Deposit as "Frozen Asset"; Magnate
Refused to Sign Joint Note

and the article said:

If it had not been for Senator Couzens' protests, the loan would have been granted.

The RFC officials and other bankers held to the belief that this loan was necessary. There followed a bitter battle with Senator Couzens, who held that it was not a safe investment for the Government. He insisted that there should be more collateral. He was called to the White House and President Hoover pleaded with him. He vowed he would go on the floor of the Senate and denounce the loan if it were made. . . .[11]

5

A more garbled version would be hard to imagine. But Couzens largely had himself to blame. For one thing, when it had leaked from the supposedly secret White House conference that he had made his "rooftops" threat, he readily confirmed that he had made the threat, but, like Hoover and Bingay, without making clear the circumstances.[12]

Later in the heat of controversy he voiced sentiments which made it look as if he himself confirmed Bingay's version or that he would have been glad if he had actually blocked the loan. For example:

"I did not stop the much disputed loan. . . . However, I'm glad to have the public think I stopped it, if the public wants to think that; because as it was presented to Washington, it was an illegal and a wicked loan." [13]

Moreover, just before the bank holiday, he had given to Jay Hayden a long interview on his views concerning RFC loans in general which made it appear that he was opposed to any kind of assistance to banks. This interview was unfortunately timed. It appeared in the *Detroit News* on Monday, February 13, the day before the holiday.

> Everybody is saying, "Let us ask the RFC for money." Now that, to my mind, raises the largest single issue facing the new administration. It is whether we shall open the treasury door to everyone or close it to everyone.
>
> I supported the RFC in its present form because I believed that, by aiding the railroads, the banks and other like industries, we would benefit the great body of bank depositors and borrowers, insurance policy holders and the like, and then stimulate recovery generally.
>
> But during the year that has elapsed, I have very carefully watched the operations of the RFC and the financial developments in the country and I have about reached the conclusion that the federal government either has to support the debt structure for all of the citizens or we have got to stop the rescue of any of them.[14]

To a good many people, later, as well as at the time, this article appeared to represent corroboration of the story in the *Free Press* two days later. Besides this, the newspapers then recalled that Couzens had denounced in the Senate an RFC loan of $12,800,000 to the

Missouri Pacific Railroad, because, as chairman of the Committee on Interstate Commerce, he was not satisfied that the way to solve the railroads' financial problems was through that procedure. He had sharply observed that the chief beneficiary would be, not the railroad, but J. P. Morgan and Company.[15] Also, he had raised questions about the Dawes Chicago bank loan in 1932, although in the end he approved that transaction when shown facts proving that if it had not been entered into, probably all of the banks in Chicago would have been forced to close. These protests, together with his sponsorship of a special Senate subcommittee to act as watchdog over all RFC loans, gave him the reputation of being irreconcilably anti-RFC as well as against helping the Detroit banks, although this was not at all his true position.[16] Even careful students of the crisis would be misled by published material about him on this point.

6

But there was still one more reason why the false version crystallized against Couzens. Usually over-quick to defend himself, he now determined that with the banks closed, it would be unpatriotic for him to stir up controversy over why the banks were in such a condition. To tell the facts, he would have to attack the bankers, and also to stress the part played by Ford. He decided not to do this. "Some day the history of all the events and personalities who played their parts, will be written, but now is not the time," he said.[17]

So, instead of devoting time to hitting back at accusations against himself, he concentrated on efforts for getting the Michigan banks reopened. "I am rushed to death with Michigan's bank troubles, plus all my own legislative work," he wrote Madeleine on February 20th.

His efforts, in which he was assisted by Vandenberg, bore fruit in the one plan that might have permitted the Guardian National and the First National to reopen. This was a proposal, embodied in a Joint Resolution, soon known as the "Couzens Resolution," which he presented to the Senate on the 20th. It authorized the Comptroller of the Currency to allow national banks, such as those in Detroit, to reopen and operate along the lines of a plan that already had been worked out in New York and in Iowa for state banks, permitting "frozen" banks to start from scratch after segregation of their non-liquid assets and obligations against them from current deposits and commitments, if state laws permitted. Disbursements would be permitted on a limited basis. In effect, this permitted insolvent banks to act as their own receivers, the while avoiding the stigma and penalties of failure.[18]

This resolution was adopted by the Senate in two days. The House concurred on February 25, and Hoover promptly signed the resolution.[19] Then, all that was needed to reopen the old banks—if the bankers so desired—was for the Michigan legislature to pass complementary legislation. Such legislation was introduced at Lansing, at Couzens' suggestion, with Kanzler acting as principal proponent.

7

Meantime the bankers and other businessmen in Detroit were working in other directions. They considered plan after plan. But each came to nothing because something that the First National directors might propose would be vetoed by the Guardian directors, and vice versa. Or cliques within the groups gave vent to expressions of rivalry and mistrust. Moreover, there was still reluctance on the part of the top financiers to put up any money.

The bankers' solution was to have one more merger, to consolidate the Guardian National and the First National. In this, they were encouraged by New York bankers and by the RFC itself. The theory was that if some $11,000,000 of new capital were subscribed for a consolidated bank, the RFC would extend a sizable loan to the new bank for unfreezing the frozen assets of the old banks. Then the Comptroller would authorize the new bank to take over the two old ones.

But an immediate hitch developed—again in the attitude of Henry Ford. As the leading depositor in both banks, his support was essential regardless of anyone else's. He was counted on to help supply the new capital—and Ford kept aloof.[20]

8

Indicative of the hysteria was a hastily written letter from Secretary of Commerce Chapin to Couzens. "I foresee by the first of the week," Chapin wrote on February 25th, "the possibility of very serious disorders. All sorts of threats are being made by depositors, and what they want—and that quick—is some form of relief. If it is not afforded, we shall have a riotous Detroit and a prostrate Michigan facing us." [21]

Two days later, the newspapers announced that the crisis was solved. Two new banks were to be established, as the bankers had urged, with Ford cooperation. The difference between this and earlier solutions was that the new institutions would be all Ford.

The Fords would put up, not some capital, but all of the capital, $11,000,000, and they would own all of the stock and designate the directors. The RFC would put up $135,000,000—$100,000,000 on First National assets and $35,000,000 on Guardian National assets. There would be an immediate payoff of 50 per cent to depositors.

At first, even by the bankers who were to be displaced, this Ford plan was greeted with hosannahs. A joint statement by the boards of directors of the First National and the Guardian National banks called it "generous and public-spirited." [22] The application for the $135,000,000 loan was rushed to the RFC. It was widely believed that the new banks would be operating in a few days.

Henry Ford gave out jubilant statements. He told newspaper reporters that he would evolve a new kind of banking system in the world. "Our policy will be an evolution," he said. Loans would be made only for "productive purposes." As for interest, it would be reduced or even "eliminated." [23] In Dearborn, Ford's town, a civic demonstration was staged, with three thousand persons parading the main street, bearing a banner that said: "BANK WITH HANK!" [24]

9

In Washington, Couzens was delighted, especially as he had been on the verge of offering to put up the capital himself for a new bank in Detroit, in answer to urgent pleas that "something had to be done" to get some kind of commercial banking going again. He had gone with Attorney Henry Bodman, prominent in the Detroit banking picture, to the office of the Comptroller to set his plan in motion.

He was greeted there by Acting Comptroller F. G. Awalt, who told him excitedly that the problem was settled. In Couzens' words later, "I, immediately, with considerable enthusiasm, said, 'Well, that lets me out!' I was glad to be out." [25]

But, almost immediately, came a great cooling off.

The fact was that almost no one, after reflection, was happy over the Ford solution, except those Detroiters whose sole interest was to get the promised 50 per cent payoff as quickly as possible.

The bankers were not happy. They did not look forward to being squeezed out of the banking business, or converted into operators

on a new kind of Ford assembly line. They gagged over Ford's
financial ideas.

Ford's business competitors were not happy.

A large number of outstate Michigan bankers immediately kicked
up a rumpus. Under the leadership of Joseph H. Brewer, of Grand
Rapids, president of the Michigan Clearinghouse Association, they
began to bombard the RFC, the Comptroller, and all of the Michigan
delegation in Congress, including Couzens, with telegrams opposing
the granting of the $135,000,000 loans to the new Detroit banks. In
the main, this was because of a ruling by the Comptroller that
deposits of the outstate banks in the two Detroit banks, amounting
to some $20,000,000, were not to be given a preferred status.[26]

10

Then Couzens himself set up some opposition. He took the position that it was against the national interest for the federal government to commit itself to a loan of $135,000,000 to the banks of one
city, even his own city, when at that time similar crises were developing in other parts of the nation. Banks in Cleveland, Toledo, and
Baltimore had just sent appeals to the RFC for large emergency
loans. When this happened, even the RFC officials began to doubt
whether they should grant the Detroit request.[27] That the federal
treasury had the ability to bail out all banks was considered highly
doubtful.

Couzens still did not at this time oppose all RFC help to the
Detroit banks. A loan should be made, he said, but he suggested
that it be limited to about $50,000,000. This would have enabled
the banks to reopen, but would have reduced the amount of the
initial payoff.[28] Couzens later explained:

> I thought it would establish a precedent for every city, county,
> and hamlet in the United States to call upon the federal government
> for its financial needs. The federal government must stand, regard-
> less of what happens to states or their political sub-divisions. When
> the national credit is gone, there will be chaos, and regardless of
> what my constituents may think of my actions concerning their
> particular affairs, I am here to use every ounce of energy and effort
> to protect the federal government.[29]

11

In the end, it was the RFC itself, regardless of Couzens' position,
which scaled down the Detroit loan. For, in the meantime, RFC

appraisers had been burrowing into the records of both banks, and now came up with reports that neither bank had assets to justify the $135,000,000 loan. All that could be granted was $78,000,000. The RFC proceeded on that basis.[30]

Couzens raised no objections to the $78,000,000 figure; it represented, in his view, a reasonable compromise. He did ask that he be given the right to "represent" the RFC in the ultimate negotiations with the Detroiters, but this request was refused.

President Hoover ordered that he be "ignored," and the $78,000,000 loan be extended without delay in order to get the new Ford banks opened.[31] Again it was announced that the crisis was over.

12

Suddenly, all was confusion again. Two things had happened.

The Ford plan, also the RFC commitment, had been predicated on the willingness of the Central Hanover Bank in New York to renew loans totaling $20,000,000 made earlier to the First National Bank. It had been thought that the New York banks would agree, as a matter of course, to the renewals. Now came the news that legal objections had been raised by the bank's lawyers, objections supported by Stanley Reed, then counselor of the RFC, later an Associate Justice of the Supreme Court.[32] The $20,000,000 renewal was out.[33]

Then a revolt against the Ford plan developed in the ranks of the officers and shareholders of the First National Bank. At 11:45 P.M., Tuesday, February 28, McKee was handed a letter from Mills of the First National Bank, which read:

> At the conclusion of the board meeting today, I was instructed to telephone Mr. Edsel B. Ford and to state to him that the general opinion of the board is that it is inadvisable to go ahead under the proposed plan in which he and his father are interested. I might add, for your information, that this action of our board was unanimous. . . .
>
> Faithfully yours,
> WILSON W. MILLS,
> Chairman.[34]

As RFC President Miller remarked to Couzens, this was a "peculiar situation." For on the same day that James T. MacMillan, a prominent director of the First National, telephoned to him to ask that an additional $20,000,000 be granted to cover the New York bank item, Wilson Mills, the chairman of the board of the same bank, telephoned to ask that this $20,000,000 not be granted.[35]

In explanation, Mills later said that while he did not "block the Ford plan," he definitely was against it. "The bank was a profitable business and Ford's plan meant keeping all the profits for Ford, as Ford would not let anyone else hold any stock. . . . We felt that the depositors were entitled to [the profits]—not the stockholders and not any special interests, not Dearborn or New York, or anybody." [36]

What this "peculiar situation" added up to was that the bankers, in particular those of the First National, had by then decided that they wanted to operate on the basis of the proposal sponsored in the Senate by Couzens. As stated by Mills to the RFC on February 28, "If the $20,000,000 is not forthcoming, the bank will seek to operate under the Couzens Joint Resolution." [37]

13

Suddenly everyone concerned, in Washington as well as in Detroit, looked for salvation to the plan that Couzens had embodied in his resolution. Eugene Meyer, then Governor of the Federal Reserve Board, had written to Hoover on February 25th:

> Recently the Board, after giving the matter careful thought with these considerations in mind, approved the joint resolution regarding the powers of the Comptroller of the Currency introduced by Senator Couzens. . . . It felt that such a measure would be helpful in facilitating the working out of existing situations in various communities without creating undue disturbance.[38]

So, despite all the curses heaped upon him, Couzens now became the man of the hour. Requests poured in on him that he leave Washington immediately for Detroit to take the lead in putting the plan into effect there. Even Ford begged him to come.[39] So did Stair of the *Free Press*, who telegraphed: "Your presence in Detroit and your help on this banking situation greatly needed." [40] Mills of the First National twice telephoned him. Senator Vandenberg, whose responsibility to Michigan was equal to Couzens', but who cautiously stayed in the background, also urged him to go. Couzens went.

CHAPTER XXXVII

THE MISSION THAT FAILED

His overnight trip might well have been screen-titled: "Couzens to the Rescue." Its importance was well underlined in a memorandum that Vandenberg hastily typed on his portable in his Senate office and had delivered to Couzens at the Washington railroad station. "This stupendous journey" was how Vandenberg referred to Couzens' mission. "We have been in complete and constant touch. You know my views and I know yours . . . I am betting on you!" Vandenberg wrote.[1]

Then, for three days, following his arrival in Detroit on the morning of March 1, Couzens was the leading actor in the drama: "The Man with the Plan." For once even big business executives acted as if they esteemed him. His every word and action was reported in detail and with the greatest respect, even by Bingay. Couzens and Henry Ford met at Dearborn. With their sons, Frank Couzens and Edsel Ford, they posed for newspaper photographers. Said the Detroit *Times:*

> The Fords and the Couzens—father and son in two great families —were evolving a new solution of the banking problem of distressed Detroit today. Behind oaken doors . . . "Henry" and "Jim" talked over the most urgent problem of their twin careers, just as in years gone by they had charted the policies of the Ford Motor Company during the era of its greatest growth. . . .[2]

2

Actually, this was optimistic overstatement. Behind "the oaken doors," Couzens and Ford had lunch at a table that buzzed with the conversation of so many Ford executives that there was no chance to talk seriously about the banking crisis.

Then Ford asked Couzens to visit a laboratory to hear a dance orchestra, after which Ford said he had to depart, and did, without letting Couzens raise the question of the banks at all.[3]

But with others, Couzens made better headway, he thought. He was even praised now for having opposed the $135,000,000 loan because of national considerations. Wilson Mills, who later lashed out at him and blamed him for the closings on this very point, was one who hailed his stand.

First National Bank–Detroit
Detroit, Michigan
March 3, 1933

Dear Senator:
While I saw you only a short time during your visit to Detroit, I cannot let an hour go by after your departure without writing to thank you for coming and for what you have done. I think you made the way seem clear to everyone in Detroit, and I know we are all doing the right thing.

I also want to state to you here and now that last Saturday I could not understand your attitude in opposing a large loan by the Reconstruction Finance Corporation to the two Detroit banks. Of course, being so near to the grindstone, I was looking only at Detroit, and I am bound to say to you that now I think your attitude was the correct one, that is, the National Government and its solvency was, is, and must continue to be the primary consideration of every one of us.

Again my heartfelt thanks.

Faithfully yours,
Wilson M. Mills

3

In such an atmosphere then, the leaders of the Guardian and the Detroit Bankers Groups finally agreed upon a simple plan. This was that the Michigan legislature should be asked to pass at once the legislation to permit limited operation of the old banks. Under that plan, the RFC would make loans to the old banks to permit a payoff of 15 per cent initially, with other payoffs to be made later. Governor Comstock and leaders of the legislature were consulted. The machinery was set in motion for the legislation to be passed when Couzens left Detroit on March 3 to be on hand in Washington for Roosevelt's inauguration.

He was confident that the situation in Detroit was now in hand. He apparently had succeeded in getting the various banking groups, shareholders, and depositors, the Fords and other business interests, to subordinate their rivalries and thus agree on united action behind his plan.

Everyone seemed grateful to him. An official statement by the board of directors of the First National said, "The Senator has been most helpful." [4]

Best of all, from the standpoint of the bankers, it appeared that the verdict of insolvency for the Guardian National and the First National banks would be escaped. There was general confidence that within a matter of days, the old banks would be reopened.[5]

4

Everyone in Detroit, however, had failed to take into consideration what was happening throughout the nation. In shocking succession, state after state had gone into banking holidays, until, as of March 3, nearly thirty states were involved.[6]

Hoover seemed to clutch at straws. On February 17 he appealed to President-elect Roosevelt for cooperation to bolster public confidence. He asked that Roosevelt join with him in a statement to the public to the effect that under the new President "there will be no tampering or inflation of the currency; that the budget unquestionably will be balanced, even if further taxation is necessary; that the government credit will be maintained by refusal to exhaust it in the issuance of securities." [7]

Roosevelt's reply was strangely delayed for twelve days. It was mislaid by a secretary, Roosevelt later explained. Regardless of that, the President-elect made it plain that he would not have made the kind of statement Hoover wished in any event. He considered Hoover's request "cheeky." [8] It certainly was asking Roosevelt to adopt Hooverian policies. As he explained politely, but firmly, to Hoover, his thought was that the bank troubles were "so very deep-seated that the fire is bound to spread in spite of anything that is done by way of mere statements." [9]

Now, on the eve of disaster, Hoover turned to Roosevelt again.

Through William H. Woodin, Roosevelt's choice for Secretary of the Treasury, Hoover asked that the President-elect at least "join in a statement reiterating confidence in the fundamental soundness of American banks and appealing to depositors to stop withdrawing funds." Roosevelt refused to make this kind of statement also. He "felt that a strong, positive, definite action should take the place of appeals." [10] Hoover then asked if Roosevelt would join him in sponsoring a special session of Congress for enactment of emergency legislation.[11] Again Roosevelt's answer was no. He did not feel that any action taken by him as "a private citizen" would be helpful.[12]

Hoover next considered two drastic, possible steps. Had he actually taken either one or both, the final result might not have been changed, but at least history might have revamped its view of him as a man incapable of bold action while President. First Hoover considered asking Congress, on his own initiative, for a government guarantee of bank deposits, at least temporarily. But before acting, he asked the Federal Reserve Board if it would support "some form of Federal guarantee of banking deposits." [13]

The Federal Reserve Board declined to support such an idea. "You are, of course, thoroughly familiar with the history of such experiments in some of the States and the inherent dangers in a proposal of this kind," Governor Meyer wrote him on March 2.[14] So Hoover backed away from the proposal, later adopted as part of the New Deal.

The other step was, by executive action, to close all of the banks in the country—a national holiday which, at least, would halt further withdrawals and maintain the *status quo*. From the first, Hoover was reluctant to take this action. His view was that "eighty per cent of the banks measured in deposits were still functioning." despite the numerous state holidays. But by then, with even the banks in New York City tottering, the Federal Reserve Board itself felt that drastic action was necessary. The Board urged Hoover to proclaim a national holiday.[15]

Was such action within the authority of the President? It had been suggested that the authority could be found in the Trading with the Enemy Act adopted in 1917 and never directly repealed, according to some lawyers.

Hoover asked the opinion of his Attorney General, then William D. Mitchell. Mitchell "advised that these war powers were so doubtful that they could be safely used only if it were certain that Congress would ratify the action." [16]

Pondering this equivocal opinion, Hoover again turned to Roosevelt, with the thought that if the new President would approve a national moratorium, ratification by Congress would be assured. But through Woodin, Hoover was told that Roosevelt took the position that "President Hoover was free to proceed as he thought best." [17] This was not, as has been represented, a refusal to approve the moratorium idea. But it certainly was another refusal by Roosevelt to join with Hoover in anything.

5

On the following day, March 3, Roosevelt, with his wife and son James, called at the White House for the traditional day-before-inauguration courtesy call. After tea, and the usual amenities, Hoover took the occasion to broach the moratorium idea to Roosevelt personally. Roosevelt said he believed the power was there, but suggested that if Hoover wanted to close the banks, he should do it, that "it made no difference who did it." [18]

Aside from the crisis, this tea was not a happy affair, either for Hoover or Roosevelt. Indeed, according to Roosevelt's secretary, Grace Tully, Hoover made one remark which caused Roosevelt to say later, "I hustled my family out of the room. I was sure Jimmy wanted to punch him in the eye." [19]

Such matters aside, it was plain that Hoover could not bring himself to act alone on a moratorium, but he was persistent with regard to Roosevelt. At 11:30 P.M., March 3, he put in a telephone call to Roosevelt at the Mayflower Hotel. There are conflicting versions as to precisely what Hoover said to Roosevelt and what Roosevelt said to Hoover at that eleventh-hour conference.[20] But the clear facts were that Hoover again asked Roosevelt to join him in proclaiming a national bank holiday, and that Roosevelt again insisted on taking no responsibility in the crisis until he had assumed the power of the Presidency.

The next morning, a matter of hours before the change in administrations, the final blow fell: In New York, the financial center of the nation, Governor Herbert Lehman proclaimed a banking holiday. Almost immediately, Governor Henry Horner of Illinois followed suit. So did ten other governors. By the time Roosevelt had taken the oath of office, nearly all of the banks of the nation were closed under state moratoria of one type or another.

Armed with an opinion by Attorney General Homer S. Cummings that the Enemy Trading Act was still valid, Roosevelt on Sunday evening, March 5, proclaimed a national holiday for all banks in the nation for four days, later extending it indefinitely. Under the terms of this proclamation, and of an emergency law adopted almost immediately afterward by Congress, no bank anywhere in the nation was to be open except under a special license issued by the Secretary of the Treasury.[21]

6

For Detroit, the result of Roosevelt's action was that even the Couzens Plan for reopening the Detroit banks had to be abandoned. The new banking legislation superseded and nullified the authority granted to the Comptroller under the Couzens Joint Resolution. The bankers there had delayed too long. The question of whether or not the Detroit banks were to be reopened at all then became a matter solely up to the new administration.

On March 12, when Roosevelt delivered the first of his "fireside chats," he emphasized over and over again that only *sound* banks were to receive licenses to reopen. Were the Detroit banks "sound?" Did "sound" mean "solvent?" These became the crucial questions.

For the emergency, Ballantine and Awalt had been retained in office by the new administration. Jesse Jones was slated to become chairman of the Reconstruction Finance Corporation. And these were the men upon whom the new Secretary of the Treasury, Woodin, relied for counsel. Their verdict was that the Detroit banks were not solvent.[22]

Couzens, who was to be denounced and slandered by the bankers and bank-stock owners, was almost the one official who tried to save the banks from this verdict.

On March 11, he protested vigorously to Secretary Woodin. Woodin called in Awalt and Ballantine and there occurred a heated scene.

"What is holding up these banks? Why don't you certify to their opening?" Couzens demanded of Awalt.

"I will not certify to the secretary that these banks are solvent," said Awalt.

And Ballantine said, "That is true. They cannot open up because they are insolvent." [23]

Couzens demanded proof as to the banks' insolvency. He threatened to "stay right here until the proof is forthcoming." He did not get proof, in facts or figures. Unfortunately for the banks, on the other hand, he was not able to present any facts to controvert the position of Awalt and Ballantine.

The Detroit bankers themselves, as he later pointed out, did not present any facts to offset the verdict of insolvency. Moreover, they were still entangled in their rivalries. They had been urged by the Treasury to take the initiative in forming a new bank. But they could not come to an agreement.

On March 14 Acting Comptroller Awalt, backed up by Secretary Woodin, let the sword fall. He named conservators for both the First National and the Guardian National. For those banks, as well as for the two groups of which they were the principal units, the action was the crack of doom. They were never allowed to reopen. Scores of investors had fortunes wiped out by this decision. Many of these then blamed Couzens, hating him fiercely to the end of his life because of this.

7

Yet, ironically, Couzens to the end had tried hard to avert the decision of insolvency. He went to Secretary Woodin and upbraided him in violent terms for having ruled that the banks could not be reopened.

Secretary Woodin—"Wee Willie Woodin," the press affectionately called him—was a likable personality, a big industrialist with a cherubic face, a financier whose hobby was music, and who had amazed most of his Wall Street associates by supporting Roosevelt and contributing heavily to the Democratic campaign funds.[24] But Couzens, characteristically, had been suspicious of him from the outset. Indeed, he had made an effort to hold up Woodin's confirmation as Secretary of the Treasury until the Senate could be informed about his "holdings." As president of the huge American Car and Foundry Company, Woodin had done much business with the railroads. On the floor of the Senate, Couzens raised a serious question. Wasn't it questionable "ethics" for a cabinet officer to be holding shares in a car and foundry company "when there is such close and obvious connection at this time between the railroads and government?" He wanted to be certain, Couzens said, that Roosevelt's Treasury head would not turn out to be another Mellon.[25]

Of course, with Roosevelt behind him, Woodin was confirmed promptly. But Couzens was never satisfied. Now he felt that Woodin was acting in the Detroit crisis in a way not at all in accord with the public interest, but more as any Wall Street banker would act. He scathingly reminded Woodin that he had been promised at a previous conference proof of the banks' insolvency before a final decision would be taken. He stormed at Woodin:

> You, during this conference, instructed your subordinates to satisfy me that the Detroit banks were insolvent, but up to this moment, not one word have I received from you or the Department. However, within an hour or so after I left, conservators

were appointed for both the Detroit banks, and I was not even done the courtesy of being notified.[26]

8

Couzens' protests, and those of the Detroit bankers, were in vain. Washington stood firm.

Then, and years later, there would be rumors that Wall Street, or the Federal Reserve Board, acting under the influence of New York interests, had played a part in this firmness. It would be alleged this was in accord with a longtime conspiracy to place the Ford Company under bankers' influence at last, though none of this was proved.

The fact was, the Treasury decision was not changed.

On March 21, the government itself, through the RFC, together with General Motors, established a new National Bank of Detroit to replace the two former institutions.[27]

On the following evening, James Watkins, police commissioner of Detroit, as spokesman for numerous Detroiters, went on the radio to accuse the government of having "played into the hands of Wall Streeters." Couzens commented in a letter to Madeleine:

"Police Commissioner Watkins raised Hell in his radio talk last night. . . . Over 10,000 telegrams reached Washington as a result. There's the Devil yet to pay over the Detroit bank problem. Wish I could have remained aloof." [28]

To which, it might be added, a better idea he never had . . . too late.

But the government went ahead. It was understood widely that Roosevelt himself had insisted that the Detroit crisis be cleanly and promptly ended. A little later there was established, also by the RFC, but with the Fords cooperating, the Manufacturers National Bank.[29] The First National and the Guardian National, with their holding companies, were gradually liquidated. In the history of Detroit finance, this was the end of an era. Almost all that remained of the wonderful group-banking idea in Michigan was the gilded tower of the ill-fated Union Guardian Trust Company, that monument to a fantastic financial era; and a seething mass of undeserved hatred toward Couzens, the one man who, though not financially involved, had tried, with willingness to make great personal sacrifice, to save the situation. And the story was not yet finished, for after an interlude, the whole thing was to flare up again.

CHAPTER XXXVIII

THE NEW DEAL ONLOOKER

ALL during these last bewildering days of the Detroit crisis, other events, equally tumultuous, had been transpiring in Washington. These were general developments in consequence of Roosevelt's inauguration and his calling of a special session of Congress the next day. With all his preoccupation with Detroit matters, Couzens tried his best to keep up with these events also.

He had liked Roosevelt's inaugural message. The ringing phrases which gave promise of driving "the money changers from the temple" and the pledges of direct federal action, if needed, to assist the "forgotten man" reinforced his earlier favorable impressions of Roosevelt. He would have agreed wholeheartedly with the comment of Karl Schriftgiesser: "Franklin Delano Roosevelt thus read the obituary of Normalcy" [1] of the Harding-Coolidge-Hoover era, against which Couzens' whole career in the Senate had been an angry protest.

The new President's inaugural speech, he told reporters, was "grand, grand!"

Indeed, in all his years as a senator, Roosevelt's message was the first of any President's he had felt like cheering.

He was pleased too by a gesture that Roosevelt made to him personally immediately after the inaugural exercises were closed. For the new President had sent word that he wished Couzens and Senator McNary to join him in an intimate gathering in "the President's Room" of the Capitol Building. When Couzens came in, Roosevelt gave him a warm handshake and his famous handsome smile.

That too was something new for Couzens from a President.

Roosevelt explained that he had sent for him and Senator McNary, who had stepped into defeated "Jim" Watson's shoes as Republican

leader in the Senate, because he desired their cooperation in per-
suading the Senate, before adjourning, to confirm immediately certain emergency appointments without reference to committees.

Couzens liked the friendly, non-pompous way in which Roosevelt
made the request to him. "You can take my word for it that these are
good men!" [2]

Couzens went away from this, his first meeting with Roosevelt,
with a sense of well-being he had not known for a long time. Roosevelt's whole manner, his seemingly utter calmness in face of general
confusion, the ready smile, the magnetic personality that caused
his crippled condition to be forgotten, all captivated him as no
other personality in his whole life had done.

One of his senatorial colleagues commented, "Quite a change,
eh?"

"Yes," said Couzens. "He's human!" [3]

2

To be sure, Couzens did not surrender to Roosevelt immediately,
or ever, completely.

Being Couzens, his fingers were crossed. The old attitude, which
back in his Ford Motor Company days caused him to be suspicious
of the hale and hearty backslapping salesmen, persisted. Roosevelt
seemed to measure up under his sharpest scrutiny, but he kept some
reservations.[4] He had not forgotten that in 1928, except for his re-
tention of Mellon, Hoover also had seemed good to him.

He did not even go along completely with Roosevelt on the request made at that first meeting. For one of his appointments Roosevelt wanted acted upon promptly was that of Woodin, and Couzens'
protests in that connection represented the first opposition that
Roosevelt encountered in Congress. Indeed, it was almost the only
important opposition, save for the attacks on the new banking legislation by Senator Huey Long, that came in those very first days of the
New Deal.

Yet, from the outset Couzens was one of Roosevelt's most fervent
admirers. He even came close to wishing he were a Democrat. Now,
with his rank on committees lowered, he considered that he would
have to be more or less an onlooker on the New Deal that began with
the special session called on March 5. "Most of the work is done
by Democrats now," he wryly wrote to Madeleine.[5]

And to Clarence Wilcox: "We are having hectic days here and

making history. I have one regret, however, and that is that I am
no part of it, because the Democratic administration is working
perfectly." [6]

3

True, there were certain aspects of the Roosevelt beginning that
troubled Couzens—the very ones, oddly, which caused so many other
Republicans to cheer the new President. The Woodin appointment
was one matter that caused him to wonder if there was to be a new
deal after all. Another was Roosevelt's appointment of Dean G.
Acheson as Undersecretary of the Treasury, to succeed Ballantine.

Couzens had checked Acheson's background and discovered readily
that, like Ballantine, Acheson was a lawyer with Wall Street connections. For example, Acheson was a partner of George Rublee, a
close associate of Dwight P. Morrow, partner of J. P. Morgan and
Company. When Morrow ran for Senator in New Jersey in 1931,
one of his ghost writers was none other than Acheson.[7] On May 17,
1933, Couzens rose in the Senate to oppose Acheson's confirmation.

"I know," he said, "that Mr. Woodin and Mr. Acheson are going
to be just as much the agents of Morgan as anyone you could put
there. . . . The Treasury now is being manned by men who, I believe, are unable, because of former connections, to serve the public
properly." What kind of a New Deal is that? he asked. Was the
New Deal intending to foist more Mellonism on the country? [8]

It was ironic, too, that just a few weeks later Roosevelt agreed
with Couzens that Acheson was too conservative, and rather un-
ceremoniously asked for his resignation when Acheson balked at
Roosevelt's monetary policies.[9] It was more ironic that still later,
this "too conservative" Acheson would be denounced as a "pro-
Communist," after he became Secretary of State under Roosevelt's
successor, President Harry S. Truman, with his friends recalling
Couzens' opposition to his confirmation in 1933 as a defense.

4

Even more exasperating to Couzens was the so-called Economy
Bill of 1933, sent to Congress by Roosevelt on March 10, which, in
keeping with his pledges for cutting the costs of government, provided, among other things, for reducing war veterans' benefits.[10]
To Couzens, this smacked too much of the old Hoover attitude, as
he saw it, of causing the poor to bear the brunt of the depression.

He noted with distrust that Roosevelt's Economy Bill had the backing of all the Old Guard elements, in and out of Congress, that on this occasion at least, Big Business was solidly behind Roosevelt, as it had been behind Hoover. Indeed, Hoover in his heyday never received the plaudits of the conservative press with such unanimity as did Roosevelt at this time.[11]

In the Senate, with all his old-time directness Couzens stormed against this measure, going so far as to charge that members of Congress were threatened by White House "representatives" if they did not fall in line.[12] Indeed, on this occasion, he made one of the longest speeches of his career, a bitter attack on the administration, as bitter as any he had made on Hoover's.

At just this time, the Treasury had arranged to float a note issue of $800,000,000, and asked and obtained approval from Congress to pay to the purchasers a higher than usual rate of interest. Couzens contrasted this with the Economy Bill.

"I hope that any member of this body who has the nerve to walk out of this chamber after having voted for this iniquitous measure will hang his head in shame for having approved of an increase of 100 to 180 per cent in interest rates for the money lender, while he would take away from the veterans 45 to 50 per cent of their small allowances."

It was untenable, he said, for the "National Economy League, the big business organizations, and the Chambers of Commerce" to argue that the credit of the nation was in danger unless the Economy Bill were passed. The per capita debt of the nation, he pointed out, was only $160, whereas for Great Britain it was $800. To him this did not indicate that the United States was in desperate straits from the standpoint of debt.

"Yet it is said that the little man who is getting $30 or $40 a month because of the service he performed for the nation must have his compensation cut. Mr. President, I should hope to be stricken dead, if I walked out of this chamber after having voted for such an iniquitous measure to do such great injustice to the people who are least able to stand it." [13]

The Economy Bill was passed the next day, with twelve senators in addition to Couzens daring to vote against it. Considering Roosevelt's popularity and the strength of other forces behind the bill— even National American Legion Commander Louis A. Johnson (later rewarded with an office) supported the veterans' cuts—it was remarkable that a dozen senators sided with Couzens.[14] Curiously, as in the Acheson matter, Roosevelt later again came around to Couzens' view, for in a matter of weeks, he began issuing a series of executive orders ameliorating the effects of the Economy Bill and in the end almost all of the veterans' cuts were restored.[15]

5

Roosevelt in the meantime went forward with enough other legislation more in keeping with the general promises of the New Deal and Couzens' hopes for it. Especially was Couzens delighted that, either from emulation or by coincidence, Roosevelt had recommended to Congress a variation of his own idea for taking care of the jobless young people who had been roaming the highways. Like Couzens, Roosevelt insisted that these youngsters had to be provided for, and proposed the Civilian Conservation Corps program.

Couzens recalled with disgust how the Army had opposed his proposal in that regard because, as he angrily told the Senate, "the aristocracy of the Army did not wish to be annoyed" with "taking care of jobless and homeless boys." Some day, he said, this same "Army aristocracy" will want these boys as soldiers, to fight for their country. But now "it did not care what happened to them." This was a "shameful attitude," he declared.[16]

When told that his proposal would be expensive, involving an additional cost to the Army of some $88,000 a day, his answer was: "We appropriate millions for the problem of migratory birds and, though it is hard to believe, there is complaint now heard when we wish to appropriate money for the care of migratory boys."

For his part, he said, he "did not care what it cost." The question was, "What are we going to do about these boys?" [17]

"During the nearly eleven years that I have been a member of the Senate, I have seen almost every kind of legislation go through in the interest of business. I have not opposed these measures. I am not against the railroads or other business. I want to see their integrity maintained. But I also want to see maintained the integrity of the youth of our land, and I want to see them preserved.

"I have heard the words 'fundamental' and 'sound policies' and 'economy' and so on, until I am sick and tired. The whole United States ought to be sick and tired of the constant repetition of such words while millions and millions of our people are in distress." [18]

His proposal had been lost in the closing days of the last Hoover

Congress. Even a large number of Democrats had opposed him, joining in charges that his scheme was "demagogic." But now Roosevelt placed all his influence behind the CCC proposal. This time the Army, if it still had objections, suppressed them, and the plan was adopted.

It turned out that of all the New Deal projects, the CCC program, with its emphasis on reforestation, although of minor significance in the larger scheme of things, was the most popular. Although it would be stated that the idea for it was Roosevelt's "own," Couzens always felt that he was at least a co-parent of it. It was certainly an example of parallel thinking on his and Roosevelt's part. A specific problem, that of the jobless youth, existed; the way to meet it was to come up with a specific act. This appealed to Couzens. At last the government was ceasing to "play ostrich."

6

There was more, much more, in this first Roosevelt phase that satisfied Couzens beyond his expectations. Roosevelt easily pushed to adoption such changes in the banking laws as compulsory divorcement of investment affiliates from commercial banks, which in itself might have prevented the Detroit disaster. He caused Congress even more easily, without even waiting for the pledged repeal of the Eighteenth Amendment, to revise the Volstead Act to permit the sale of 3.2 beer. "I think this would be a good time for beer," Roosevelt said, and it was done.[19] Here also was personal vindication for Couzens—ten years after he had said, in opposition to Harding and the Anti-Saloon League, that the Volstead Act ought to be modified.

In breathtaking succession, came a new act for the small-home owners of the nation, a Home Owners Loan Corporation, which substantially met Couzens' objections to Hoover's Home Loan Bank act, for it provided direct aid to the home owners; and the Tennessee Valley Authority Act, which at long last decided the question of Muscle Shoals as Couzens as well as Norris and, of course, other progressives and liberals of both parties for years, had wanted it decided. As Couzens wrote to a protesting constituent, "My approval of TVA was the result of years and years of fighting here in Congress about what was to be done with Muscle Shoals." [20]

Then came an unemployment relief act, which willingly, rather than grudgingly, made federal funds available for direct relief to the needy as well as for providing jobs. Also an act for federal regulation of the sale of investment securities, which for the first time enacted into law, in so far as this field was concerned, a code of ethics which Couzens, along with such liberals as William O. Douglas, had always insisted ought to prevail among bankers; and an act for emergency railroad legislation that incorporated many of the views Couzens had fought for against Hoover, in his capacity as chairman of the Senate Committee on Interstate Commerce.

Indeed, as it began to take shape, the New Deal was in fact already an enactment of so many of the ideas Couzens, along with other independents and progressives, had been plumping for since the days of the elder La Follette, that it could properly, in a way, have been styled as much a Couzens program as a Roosevelt program. No wonder that Senator McNary—who had not long before got a laugh from Couzens by sending him a crate of prunes from his Oregon farm with a note, "These are of a new variety, thus somewhat radical"—observed:

"Couzens fell in love with the New Deal." [21]

7

This was true.

Toward the end of May, Roosevelt came up with the most sweeping of all his measures in his honeymoon period—the National Industrial Recovery Bill (NRA).

Couzens felt cause to be truly elated over this many-sided measure. Here in one package were recommendations in principle if not in exact detail which constituted implementation of most of the major positions he had championed ever since he had been in public life, a program harking back to his mayoralty, when Detroiters called him a "Bolshevik" for the way he took care of the unemployed during the depression of 1920–1922: prohibition of child labor; the right of working men to organize; shorter working hours to stagger employment with decent wage levels protected; and a gigantic public-works program precisely in line with that "fantastic" interview he had given to Ray Tucker back in 1931.

True, the NRA also involved some provisions, notably the "codes" permitting exemptions from the anti-monopoly laws, and also some omissions in the matter of wage rates on public-works projects, to which he would find himself in disagreement, or not certain of. But on the whole, the NRA, as it was first projected, appeared almost a millennial event from Couzens' point of view. On the basis of his past, this was precisely the kind of program he would have come up with, had he been President.

Taken with Roosevelt's boldness in going off the gold standard, which reversed the deflationary trend of the Hoover era, and the drastic farm-relief measures, which for once all the farmers' organizations agreed upon and practically drafted themselves, a fact that persuaded Couzens to vote for them, the NRA looked like a complete break with the Old Guard traditions in America, albeit even Hoover had been moving against his will in the same direction.[22]

As Frank Kent correctly observed at the time, the new Democratic administration had really taken over the program, not of the historic Democratic party, but of the Progressive insurgents in the Republican party, in which Couzens, if anywhere, actually belonged.[23] The "nice and decent revolution," forecast by William Allen White ten years earlier, almost to the day, had come to pass, apparently. To accomplish it, Roosevelt had supplied the needed cohesive force, which the Progressives, all intensely individualistic, never achieved.[24]

Moreover, Roosevelt's legislative assistants had on several occasions showed a marked disposition to do what the previous Republican administrations almost never did—consult with Couzens as well as other independent Republicans, on the drafting of legislation.

A case in point was the securities regulation bill. The New Deal historians Joseph Alsop and Robert Kintner would say that Couzens was responsible for the securities bill having been introduced and passed much earlier than Roosevelt had intended. "Prepared at the mere request of one of Ferdinand Pecora's assistant investigators, it was only introduced because Senator Jim Couzens suddenly decided the time was ripe for an exchange bill." [25] This was not the whole story, but there is enough truth in the statement to show how things had changed in his relations with the White House.

8

Yet after the first excitement over the Roosevelt approach had died down, Couzens was not really as happy as he had expected to be. Across the land, people hummed the New Deal theme song, "Happy Days Are Here Again!" There was a feeling that Roosevelt would take care of all the nation's ills. But Couzens still saw the heartbreaking effects of the continuing depression.

True, people no longer faced the danger of actual starvation amidst plenty. But there was still much hardship, and the basic causes remained.

"The misery I am going through here because of nationwide conditions is beyond telling in a letter," he wrote his brother Albert on May 26, 1933, nine days after Roosevelt sent the NRA bill to Congress.

This comment pointed up a facet of Couzens' nature that few people recognized. As with crippled children, he identified himself emotionally with victims of the depression. "He suffered physical pain that was real over the plight of the unemployed," Hiram Johnson observed.[26]

Each day's newspaper continued to emphasize millions of Americans still were without jobs, that relief rolls were still growing. For once, he even sympathized with some rich persons, whose investments had turned sour, especially in Detroit bank stocks. "I never expected to live to see the day when so very many even wealthy people are absolutely broke, when heretofore well-known rich people hardly know how to get a living," he told his brother.[27]

On top of this, all the aggravation of the bank crisis had taken from him a physical as well as mental toll. More than ever, he suffered from sleepless nights. He was desperately in need of a rest. But instead of relaxing, he plunged now, during that spring of Roosevelt's first period, with all his bulldog strength into an investigation of J. P. Morgan and Company, an activity not calculated to be a sedative for his nerves.

CHAPTER XXXIX

THE INVESTIGATOR AGAIN

THE inquisition of the House of Morgan began May 23, 1933, in the marble-floored conference room of the Senate Committee on Banking and Currency. In certain quarters it would be labeled a "circus," especially after the incident engineered by a press agent of having a midget suddenly plump himself on Mr. Morgan's lap.

But in truth this inquisition was one of the most important ever conducted by a Congressional committee in terms of its revelations as to the inner workings of interlocked finance and politics.

It was a continuation of the investigation into stock-market practices that the same committee had been conducting off and on for more than a year. In a large sense, it was also an extension of the investigation by the Senate Finance Committee two years earlier into the processes by which Americans had lost so heavily on Cuban, Peruvian, and other foreign bond issues. Taken together, the two inquiries furnished an especially candid picture of both domestic and foreign financial practices in the era of "wonderful nonsense."

Even before the House of Morgan was subjected to inquiry, the stock-market investigation, called off during the 1932 election campaign, already revealed enough to permit Charles and Mary Beard to summarize:

> Page after page of sworn testimony showed that mighty men among the Lords of Creation had formed "pools" for particular stocks and bonds, run up the price of securities, poisoned the news of financial columns by the bribery of reporters, drawn unwary sheep into the pens of bulls and bears and sheared them as the bottom fell out of liquid claims to wealth.[1]

While J. P. Morgan and Company had been mentioned now and then in some of these amazing transactions, and one of its prominent partners, Lamont, had been questioned by the earlier Senate Finance Committee inquiry into foreign loans, the impression had persisted that, on the whole, it had been above yielding to any challengeable practices. The House of Morgan, it was believed, was so strong and so circumspect that it had no need to adopt methods that could not stand senatorial scrutiny.

2

Now, however, the House of Morgan was subjected to its first thorough investigation since the Pujo inquiry of two decades before. It was understood that Roosevelt urged this personally, on the theory that the more adverse attention obtained by J. P. Morgan & Company, the more amenable Congress and the nation would be to New Deal legislation. In the words of Ernest K. Lindley, "To put the House of Morgan on the defensive immediately was to the Administration's advantage. To establish definitely and expose its position in the economic and political world was a necessity preliminary to reforms that would go far beyond the improvement of the banking system." [2]

In this inquiry, Couzens, even though now a minority member of the Banking and Currency Committee, played a prominent role. He was "merciless in his judgments and caustic of tongue," recalled Stokes.[3] Indeed, even though the committee finally retained Ferdinand Pecora, a hard-hitting New York City prosecutor, as counsel, it is doubtful if the House of Morgan investigation would have been so incisive if not for Couzens' participation.

A number of the other senators, including even the usually acid-tongued Senator Glass, seemed overawed by the prestige of this firm and especially of its head, J. P. Morgan himself. They reflected the attitude, reported on by Frank R. Kent in the *Baltimore Sun,* of "a number of people who talk about the 'terrible outrage' of a Senate committee dragging Mr. Morgan and his partners down here, cross-examining them like a lot of chicken thieves, and making it all a sort of Roman holiday." [4]

There was a tendency to handle Morgan with soft gloves, to show deference to him that was denied other bankers. Couzens put a stop to that. He had no more reverence for Morgan than he had possessed for Mellon. He agreed wholeheartedly with Frank R. Kent. "There should be nothing sacrosanct about the House of Morgan." [5]

At one point, Couzens engaged in a row with Senator Glass when the Virginian declared that Pecora should be more respectful and less barbed in his questioning of Morgan. "I insist that Mr. Morgan be treated like anyone else here!" snapped Couzens. He pounded the table. Glass backed down,[6] and from then on, Pecora, with Couzens' backing, went after Morgan without gloves.[7]

3

The results were startling enough to shake even a man so suspicious of other wealthy men as Couzens. The inquiry disclosed that J. P. Morgan and Company not only had engaged in many, if not all, of the practices common to the other firms already investigated, but, in one respect, had gone even further. Thus, while other firms had seduced mere newspaper editors and reporters to help win their cooperation for unloading inflated stocks on the public, the House of Morgan, it was now revealed, had apparently succeeded, by the device of so-called "preferred lists" in winning the influence, favor, or silence, of many of the most outstanding public figures of the nation. This seemed at least a fair inference when it was revealed that persons on the House of Morgan "preferred lists"—men permitted to purchase stocks in advance of the public sale at prices considerably lower than the public paid—included such public dignitaries as:

Former President Coolidge; Newton D. Baker, President Wilson's Secretary of War; Charles Francis Adams, Hoover's Secretary of the Navy; Charles D. Hilles and J. R. Nutt, officials of the Republican National Committee; Silas H. Strawn, former president of the United States Chamber of Commerce and law partner of Garrard Winston, Mellon's Undersecretary of the Treasury; Norman H. Davis, even then functioning as Roosevelt's ambassador-at-large in Europe on the question of war debts; John J. Raskob, former chairman of the Democratic National Committee; John W. Davis, 1924 Democratic Party nominee for President; General of the Army John J. Pershing; William G. McAdoo, Secretary of the Treasury under President Wilson and then Democratic Senator from California; and—most interesting of all to Couzens—William H. Woodin.[8]

It seemed obvious from this list that, in the game that was being played, the leaders of both parties were on equally good terms with the House of Morgan.

Couzens was among the first to comment pointedly on this bipartisan financial policy of the nation's great. "When it comes to money," he told the press, "there are no Republicans or Democrats. Rich men never fight each other seriously. There is the finest coalition of all parties when it comes to control of the Treasury of the United States." [9]

This is what he had contended all his public life, and now evidence demonstrating his position had been produced.

The Morgan partners insisted that in most cases they did not even know the political affiliation or standing of their "preferred" clients and that "influence" was the last thing the firm had counted upon in letting these individuals in on chances to make gigantic killings in the stock market.[10] Probably some persons believed these disclaimers. Couzens was not among them.

Couzens questioned George Whitney, partner of J. P. Morgan and Company, also director in large corporations, on the motives behind the preferred lists. The banker protested, "perhaps too vehemently," he later conceded under questioning by Couzens,[11] that the lists were for purely business purposes, not for getting favors from high-placed individuals in politics and government.

It had been brought out, as one example, that J. P. Morgan & Company had distributed to the individuals on its preferred list shares of Johns-Manville Corporation at 47½ in June 1927, whereas when the stock was offered to the public a few weeks later, the stock sold at 79, "representing a potential combined profit to the members of the selected lists of $12,037,500.[12]

SENATOR COUZENS: You said the only object was that these men you distributed the stock to would make money?

MR. WHITNEY: I did not say our only object. I said we hoped they would.

SENATOR COUZENS: That was not the only object you had?

MR. WHITNEY: No sir.

SENATOR COUZENS: You hoped they would reciprocate?

MR. WHITNEY: No, really.

SENATOR COUZENS: You did not give them this price so that they would reciprocate and keep on good terms?

MR. WHITNEY: No, really. That is, of course, the suggestion that has been carried in the testimony yesterday, and in the papers, but I can only tell you that is not so.

SENATOR COUZENS: I never heard of anybody quite so altruistic in my life![13]

4

Nor did the Senate committee as a whole believe that altruism was the explanation, for it finally summed up:

The preferred lists strikingly illuminate the methods employed by bankers to extend their influence and control over individuals in high places. The persons upon whom princely favors were bestowed in this manner were . . . persons prominent in all the financial, industrial and political walks of our national life. The granting of these preferential participations . . . augured well for their mutual welfare and ill for that of the public.[14]

Of special interest to Couzens was testimony about certain taxation practices of the House of Morgan. This part of the inquisition produced unexpected corroboration of the significance of his investigation of Mellon and the Bureau of Internal Revenue almost a decade earlier. He had charged then that the Bureau, under Mellon, had favored wealthy individuals and corporations. The House of Morgan was not then involved. Now it was.

Mr. Morgan himself was forced to give testimony showing that the Bureau of Internal Revenue, during the period that Mellon was Secretary of the Treasury, exercised exceptional discreetness in matters in which the House of Morgan was concerned.

The committee later said in its report:

> Internal-revenue agents accepted without examination income-tax returns prepared by J. P. Morgan & Co. on the assumption that preparation by that firm *ipso facto* established the correctness of the returns. For example, the tax return of Mrs. Margaret Y. Newbold for the year 1928, prepared by J. P. Morgan & Co. bore the following legend:
>
> "Returned without examination for the reason that the return was prepared in the office of J. P. Morgan & Co., and it has been our experience that any schedule made by that office is correct. The books of the taxpayer are located in Philadelphia, and if necessary schedule C may be verified in that city. This office, however, recommends that the return be accepted as filed. C. M. Sheppard, Internal Revenue Agent."
>
> Many other returns, particularly of partners in large banking houses, were likewise exempted from adequate scrutiny. When examinations were made, the time devoted to them was comparatively short, in view of the wealth of the taxpayers and the complex nature of their transactions. Thus, in 1930, according to the Bureau's own records, 1 day was spent in checking the partnership return of J. P. Morgan & Co., and Drexel & Co.—the most powerful banking group in the world. This return was not subjected to any field examination, and apparently the agent's explanation was sufficient to satisfy the Internal Revenue Bureau that none was necessary.[15]

The Senate committee reported: "For the year 1930, 17 Morgan partners, including J. P. Morgan, paid no tax and 5 paid aggregate taxes of about $56,000. For the year 1931, not a single Morgan partner paid any tax. For the year 1932, not a single Morgan partner paid any tax." [16]

It was all dramatic vindication of Couzens' crusade against Mellon-ism, which Senators Moses and Watson, as well as others, including Mellon himself, characterized as merely a "private feud," or just a demonstration of Couzens' "terrible temper" and nothing more.[17]

5

There was still further personal vindication for Couzens in these hearings. He had been criticized back in the spring of 1932 for having opposed a loan of millions of dollars from the RFC to a rail-road because, he charged, the loan actually would go to J. P. Morgan & Company, which did not need it. The inquiry brought out that it was the House of Morgan that had suggested that the railroad apply for the loan and press it, over disapproval by the Interstate Commerce Commission, and that $5,850,000 of the government money promptly found its way into the coffers of the banking firm.[18]

Supremely corroborative as they were of much of Couzens' career in the Senate, such revelations did not, however, really please him as much as many persons supposed. Reporters and others took it for granted that the "Scab Millionaire," who preferred needling rich men to anything else, as it often was said of him, would be ecstatic over the House of Morgan inquisition. Actually, he was not. Such revelations merely added now to his painful frame of mind.

Coming on top of the Detroit bank episode, the findings of the Senate committee left him more acutely depressed than ever. He was being eaten up inwardly by suppressed hostility toward men like Morgan, who, he felt, ought to have behaved differently than he feared they had. He was not at all anxious to have it proved that the whole American business system, as it seemed to him, had been corrupt to the very highest pinnacle.

The day-after-day testimony to greed, irresponsibility, chicanery, and corruption, not of politicians and gangsters, but of the most respected persons in society, left him appalled. Former Governor James M. Cox of Ohio later had some conversations with him which caused Cox to conclude: "The world he was living in . . . gave him great concern, and he worried too much about it." [19]

This was all too true. He was more and more tense; more and more in need of a change of scene.

CHAPTER XL

THE DELEGATE TO LONDON

ROOSEVELT unexpectedly opened the way to his needed change of scene. Summoning him to the White House for a 9 A.M. meeting, but without telling him the purpose, Roosevelt had Couzens ushered into his private apartment. The President was still in bed, having breakfast and reading the newspapers, which informality (inconceivable with Coolidge or Hoover) so impressed Couzens that instead of setting down in his notebook the reason for the visit, he wrote: "Saw Roosevelt in his pajamas." Roosevelt promptly sprung on him the offer of an appointment as a delegate to the World Economic and Monetary Conference scheduled to open in London in June.

Roosevelt had been scouting around for a suitable Republican on an otherwise Democratic delegation, and Senator McNary mentioned Couzens' name to him. With certain other Republican progressives, McNary had begun hinting to Roosevelt that Couzens would be a good man in his cabinet as Secretary of the Treasury, if only because of his stand against Mellonism. The London assignment looked to McNary like a step in that direction. Besides, McNary was worried over Couzens' health and believed the trip would be good for him. Though wary of Couzens' independence, Roosevelt quickly fell in with the suggestion. He saw that Couzens fit exactly what he had in mind—a Republican who was sympathetic, openly so, toward the New Deal.[1]

With Mrs. Couzens, John Carson, and Jay Hayden, whom the *Detroit News* assigned to cover his activities, he sailed for England on June 6, 1933.

2

This was his fifth transatlantic crossing. His first, back in 1891, when he accompanied his father on a visit to London, was made just after he had begun his life in Detroit, still a Canadian. Oddly, in view of the purpose of this latest crossing—to help solve the deepest world monetary questions—his main impression of his first visit to London was the trouble he had experienced in keeping his American money straight in terms of pounds and shillings.[2]

The second and third trips abroad, in 1907 and 1909, had been in connection with the Ford Motor Company. Memories, some sharp, even poignant, naturally would be evoked from thinking of those days—of his early association with Ford, of Malcomson (dead ten years by 1933), of the Selden case, of the negotiations with Durant for selling the Ford company which, if they had gone through, would have left him one-fourth owner of General Motors (bigger than Ford now), of the five-dollar-a-day plan . . . of, indeed, the many phases of the whole Ford story.

Not all such memories were wholly pleasant. The break with Malcomson had not been pleasant. Nor the break with Ford. Then, too, there was the great sadness of his life, the death of that promising boy, Homer. Nobody else could ever know how deeply that tragedy had affected him, of what pleasure in life it had robbed him. Never had he ceased to reflect on the shining hopes of achievement he had held for Homer.[3]

True, his other son, Frank, had not done so bad. Indeed not! In 1933, Frank was the Mayor of Detroit. That had happened because Roosevelt, two weeks before he asked Couzens to go to London, appointed Mayor Frank Murphy as High Commissioner of the Philippines. As president of the Detroit Common Council, Frank Couzens succeeded to Murphy's job as Mayor. "I've lived pretty well, don't you think, to have raised a mayor?" Couzens said to reporters who interviewed him just before he left for London.[4]

Thoughts of Frank in his own former office in the grimy old Detroit City Hall were bound to bring to mind his own mayoralty, as well as his earlier term as police commissioner. How serene the world had appeared to most persons in that era! Possibly some remembered that on returning from his fourth visit abroad, in 1923, he had pointed to danger signals in Europe and suggested a receivership for Germany. These ideas were laughed at or denounced, and especially was this true of his assertion that the United States ought to play a more positive role in international affairs so as to help avoid another world war which he felt was brewing already in Germany. Now, ten years later, this conference, to which he was a delegate, had been called precisely because such warnings had been ignored. The economy of the whole world had gone to pot, just as the economy of the United States had gone to pot, and another world war would, in fact, be the result in six more years. In Germany Hitler was already in power.

Coolidge had been President when Couzens returned from that fourth trip. Just ten years ago—and it seemed centuries.

Poor Coolidge! Only the previous January 1933 he had died, heartbroken, it was said, because even to him it was plain that "Coolidge prosperity" had been built on sand. Coolidge had seemed so wise in saying, "The business of America is business," or when, on the international debt problem, he had commented, "They hired the money, didn't they?" Yet he lived long enough to realize that such "Yankee talk" was not so statesmanlike as he had supposed. The Coolidge world—Andy Mellon's too—had crashed utterly. Even the banks in Northampton, Massachusetts had closed.[5]

That the London conference, for which he was making this new trip to Europe as he was turning sixty-one, would help the world to recover economically was a hope that Couzens shared with many others. He had seldom talked in the Senate about foreign affairs, yet he had a greater awareness than most of his colleagues—certainly more than most of his fellow Middle Westerners, especially the other progressives—of the perilous position of the world and the impact of foreign conditions upon the United States, as witness his warning in 1923 to Coolidge about "Hiram Johnson's isolationism." He knew that the major powers, the United States included (with the Smoot-Hawley tariff act of 1932 especially), were engaged in a form of economic warfare. He hoped that the London conference might change this pattern and bring "economic disarmament" as a step for preventing the resort to military force. "On every side there are possibilities . . . more ominous than any since 1914," said James W. Angell, American member of the Preparatory Commission of the conference, in March 1933. And Couzens agreed as he sailed for England.[6]

3

Unhappily, the London conference proved unworthy of the hope it had inspired. It had been ill timed. It ought to have been held many months earlier, when first planned under Hoover, or not at all. For economic stabilization, as a condition precedent to the breaking down of barriers to international trade, was the principal goal, yet stabilization at that juncture was precisely what the Roosevelt New Deal was against. For stabilization then meant settling for the deflationary level of the depression. "Reflation," not stabilization, in the United States, was the Roosevelt goal, and he had flatly said in his inaugural that this must come ahead of international arrangements.

On arriving in London, Couzens found himself in an atmosphere of gloom because no one expected the meeting to succeed. "Everything within the delegation was all so riotously unhappy," recalled Herbert Feis, economic adviser to the United States State Department.[7] Nor were matters helped by the British. It had been specifically agreed, or so it was thought, that the question of war debts would not be brought up. Yet Prime Minister Ramsay MacDonald in his opening address, seconded by Neville Chamberlain, then the Chancellor of the Exchequer, brought up precisely this question.[8] Then, just after Couzens arrived, the conference faced a kind of sit-down strike. No monetary stabilization, no action on anything else that the agenda provided, such as toning down tariffs, exclusive trade agreements, dumping, and the other impediments to free trade in the world—such was the tacit position of France. It was no wonder that Couzens later said he was under "a terrific strain" there "trying to be diplomatic." [9] Frustration engulfed everyone.

4

He was appointed to the monetary and financial commission. It was there that the struggle over stabilization centered. As always, he took his responsibility seriously and worked hard at it. Mrs. Couzens wrote to Madeleine, "Daddy's hours are from 9:30 in the morning until 7:30 in the evening, sometimes later. . . . He is quite tired." [10] But he was not long in discovering that the conference was involved in an irreconcilable conflict: nationalism versus internationalism.

On June 19 he expressed himself candidly to the conference on this impasse. "The nations have not suffered enough to be willing to meet in complete humility. . . . Most nations are still rather cocky about their nationalism and feel confident that they can paddle their own canoes, whether anything comes out of the conference or not." [11]

Of all the utterances at the gathering, this most bluntly exposed the impasse. The *Times* of London placed over it a headline that showed that in one statement he had been capable of making in

London the same impression for which he was most noted in Washington: "PLAIN SPEAKING."

5

Not even the American delegation was in agreement within itself on a program. There were some in the delegation who wanted to agree to currency stabilization after all, in spite of Roosevelt. A resolution to that effect was drawn up, but word came from Roosevelt that he was against it. "The whole conference very nearly broke up in disorder," recalled young James P. Warburg, one of the advisers to the American delegation.[12] Couzens sided with Roosevelt. "We must work together," he said in a statement showing that he was shelving his mild internationalist views, at least temporarily, to embrace fully Roosevelt's program of "First things first." [13]

But unity remained the one thing the delegation could not achieve. "On one day at the conference," recalled Raymond Moley, then a confidant of Roosevelt and Assistant Secretary of State, "Senator Couzens spoke against tariff reductions and, on the next, Representative McReynolds asserted that lower tariffs were necessary to recovery. To complete the impression created by this episode, McReynolds denounced the Republican party as though he were making a speech on the floor of the House." [14] This was typical.

When it was suggested at a meeting of the American delegation that no one speak for publication without the approval of Secretary of State Cordell Hull, the delegation chairman, Couzens refused to be bound by such a rule. He "intended to voice his opinions to the press on all matters at any time," he said.[15]

His insistence on his independence did not endear him to Hull, who later asked Moley to convey to Roosevelt a pointed message. The President should "not give Progressive Republicans too prominent a place in the administration, since they didn't seem capable of working with anybody." [16] Roosevelt of course knew that Couzens in London was more in line with "the administration" than was Hull, for Hull did not believe that economic recovery in the United States could come from domestic action alone.[17] After a row with Hull, one of several, Couzens threatened to resign.[18] Mrs. Couzens expressed his feelings when she wrote to Madeleine: "If the policy of this conference does not change and get a little more pep and sense into it, I am sure Daddy will pack up and get out of it all. This crowd is going around in circles." [19]

Only Hull's pleas that Couzens' resignation would prove a serious embarrassment and that he should at least stand by until the expected arrival from Washington of Moley, caused Couzens to stay on. But after this, he devoted himself mainly to championing aggressively the Roosevelt program for increasing employment in the United States through public works and to urging all other nations to do likewise. "I am enthusiastic about what President Roosevelt is accomplishing, if press reports are correct," he wrote to Tom Payne concerning news about the NRA, which went into effect on June 16. In the same vein, during a formal speech before the monetary and financial commission, he argued that the nationalistic Roosevelt program be made international, that all the nations do as the New Deal was doing—an idea that Roosevelt, cruising on a destroyer off the Atlantic coast, almost at the same moment was expressing to Moley.[20] Thus did Couzens try personally, albeit naively, to bridge the unbridgeable gap that then existed between nationalism and internationalism.

6

When Moley arrived in London on the next day, he immediately took the spotlight as one who had recently been with Roosevelt. Would Moley be able to break the deadlock on the question of monetary stabilization? He tried his hand. At the American embassy, during a secret meeting which Couzens attended, he drafted the text of a suggested resolution which was forwarded to Roosevelt. It committed no nation to anything except a desire to return to the gold standard when it was deemed proper to do so. Couzens sensed that Roosevelt would not approve even this innocuous resolution.

Thoroughly disgusted by then—the more so since Hull had raised objections because he had been in on the embassy meeting, whereas Hull had known nothing of it—Couzens informed Moley that he wished to resign forthwith.[21] But again yielding to an appeal not to bring into the open the pitiful division within the delegation, he agreed to remain at least until Roosevelt responded to the resolution forwarded by Moley.[22] "If this conference does not come to some understanding soon, poor Daddy will blow up," Mrs. Couzens wrote to Madeleine.[23]

When Roosevelt responded on July 3, his message said that the conference should not "allow itself to be diverted by the proposal of a purely artificial and temporary experiment affecting the monetary exchange of a few nations only. . . ." [24] Whatever was Roosevelt's intent, the effect of his pronouncement was to bring the conference to an end for all practical purposes.[25] Again there was talk of resignation, this time not by Couzens, but by Hull.[26] Indeed, it was Couzens, in the unusual role of pacifier, who stood out among those who tried to save the conference from wreckage. He made a speech attempting to explain America's position and urged: "The conference must go on with the work for which it was summoned." [27] But almost no one shared his view that anything still could be accomplished, and his heart was really not in the effort.

7

After this, the conference became just an occasion for social gatherings. These were interesting, of course. At one of them Mrs. Couzens met "the lady that the Prince of Wales is so devoted to, and had a charming visit with her." But soon even the parties grew boring to everyone. London's weather turned uncommonly hot. "Poor Daddy will be a wreck—it is so hot," Mrs. Couzens informed Madeleine on July 7. "Besides, everyone of our delegates is very unhappy over the turn affairs have taken and are undecided what to do." [28]

But Couzens knew what he intended to do. He made reservations to sail for home without waiting for the official adjournment. He did not, however, get away before being involved in one more irritating incident. Roosevelt had asked Moley to send him a confidential estimate of the American delegation. In complying, Moley deprecated in frank terms all the delegates except Senator Pittman. He had marked the message "Secret from Moley, to the President Alone and Exclusively." But an embassy employee showed a copy to Ambassador Robert Bingham, who showed it to Hull, who saw to it that Couzens, among the others mentioned, read the Moley comments. Especially wrathful because just previously Moley had "particularly praised him to his face," Couzens gave Moley a tongue lashing. No wonder John Franklin Carter summed up the whole conference as a "diplomatic bedroom farce." [29]

Thus at the end as at the start, this interlude, "a Donnybrook Fair," as Moley accurately called it, proved a poor sedative.[30] Especially was this so in view of still another eruption, one occurring in Detroit, that disturbed Couzens as much as the frustrations in London, indeed even more.

CHAPTER XLI

THE SMEAR

THE Detroit bank case had re-exploded.

Couzens first learned of this development between sessions in London when Jay Hayden showed him a cable from his newspaper, the *Detroit News*. The cable asked Hayden to get Couzens' comments on testimony given before a one-man grand jury that day by Clifford Longley, the Ford attorney and the latest president of the defunct Union Guardian Trust Company.[1]

Asked why the original RFC loan to the Guardian Group did not go through, Longley had said, "There was considerable opposition in Washington."

"Why and by whom?"

Longley had paused for a moment. He laced his fingers together, and smiled. "Well, I think the largest single opposition to the loan in the amount we were asking came from Senator Couzens." Couzens "was very antagonistic," he said.

He "gathered" that "Couzens was very much put out because of our not coming to him in the first place." He "gathered" that "Couzens opposed the loan very strongly." He "gathered" that "Couzens' opposition stopped the loan."[2] All of which was reason enough for most of the Detroit and Michigan newspapers to carry banner lines on one theme:

COUZENS BLOCKED LOAN FOR BANKS!

2

It was soon apparent that this grand-jury investigation, presided over by Judge Harry B. Keidan, supposedly called to reveal the facts behind the bank crisis, actually was maneuvered from the beginning into an elaborate device for pinning the blame for the whole tragedy on Couzens personally.

At first, Couzens was not overly disturbed. Not even when a cable reached him from his lawyer-friend, Tom Payne, asking his permission for Payne to go before Judge Keidan to ask that the inquiry not be adjourned until after Couzens had testified. Couzens cabled the permission, and also dictated to Hayden a rejoinder to the Longley testimony to be published in Hayden's paper.

His answer to Longley was a notably calm statement, wholly devoid of acrimony. In it he reviewed briefly the Guardian Group loan application of January 1933. He pointed out that none of the RFC directors had approved the loan application, and that this was also true of those who attended the White House conference. Recalling that Senator Vandenberg attended the White House meeting, he suggested that Vandenberg be "consulted for details." [3]

The *News* did query Vandenberg. From Grand Rapids, he issued a statement which, while cautious, fully upheld Couzens.

"There is no question," Vandenberg said, "that Senator Couzens is correct when he says that at the initial conference no one felt, on the basis of the figures submitted by the RFC, that the program could be put through as originally requested. This included Ogden L. Mills, Secretary of the Treasury, Charles A. Miller, president of the RFC, and President Hoover himself." [4]

3

That seemed to take care of matters very well. On June 22, Couzens wrote to Payne, "Do not hesitate to make any expense to keep me informed and to protect my name, because I have nothing to hide and no financial interest to protect or to hazard." [5] Then he placed the matter pretty much out of his mind as he concentrated on the problems of the conference. But in the following week came news from Detroit that was more of a "bombshell" to him than was President Roosevelt's July 3 rebuke to the gold-bloc nations of the conference.

This concerned some fantastically irresponsible testimony. For H. R. Wilkin, a vice-president of the Guardian National Bank, later convicted of fraud in connection with operations of one of the group units, had implied that Mrs. Couzens had made a "smart money" withdrawal from the Union Guardian Trust Company just before the bank holiday.

Illustrating the careless manner in which the grand jury investigation was conducted, Wilkin had injected Mrs. Couzens' name into the hearing knowing, as his testimony itself shows, that his assertions were based on hearsay, a knowledge that also was shared by everyone else concerned.

Wilkin was being questioned at the time by Harry S. Toy, then Wayne County prosecutor. Toy had asked Wilkin to comment on reports that certain large withdrawals had been made from the Union Guardian Trust Company prior to the holiday. Wilkin mentioned that a bank in Houston, Texas, the bailiwick of Jesse Jones, the RFC board member, had withdrawn about $165,000 between February 8 and 11. Then:

Q—Were there any other large withdrawals made prior to the holiday?

A—Not to my knowledge.

Q—What do you mean to your knowledge? Did someone tell you about them?

A—Yes. One of the officers of the bank told me Mrs. Couzens had withdrawn nearly all her balance the Saturday before the holiday.

Q—How much did she withdraw?

A—I don't know.

Q—Did you ever try to find out?

A—Yes, I saw the ledger card and it showed a pretty scant balance. Later I tried to find out from the receiver of the bank, (B. C.) Schram, and he told me he could not divulge the amount of the withdrawal without permission of the comptroller of currency.

Q—You say this withdrawal was made the Saturday before the holiday?

A—Yes.

Q—When was this withdrawal cleared through the Detroit Clearing House?

A—The clearing house cleared approximately $4,000,000 on the fifteenth. . . .

Q—Would the check of the average depositor have been cleared the same as the check of Mrs. Couzens?

A—Yes, I think so.[6]

That was all there was to this line of testimony. But it was enough to inspire headlines and stories all over the world which, if they did not say so directly, gave the impression that Mrs. Couzens had made a "smart money" withdrawal of a really substantial amount.

The facts? Mrs. Couzens had made a withdrawal from a personal account in the Union Guardian Trust Company. It was for approximately $5,000, which she requested transferred around February 6 to the Riggs National Bank in Washington, to be used by her for customary contributions to charities in which she was interested.[7]

Obviously this was not a "smart money" withdrawal, nor was it important in any respect to the fate of the trust company.

However, as a result of the way the Wilkin testimony was presented, Couzens, in London, experienced the jolt of his life when he saw on the front page of the Paris edition of the *New York Herald* the headline:

SENATOR'S WIFE BLAMED
FOR WRECKING MICHIGAN BANKS
BY SMART MONEY WITHDRAWALS

4

He turned red—and he saw red. Ever afterward, he could never recall this incident without feeling anger. "I was stabbed in the back, and my dear wife's name was dragged into this mess. I'll never rest until I get even with them," he was later quoted as saying.[8] Whether or not he used precisely those words, this was certainly how he felt. In this mood he returned to the United States, an angry man, determined to go before the Keidan grand jury and at last tell all he knew about the bank crash.

There was no longer any reason anyway, he concluded, to hold back the facts. He needed certain documents to back up what he had learned—reports and letters in the possession of the Comptroller of the Currency. So, before going to Detroit, he made it a point to call on President Roosevelt to report personally on the London conference, and obtained from the President permission to have access to the Comptroller's records of the Detroit banks, including copies of confidential reports filed by various bank examiners.[9]

5

Couzens appeared as a witness before Judge Keidan on August 17, 1933. Up to then, the investigation had proved worthless as a fact-finding process. Even State Attorney General Patrick O'Brien, who had initiated the inquiry, had become disgusted. "We are getting nothing but speeches," he said. However, after Couzens had been on the stand for two days, the Attorney General changed his mind. "I am satisfied to go on," he said. "Now we are getting facts." [10]

The kind of material that Couzens now presented was illustrated by a report drawn up in May 1931 by the examining committee of the Guardian National Bank of Commerce. This report, written by officers of the bank itself, said:

The committee finds in the list of bad loans many loans that obviously have no other purpose than speculation on the stock market. The makers of these loans had only limited earnings and no prospects of the payment of the loan otherwise than the rise in stock prices. They were made to clerks, stenographers, bank officers, and bank clerks, salesmen and others whose incomes were not sufficient to warrant any substantial credit. . . .

The committee also finds in the list of bad loans, loans to officers in other banks which were clearly made to assist or further stock market operations. . . .

We find on the list of loans a substantial number of individuals who have been recommended by directors of the banks for such loans, loans to associates of directors in business, and loans to concerns in which the directors are interested or in which they were officers.[11]

If this document, and others of similar import, reflected fairly how the Detroit banks were being operated, what remained of charges that Couzens, Mrs. Couzens, or any other outsider—even the RFC, let alone "radicals"—had wrecked the banks?

6

But no one connected with the grand jury was happy over this kind of evidence. Prosecutor Toy, presumably intent upon getting the facts, proceeded to badger Couzens. The *Free Press* under Bingay carried articles to the effect that up to then the inquiry had been proceeding properly, but Couzens, by "casting a spell," because of his position in public life, had changed the course of the inquiry into undesirable paths. Editorials by Bingay in the *Free Press* chided the prosecutor for being "awed" by Couzens. Prosecutor Toy should break through the "spell" by getting tougher, the editorials said.[12]

Toy obviously sought to comply. He subjected Couzens to a good deal of harassment. However, it was plain that Couzens had transformed the hearing into a true fact-finding inquiry, not by any "spell," but through the force of facts.

Indeed, he furnished a classic example of the explosive nature of Truth in a controversy, of how it shatters the most carefully constructed alibis and melts through the layers of the most expertly contrived makeups.

7

At times, his anger betrayed him into a too-sweeping indictment of bankers in general. He included some individuals who apparently were blameless, notably certain directors of the First National Bank. This left him open to some equally anger-inspired counterblasts, such as one from James O. Murfin, a First National director, who said: "I can shorten this testimony by saying every time Jim Couzens mentioned my name, he lied!" [13]

Then, Longley returned to the stand to say "Couzens didn't know anything about the [Guardian] assets at the White House. He didn't know anything about them when he testified here. I don't think he knows anything about them now." [14] The press featured these blasts, and Couzens was placed on the defensive.

His recital of why the banks failed also suffered at times from disorganized presentation of his material. This was not wholly his fault, although his emotional tenseness tripped him up in this respect. To reconstruct properly the whole story, months, even years, would be needed. Moreover, all the facts—the minutes of the RFC for example—were not then open to him or anyone else. His presentation suffered too, because he still chose to play down the part played in the whole episode by the Fords. But these flaws and errors were really matters of minor detail. The fact was, as a result of his appearance in five sessions scattered through August and September, Detroit really began to see for the first time what had happened to its banks.

8

Yet, the effect of Couzens' presentation was not at all what should have been expected. Judge Keidan was strangely impatient with Couzens. Concerning Couzens' declarations that the banks were undoubtedly insolvent, the judge demanded to know how this could have been the case inasmuch as the federal government permitted the banks to continue to operate until the holiday.

Was it not the law that the Comptroller of the Currency must close insolvent banks?

As the Comptroller did not act, was that not sufficient evidence that the banks were in fact solvent?

Such questions had logic in them. But Couzens answered them with some amazing evidence. He produced documents to show that the Comptroller of the Currency, J. W. Pole, had adopted a policy of extraordinary leniency with the nation's banks. One such document read as follows:

October 6, 1931

A. P. Leyburn,
Chief National Bank Examiner,
164 West Jackson Boulevard, Chicago, Ill.

Please instruct all examiners to exercise extraordinary discretion in their work and to use every effort to encourage and sustain the morale in banks examined.

Leniency consistent with proper regard for public interest should be extended. Present conditions demand sympathetic treatment on the part of this office, and examiners can in important measure contribute to the alleviation of the difficult problems with which we are temporarily faced.

J. W. POLE, Comptroller.[15]

Couzens showed that later the Comptroller reiterated such instructions for "leniency." In the following December, all national bank examiners were instructed by Pole that in cases of greatly depreciated securities held by banks, the examiner "should discuss the situation with the directors and urge recourse to methods by which the bank may be strengthened, *but should make no mandatory demands.*" [16] In July 1932 the Comptroller had circularized all chief national bank examiners with a communication that criticized examiners for being too strict in their appraisals of securities.[17]

Couzens quoted a statement made in the Senate on May 1, 1933, by the "father of the federal reserve system," Senator Glass:

For the last 12 or 14 years there has been no espionage on the weak national banks. The comptroller of the currency admits that if he had enforced the law he would have closed half the national banks of the country. This means that the comptroller's office has not done its duty. It has allowed banks to engage in irregular and illicit practices. It has endangered the whole banking community. . . .[18]

Judge Keidan wanted to know why the federal government adopted such a policy. "On the theory," Couzens answered, "that prosperity was just around the corner. Public officials, from the President down, were holding out that hope to the people." [19]

He then made a point that later drew a vigorous protest from Hoover, who felt that it was a reflection upon his administration.[20] Couzens said:

"Your Honor must remember that there was a political campaign on and that there was undoubtedly a disposition on the part of the powers that be not to cause a bank collapse or bank difficulties while a political campaign was on." [21]

9

Of course there was another side to this picture. Strict enforcement of the banking laws would have hastened the closing of many more banks than were closed, and nobody could be sure that this was correct national policy. But Couzens' purpose was not to question the policy, rather to show what the banking situation had been.

In this, he not only received little cooperation from the judge, but more antagonism from County Prosecutor Toy. His statement that the political campaign influenced officials to be soft toward actually insolvent banks was hooted at, though he had merely anticipated the verdict of a well-known banking student, Professor Westerfield of Yale, who later wrote: "Most of the banks had portfolios choked with immobile and worthless loans and investments; banking supervisors had been restrained for political and other reasons from exacting obedience to bank law and had ceased to require banks to write off losses." [22]

A good deal of the material that Couzens presented was from so-called "yellow sheets." These were letters that bank examiners had sent to Washington as supplements to their regular reports. They were confidential letters, designed only for the eyes of the Comptroller—letters in which the examiners told exactly what they thought about the banks they had examined, in which they set down comments which, for reasons of policy, were not included in the regular reports.

Because of their nature, these "yellow sheets" often were more revealing than the official "white sheets," and especially so during the period of Pole's "leniency."

But because they were not "official," Prosecutor Toy, backed up by Judge Keidan, proceeded to develop the theory that they were unreliable. The prosecutor scoffed at them. Who had ever heard of the "yellow sheets," he asked, in effect. Why, no one had! This was precisely the point about them—that they were confidential. But to the prosecutor that vital point was enough to damn them as evidence.

Couzens asked that the bankers be recalled to the stand. They were. It was soon obvious that they were summoned not to be questioned on the records and the transactions he had mentioned, but to give them an opportunity to heap denunciation upon him. This they did in full measure. Indeed, the proceedings then became, rather than an investigation of the banks, a forum from which witness after witness assailed Couzens.

Even former Governor Groesbeck, Couzens' original sponsor for the Senate, now receiver for the Guardian Union Detroit Company, joined in the attack. So also did aging Judge Connolly, whom Couzens had defeated for mayor back in 1919, now receiver for the Detroit Bankers Company.[23] Once again, almost all that was heard in Judge Keidan's court was the refrain: "Couzens wrecked the banks!"

10

There was much cruelty in the way he was attacked, both in and out of the courtroom. Frederic L. Smith, who had become an admirer of Couzens since the days back in 1903 when Couzens had defied Smith's Selden patent association, wrote him that the easiest way to start a row in the Detroit Club to which both belonged, was for someone to make a remark in his defense. "I tried this," said Smith, "and ran the risk of being thrown out." [24]

How this group of Detroiters felt about him was made clear to Couzens in an experience of his own. On his going to his accustomed table for lunch at the Detroit Club, several of the men who had shared that table with him for years stiffly rose and carried their plates to another location.[25] Ever since he had joined the club many of the members had tolerated his general criticisms of the economic system by which they had become the industrial and financial leaders of Detroit. But now that he had become specific, and worse, had declared open war upon the most respected leaders of the city, the bankers and bank directors, they felt that he had put himself beyond the pale of polite society. Even for a "scab millionaire," he had gone too far, they decided.

This bitterness toward him was more intense than any he had generated during his entire previous career, greater than that caused by his fight for M.O., his attack on the Mellon tax plan, or his opposition to Warren for Attorney General. Not since the 1890's, when Mayor Hazen S. Pingree was expelled from his clubs and his church for advocating the reforms in municipal politics that Couzens was to carry out, had Detroit seen anything like it.

The whole atmosphere was distinctly that of a pack, snapping and snarling. The furor surpassed even the anger he had aroused back in 1914, when he had denounced the Board of Commerce members' labor policies, the incident that had evoked a description of him in the *Detroit Journal* as a "commercial Savonarola." This newspaper, now long out of existence, had said: "Society has an unpleasant way of crucifying those who tell it the truth one generation too soon. And woe to Couzens for his truth indulgences were he less strong in this community! For banks can crush and capital can ostracize." [26]

In the hot summer of 1933, those passages in the editorial printed in the long-ago winter of 1914 must have seemed highly prophetic to Couzens. He probably remembered them, for during the height of the storming, he once wryly remarked, "I'll be lucky not to be hanged in person, not merely in effigy." [27]

II

But Couzens was neither crushed nor silenced. Because he had not been able to present before Judge Keidan all of his material gleaned from the government documents and, concluding from the judge's attitude that he would not be permitted to do so, he attempted to proceed through direct action. He invited Prosecutor Toy and members of the prosecuting staff to come to his office in Birmingham. There he laid before them a mass of records, with the hope that they would make use of the material on their own. The prosecutors were strangely unprosecutorlike. They did nothing. Couzens then offered the material directly to the newspapers. The newspapers were decidedly cautious, perhaps for good reasons, in their view.

Indeed, almost the only result of this move was that, on September 14, he became involved in a furious argument with Malcolm Bingay when that journalist, instead of welcoming the material, proceeded to upbraid Couzens for "keeping up this endless argument and flinging of personalities." [28]

There was still Judge Keidan's court. It was only right that Couzens should have the opportunity to testify there again, especially in view of the assaults made upon him. So he made ready to present new material to the grand-jury investigation. Day and night, "and Sundays included," in his office in the Wabeek Building in Birmingham, he labored over the reports and figures. On September 15 he wrote to Judge Keidan that he had "considerable new evidence concerning the Guardian Detroit Union Group" and asked the judge to advise him when he might be permitted to testify again.[29]

Before his letter could reach the judge, Couzens heard incredible news—Judge Keidan planned to adjourn the inquiry immediately, without hearing him. He promptly telephoned the judge, who agreed to meet him the following morning at Frank Couzens' home. "Judge Keidan . . . argued against my again appearing on the witness stand for the reason that I might introduce new evidence, which would cause the bankers to again request a chance to be heard and further delay the conclusion of the grand jury," Couzens later related. Finally the judge grudgingly consented to let him testify once more, on a condition: Couzens was to confine himself to answering the attacks made on him. Under no circumstances, said the judge, was he to bring up anything new.[30]

With respect to influencing the findings of Judge Keidan, Couzens might well have saved himself that final three-hour exertion at the grand jury session. For as soon as Couzens finished, the judge ruled that the inquiry was over, and at once produced a previously prepared document setting forth his findings. This gave the bankers and the banks a clean bill of health.

12

Judge Keidan had enjoyed the reputation of being one of the most judicial of judges on the bench in Detroit and an honorable man. Couzens had esteemed him, at one time considered recommending him for a place in the federal judiciary. No breath of scandal or of venality of any kind had ever touched him. But it was clear from his conduct throughout the grand jury, and especially from his statement of findings, that Judge Keidan, for whatever reason, had no stomach for exposing any wrongdoing on the part of the bankers. He, at least, was no Savonarola.

The judge revealed clearly in his statement that his major concern was to have the grand jury create public pressure which would cause the federal government to come through quickly with money for paying off the depositors. He wrote: "In the final analysis, the public is interested in this help. Criminations and recriminations are futile." [31]

In short, Judge Keidan's view was to let sleeping dogs lie. The thing to do was to thaw out the frozen assets. He wanted no part of Couzens' program of getting the causes of the banking crisis presented to the public.

13

Couzens then took to the speaking platform. At a meeting of depositors at the Northwestern High School Auditorium in Detroit, he gave a fiery two-hour speech. "I am satisfied," he told this audience, "that a determined effort to get at all the transactions of the bank holding companies and their subsidiaries will convict somebody of a crime." [32] He was angry; no doubt about that.

However, he soon decided that such meetings would really get him nowhere. Obviously speeches were no weapons in the war that quickly opened up between him and Bingay of the *Free Press,* which then—this was before the *Free Press* came under a new and more objective management, that of the Knight Newspapers—was openly feuding with him. That he was at a disadvantage in this feud was brought home to Couzens when that newspaper devoted nearly three columns of its front page to an article which carried these headlines:

COUZENS ADMITS REVENGE
SPURS HIM ON IN ATTACK
UPON BANKS OF DETROIT

Says He Is Moved
By Personal Hate

Feels Safe Because
of Wealth and Office [33]

14

Malcolm Bingay had written the article on the basis of the argument that they had engaged in on September 14. It was printed, said the *Free Press,* because "the strange attitude of Senator Couzens requires explanation"; because "it is necessary now for the people of Detroit and Michigan who have for so many years honored James Couzens to know his mental attitude." As summed up by Bingay, there was nothing to Couzens' efforts to bring out the facts in the bank situation except hatred of the bankers and a desire for revenge. Bingay shored up his thesis by quoting utterances by Couzens made in the heat of their personal argument in Couzens' office in Birmingham.

After the heat of the bank controversy died down, it was plain what Bingay had done. He had goaded Couzens into a personal argument, knowing how easily Couzens lost his temper, and then had printed the result as if it were an "interview."

True, Couzens had asked for this treatment. He had flown off the handle with a newspaperman. His ingrained outspokenness and anger had betrayed him into making remarks he obviously would not have made had he believed he were being interviewed for publication. A calmer man would never have let himself get into such a position.

To friends, he pretended that he was not bothered by Bingay's article. Actually he was a good deal upset over it.[34] He promptly called off any further speaking engagements on the bank situation. He felt keenly that the public had been poisoned against him, that most Detroiters really believed that he had been responsible for wrecking the banks. He talked moodily with intimates about how his reward for twenty years and more of public service was that he had become an object of scorn. "I went through Hell," he told Tom Payne.[35]

15

Actually, it had been a mistake, from any angle, for him to participate in the Keidan grand jury investigation. As a Senator, he had at hand the most effective medium in the country for producing facts—a Senate investigation.

As early as the previous March, various persons had suggested that the Senate Committee on Banking and Currency, still probing into the New York Exchange and other financial institutions, might well turn its attention to the Detroit affair. In June, the City Council of Detroit adopted a resolution asking that the Senate committee "come to Detroit and conduct a thorough and public investigation." [36]

As a member of that committee, Couzens was not then convinced that the Detroit situation warranted a full-dress Senate inquiry, especially as new banking legislation already had been adopted, presumably for making impossible a repetition of the Detroit bank organizational defects.[37]

However, after the Keidan investigation fiasco, he changed his mind. Besides, his spirits were now considerably elevated, in consequence of a special mayoral election held in Detroit at just this time that resulted in Frank Couzens' being elected mayor by a handsome majority.

"I guess that shows that I haven't ruined the family reputation after all!" Couzens exclaimed.

He was ready to fight again.

When he returned to Washington on October 1, he discussed with Pecora, still counsel to the Senate Banking and Currency Committee, the possibilities of a fruitful inquiry by that committee into the Detroit banking mess.[38] Soon after, the full committee, of which Senator Duncan U. Fletcher of Florida was chairman, voted to conduct such an inquiry.

This Senate investigation of the Detroit banks, which began in Washington on December 19, 1933, was decidedly different from the Keidan grand jury investigation. It laid bare in minutest detail the full story of the Michigan bank holiday, its causes and its aftermath. Almost everyone who had anything to do with the banks and the holiday was called to testify and subjected to searching examination by the expert cross-examiner, Pecora. Edsel Ford was called, though not Henry Ford, and from Edsel the role of the Fords was brought out clearly.

There were no "speeches" at this investigation, and no hearsay. Only facts. The facts filled 1,647 closely printed pages in the four volumes published by the Senate.[39]

A study of those volumes leaves no doubt as to where the fault lay for the holiday, nor for the conditions which led up to it. The bankers themselves had wrecked their banks, albeit, the final Senate report in words approved by Couzens, rather obliquely put it: "Nor can the failure of these companies be attributed *solely* to the constituency, competency, or honesty of the persons controlling these institutions.[40]

True, some of the truly shocking actions laid bare had been forced on them by the depression and represented desperate efforts to prevent the crash. But careful and honest banking, rather than recklessness and speculation and worse, obviously would have avoided the full extent of the crash. Moreover, it was unquestionably established that Couzens had nothing to do with the refusal of the RFC assistance asked for in the beginning, nor even with the scaling down of the ultimate loan granted.

If any one person had forced the bank holiday, this person was, not Couzens, but Henry Ford.

All this was placed on the record.[41] That record constitutes more than a defense of the accusations against Couzens; it is a detailed description of the Michigan banking "magic" which turned out to be, not magic, but financial buccaneering on a scale beyond ordinary comprehension.

Studied efforts were made to discredit this Senate investigation. It was dubbed solely a "Couzens affair." [42] The truth was precisely the opposite, as even a cursory examination of the record shows. But angry men will say many things; Couzens did, and so did those who opposed him for one reason or another.

16

The Senate investigation came to an end exactly on the anniversary of the White House conference on the bank crisis. "We concluded our Detroit bank hearings at five o'clock tonight, and, I feel, with a blaze of glory, because today's testimony was quite corroborative of my position," Couzens wrote to Tom Payne.[43]

He did not exaggerate. On that day the committee had heard Ballantine, Leyburn, and Awalt. Their combined testimony underlined emphatically what was plain to anyone who bothered to follow the hearing—that the bankers themselves, by the type of banking they had developed, had been at fault. There could be no doubt of that.

Frederic L. Smith, who, like Couzens, had lived through the panics of 1893, 1907, and 1921–1922, and had observed such Congressional investigations as the Pujo inquiry into the "money trust," wrote to Couzens: "Your investigations have been more truly constructive, timely, and, I believe, ultimately 'curative' than those of any government-run investigations since I began to take notice. . . . They have opened the eyes of the man on the street."

Couzens answered that, while he was "distressed" over the disclosures as to how the banks were operated, he was satisfied "they had to be made in the public interest. . . . What I wanted was for the Senate and the country to know." [44] This he had accomplished.

He had shown, among other things, that so far from having been "responsible" for the closing of the Detroit banks, he had tried to do more than almost anyone else to keep them open, having gone to the length of offering a good slice of his personal fortune to save the situation, even though he had no stock in any of the banks and very little other personal financial interest. He had shown, too, that his objections to an "immoral" RFC loan were not at all a factor in the crisis—that no one else in the government approved the original loan requested after the facts were known. His statement about "shouting from the rooftops" was not at all a "cause" of the crisis. It had been torn out of context and used to misrepresent his position, also to make of him the scapegoat for the crisis brought about by others.

He had shown that the Detroit crisis was not something that had developed suddenly, but was long in the making, in large part because of "general conditions" and some unwise mergers, and also because of unsound and in some cases immoral as well as illegal banking practices. He had established also that whereas the Fords were involved in the crisis, his own relationship with the Fords, friendlier then than at other periods, was not a factor. Above all, he had shown that had the bankers as a class followed the safe, sane, and strictly ethical principles which he himself, when a banker, had epitomized, the situation might not have developed, certainly not so critically. Having established a record showing all this, he had good reason to be satisfied with the verdict of history.

17

On August 1, 1934, largely in consequence of the revelations at the Senate investigation, the Department of Justice obtained federal grand jury indictments against twenty-eight of the leading bankers in both groups on charges of technical violations of the federal banking laws.[45] Complicated cases brought some complicated results. In 1935 three bankers in the First National group were acquitted. But in 1936 three others of the same group were found guilty and fined, though the verdict in the case of one was later set aside. In 1937 all of the cases were dismissed after still another trio entered pleas of *nolo contendere* and were fined $1,000 each.[46]

One banker did get a prison sentence on criminal-count conviction in a state court. This was Wilkin, the witness who had brought Mrs. Couzens' name into the controversy before Judge Keidan. He was held responsible for "window-dressing" of the Union Industrial Bank of Flint, a unit of the Guardian Group.[47]

As for Couzens, after the Senate investigation was over, he was content to let the bank matter pass into history. His principal interest after this was in the further unfolding of Roosevelt's New Deal. And to this he devoted himself with much of his old-time zeal.

CHAPTER XLII

THE NEW DEAL REPUBLICAN

By THEN, in 1934, Roosevelt's honeymoon was over. As the banks stayed open and business indices rose, as everyone began to feel better about the state of the nation, the earlier fear disappeared. Then many stand-patters turned on the new President and there occurred, with Couzens playing a part, increasingly bitter debate over the policies of the new administration.

In August 1934, on the occasion of his sixty-second birthday, Couzens was interviewed by the North American Newspaper Alliance. He took the occasion to rebuke those who, without offering an alternative, criticized the New Deal, saying: "This is not the time for mere words. The country is in the fifth year of depression, and action, rather than words, is needed." [1]

In the following November, he told the Detroit Optimist Club:

> The thing to do is for everyone to show a continued faith in President Roosevelt's policies. . . . There is no light in the future of America unless we get away from the idea of "rugged individualism" which means, I believe, that a few can become wealthy at the expense of the many. . . .[2]

No one was more disgusted than he with the propaganda line of New Deal opponents which pictured certain Roosevelt advisers, notably Professor Rexford G. Tugwell, then of Columbia University, later of the University of Chicago, as "communists" bent on undermining the nation.[3] He told Madeleine: "Most of these yarns about communism, dictatorship, etc. are smoke screens, or evidence of fear that someone's money may be lost." [4] When one of his constituents in Detroit wrote him to urge that he try to get rid of Tugwell before America was "sovietized," Couzens answered:

> "I am unwilling to sit by and see millions of our people in distress because they are unable to secure work, and if that is what Professor Tugwell is driving at, then I am for it." [5]

2

By no means, however, was he always on Roosevelt's side.

He was still Couzens, still the individualist who stubbornly hoed his own row; still the natural critic. Hence, he often let loose blasts at the Roosevelt administration as trenchant and resounding as any set off by the "Stop Roosevelt" bloc then active. A case in point occurred when Secretary Woodin, because of illness, resigned from the Treasury, and Henry Morgenthau, Jr., was named his successor. Couzens did not object to Morgenthau; rather, he approved.[6] But he did object to Morgenthau's plan to retain in the Treasury department as a principal assistant Earl Baillie, member of J. & W. Seligman & Company. In Couzens' view, this was "another Acheson type of appointment." Baillie's banking firm was one of those involved in the foreign-loan scandals unearthed by the Senate Finance Committee. Indeed, it was the very firm that had floated the discredited Peruvian loan of unpleasant memory. Couzens let it be known that unless Baillie went, he would conduct a fight against the confirmation of Morgenthau. He "laid down the law," and Baillie resigned.[7]

3

Certain New Deal projects went wholly against Couzens' grain. The public housing program was one. As did the remaining stalwart Republicans and conservative Democrats, including a new and inconspicuous senator from Missouri, Harry S. Truman, he voted against the bill establishing the United States Housing Authority.[8] His general opposition to public housing was that it represented a subsidy to employers. "I never quite understood the theory of some people," he wrote, "that the taxpayers should supply houses for certain low income wage workers to enable private employers to get these workers at low wages." [9] His attitude seemed an about-face from his own stand as Mayor of Detroit, when he proposed a municipal bond issue to build homes because of the wartime housing shortage. But he viewed his proposal as different from the New Deal program of raising the standards of homes that existed.

As in the days when he suggested the five-dollar-a-day plan at the Ford Company, he held to the view that it was up to the industry to pay wages high enough so that workers could arrange for their own housing. Or, he maintained, let employers pay the whole bill in higher corporation taxes, rather than assess the cost to the general taxpayer.[10]

One phase of New Deal housing, the subsistence homestead projects, had his sympathy for these represented fruition of an idea that he and Ford had toyed with back in the days of the five-dollar plan. The concept was that factory workers would also be small farmers. Couzens was glad to see the New Deal experiment in that direction. But here he felt that the approach was wrong, in that the first such projects were located in areas that lacked factories, notably the so-called Red House project in West Virginia.

With Roosevelt, and also with Harry Hopkins, relief administrator, Couzens carried on an extended argument over this. It was foolish, he told them, "to go out in a field and build some houses under the assumption that eventually some industry would come in. . . . He felt that it was far more sensible to build the houses somewhere adjacent to where industries already were established." The New Dealers, he said, were "cockeyed" in their approach.[11]

Curiously enough, as a result of this discussion, he found himself sponsoring a housing project, even though he was opposed to the general idea.

"How much did the Red House project cost?" he asked Hopkins.

Hopkins guessed that the cost was $550,000.

"All right," said Couzens. "I'll put up $550,000 for a project to show that I am right. But if the Red House project cost more, and I think it did, you put up the balance." [12]

The Red House project cost $850,000. So the arrangement was made for Couzens to donate $550,000 to the State of Michigan, to which the federal government added $300,000, and there was born the non-profit "Oakland Housing, Inc.," for building West Acres, a community of 150 six-room homes located on a 1,000-acre tract nine miles west of Pontiac, in close proximity to the automobile industry.[13] There, low-income families who were subject to the seasonal unemployment then characteristic of the automobile industry, were permitted to acquire on easy terms homes on sufficient land to enable them to fill in their income through raising garden products.

But he was sorry that he had made this housing gift almost as soon as he had made it. His doubts about it were clearly revealed in the announcement that was made to the public.

This project is not economically sound if there is any fundamental soundness in our capitalistic system. It is merely a bridge. . . . Our fundamental job is to readjust national income, wages, and working conditions so as to provide more of these men with a living income. . . .[14]

4

This ambivalence, well-founded, regarding West Acres really reflected his basic attitude toward the way the New Deal was being administered. Roosevelt himself admitted that he often considered himself "a quarterback" who followed one line and then another, depending on how the game was going.[15] Couzens noted this, was disturbed, and complained. He frankly told Roosevelt that good laws were being ruined by "abominable administration." In one such talk with Roosevelt he said, "Do you know what's wrong with your administration? You haven't anyone in it who ever earned a dollar. That's what's wrong!" [16]

To Dr. Freund he wrote: "While I have a very definite conviction that where the President wants to go is right, I am not always sure that he is on the right road and neither can anyone else be." [17]

In the following spring he complained to a friend in London: "Things are in a terrible turmoil, and I haven't the slightest idea where the New Deal is going. . . ." [18]

Yet it was always apparent that his criticisms of the New Deal were those of a friend who wanted a new program to succeed. Often the fault he found with the New Deal was that it was not liberal enough.

5

In April 1934 he drew upon himself much of the abuse generally reserved for Roosevelt, when he initiated an amendment to an appropriation bill for increasing surtaxes on large incomes by a flat 10 per cent as the most equitable way to pay the cost of unemployment relief.

It was his old fight on Mellonism over again.

In San Simeon, California, Publisher Hearst was enraged by Couzens' tax plan. The Hearst papers soon campaigned against it in 120-point type. Hearst was especially bitter, it appeared, because Hiram Johnson had endorsed Couzens' amendment, thus, for once in this period, taking a non-Hearstian stand.

"Hearst called his editors in a violent wrath in the dead of night and ordered them to crucify Johnson and Couzens with him. . . . Hearst screamed: 'That man Couzens has all the money he wants and now he's trying to feather his political nest by appearing to help the people. We'll have to throw Couzens out. His money has turned Johnson's head!' " So one Hearst editor recalled.[19]

B. C. Forbes, in earlier years author of several articles friendly toward Couzens, sent nationwide a bitter attack on Couzens. "The foremost 'Soak the Rich' advocate in America is a rich man, a very rich man, a multi-millionaire," wrote Forbes. "This extremely wealthy soaker of the rich has placed himself largely beyond the reach of the kind of soaking he vehemently urges for others, for his fortune is in tax-exempt bonds." Not patriotism but demagoguery motivated Couzens, Forbes said.[20]

In the Senate, although not in the House, Couzens obtained passage of his proposal.[21] Then he delivered an attack on Hearst, referring to him scornfully as a "yellow journalist." [22] Hearst stood for "soaking the poor," he said. He sarcastically noted that Hearst had finally changed his slogan against his plan from "Soaking the Rich" to "Soaking the Thrifty" because "somebody must have tipped him off to the absurdity of the 'soak the rich' slogan, as there isn't anybody else to soak." He reminded the Senate that Hearst was the foremost supporter of a general sales tax. "I compliment the American Congress," he said, "for never having fallen for the stupid and unscrupulous general sales tax, in spite of the years and years of propaganda for it by Mr. Hearst." [23]

His main purpose in answering the Hearst attacks, he said, was to comment on a more important and dangerous propaganda line then prominent in Hearst editorials. This was that England, then under a Tory government, had staged a greater recovery from the depression than had the United States, by balancing her budget and planning to lower taxes. If England had indeed balanced her budget, went on Couzens, she had done so by postponing payment of her debt to the United States.

"We could balance our budget and reduce our income taxes if we repudiated all of the money we borrowed from our citizens to loan to Great Britain and other countries." [24]

6

Not long after that he again rubbed persons of wealth the wrong way when, as in the Mellon days, he plumped for publicity on income tax payments, holding that "secrecy . . . breeds favoritism, corruption, dishonesty, graft and maladministration." As he wrote to an editor of the *Detroit News:* "If the income tax returns had been matters of public record, Congress long ago would have discovered the means of evasion adopted by the Morgans, Mitchells, and others to avoid all taxation for the years 1930 and on. . . ." [25]

He conceded that one argument against the publicity proposal was valid: gossip would be encouraged. But, he declared, "there are many things in a democratic society which have to be done to maintain our country." [26]

In this battle, one that stirred up a great heat, much abuse was directed at Couzens. Bingay devoted a column to the old charge that Couzens wanted to embarrass other rich men, whereas "Jim has $60,000,000 in tax exempt bonds." [27] A few weeks later, the *Chicago Tribune* published a long magazine-section article under the headings:

'SWAT THE RICH' IS COUZENS' CRY
$30,000,000 SENATOR HAS TAX-FREE FORTUNE [28]

However, the real complaint against Couzens by staunch Republican organs was more fundamental than mere outrage over his views on taxation. He was now looked upon, with Norris, young La Follette, and Hiram Johnson, as a real threat to the continued existence of the Republican party. His evident friendliness toward the New Deal was interpreted as playing into the hands of a Rooseveltian scheme to bring about a new political alignment in the United States, by which the old parties would give way to a Liberal and a Conservative party. The inclusion in Roosevelt's cabinet of two Republicans, Henry A. Wallace and Harold L. Ickes, was seen as one step in this direction. Another would be the winning permanently of the allegiance of the old Republican insurgents.

So Couzens was now anathematized in the conservative Republican papers as a "New Deal Republican" or, worse, a "Roosevelt New Dealer," who had turned traitor to his own party and class. "Party wheelhorses are taking the position that anything that could be done to discredit Couzens would be to the Republican advantage," Jay Hayden wrote.[29]

7

But Couzens did not at all resent the New Deal label. More than ever, he was convinced that not just recovery, but a new deal in fact, was needed in America. It would be stupid, he felt, to go back to the old order, and thus merely assure a repetition of the Great Depression. Until a better new deal was produced, he would support Roosevelt's, regardless of partisan considerations.

Temperamentally, this decision meant disciplining his trait of independence. It would have been easier on his emotions to let this trait now take him along the path followed, for example, by Senator Borah. For by 1935 Borah, once denounced as a dangerous radical, had become, strangely, a hero of the conservative Republicans. He had decided that the whole New Deal was "unconstitutional," its tax program, in particular, a "spread the poverty" scheme that would lead to "dictatorship." [30] In effect, Borah had committed insurgency against himself. With him on his circuitous route, Borah took along an oldtime admirer, Vandenberg. For a time Vandenberg had surprised Couzens, and, perhaps, even himself, by standing for certain New Deal proposals and even going further than Roosevelt wished, as in sponsorship of federal insurance of bank deposits. Now, like Borah, Vandenberg was declaiming against the New Deal as a threat to American institutions. His slogan was: "Roosevelt must be stopped." [31]

To Couzens, Borah's position was illogical—opposition to the New Deal for mere opposition's sake, something of which he himself had been often accused. If Borah were motivated by a desire to preserve the old party labels—perhaps to get the Presidency in 1936— Couzens was even less sympathetic. During the crisis, he was for postponing all partisan activity. Thus in December 1934 he turned down an invitation to participate in a conference of Republican leaders, even when the meeting was ostensibly to be held for the purpose of reorganizing the Republican party along liberal lines.[32]

A few months later, he still held to this position even to the extent of creating a new breach between himself and the Republican leadership in Michigan. Howard C. Lawrence, state chairman, had asked him to send a message to the regular Republican state convention, scheduled to be held in Lansing in March 1935. A mere greeting would have served. Couzens declined even this. He bluntly informed the state chairman that he did not believe a political convention should be held at that time, in view of the critical problems which the nation faced. It was "inopportune" to discuss "partisan politics" in such a crisis, he said.[33] Of course, the party leaders were offended, retaliating at the convention by passing a resolution praising Senator Vandenberg but pointedly ignoring Couzens. It was 1924 all over again.[34] It was also a forecast that if Couzens were forced to choose between Republicanism and Roosevelt, Roosevelt probably would win.

CHAPTER XLIII

THE UNBOWED HEAD

THAT spring Roosevelt sent to Congress a request for an emergency public-works program to cost $4,800,000,000. It was a measure, one which made possible not only big public works, but also the WPA projects of "made work," the National Youth Administration, and other agencies to supply jobs for the unemployed, that sent the conservative opposition into a kind of frenzy. Such an expenditure, though only a fraction of the size of federal appropriations some of them lived to see and even approve, would "wreck the nation," they declared.

Vandenberg, now often mentioned as a Republican candidate for President in 1936, took this line, and delivered a lengthy oration in the Senate on the theme that so vast a project must lead first to bankruptcy, then to a dictatorship.

Couzens naturally favored the public-works program. It had been his own idea also. Yet he also took part in this furious debate as critic, as well as defender, of Roosevelt. He agreed with Vandenberg that the bill, as originally drafted, gave too much power to the President in determining what projects were to be undertaken.[1] His most vigorous objection, however, was not at all a conservative one. It was against a provision that workers on the projects were to be paid a so-called "security wage," averaging about fifty dollars a month, or less than half of the prevailing rates. He told the Senate:

"The industry that supplies the lumber has no limitations on its prices at all, but the most defenseless group of our citizens is told, 'You will take what you are given and you will perform a day's work for half what any other citizen gets for performing the same work.' " [2]

This, he insisted, was unjust and ought not to be tolerated by the New Deal, not for economy reasons, not even to placate Southern leaders, who feared high wage scales for Negroes. When an amendment was adopted which met Couzens' objections to the "security wage," he quite happily voted for the bill.[3] He did not think much of Vandenberg's fears that a $4,800,000,000 outlay to put men to work could "bankrupt America."

2

Up to then, Roosevelt's program in the main had concentrated on relief and recovery. Now the New Deal moved more in the direction of reform, with the Social Security Bill, the Wagner Labor Relations Act, the Public Utility Holding Company Act, and the first major New Deal tax program imposing higher income tax rates as well as greatly increased levies on inheritances and gifts.[4] Couzens favored all of these proposals, especially the tax program.[5] In a sense this was his real victory at last in the battle he had waged for progressive principles on taxation when Mellon was in office.

Even before this, it was obvious that he was almost always in Roosevelt's camp when the chips were down, more so, in fact, than many members of Roosevelt's own party. He stood with Roosevelt for adherence to the World Court, in face of an unprecedented barrage of letters in opposition generated by Father Coughlin and the Hearst papers, thousands of which descended upon him from Michigan.[6]

He likewise stood with Roosevelt against the Patman Bill for immediate payment of the soldiers' bonus, which Roosevelt vetoed. He was bitterly denounced as a "turncoat" by veterans' groups for that vote, for he had been a bonus advocate during the Coolidge and Hoover regimes, and he had opposed Roosevelt's veterans' cuts in March 1933. But he now agreed with Roosevelt that, with all the relief provided by the New Deal, the war veterans did not need special treatment.[7]

3

Two other measures with wide popular support, the Townsend Old Age Plan, and the McLeod Bill for having the federal government make a payment of 50 per cent to all depositors in closed banks, likewise found him standing with the administration, whereas there were wide defections from Roosevelt within his own party on these issues. For Couzens, like Roosevelt, opposed these popular measures.

Even Borah, then the "constitutionalist," supported the McLeod

Bill, which the Hearst press advocated. It was a popular measure, especially in Couzens' home state, with all its closed banks.

Among thousands of others, Couzens' own brother, Homer, urged that he support it. "For the love of Mike," begged Homer, "get behind the McLeod Bill . . . so I can pay off on our new home." [8] But Couzens told Homer what he wrote to others. The McLeod Bill was "stupid." For the government to pay off closed bank depositors out of government funds perhaps looked like relief to the average citizen, but actually meant pouring billions into the coffers of a few corporations and wealthy persons, who owned the bulk of bank deposits in closed or open banks. He told the Senate that "anyone so lacking in judgment as to endorse the so-called McLeod Bill is not entitled, in my judgment, to vote on the floor of the Senate." [9] In particular, he meant Borah, now in his view a fallen idol of progressivism and independence.[10]

4

However, the big fight was on Roosevelt's reform measures. Against these the Republican Old Guard, conservative Democrats, Borah, Vandenberg, the Hearst press, and a newly formed, supposedly nonpartisan, American Liberty League (of which Alfred E. Smith, John W. Davis, and John J. Raskob were leaders) began a tremendous campaign on the theme that the New Deal was intent on tearing down "the American system."

Of this American Liberty League, Couzens was scornful. It might have been nonpartisan, he said in an interview, but this was only true with regard to the formal political affiliations of the members. The leaders were all rich men, Democratic as well as Republican, so there was no question in his mind that they represented "the same convictions." The nonpartisan claim was "humorous" to him, he said.[11]

When the great debate opened, the tension heightened by Supreme Court decisions that held invalid certain portions of the NRA and the Agricultural Adjustment Act, Couzens prepared to participate prominently.

In particular, he planned to defend the Roosevelt tax program against the attacks on it by Hearst, Borah, and Vandenberg.[12] Roosevelt supporters were delighted with the prospect of his aid, for his status as a multimillionaire defending the New Deal seemed in itself a refutation of the charge that the New Deal was a "communistic plot." This debate had only begun, when, just as had happened to him in 1924, at the crisis of his Mellon fight, he had to leave the arena because of a new siege of illness.

5

"I am tired. . . . I am tired. . . ." For some months there had appeared in his letters to friends and family this warning phrase. In March 1935 he told Madeleine that his "very conflictual" mail from constituents had become enormous, and that keeping up with it was wearing on him.[13] His sister, Rosetta, suggested that he take at least a year off. But he could not see himself doing that. "When I am unoccupied, I have a great deal of mental distress," he said.[14]

So he continued to drive himself, although obviously suffering from acute fatigue. He began to lose weight noticeably. He complained of a peculiar numbness. Dr. Freund came from Detroit to see him, and arranged immediately for a medical conference with several Washington doctors. The discovery was made that he was a victim of diabetes. He was ordered to be hospitalized at once, not in Washington, but at Harper Hospital in Detroit.

"What the Senator needs is a good long rest," Dr. Freund said in a public announcement.[15] Actually, Dr. Freund knew that his patient needed that and a good deal more.

When he had been at Harper for ten days, there came worse news. The old bladder condition had become acute again,[16] so acute that it was decided to rush him to the Mayo Clinic at Rochester, Minnesota. At Rochester he underwent two major operations, and remained there for seventy-eight days.

6

For weeks he was a man in torture. The pain that he suffered was monumental. Once he exclaimed to Dr. Freund, "I've given twelve million dollars for the Children's Fund. I'd give another twelve million dollars if you could find a way to end pain!" [17]

Yet by November 1935 he was well enough, he thought, to go with Mrs. Couzens to Phoenix, Arizona. His stay there, at the beautiful Arizona Biltmore, did not turn out nearly so well as he had expected. For one thing, on top of all else, he now developed sinus trouble. Spells of pain returned. He suffered from a peculiar weakness which showed up in all his movements. On November 11, 1935, he wrote to his friend, Senator McNary, in a shaky script:

"My legs seem to be in about as desperate a condition as the Republican party; they wobble like Hell. This is the most unsatisfactory period I have ever had to go through."

What added to his physical distress was the old protest against inactivity. "Just sitting around" a hotel depressed him. In December, he wrote to Madeleine, "I think I am about through with active business and work." [18] Soon, however, he began talking about cutting short his stay at the winter resort to return to the Senate.

His doctors argued against this, but on December 15 he and Mrs. Couzens were on a special train, Washington-bound. And when the Seventy-fifth Congress convened, January 3, 1936, he was there, applauding Roosevelt's State of the Union message in which the President, concerning the New Deal, declared: "I recommend to the Congress that we advance; that we do not retreat." [19]

Just hearing Roosevelt again was a tonic for Couzens. He was glad he had defied his doctors and returned to work. To his colleagues, he insisted that he felt "just fine," though he didn't. But he stayed on the job, wracked but unbowed by the massive pain that so often attacked him. Jay Hayden once found him writhing on the desk of his office in the Senate Office Building because of pain—because he refused to call a doctor, which, in his view, would have been a sign of giving up.[20]

CHAPTER XLIV

THE POLITICAL DILEMMA

HE WAS never to feel really "fine" again. The incisions were slow in healing. He had to have injections of insulin. The attacks of terrible pain recurred. He was disappointed and depressed over his physical condition, he wrote to John C. Manning, nephew of Mrs. Couzens. But for the most part, his mood was to rise above his physical distress and carry on.

He certainly demonstrated very early in the new Congress that he still had plenty of fight left in him. For he took the lead in opposing, as did Roosevelt, a new soldiers' bonus bill. When Roosevelt vetoed the "new veterans grab," as it was called, Couzens was among only nineteen senators to vote to sustain the veto.[1]

To Madeleine's husband, William R. Yaw, of whom he had become very fond, he commented: "By this time you will have seen how much in the minority I was when I voted against the payment now of the adjusted compensation certificates for veterans. That vote undoubtedly will lose me votes. However, I do not suppose I will ever have the courage to quit and so it may be to my own interest to be defeated. Whatever happens will satisfy me."[2]

2

Then, in February 1936, he conducted a vigorous one-man campaign against what seemed to him to be an especially flagrant abuse of patronage power by the administration. His target was Walter C. Cummings, a Des Moines and Chicago streetcar manufacturer, who had been introduced into the administration as Assistant Secretary of the Treasury by Woodin.

Couzens pointed out to the Senate that Cummings received some unusual patronage plums, unusual in salary and in number. Cummings was installed, through the RFC, as chairman of the huge Continental Illinois National Bank and Trust Company of Chicago, at a salary of $75,000, as trustee of the Chicago, Milwaukee, St. Paul and Pacific Railroad, at another salary of $15,000, and, also through the RFC, as board member of a large insurance company, the Maryland Casualty Company. Undoubtedly, Cummings was an exceptionally able man, and Couzens did not deny this, nor did he question his integrity.

But what compounded the case, in Couzens' view, was that Cummings was then also the treasurer of the Democratic National Committee. He denounced what he described as "the possibility of interlocking directorates, political appointments, the tying in of politics with business and the tying in of railroads with bankers, and so on down the line," all apparently personified in Cummings.[3] Not long after this, Cummings resigned as treasurer of the national committee, though he still headed the big Chicago bank.

3

This episode, which, the *Chicago Tribune* said, "gave Democratic party leaders the jitters,"[4] did not mean that he had by any means deserted Roosevelt. It merely meant that, as before, he reserved the right to criticize the Roosevelt administration, even while supporting it. On this point, referring to the position Cummings was in, to solicit, if he desired, campaign contributions from corporations with which he did business in his various financial posts, Couzens told the Senate:

"I happen to know that during the Republican administrations . . . millions of dollars [in campaign funds] were collected from parties who had income tax claims pending before the bureau of internal revenue. So my complaint now is in no sense political or partisan. It involves a question which I have vigorously fought here for some thirteen or fourteen years, and I intend to continue to find fault, regardless of what administration may be in power."[5]

4

As 1936 wore on, his affinity for the New Deal caused considerable concern to certain of his political well-wishers. That was the year he was up for re-election, if he wished to remain in the Senate. They worried especially over the problem of how he could expect to win a Republican nomination, in a Republican primary, if he stuck by his New Dealism with no organization of his own.

He had become quite friendly with George Averill, editor of *The Eccentric,* the local newspaper in Birmingham, Michigan. Averill sketched quite early to him a plan to solve his dilemma. He suggested that Couzens adopt the view that while he supported the Roosevelt program "in principle," he had decided that the Republican party could do a better job and therefore Roosevelt ought to be defeated in 1936. If he adopted that position, said Averill, he could be re-elected easily.[6]

Essentially, this was how Vandenberg had won his re-election in 1934. Couzens rejected such advice offhand. His record of supporting Roosevelt, as well as Roosevelt's principles, was made, and he could not repudiate it. He would not "stultify" himself, he told John Manning.[7]

5

The primary was the critical hurdle. In the general election itself, he could expect, as before, the support of voters of all parties, including especially the followers of Roosevelt. Not so in the primary. Roosevelt's very popularity had set up an additional obstacle to Couzens there. He saw this new situation clearly:

> Until 1932 there was practically no Democratic party in Michigan and so nearly everybody (in the primary) went in and asked for a Republican ballot, and in that case my sledding was easy. Now, however, they have a Democratic party in Michigan and all of the Democrats and Roosevelt supporters will undoubtedly go in and ask for a Democratic ballot. My name will not be on that ballot and so I will not be able to get their vote.[8]

This meant that, in the Republican primary, his candidacy more than ever would be at the mercy of the organization politicians of the Republican party.

There was not much doubt but that those elements, as before, would be against him. Already they were lining up behind young Wilbur J. Brucker, who had been governor and who in 1955 was to be Secretary of the Army in the Eisenhower administration, as the candidate in place of Couzens. At the state Republican convention in March 1935, at which Couzens had been snubbed, Brucker, then an Old Guard type of lawyer with a flair for oratory, was ostentatiously idolized along with Vandenberg. It was plain that Brucker would be run against Couzens, with the support of the whole Republican organization of the state.

In 1924, Couzens had overcome with ease the opposition of the organization Republicans. But 1936, obviously, would not be 1924.

As he himself said, "I am not under-rating the many enemies I have accumulated during the past five years. When you frankly oppose the payment of the soldiers' bonus, the Townsend Old Age Pension Plan and other crazy schemes (like the McLeod Bill), you obviously collect a bunch of enemies, in addition to those I have accumulated through the misrepresentation about the bank closing." [9]

6

Back in February 1935, former Mayor Frank Murphy, then Governor-General of the Philippines, later Governor of Michigan and named by Roosevelt to the Supreme Court, had a conversation with John Manning which pointed to an interesting solution of Couzens' problem. Couzens should change parties, Murphy said, and seek the Democratic nomination for senator.

Coming from Murphy, then emerging as the leading Democrat of the state, this suggestion was by no means mere conversation, especially as Murphy then was preparing to run for governor on the Democratic ticket in 1936. If Couzens would agree to seek the Democratic nomination, said Murphy, the Democratic organization would not put up a candidate against him.

"I know I can manage it," Murphy told Manning. "Connolly and some of the Old Guard Democrats would fume, but they are done; their power is gone." [10]

Murphy told Manning that this idea came to him after a group of wealthy Detroiters had approached him with the offer of backing him for senator against Couzens. As related to Couzens by Manning:

"Three friends of Ed Stair actually met Murphy in Honolulu and tried to sell him. . . . Murphy asked why they were approaching him—a Democrat and fully as radical as you—instead of grooming one of their conservative Republicans. . . . He considered it an . . . illustration of the extent of their hatred for you, that in their desperation they would go to a man like him to run against you." [11]

Murphy declined the suggestion. "Senator Couzens stands for the same things in government that I do. He is for the people. He is head and shoulders above every other man in the Senate in integrity and independence and unswerving devotion to the interests of the great mass of people. We need men like him in our government. His way should be made smooth rather than hampered." [12]

Murphy later added to this: "They offered me a half million dollars for a campaign fund. They considered Couzens a traitor to his class. They wanted to beat him, desperately." [13]

In Washington a few days after his talk with Manning, Murphy called on Couzens himself and made the same suggestion to him directly, that Couzens seek the Democratic nomination.[14] "Your position in the Republican party is untenable," he said. "You never have voted with the Republicans. You belong in the Democratic party. You can't win as a Republican. You can win as a Democrat." [15]

Couzens protested on this occasion that he had "started as a Republican and wanted to stay a Republican." [16] But he did not close the door tight against Murphy's suggestion. There was yet time to decide, he said.

Could he do as Henry Ford had done in 1918, and run as both Republican and Democrat? Hiram Johnson had done that in California, and had run on a third-party ticket to boot.

He asked Senator Vandenberg to obtain a formal opinion from Harry S. Toy, by then the Attorney General of Michigan, on this point. Toy's opinion was that it was legal to be a candidate on both tickets, but that in the general election he would have to designate himself as either a Democrat or Republican. This meant that if he entered both primaries and won only in the Democratic primary, he would have to call himself a Democrat.[17] He shied from that, and postponed a definite decision.

7

In November 1935 still another overture from the Democrats was made to Couzens. G. Hall Roosevelt of Detroit, brother of Mrs. Franklin D. Roosevelt and a close political associate of Frank Murphy, called on Frank Couzens. He told Frank that the Democratic party in the state "might" endorse Senator Couzens for reelection, but wanted to be certain beforehand that the Senator would not "slap back at them." [18] He asked Frank to sound out his father in secret. Couzens' response to Frank was:

"I think I told you that numerous prominent Democrats had talked to me along the same lines . . . but on each occasion I was silent or at least noncommittal. I would not, under any circumstances, make any private arrangements with anybody. Whatever I do with respect to my campaign, will be done publicly." [19]

But what would he do? He did not know.

8

Apparently with the idea of coaxing him to accept the Democratic overtures, certain Democrats began feeding newspaper writers "inside information" that he would run as a Democrat. Among other publications, the *Free Press* said that there had been a deal: Postmaster Farley was backing Couzens. In the *Review of Reviews,* there appeared an item that said:

> The real political fight looming in Michigan will be an effort by the now thoroughly entrenched Republicans to oust Senator Couzens as an independent Republican New Dealer. The violent-tempered multimillionaire is Farley's only hope in Michigan.[20]

Publicly, Couzens ignored these assertions. But to Tom Payne, he wrote, "I can say to you, in confidence, of course, that no such offer was ever made to me by Mr. Farley." [21] He also denied the Farley reports in private correspondence with Governor Frank D. Fitzgerald, who had announced that he, at least, among leading Republicans, favored his renomination as against Brucker. To Governor Fitzgerald, he added:

> While the necessity of filing petitions and the primaries are somewhat in the distance, I know of no reason why I should not run on the Republican ticket, unless it be that the party again comes under the standpat and reactionary leaders who have heretofore had control of the party.[22]

9

Which way the wind was blowing in the Republican party appeared to be well indicated by the sentiment at a dinner held in Detroit in February 1936 by the Wayne County Republican Party. A headline on February 21 told the story:

JAMES COUZENS' NAME
BOOED AT G.O.P. DINNER

In April, Brucker formally announced his candidacy for the Senate on a typically Old Guard platform: anti-Roosevelt and anti-Couzens.

Couzens' friends now urged that he also announce. "Every day you lose in making clear your stand will require at least two days of vigorous work . . . to win back the support you seem to be losing," wrote George Averill.[23] That was all too true. But he still hesitated.

In May he told Tom Payne, "I think finally it will be my decision to enter the Republican primaries." Then, only a week later, he asked Payne to find out if he could legally run as an independent. Shortly after he inquired of Payne: "How would we go about organizing another party?" [24] That same month, the Democratic party in Michigan, without consulting him, adopted a resolution endorsing him for re-election on the Democratic ticket, if he chose to accept. Would he accept? He declined to say.

10

"There is no doubt that Senator Couzens seriously considered running on the Democratic ticket," Prentiss M. Brown, then Democratic Congressman from Michigan (later Couzens' successor in the Senate) recalled. Brown himself, among other Democratic Congressmen, urged that Couzens head the Democratic ticket in Michigan. He was also "authorized from a much higher authority to express the hope that the Senator would run," said Brown.[25] But an affirmative answer could not be pried from Couzens.

One reason for his indecision was that, at times, he considered not running at all. His secretary, Carson, had in fact urged that decision upon him. Carson felt that the prospects for victory were too slim, and, besides, that Couzens was not in good enough physical condition to undertake another campaign. He discussed with Couzens the possibility of his accepting some worthwhile appointment from Roosevelt. "Without actually committing him, I got him to say that he would accept an appointment," Carson recalled.

So Carson began consulting with certain men close to Roosevelt. His own hope, he later said, was that Roosevelt might offer Couzens the post of Secretary of the Interior, in place of Ickes, albeit this was only a hope on the part of Carson, who did not like Ickes. Among others, Prentiss Brown was interested in Carson's efforts.

Slated to be the Democratic candidate for Senator, Brown was only too glad to avoid the possibility of a contest between himself and Couzens. He agreed to talk with Roosevelt about Carson's proposal.[26] But Brown encountered delay in seeing the President. Couzens himself did nothing to press the matter.

11

In June, he was forced by the political calendar to make a decision one way or another. Democratic friends, including Murphy and Brown, continued to press him to accept a Democratic nomination. He finally turned that down. He told Murphy that to run as a Dem-

ocrat, would mean he would be called "a turncoat," and he could
not "tolerate" that.[27]

To Brown he gave yet another excuse. His son Frank, by the kind
of administration he was giving Detroit as mayor, was now launched
on a promising political career. "If I became a turncoat, it would
harm Frank's political future," he told Brown. He did not wish to do
that.[28]

Actually, there was a deeper reason for his rejection of the Democratic nomination. He had made a career of being an independent
man. Now, in his last years, how could he most clearly demonstrate
his independence? By seeking refuge in another party? Or by insisting
that he was a Republican even though the Republicans denied it?

His answer to that was inevitable. On June 15, he announced that
he would be a candidate for the Republican nomination. "I am,"
he said, definitely, "a Republican." [29]

Three days later, while he was packing to leave Washington for
Detroit, Congressman Brown received the long-awaited message from
the White House to confer with Roosevelt on "the Couzens matter."
Couzens was already at the railroad station when Brown later reported to Carson on his talk with Roosevelt. The President had indicated to Brown that he was ready to make a worthwhile offer to
Couzens. There was a distinct possibility that Farley might retire
temporarily, for the duration of the campaign, as Postmaster General,
Roosevelt indicated. Politically, this seemed an expedient thing, as
the Republicans appeared intent on making a serious campaign issue out of "Farleyism." Even Senator Norris had been stirring up
sentiment against the administration over Farley's handling of patronage.

Roosevelt would be glad to have Couzens become Postmaster
General for that period, with the understanding that another post
would be found for him after the election.[30]

Carson hurried to the station to tell Couzens. "We walked up and
down the station and talked it out," Carson related. The offer had
come too late, Couzens finally said. Had it come earlier, before he
had announced his candidacy, he might have accepted. "To take the
offer at that hour would make it look as if he had been bought off.
He could not take it." [31] So he entrained for Detroit for his third
campaign for the Senate.

CHAPTER XLV

THE INDEPENDENT MAN

2

IN TRUTH, there was no campaign. He still had no organization with which to make one, a price he paid for having eschewed patronage in politics.

After fourteen years as a Senator, he was in the pitiful position of a political leader unable to count on more than a dozen men in the whole state to serve as the nucleus of a strong campaign committee. Then, too, he declined to give the signal for the start of any kind of real effort to get his story to the public.

He made only one speech, a talk to the Detroit Optimist Club, in which he scarcely referred to his candidacy. "I will be entirely content," he said, "if the people of Michigan say I am through, if they are dissatisfied with my work."

Most of the time during this appearance, he spent in answering questions concerning his attitude toward the Roosevelt administration.

"Was Roosevelt bankrupting the nation?" he was asked.

"Certainly not," he answered. "I have been disgusted with this constant talk about balancing the federal budget. How could anybody have balanced it?"

Did he expect a "Red government" in Washington as a result of Roosevelt?

"Absurd," he said. "All three branches of our government, the legislative, executive, and judicial are functioning."

He made no reference to Brucker, his opponent. Nor did he mention Alf M. Landon, the Republican nominee for President.

2

Whereas by all the rules, with his opponent going up and down across the state, he ought to have been out on the hustings himself,

311

he instead chartered, from Leon Mandel of the Chicago department store, a yacht, the *Buccaneer*, and spent most of his time cruising with Frank, William J. Norton, and others on the Great Lakes. It would be said that he was a man "sulking on his yacht," because of chagrin over the impossibility of being renominated. If so, his sulking was a most agreeable kind, for friends who joined him on the *Buccaneer* from time to time found him more relaxed and amiable than they had ever known him. He had, as he wrote to Senator Vandenberg, "a most delightful and restful summer and, of course, time to think and think and think." [1]

He did a great deal of fishing. He told stories. One night he held his guests "enthralled past midnight as he told the true story of the founding of the Ford Motor Company."

He talked of his lost boy, Homer. As he recalled that boy, he wept openly for the first time. Apparently, somewhere in him an emotional dam had broken. He felt all the better for this, and was able at last, after twenty-two years, to speak of Homer without bitter regret over his death.[2]

Once while the yacht was on Lake Superior, someone pointed to the Canadian shore and commented: "If you had not been born over there, in Chatham, you might have been President." He laughed. This was very nearly the same comment he had made to his mother fifty years before.[3]

3

His friends kept pressing him, as the summer wore on, to let some kind of campaign be put up for him. But he delayed giving his approval. He put them off usually with the assertion that the people knew his record, so the usual activity was unnecessary.

His real reason was something else. He could not envision himself making an appeal for renomination without making his stand clear on the one big issue—Roosevelt. Obviously, he was for Roosevelt. But should he say so? And when?

His opponent, Brucker, was demanding that he declare himself. On August 5, at Petoskey, Michigan, Brucker, who twenty years later would find himself defending Republican President Eisenhower against the charge of "New Dealism" and "socialism," asked, "How can the Republican Party put up a united front against President Roosevelt and his socialistic doctrine, if the head of the federal ticket in Michigan is a New Dealer?"

At Cadillac, Brucker said, "I dare Couzens to tell the people of this state whether he is supporting Alf M. Landon, the Republican nominee for President, or President Roosevelt." [4]

At Detroit, in a radio broadcast, Brucker said: "Mr. Couzens has utterly failed . . . to say whether he supports Landon or Roosevelt. . . . The people are entitled to know. . . . Why isn't Senator Couzens out working for Landon's election? Senator Vandenberg is out on the stump for Landon, while Mr. Couzens won't even declare himself." [5]

4

The politically wise advice to Couzens was to refrain from answering Brucker. To state openly that he favored Roosevelt's re-election could not possibly help his own cause in the Republican primary. On the contrary, such a statement could only harm his already slim chances of winning, if not cinch his defeat. If he insisted on coming out for Roosevelt, he should hold off until after the primary.

On the yacht, Couzens pondered that problem. The primary was set for September 15. Early in August, Bill Yaw, his son-in-law, began pressing him to approve an advertising budget for a campaign keyed to two themes—that Couzens was a Republican and that a big Republican vote was desirable. Henry T. Ewald, the advertising-agency head, had prepared the campaign. Radio time had to be reserved.

On the afternoon of August 12, as the *Buccaneer* was off St. Ignace Island, Couzens reached his decision. On a radiogram blank he wrote out a message to Yaw:

> I intend to announce myself as desiring Roosevelt's election. Therefore tell Ewald and Carson all plans cancelled. . . . Also tell Ewald I do not desire any radio reservations and am unconcerned about plan of getting Republicans out to vote. . . . [6]

He handed the message to John P. Frazer, a friend of Frank's who was on the yacht, and asked that he send it. Frazer read the message and blanched. He argued with Couzens that he should "wait." Couzens said no, he had "decided."

"I won't send it!" said Frazer.

"If you don't, I'll get it on the radio myself," Couzens replied.

Frazer pleaded some more. But it was no use. The radiogram was sent. [7]

5

Efforts were made by Bill Yaw, Tom Payne, and others to get him to change his mind. All they succeeded in doing was to get him to hold up for awhile public announcement of his decision. Maybe something would turn up, they hoped. They knew that for a Republican candidate for Senator to come out openly for Roosevelt would doom even a slight chance of winning in the Republican primary. It just could not be done—not in 1936.

Couzens insisted that it would be "dishonest" not to make known, before the primary, clearly and unequivocally his decision. He recalled that back in 1924, Brookhart had been accused of "fraud and deception" because he favored La Follette, but did not say so until after he had won the Republican party nomination in Iowa. That was one of the reasons the Old Guard in the Senate gave for refusing to let Brookhart take his seat.[8]

Couzens would not lay himself open to that kind of thing. He would not "stultify" himself, he repeated. The Republican voters had a right to know.

Madeleine Yaw tried her hand at getting him to change his mind, when he visited her in Harper Hospital, where she was expecting her fourth child—Couzens' twelfth grandchild.

"Well, Pete," he greeted her. "I won't be re-nominated."

"Why not?" Madeleine demanded.

"Because I am coming out for Roosevelt."

"But you don't *have* to do that."

"Yes, I do. That's the honest thing."

Madeleine agreed in her heart. But she felt it was not "good" for him to be defeated. So she kept on arguing with him. But it was no use.[9]

On Sunday, August 23, three days before his sixty-fourth birthday, the newspapers all over the nation carried his statement:

> Believing as I do that the most important matter confronting the nation is the re-election of President Roosevelt, I intend to support him.
>
> The outcome of my own candidacy is neither important to the nation nor to me, but I do believe it is important that my many loyal supporters in Michigan be advised in advance of the primary. . . .

This was the real end of his campaign, such as it was, for re-election. It was clear immediately that his senatorial career was over, ended in the way he had started it, by an affirmation of what had been his greatest aim—to be Couzens, the independent man.

CHAPTER XLVI

THE TRIUMPHANT DEFEAT

HE KNEW only too well the consequences. "I have written myself out of the Senate," he wrote to Senator McNary.[1] Friends said, "Too bad, too bad." His response was, "Not at all. The important thing is that the New Deal, what it stands for, be firmly entrenched. That means another term for Roosevelt is necessary. Otherwise the country will swing back. What happens to me is not important, next to that consideration."[2]

Vandenberg was dismayed and suggested to Couzens that he had yielded to impulse while "mentally disturbed." "That is not the fact," Couzens told him. "On the boat, I had days and days to consider the future of my adopted country."[3]

"The odd thing about it," said Senator McNary, who got to know Couzens perhaps better than anyone else, "was that Couzens meant it when he said he acted solely from his view of the good of the country."[4]

2

The chief beneficiary of his announcement, Roosevelt, was then on a tour of Western states. Roosevelt was both elated and surprised, all the more as he knew that Couzens had turned down a chance to run as a Democrat in place of Prentiss Brown.

THE WHITE HOUSE
Washington

September 8, 1936

DEAR JIM:
It is one of the fine things about public life that every once in a while the usual rules of the political game are not followed! Your announcement is not only fine in itself but it is especially so because it came without solicitation or suggestion on my part or on that of any member of the Democratic organization.

Frankly, I was just as much taken by surprise as, I imagine, Brother

Landon was. I want you to know that I appreciate not alone what you have said and done but also your manner of doing it—for you have shown a very deep courage based on conviction and may lose your Primary as a result.

Perhaps you have not seen this typical vile editorial in the Chicago *Tribune* which came to me the other day. I do not give a continental under which party label you or I may happen to enroll ourselves but I do know that very fundamentally you and I have the same ethical standards.

Always sincerely,
FRANKLIN D. ROOSEVELT [5]

3

The "vile editorial" to which the President referred was an example of the anger Couzens' announcement had provoked. His support of Roosevelt was part of a conspiracy between him and Roosevelt of long standing, the *Tribune* said. "It is established now that he [Couzens] helped in creating a hero role for Mr. Roosevelt in 1933." Had he not caused the nation-wide bank crisis by "blocking" the RFC loan to the Detroit banks? And had not Roosevelt, too, opposed aid to the Detroit banks? It was all now clear. They had purposely set the stage for Roosevelt to win acclaim for saving the financial system that they themselves had "wrecked." "Now the people of Michigan will have an opportunity to wreak their vengeance upon the two men primarily responsible for that state's worst calamity." [6]

Loyal Tom Payne also received a letter—typical of the reaction of certain war veterans who resented Roosevelt's and Couzens' attitude on the latest bonus proposal.

This . . . written against the man you are working for politically, Senator James Couzens. . . . He has deserted the honest, the upright, the noble, for the degrading position of a bootlicker to the most dangerous, damaging demagogue that ever sat in the President's chair. No good can ever come from a turncoat. . . .

4

After docking at Detroit for the day to make his announcement, Couzens promptly sailed away again on the *Buccaneer*, to be gone, except for one short visit to Wabeek in the interim, until primary day. He did not share the gloom of his associates. Indeed, he was now noticeably in especially good spirits. He was like a man who had cast off a great load. He had followed his conscience. As expected, he was badly defeated. The surprising thing was that he still received 199,204 Republican votes against the 328,560 for Brucker. [7]

5

Three days after the primary, G. Hall Roosevelt arrived in Detroit with a confidential letter from the President.

THE WHITE HOUSE
    Washington

                                                    September 17, 1936
Personal
DEAR JIM:
    Hall has been with me here in Washington while the returns were coming in. I need not tell you that you were a good sport because you were a lot more than that—you lived up to your own ideals. Actually, your run was a feat unprecedented in political history and will always be remembered.
    What I want to convey to you in very simple terms is that you and your ideals and ability must not, because of a political system be lost to the country. As you are aware, one of the most difficult problems before us is that of American shipping. Ever since the mail subsidies of the eighteen forties, when the Merchant Marine legislation was first passed, shipping has gone through ups and downs but always more or less the victim of party politics or of shipping lobbies.
    Today I am confronted with constituting a Maritime Commission under the new bill, which, although not perfect, is very definitely a step in the right direction, giving powers to this independent Commission which are far greater than any previously granted. In fact, this new Commission *can* put our sea borne trade back on its feet in an honest way. . . .
    What I need and what the country needs is a fearless Chairman of this Maritime Commission, who will take the responsibility in setting up and putting through a new and permanent Mercantile Marine policy. Experts on engineering, ship design, ship management, etc., can be hired, but a Chairman with the capacity and the courage I seek cannot be hired; he must be drafted. That is why I want you on the first of January to undertake the task of heading the Maritime Commission. . . .
    In sending you this note by Hall, I can only reiterate that irrespective of party affiliations the country needs you in public service, and I cannot conceive of any higher or more important duty than getting the Maritime Commission started under real leadership and under auspices that will be considered neither political nor tinged with any special interest. I have emphasized courage because it will take courage to end many abuses which have grown up in the shipping industry in the past. You have that courage.

                                        My warm regards,
                                        Faithfully yours,
                                            FRANKLIN D. ROOSEVELT [8]

6

This letter pleased Couzens, but he was not certain that he wanted to accept the chairmanship of the Maritime Commission. "I do not know the first thing about water shipping, naval construction or design, yet . . . I would have to assume the responsibility of the decision of your so-called experts," he replied to Roosevelt. He did not, however, reject the offer flatly. He left the matter open until he would return to Washington, "probably about election time."

The more immediate thing, he told Roosevelt, was the election. He wrote to him:

> I want . . . to emphasize . . . that the election is not won and I think there is a lot of work to be done. Great headway could be made . . . by pointing [up] your Good Neighbor policy and your endeavor to keep us out of foreign conflict. . . . Some simplified form has to be adopted for ridiculing our national debt. I told Hall that I wanted to be helpful in your campaign and I still do.[9]

7

From Vandenberg, he received an interesting testament.

> The returns are in—and it appears that we are "parting company" as Senate colleagues. Under the circumstances, I cannot refrain from this reminiscent note. I cannot explain my very real affection for you —but I have it—and there it is.
>
> Many times in the last eight years you have made me "mad as Hell" and I know that I have had the same effect on you. But most of the time we have travelled comfortably in double harness and I have deeply cherished the privilege of knowing you with an intimacy denied to most other men.
>
> I know that my legislative association with you has been distinctly and usefully tempering to what was originally too "conservative" a view on my part, and you have had much to do with instilling in me a sense of "social responsibility" which I hope I may never lose.[10]

Grateful for this from Vandenberg, he yet could not resist the urge to take advantage of the opportunity to tell Vandenberg that he believed him wrong for supporting Landon, even for the sake of party regularity.

> Let me say to you, Arthur, that if the great mass of our people who live on an economic precipice ever get the idea back in their minds that their government has no interest in them and that their government is only interested in the "big boys," we will never be

able to stop the growth of communism and the other isms that are being propagandized in our country. That is one of the reasons I do not want Mr. Landon elected. I think it would be a setback. . . .

Nor did he resist telling Vandenberg that he hoped he would not have Brucker as a colleague. He frankly asserted that Prentiss Brown should be elected, "in the interest of Michigan and our country." He noted that Vandenberg had told him that his advice would continue to be welcomed.

This leaves me free to be as candid with you in the future as I have been in the past and I think that over the years I probably will be availing myself of it. You know we still have a Washington house and I am going down there after the election to spend some considerable time. . . .[11]

8

What he expressed there was only a hope. For within a week after the primary his health took another bad turn. Just after his talk with Hall Roosevelt on September 18, in his office in Birmingham, he felt so weak and feverish that he went home early in the afternoon and to bed. Feeling the need for more air in the room, he got out of bed to open a window. He came close to collapsing from the sudden pain caused by the exertion—and it was found that he had injured his sacroiliac.[12]

Five days later he was ordered to Harper Hospital in Detroit "for treatment," as he himself recorded in his notebook, "for jaundice, diabetes, and sacroiliac." [13]

A postscript to his letter to Vandenberg told the story:

I am signing this in the hospital, so forget the errors. I am feeling very rotten. JIM.

Bill Yaw visited him on October 1. That afternoon he wrote to Carson:

Frankly, I am quite concerned about the Senator's health. . . . I am not at all pleased about his general condition. . . . I have an idea that he really feels his defeat more than he thought he would, although I am sure that he has no regrets that he was unwilling to compromise his convictions.

On October 2 Couzens decided to leave the hospital. The old rebellion against being inactive returned. As a compromise, he took a suite at the Book-Cadillac Hotel, where Dr. Freund could be closer to him. He had "things to do," he insisted, like preparing to help the Roosevelt campaign and also for paying a visit to Madeleine and her new baby, a boy, James John Yaw, born on August 28, two days after his own birthday. He felt so well that during the next few days he took Mrs. Couzens to several shows, including a performance of *Romeo and Juliet*. They even drove out to Wabeek.

On October 7 Marvin McIntyre, one of Roosevelt's secretaries, called from Washington to ask him if he would be in Detroit on October 15, when Roosevelt was to make a campaign visit there. The President wanted to see him on that occasion.[14] Couzens said that he would, and that certainly he would be glad to see Roosevelt.

On the 10th a letter from Roosevelt himself arrived. It said:

> . . . You are right about the campaign not yet being won. I expect to spend one day—October fifteenth—in Michigan, and I hope that I shall see you at that time, if only for a few minutes. It would help me if you were seen with me! [15]

9

He accepted the position of honorary chairman of the committee in charge of the Detroit reception for Roosevelt.[16] On Monday, October 12, he invited Arthur Krock, Washington correspondent of the New York *Times*, out to Wabeek for an interview on the political situation. He predicted that Roosevelt would sweep Michigan.[17]

He seemed then to be in fairly good shape. But on Wednesday, October 14, Dr. Freund ordered him back to Harper Hospital when he developed a stomach disorder that prevented him from keeping down any food. So he was at the hospital in Detroit when Roosevelt came into Michigan from Chicago on a special train.

At Flint, Frank Murphy, campaigning for governor, told Roosevelt of Couzens' new illness. The President said he would go to see Couzens at the hospital. But Couzens would not "stand for it." "It wasn't right for the President to come to him." [18] He said he would keep his date with the President, if he were at all able.

So, in the late afternoon of the 15th, he left his bed at Harper and went by automobile to the Grand Trunk Railway yards in Highland Park to greet Roosevelt in his campaign car.

While waiting for the President's train to be switched into place, he talked with a local Democratic leader about his own political position. "Some people have asked me why, if I would not join the Democratic Party, did I not lead a third party in Michigan. The answer is that I am too ill for anything like that."

He did not have to emphasize that he was ill. It showed in his face and in his posture. He had had no nourishment for two days. In the President's car he was to have dined with Roosevelt. He joined the President, but all he took was a glass of milk.[19]

10

He stayed with Roosevelt through the whole strenuous evening. He was in the parade through the city. He stood with the President at a rally in Hamtramck Stadium, built by the PWA. At a great mass meeting that night in front of the Detroit City Hall, he was there, ill as he was.

Detroit had never before seen such a turnout for any candidate. But that mass meeting was really for Couzens as well as for Roosevelt. For when he was introduced to the throng, a "thunderous cheer" went up for him.[20]

He was pleased by the speech Roosevelt gave that night. The President talked of the importance of building up mass purchasing power. He spoke of the need for more security for labor—and got down to cases with mention of the automobile industry. "It is my belief that the manufacturers of automobiles and the manufacturers of many other necessary commodities must, by planning, do far more than they have done to date to increase the yearly earnings of those who work for them." [21]

This was almost precisely what Couzens had in mind nearly twenty-two years before when, just a few blocks away, he had addressed the Board of Commerce on the responsibility of Detroit's employers to their employees.

He had been called names for having made that speech in 1914. He had been denounced for the five-dollar-a-day plan. And now here was the President of the United States enunciating those views as government policy. So this night was one of triumph for him, triumph despite his personal defeat. He might be out of the Senate, but Roosevelt would be re-elected, he felt, despite a *Literary Digest* poll that forecast an overwhelming Republican landslide.

Thus his own policies would be carried on.

Roosevelt gave him a warm handshake in thanks for his having come out that night.

"Take good care of your father," said Roosevelt to Frank, who, as Mayor, was the President's official host. "We need him." [22]

CHAPTER XLVII

"THE END OF THE ROAD"

WHETHER or not the exertion of being with Roosevelt that night had harmed him, none could say. He was obviously exhausted. Frank and Bill Yaw escorted him from the Roosevelt meeting to the Book-Cadillac Hotel, where Dr. Freund was waiting to take him back to the hospital.

Dr. Freund saw that he was over-fatigued. "Was it worth it?" he asked, after they were settled in an automobile on the way to Harper.

"Yes. Definitely," Couzens answered.

"Just why do you think it's so important to re-elect Roosevelt?"

"Here's something I have never told anyone," Couzens said. "The President has told me that he is afraid that war is coming. It may come from Japan. If that happens, all this opposition to the New Deal will not mean anything. I think Roosevelt is the one man to be our leader if we have a war. That's one reason I feel he must be re-elected even though I am a Republican." [1]

2

He was glad to get into bed at the hospital. "I'll never be back with you at Wabeek," he told Madeleine.[2]

On October 20, his condition was such that his daughters Margo and Betty were called from Washington to be at his bedside, along with Madeleine, Frank, and Mrs. Couzens. By then Dr. Freund and consulting physicians had determined that he was a victim of uremic poisoning. on top of all the other ailments. Through Carson, Roosevelt was advised that Couzens' condition was desperate. The President sent a telegraph message which, he hoped, would help rally Couzens' spirit.

I KNOW THAT YOU LIKE A FIGHT AND I AM PUTTING ALL MY FAITH IN THAT DOGGED DETERMINATION OF YOURS. IT HAS WON MORE THAN ONE

FIGHT FOR YOU AND IT IS STILL OUR BEST BET. I HOPE YOU WILL BE
YOURSELF AGAIN VERY SOON. I NEED YOU AND SO DOES THE COUNTRY.

FRANKLIN D. ROOSEVELT.[3]

He did seem to rally. On the 21st, Dr Freund said that he believed
he was gaining. "The pulse and temperature are normal." [4] But on
the following afternoon his temperature went up again. A medical
consultation was held. Then Dr. Freund said to him: "Senator, we
are not satisfied with the way you are getting along." Dr. Freund
decided that another operation was necessary.

3

He had been through this before—seven, eight, nine, even more
times—too often to count accurately. Each time before, he had put
up some kind of protest. But not now. The old spirit was ebbing.
"All right. It's all right with me." [5]

Frank, who had sat in on the medical consultation, expressed
dismay that another operation was ordered. But his father smiled
at him. "Don't worry." he said. "They can't kill an old dog like me."

Mrs. Couzens was permitted to see him for a moment before he was
wheeled from the room. He held out his hand to her and she clasped
it. "I'll see you later, Mother. Don't worry."

They operated at 3:00 and he was brought back to his room at
4:00. Dr. Freund said to Mrs. Couzens, as they waited his awakening
from the anaesthetic, "It was the only thing to do. It was the end of
the road." [6] So it was—October 22, 1936. He did not wake up.

4

Death is the Great Biographer.

For some time, the attacks on James Couzens in the conservative
press and by the politicians, notably in connection with the bank
case, had obscured the esteem with which he was held by the people.
Likewise, they had obscured his truly remarkable career.

Now, suddenly, on every side, it was remembered that he had been
more than a man in politics. Suddenly, it was remembered that he
he had been one of the great builders of American industry, starting
from scratch; that he had struck mighty blows for the workingmen
while still an industrialist; that, after making millions, he had retired not to leisure, but to public service; that he had been a great
and constructive mayor before he had become an outstanding senator;
that he had been a benefactor of children through philanthropy

equaled by few; that he was that rare thing, an honest man in politics. In the words of a writer in the *New Republic,* he was the "perfect example of the honest man in politics . . . the most intellectually honest man . . . in Washington." [7]

5

Even men and women who had been taught to dislike him, suddenly realized that a great void had been caused by his passing, that a man of uncommon strength had been among them. All this was reflected in the honors that were paid to him, by adversaries as well as admirers, now that he was gone. Never in the history of his city and his state was any man so honored in death as was this man who had come there forty-six years before—a youth from a small town in neighboring Canada.

The city government of Detroit asked that his body lie in state in the City Hall, the resolution for that being introduced in the Common Council by Councilman John Lodge, with whom Couzens had had one of his celebrated "rows" as mayor. The flags of all public buildings in the city were ordered kept at half-staff for thirty days. Long was the line that passed by the coffin in the City Hall, a line composed almost wholly of wage-earners. Perhaps never had a millionaire been mourned so sincerely by so many from the common ranks of a community. Their outpouring emphasized the strangest and also strongest aspect of his life, that with all his great wealth he made himself a symbol of opposition to arrogant wealth and a champion of those who lacked any wealth at all.

At Bath, Michigan, the children in a school that he had erected there to replace one wrecked by a maniac in 1927, spontaneously contributed pennies for a floral tribute. There was sadness among the attendants at the Children's Hospital of Michigan. They remembered that the work they were doing for their crippled charges had largely been made possible by his generous giving. There was sadness in the hearts of countless fathers and mothers of the poor who knew that their children's lives had been enriched because he had established the Children's Fund of Michigan, then in its sixth year. They would not have understood the comments of certain politicians and industrialists to the effect that he was a "cold man."

6

Tributes poured in from all over the nation, for the man who had been the boy in Canada who made himself not just a Detroiter and a Michigander, but an American "of unique renown," [8] For once all the tributes were honest, as if his candid—often too candid—spirit controlled them. There were no false notes, no generalities to fit any public man.

Roosevelt interrupted a speaking tour in Connecticut to say:

> In the death of Senator Couzens the Senate of the United States and the people of Michigan and the Nation have lost a leader whose convictions were a part of the best that America aspires for and whose courage was a match for his idealism.
>
> Senator Couzens did not enter public life because he sought either fame or power, but rather because of a service he believed he could render to the cause of progressive thought and political uprightness. He was a party member. But his prior obligation was to the well-being of the people whom he served. He never hesitated in that service.
>
> The death of Senator Couzens to me is a great loss. But, more than that, it is a great loss to the multitudes of Americans whose needs and problems were always in the forefront of his thought and action.[9]

All city and county offices in Detroit were closed for the funeral on October 26. Recalling that he had established the municipally owned transportation lines, the Detroit Street Railway brought every streetcar and bus in Detroit to a halt for a minute at the hour the body was placed in the mausoleum in Woodlawn cemetery.

Recalling his services as commissioner of police, nearly all of the city's policemen lined the highway of the funeral procession from Wabeek to the cemetery.

More than two thousand persons were present at the interment. The honorary pallbearers were men who had known him or had been associated with him in all the phases of his career—Ernest C. Kern, Joseph Mack, Clarence H. Booth, William O'Leary, Dr. Freund, William J. Norton, John P. Frazer, C. H. Haberkorn, Jr., Thomas Payne, George B. Judson, Clarence E. Wilcox, and Henry Ford.

7

In the week after the funeral, there was held at Traverse City, Michigan, where only that previous June his Children's Fund had dedicated the Central Michigan Children's Clinic, a spontaneous community-inspired memorial service. There, William J. Norton, the director of the Fund, gave a nearly perfect tribute, an honest appraisal.

This man was a rugged and dauntless fighter. He was no molly-coddle. He was a warrior's captain. . . . He fought always on the side of justice and human rights. His sword was never drawn in the cause of special privilege. Mistakes of the mind he no doubt made in some of the causes he espoused, for he was intensely human, but mistakes of ethical purpose—never.

His conscience held the most finely etched pattern as a guide for his own conduct that I have ever seen in any man of wealth or dominance. Simple honesty, complete integrity, a sense of great re-sponsibility, cold-blooded objective justice, perfect faith in the demo-cratic ideal, and a love for gentle charity were all burned clearly and distinctly into that ethical pattern that acted as his sole governor in all of his public relations. . . . Those ethical mandates were the only masters he acknowledged. . . .

On the first anniversary of his death, Edgar DeWitt Jones, the minister, in a nationwide radio broadcast, came close to voicing in seven words the complete epitaph: "He preserved his individuality to the end."

In a large sense, to do this had been his career.

Appendices

NOTES

BIBLIOGRAPHY

INDEX

NOTES

PROLOGUE: *October 12, 1915*

1. The scene between Couzens and Ford is based on the transcript of an interview given by Couzens to Judge Neil, a magazine writer, on July 27, 1926, and approved by Couzens as authentic. Copy in Couzens' papers. The interview, in substance, was published in *Real America*, April 1934. John C. Lodge's comment was made to author, 1941. See his book, *I Remember Detroit*, in collaboration with M. M. Quaife, 1949.
2. Before U.S. Board of Tax Appeals, 1927, *Transcript*.
3. Milo M. Quaife, *The Life of John Wendell Anderson*, p. 140; also in U.S. Board of Tax Appeals, 1927, *Transcript*.

CHAPTER I. *The Beginning*

1. Homer Couzens, brother of James Couzens, interview in Detroit, 1940.
2. "Historical Chatham," supplement with *The Planet Souvenir* of Chatham, Ontario, 1904.
3. Homer Couzens, interview; and Alice Couzens Lund to author, September 23, 1941.
4. Mrs. James Couzens, interview.

CHAPTER II. *The Canadian Boy*

1. Homer Couzens, interview.
2. Alice Couzens Lund, a sister, in a letter of September 23, 1941.
3. Ross Schram, an unpublished story of James Couzens' life to about 1920, in Couzens' papers. A Detroit newspaperman, Schram had served Couzens temporarily as secretary.
4. *Detroit Journal*, January 26, 1915.
5. Homer Couzens, interview.
6. *Detroit Journal*, January 26, 1915.
7. Alice Couzens Lund, letter, April 18, 1940.
8. John Carson, secretary to Couzens, to author, 1941.

CHAPTER III. *The Money-Making Machine, I*

1. Interviews in Chatham: William Mann, Frank Baxter, Charles Donovan, *et al.*, 1941.
2. James Couzens, article in *Nation's Business*, December 1926.
3. Charles Donovan, memorandum for author, 1941.
4. Victor Lauriston, Chatham, unpublished article loaned to author, 1941.
5. Albert L. Couzens, letter, September 23, 1941.
6. Alice C. Lund, letter to author, September 7, 1940.
7. *Pipp's Weekly*, June 16, 1922.
8. Charles Donovan of Chatham, letter to author, October 1940.
9. Homer Couzens, interview.
10. Arthur Stringer, Canadian novelist, boyhood friend of James Couzens in

329

Chatham, author of the book about a Chatham boyhood, *Lonely O'Malley;* letter to author, December 19, 1940.

11. William Mann and Frank Baxter, boyhood friends of Couzens in Chatham, interviews, February 7, 1941.

12. Interview with Bill Turtle in Chatham, February 6, 1941.

13. *New York Times,* December 20, 1922, and Detroit papers—stories based on interviews with James Couzens after his appointment to the U.S. Senate; also *Detroit Journal,* January 26, 1915, a basic item on his youth.

CHAPTER IV. *The New Detroiter*

1. Homer Couzens, interview: also Daniel Hackett, fellow worker at the Michigan Central Railroad and the late mayor of Jackson, Michigan, interview, 1940.

2. Schram, unfinished study of Couzens, *op. cit.;* also Catlin, *The Story of Detroit,* and the works of Milo M. Quaife.
Concerning the automobile industry and its founders, the most recent study, also the fullest and no doubt the best, with certain reservations as to interpretations, is by Allan Nevins, in collaboration with Frank Ernest Hill and others of Columbia University, published in 1954 under the title *Ford: The Times, The Man, The Company.* It is cited here as Nevins, *Ford, I.* A second volume of this important study, entitled *Ford: Expansion and Challenge 1915–1933,* was published in 1957, and is cited here as Nevins, *Ford, II.*

For readers who may be curious about certain similarities between that study and this book with respect to the treatment of James Couzens and his role in the Ford Motor Company from its founding to 1915, the explanation is that, as a matter of academic cooperation, the typescript of this work, before it was put in final form, was made available to Professor Nevins, as courteously acknowledged in the Nevins study. The typescript of the unfinished version of this book is cited in the Nevins study as "Harry Barnard, *James Couzens of Detroit,*" which was the working title of this book. For an especially excellent though short study of Henry Ford and the company see Roger Burlingame's *Henry Ford: A Great Life in Brief,* 1955.

3. Sidney Glazer, in Quaife and Glazer, *Michigan, From Primitive Wilderness to Industrial Commonwealth,* pp. 247 and 281.

4. Catlin, *op. cit.,* pp. 586–606.

5. Couzens to Daniel Kiefer, March 5, 1917.

6. Daniel Hackett.

7. A. T. Dempster, a Michigan Central employee, interview.

8. *Ibid.,* and *Detroit News,* April 13, 1924.

9. Arthur J. Lacy, Detroit attorney, whose firm, Anderson, Wilcox and Lacy, handled Couzens' legal affairs over a long period, interviews, 1940.

10. A. C. Goodson of the Michigan Central, in *Detroit News-Tribune,* October 27, 1915.

11. Daniel Hackett, memorandum for author, 1940.

12. Daniel Hackett, *op. cit.*

13. Michigan Central Railroad records, copy prepared for author.

CHAPTER V. *The Coal Clerk*

1. John Gunther, *Inside U.S.A.,* p. 403. Mr. Gunther did, as he wrote, find out that Malcomson was an original stockholder in the Ford Motor Company, owning an amount of shares equal to Ford's. He said, "Ford must, of course, have bought him out many years ago, as he bought out Couzens." But it is no wonder that Mr. Gunther did not come out with the full story about Malcomson. Until recently, most accounts of the Ford company left Malcomson out, or included him only glancingly, especially the stories supposedly authored by Ford.

2. *Detroit Journal,* October 27, 1902.

3. A. R. Malcomson, interview, 1942.

4. *Detroit Free Press,* April 1, 1903; see also Jere C. Hutchins, *A Personal Story,* pp. 283–84.

5. A. R. Malcomson, interview; also comments by Helen Malcomson Gore, his daughter, in a letter to the author dated July 25, 1942.
6. Ross Schram, *op. cit.*
7. *Ibid.*

CHAPTER VI. *The Family Man*

1. Mrs. James Couzens, interview, 1940.
2. *Ibid.*
3. *Ibid.*
4. Frank Couzens, interview, February 13, 1941.
5. Mrs. James Couzens, *ibid.*
6. Couzens to his daughter, Madeleine C. Yaw, November 14, 1933.
7. Mrs. David Huffman, letter to author, August 27, 1941.
8. Jay G. Hayden of the *Detroit News,* interview, April 17, 1940.
9. Mrs. James Couzens, interview.

CHAPTER VII. *The Ford Motor Company*

1. In *My Life and Work,* 1922, p. 36, actually written by Samuel Crowther, a work to be read with great caution. See Burlingame, *Henry Ford,* p. 185, for pertinent comments. Data about Malcomson and Ford, based on interviews with various persons who knew them both, including A. R. Malcomson and Mrs. Couzens, and also Schram's work.
2. McManus and Beasley, *Men, Money, and Motors,* p. 1. This work is exceptionally well authenticated, for many principals read it over before publication, and it rates as a primary source on Ford and others. It is cited hereafter as "McManus."
3. McManus, *op. cit.,* pp. 1ff.; see also Nevins, *Ford I, op. cit.,* p. 185.
4. McManus, *op. cit,* p. 2; see also Glasscock, *The Gasoline Age,* pp. 50–52, and Doolittle, *The Romance of the Automobile Industry,* 1916.
5. McManus, *op. cit.*
6. *Detroit News,* July 11, 1919; Nevins, *Ford, I,* includes an extended account of the Henry Ford Company, pp. 206ff.
7. Burlingame, *Henry Ford,* p. 29; also interviews in Detroit by author.
8. Charles B. King, *Psychic Reminiscences,* pp. 18–19.
9. John W. Anderson, testimony, in *Dodge, et al., v. Commissioner of Internal Revenue, U.S. Board of Tax Appeals, 1927* (known as the tax case brought against Couzens by Secretary of the Treasury Andrew W. Mellon; see *infra.*), *Transcript,* pp. 1270–72. Hereafter the record of this case will be cited as *Board of Tax Appeals, Transcript* See also Nevins, *Ford, I,* pp. 226ff.
10. Quaife, *The Life of John Wendell Anderson,* privately printed in 1950, pp. 89ff. A copy of this book was courteously loaned to the author by Milo M. Quaife.
11. *Ibid.,* p. 107; also interviews by author.
12. Schram, *op. cit.*
13. Schram, *op. cit.* Schram's account is based upon talks with Couzens himself.
14. Benson, *The New Henry Ford,* p. 103. Benson talked with Couzens as well as Ford.
15. *Ibid.*
16. J. C. Long, *Roy D. Chapin,* 1945, p. 35, concerning the Dodges' work for Olds. Chapin, who became head of Hudson Motor, started with Olds.
17. Benson, *op. cit.,* p. 103.
18. John W. Anderson to his father, Dr. Wendell A. Anderson of LaCrosse, Wisconsin, June 4, 1903. This letter is a primary source of exceptional value on the founding of the Ford Motor Company. A copy was made available by Anderson's associates. Quaife, in his *Life of Anderson,* publishes it in full, pp. 94ff, and also it is in Schram, *op. cit.*
19. *Ibid.*
20. *Ibid.*
21. John W. Anderson, *Transcript, op. cit.,* 1273.

22. *Philadelphia Evening Public Ledger*, interview, December 4, 1922.

23. McManus, *op. cit.*, p. 28.

24. Charles T. Bennett, president of the Daisy Air Rifle Company, interview with author, July 11, 1941. Bennett put $5,000 into the Ford Motor Company, but sold out later.

25. McManus, *op. cit.*, p. 29.

26. *Detroit Free Press*, April 1, 1903.

27. Benson, *op. cit.*, p. 115.

28. McManus, p. 31. Couzens also tried to enlist share buyers, but from book to book, a story has been printed, as in Simonds, *Henry Ford*, 1943, to the effect that, once after failing, Couzens sat on a street curb and burst into tears, which sidelight on him may be dismissed as incredible.

29. Quaife, *Anderson, op. cit.*, p. 102.

30. Merle Crowell, in *American Magazine*, February 1923.

31. McManus, *op. cit.*, and others.

32. Anderson letter, *op. cit.*

33. Mrs. James Couzens, interview, June 27, 1941.

34. *Ibid.*

35. *Detroit News*, January 20, 1927. Several books erroneously refer to Couzens' sister Rosetta as having taught school in Detroit. It was in Chatham.

36. Schram, *op. cit.*, and interviews.

37. *Ibid.*

38. Minutes of the Ford Motor Company, in *Board and Tax Appeals Transcript*, p. 425.

39. *Ibid.*

40. A. R. Malcomson, interview, June 23, 1941; also Mrs. James Couzens, interviews.

41. Anderson, *op. cit.*

CHAPTER VIII. *The Business Manager*

1. *Detroit Times*, December 3, 1922.

2. See Nevins, *Ford, I*, p. 229, for example, concerning Ford's appreciation of C. Harold Wills' "severity"; also Marquis' *Henry Ford, An Interpretation* (1923), in many ways perhaps still the best study of Ford the man. Pertinent, too, of course, is the relationship between Ford and Harry Bennett, among others, after Couzens left. See Bennett's remarkable story, *We Never Called Him Henry*. Also Robert Coghlan's superlative piece in *Life*, February 28, 1955.

3. See Nevins, *Ford, I*, p. 503; also Marquis.

4. B. C. Forbes, "Why Multimillionnaire Couzens Quit Business," in *Forbes Magazine*, December 1922.

5. Couzens interview, *Philadelphia Public Ledger*, December 4, 1922, and Forbes, *op. cit.*

6. Vernon Fry, interview with author, June 1941.

7. *My Life and Work*, p. 56.

8. Anderson, *op. cit.*

9. *Ford Times*, July 1, 1908, p. 8; in Nevins, *Ford, I*, p. 214.

10. Stipulation on Ford history, *Board of Tax Appeals, Transcript*, pp. 424–25.

11. *New York Times*, October 14, 1915.

12. McManus, *op. cit.*, p. 20.

13. Quaife, *op. cit.*, p. 105.

14. Couzens to J. W. Anderson, "Statement of Business, October 1, 1903."

15. *Detroit News*, January 23, 1937.

16. McManus, *op. cit.*, p. 20.

17. Stipulation, *Board of Tax Appeals Transcript*, pp. 425 and 435; also Nevins, *op. cit.*, p. 262.

18. McManus, *op. cit.*, p. 25; also B. C. Forbes interview; see also Garet Garrett, *The Wild Wheel*, 1952, p. 113, among the most perceptive works on Ford, although quite subjective.

19. Testimony of P. E. Martin, *Transcript*, pp. 846–50.

20. Stipulation, *Transcript*, p. 426.
21. Norval Hawkins, *Transcript*, p. 1610.
22. *Ford Times*, July 1, 1908, p. 8.
23. Garrett, *The Wild Wheel*, p. 113. See also, for Couzens' role in the company, Charles E. Sorensen, *My Forty Years with Ford*, pp. 36, 43, 84, 86–88, and 153.

CHAPTER IX. *The Cloud*

1. *Ford Times*, July, 1908.
2. Couzens notebook, 1906.
3. Bennett, interview, *op. cit.*
4. *Detroit News Tribune*, October 19, 1915.
5. James Couzens, "What I Learned About Business From Ford," *System* magazine, September 1921, p. 261.
6. *Ibid.*
7. *Ibid.*
8. *Ford Times*, September 15, 1908.
9. Couzens, *op. cit.*, p. 262.
10. Schram, *op. cit.*, p. 252.
11. Article by Oscar E. Hewitt, in the *Chicago Herald*, October 23, 1916.
12. Milton R. McRae, *Forty Years of Newspaperdom*.
13. *Detroit News*, October 19, 1915.
14. Ida M. Tarbell, manuscript of planned book on Ford Motor Company, loaned to author, 1942.
15. *Transcript*, p. 1281.
16. George D. Selden, in *Rochester Alumni-Alumnae Review*, February–March 1940, p. 16.
17. *Ibid.*
18. Patent No. 549,160, U.S. Patent Office.
19. George Byers, in *The Patent Office Journal*, October 1940, p. 725.
20. See Nevins, *Ford, I*, 98n. and 284ff., and other sections, for a superb description and analysis of the Selden patent matter, the best and most complete ever done. For the text of the licensing agreement, a curious document, see appendix of Epstein, *The Automobile Industry*.
21. Quaife, *op. cit.*, p. 116.
22. Anderson testimony, *Board of Tax Appeals, Transcript*, pp. 643–44.
23. *Transcript*, pp. 643–44.
24. In *Detroit Saturday Night*, quoted by Glasscock, p. 141.
25. *Transcript*, p. 1284; also Glasscock, p. 78.
26. Glasscock, *op. cit.*
27. McManus, *op. cit.*, p. 56. It should be noted that nearly everyone who writes about the decision to fight the Selden patent gives credit for the decision to a different person. Quaife, in *Anderson*, seems to give it to Anderson. Nevins, in *Ford*, seems to give it to Ford and Ralzemond A. Parker. Burlingame is quite neutral on this point. The McManus and Beasley account is used here as most objective, based, in the author's judgment, on the best sources. The final decision, of course, was a cooperative one.

CHAPTER X. *The Realignment*

1. Anderson testimony, *Transcript*, p. 1284.
2. *American Encyclopedia of the Automobile*, pp. 176–77.
3. Frederic R. Coudert, one of the attorneys, letter to author; and Mrs. James Couzens, interview. For watching carefully the expenses of some of the lawyers, Couzens not surprisingly incurred the antipathy of one or two, as witness the slurring comments about his role in the patent case attributed to a son of one lawyer, in Nevins, *Ford, I*, p. 424n.
4. *The Automobile Review and Automobile News*, October 15, 1903, p. 156.
5. *Transcript*, pp. 674–76.
6. Appel, *The Business Biography of John Wanamaker*, p. 155.

7. Couzens article in *System, op. cit.,* p. 263.
8. *Harper's,* March 16, 1907.
9. *Ford Times,* June 15, 1908.
10. *Transcript,* p. 755.
11. Rackham testimony, *Transcript.*
12. A. R. Malcomson, interview, June 23, 1941.
13. McManus, *op. cit.,* p. 20.
14. Couzens to Madeleine C. Yaw, January 30, 1928, quoting Ford.
15. Mrs. James Couzens, interview, June 27, 1941; also A. R. Malcomson, June 23, 1941.
16. A. R. Malcomson, interview, June 23, 1941; also C. H. Bennett, interview.
17. McRae, *Forty Years in Newspaperdom,* p. 393.
18. *Detroit News,* May 23, 1917.
19. *Ibid.*
20. Benson, *op. cit.,* p. 116.
21. Minutes, Ford Motor Company, September 9, 1905, in *Transcript.*
22. Board of Tax Appeals, *Petitioner's Statement of Facts,* p. 47.
23. *Ford Times,* August 17, 1904.
24. McManus, *op. cit.,* p. 144. There is a suggestion, in Nevins, *Ford, I,* p. 247, that there was some basis for dissatisfaction over the quality of work done by the Dodge brothers, implying that this was a factor in the Ford Manufacturing Co. scheme. This is certainly debatable, as the Dodge Brothers, then as later, were universally known to be dependable manufacturers. They would be criticized, but not for the quality of their products.
25. Vernon Fry, interview; See also testimony by Norval Hawkins, *Transcript,* pp. 1960–61, and Sorensen, *My Forty Years with Ford,* pp. 72–78.
26. Minutes of the Ford Motor Company, November 17, 1905.
27. Michigan Corporations and Securities Commission records, November 29, 1905.
28. *Ibid.*
29. Malcomson's letter in minutes of Ford Motor Company, December 22, 1905; also in *Detroit News,* February 22, 1927.
30. Minutes for December 22, 1905.
31. *Automobile Magazine,* May 1906, p. 354.
32. Sinsabaugh, *Who Me?,* p. 222.
33. A. R. Malcomson, interview, June 23, 1941.
34. See Nevins, *Ford, I,* pp. 278 and 330.
35. Minutes of Ford Motor Company, quoted in *Detroit News,* February 22, 1937; also interview of Fry by author, July 8, 1941.
36. In 1955, the Ford Motor Company, under Henry Ford II, and in connection with the Ford Foundation, for the first time became a public corporation, with Ford shares available to the public.
37. Ford to Couzens, cablegram, November 19, 1906, in Couzens papers.
38. Couzens to Judge Neil, interview, July 27, 1926.
39. Mrs. Couzens, interview; see also Nevins, *Ford, I,* generally.
40. *System, op. cit.,* p. 262.
41. See Sorensen, *My Forty Years with Ford,* pp. 36, 43–44, 86–88.

CHAPTER XI. *The Money-Making Machine, II*

1. Gibbons, *John Wanamaker,* II, pp. 122 and 128.
2. Testimony, Frank W. Blair, president, Union Trust Co., in U.S. Senate Committee on Banking and Currency, *Transcript of Hearings, 73d Congress,* 2d Sess., p. 4766.
3. *Ford Times,* December 1, 1908.
4. See Sward, *The Legend of Henry Ford,* pp. 22ff.
5. *Ford Times,* October 15, 1908, p. 10.
6. *Ibid.,* 14.
7. *Ibid.,* September 15, 1908.
8. Crowther interview of Couzens, *System, op. cit.,* p. 264.

9. Minutes of April 22, 1907.
10. *Transcript,* U.S. Board of Tax Appeals, pp. 430 and 440.
11. Fred H. Colvin, *Sixty Years With Men and Machines,* p. 131.
12. *Electric Vehicle Co., et al., v. C. A. Duerr & Co., et al.,* 172 Fed. 923, 1909.
13. *Ibid,* 935.
14. *Columbia Motor Car Co., et al., v. C. A. Duerr & Co., et al.,* 184 Fed. 893, 1911.
15. Board of Tax Appeals, *Transcript,* pp. 430 and 440.
16. *Petition on Appeal,* Board of Tax Appeals, p. 34.
17. *Ibid.*
18. *Transcript,* p. 1156; also see Sward, *op. cit.,* p. 44.
19. *Transcript,* pp. 819 and 1705.
20. See Burlingame, *Backgrounds of Power,* p. 256.
21. *Detroit News,* November 22, 1913.
22. Testimony before Judge Harry B. Keidan, August 22, 1933, in one-man grand-jury investigation of the Detroit bank crisis.
23. Couzens to A. E. Stilwell, March 1, 1911.
24. *Toronto Daily News,* October 21, 1915.

CHAPTER XII. *The Crisis*
1. Frank L. Klingensmith, interview. Klingensmith became vice-president of the company in 1915.
2. Transcript of Couzens' interview with Neil, *op. cit.*
3. See Seltzer, *A Financial History of the American Automobile Industry,* pp. 34-35; McManus, *op. cit.,* p. 68; Epstein, *op. cit.,* p. 225; Pound, *The Turning Wheel, A History of General Motors;* Kennedy, *op. cit.,* p. 49; Glasscock, p. 136; Briscoe, in *The Detroit Saturday Night,* June 1908; Richards, *The Last Billionaire,* and Simonds, *op. cit.,* pp. 114 and 123. The facts about the contemplated sale of the Ford Motor Company are corroborated by William C. Durant, in material from his memoirs, loaned to the author; and by Herbert L. Satterlee in letters to the author, 1942. The references cited in the Ford biography by Simonds, a Ford publicist, may be accepted as confirmation finally coming from Henry Ford himself, in 1943.
4. Herbert L. Satterlee to author, letter, March 12, 1942. He later helped organize General Motors for Durant.
5. Durant memorandum, *op. cit.*
6. Couzens notebook, 1908.
7. Satterlee and also Seltzer, *A Financial History of the American Automobile Industry,* pp. 34-35.
8. Durant, *Memoirs,* excerpt, *op. cit.*
9. Concerning W. C. Durant, for a good though short account, see David L. Cohen, *Combustion on Wheels,* pp. 112ff.
10. McManus, *op. cit.,* p. 72.
11. Durant, *Memoirs,* excerpt, *op. cit.*
12. *Ibid.*
13. Couzens notebook, October 5, 1909.
14. Durant, *Memoirs, op. cit.*
15. William C. Richards, *The Last Billionaire,* New York, 1948, p. 350.
16. Durant, *Memoirs, op. cit.*
17. *Ibid.*
18. Richards, *The Last Billionaire,* p. 350. Richards, an associate editor of the *Detroit Free Press,* was quite friendly with Henry Ford.
19. Minutes of the General Motors Corporation, quoted by Seltzer, *op. cit.,* p. 36.
20. *Ibid.*
21. Couzens notebook, October 24, 1909.
22. McManus, *op. cit.,* p. 72.
23. Durant, *Memoirs, op. cit.*
24. Harry B. Harper, interview, November 23, 1940.
25. Player to Couzens, December 24, 1934, and Hay, interview.
26. T. J. Hay interview, August 13, 1940.

27. See Keith Sward, *The Legend of Henry Ford,* pp. 43ff.
28. Malcolm Bingay, for example, in *Saturday Evening Post,* June 29, 1940.
29. Mrs. W. R. Yaw (Madeleine Couzens) to author, interview.
30. Couzens to Madeleine Couzens, May 11, 1925.
31. *Ibid.,* April 1, 1925.
32. *Ibid.*
33. Couzens to Edward W. Alexander, December 7, 1915.
34. Neil interview, *op. cit.*
35. Couzens to R. L. Jobling, October 12, 1912.
36. See Fay L. Faurote, "The New Ford Line-up," *Engineering Magazine,* January 16, 1916.
37. Garet Garrett, in *Everybody's Magazine,* April 1914.
38. Nevins, *Ford, I,* p. 573.
39. John C. Lodge, interview, July 3, 1941.
40. Couzens to J. H. Neil, interview, *op. cit.;* Frank L. Klingensmith, interview with author, June 30, 1941. Mrs. Ford's attitude toward Couzens is confirmed in Sorensen, *op. cit.,* p. 15.
41. Frank L. Klingensmith, interview.
42. Nevins, *Ford, I, op. cit.*
43. Couzens interview with Judge Neil, *op. cit.*
44. *Ibid.*
45. *Ibid.*
46. *Ibid.,* also Richards, *The Last Billionaire,* pp. 244–45.
47. Charles W. Duke, in *Philadelphia Public Ledger,* July 2, 1933.
48. B. C. Forbes, *op. cit.*
49. See *Reply Brief on Behalf of James Couzens,* U.S. Board of Tax Appeals, May 12, 1927, prepared by Arthur J. Lacy and Clarence Wilcox, pp. 66–67. Subjoined to the statements quoted from this brief was the following significant comment: "Eliminating Henry Ford, it is reasonable to believe that this program (of expansion) would have been carried out exactly as planned. Henry Ford was not in charge of that expansion program, although he agreed with the rest as to its desirability. The minutes show that it was projected and effectuated by James Couzens and others acted under his direction."
50. *Detroit News,* December 30, 1921.

CHAPTER XIII. *The Five-Dollar-A-Day Plan*

1. Mrs. James Couzens, letter to author, July 24, 1942.
2. Couzens to Edward W. Alexander, December 29, 1912.
3. Couzens notebook, entry for July 24, 1912.
4. Nevins, *Ford, I,* 581*n.*
5. Couzens to Chapin, December 18 and December 31, 1912, and January 10, 1913. Excerpts in J. C. Long, *Roy D. Chapin,* pp. 109ff.
6. Jay G. Hayden, a history of the Detroit railway commission, in mss., loaned to author.
7. Hayden, mss.; *Detroit Free Press,* August 4, 1913.
8. Forbes, *op. cit.*
9. Villard, "The Unique Millionaire," *Forum Magazine,* January 1937.
10. Belle C. and Fola La Follette, *Robert M. La Follette,* p. 352.
11. Gibbons, *op. cit.,* p. 258.
12. Board of Commerce *Minutes,* 1912.
13. *Chicago Tribune,* June 2, 1935, article by Willard Edwards.
14. Mrs. Couzens, interview; and Keith Sward, *op. cit.,* p. 50.
15. *Highland Park Times,* October 6, 1916.
16. From a stenographic copy of Miss Tarbell's notes, as dictated on a record for John S. Phillips, editor of *The American Magazine,* May 28, 1915. Loaned to author by Miss Tarbell, March 20, 1942. Also her manuscript of chapter 111 of unfinished book, "Making Men and Fords," loaned to author, 1941.
17. James Couzens, article in *Michigan Manufacturer and Financial Record,* October 26, 1918.

18. John R. Lee, "The So-called Profit Sharing System in the Ford Plant," *The Annals of the American Academy of Political and Social Science*, May 1916, Vol. LXI, p. 299.

19. *Ibid.*

20. Tarbell, *op. cit.*

21. *Ibid.*

22. Tarbell, *op. cit.*, also *Detroit News*, November 25, 1914; also McManus, *op. cit.*, p. 154.

23. B. C. Forbes, "Multimillionaire Couzens Tells Why He Quit Business," *Forbes Magazine*, December 22, 1922.

24. Tarbell, *op. cit.*

25. McManus, *op. cit.*, p. 156.

26. *Chicago Tribune*, June 2, 1935.

27. Interview with Henry Nimmo, *Detroit Saturday Night*, December, 1914.

28. Margaret Moors Marshall in *New York Evening World*, December 4, 1922, quoting Couzens.

29. Tarbell, *op. cit.*, and McManus, *op. cit.*; also *Chicago Tribune*, June 2, 1935.

30. See Simonds, *op. cit.*, p. 138.

31. Theodore McManus and Norman Beasley, *Men, Money and Motors*, pp. 157–58. Frank L. Klingensmith, vice-president of the Ford Motor Company, to author, March 5, 1942: "*Men, Money and Motors*, by McManus and Beasley, is an absolutely authenticated book, every word in it having been proofread and approved by representatives of the various companies mentioned. While the incident of the wage raise is told in narrative form, the facts are there and I will stand by every word that Beasley wrote. When it was written (1929) the time had not been so long, and the facts were fresh in our minds, and I personally O.K.'d the article. I don't care what Stidger (author of *Henry Ford; The Man and His Motives*, 1923) or anyone else says!" Ordway Tead, editor of Harper & Brothers economics books, who published *Men, Money and Motors*, to author, October 7, 1942: "I never saw or heard of it being challenged."

32. Couzens to *New York World*, December 4, 1922; and Ida M. Tarbell, notes.

33. Tarbell notes; also McManus, *op. cit.*, p. 158; Forbes, *op. cit.*; also Sward, *op. cit.*, p. 51.

34. Pipp, *Henry Ford, Both Sides of Him*, p. 48. Pipp quotes Ford as having said that he (Ford) first had the idea of increasing wages in order to step up production, to increase profits, and that he finally decided to make the basic scale $4.84, when Couzens suggested the five-dollar rate.

35. McManus, *op. cit.*, p. 158. In the lawsuit of *Henry Ford v. The Tribune Company, et al* (1919), Transcript of Record, pp. 2713–2716, John R. Lee, first head of the Ford "sociological department," testified under oath: "Mr. Couzens, as I remember it, finally mentioned the $5-a-day and Mr. Ford readily agreed with him." He also testified: "Mr. Couzens had been urging him (Ford) largely; I think it was a result of his urging that Mr. Ford came to this profit-sharing idea." John Dodge, in the same law suit, agreed. Transcript kindly loaned to author by the *Chicago Tribune's* law firm in Chicago, Kirkland, Fleming, Green, Martin, and Ellis, October, 1942.

36. *Minutes of Ford Motor Company*, for January 5, 1915, quoted in Board of Tax Appeals, *Transcript*.

37. Flynn Wayne, "Couzens: A Master Builder in Business Efficiency," *National Magazine*, September 1915.

38. Garrett, "Henry Ford's Experiment in Good Will," *Everybody's*, April 1914, p. 462.

39. Excerpts from pamphlet by Ford Motor Company, "Helpful Hints and Advice to Employees," in 1915.

40. See Sward, *op. cit.*, pp. 58ff.

41. *Detroit Saturday Night*, January 1916.

42. Sward, *op. cit.*, p. 52.

43. Couzens to William Robins, February 23, 1916.

44. Couzens to William Robins, November 15, 1915; Sward, *op. cit.*, p. 51.

45. A great many versions of the birth of the five-dollar-a-day plan have been published, some of them cited in the footnotes, but most are unreliable. The author is

satisfied that the version here given—one backed by sworn testimony in several court proceedings, is the correct one. Couzens, of course, explained the differing versions when he said that it was the Ford company policy, in which he had participated, that Ford was to get the credit exclusively as a matter of company advertising and public relations. In all probability, this particular Ford myth will never die. Two books on Ford published in 1954, Burlingame's *Henry Ford* and Nevins' *Ford, I,* may help dispel the myth. Nevins, in a footnote on page 532, makes an interesting comment: "After the lapse of forty years, the precise facts about this fateful conference (when the wage scale was adopted) are irrecoverable." In 1956 Charles E. Sorensen, in *My Forty Years with Ford,* presented a version giving the full credit to Henry Ford, pp. 5 and 136–40, but it suffers from defects common to other versions based upon one perspective.

CHAPTER XIV. *The Final Break*

1. Klingensmith to Couzens, February 6, 1914.
2. *Ibid.,* March 27, 1914.
3. See Sward, *op. cit.,* pp. 54–55.
4. Garet Garrett, "A World That Was," *Saturday Evening Post,* June 8, 1940.
5. Alfred P. Sloan, "Adventures of A White Collar Man," *Saturday Evening Post,* August 31, 1940.
6. Garrett, *The Wild Wheel,* p. 9.
7. Garrett, *Saturday Evening Post,* June 8, 1940.
8. McManus, *op. cit.,* p. 164.
9. Couzens to E. D. Stair, January 8, 1914.
10. *Ibid.*
11. *Detroit Times and Tribune,* December 22, 1914.
12. *Detroit Labor News,* November 1, 1918.
13. *Detroit News,* November 25, 1914.
14. Simonds, *op. cit.,* p. 147.
15. Henry S. Morgan, interview; also letter to author, August 21, 1942; see Richards, *The Last Billionaire,* p. 244.
16. Copy in Couzens' papers.
17. Morgan, interview.
18. Mrs. James Couzens, interview.
19. Klingensmith, interview.
20. *Chicago Tribune,* June 7, 1919. See also Nevins, *Ford, II,* pp. 26ff., for Ford's peace views and anti-war activities.
21. *Toronto Daily News,* October 21, 1915.
22. Couzens to Glenn Frank, May 2, 1917.
23. McRae to Couzens, November 14, 1911; Couzens to McRae, October 19, 1915; November 19, 1915. Also, McRae, *Forty Years of Newspaperdom,* p. 394.
24. Klingensmith, interview, June 30, 1941.
25. Jay G. Hayden, interview, April 17, 1940.
26. Couzens to Louis B. Block, October 14, 1915.
27. Pipp, *Henry Ford, Both Sides of Him,* pp. 14–15; see also Sward, *op. cit.,* pp. 64–65, Richards, *op. cit.,* pp. 70–71; and Nevins, *Ford, II,* pp. 10–11, 23–24.

CHAPTER XV. *The Job-Seeker Again*

1. *Toronto Evening Record,* December 6, 1915.
2. Hutchins, *op. cit.,* p. 244.
3. Catlin, *The Story of Detroit,* pp. 633–72.
4. *Detroit News-Tribune,* Oct. 31, 1915.
5. Catlin, *op. cit.*
6. Jay G. Hayden, manuscript, *op. cit.*
7. Couzens to McRae, May 6, 1929.
8. Couzens to Townsend, June 15, 1916.
9. Couzens to Warren, September 27, 1916.
10. *Detroit News-Tribune,* June 11, 1916.
11. William J. Norton, address at Memorial Services for James Couzens, Traverse

City, November 1, 1936. Published by the Kiwanis Club, Traverse City; also Catlin, *The Story of Detroit*, pp. 672–73.
12. *Detroit News*, December 22, 1924.
13. *Ibid.*, September 28, 1916; also Catlin, pp. 673.

CHAPTER XVI. *The Police Commissioner*

1. *The Story of Detroit*, p. 673.
2. *Detroit News*, October 2, 1916.
3. *Detroit Saturday Night*, October 9, 1916.
4. *Detroit Times*, October 6, 1916.
5. *Grand Rapids News*, September 30, 1916.
6. *Detroit News*, November 6, 1924.
7. *Ibid.*, October 13, 1916.
8. Charles W. Wood, "He Had Millions but Wanted a Job," *Collier's*, August 5, 1922.
9. *Detroit Free Press*, May 19, 1917.
10. *Detroit News*, March 27, 1917.
11. *Detroit Free Press*, April 17, 1917.
12. Barry, *The Outlook*, December 20, 1923.
13. Hard, William, "Coming: Couzens of Detroit," *Hearst's International*, May 1922.
14. William J. Norton, interview.
15. Frank Couzens, interview.
16. *Detroit Times*, December 5, 1916.
17. *Detroit Journal*, March 23, 1917.
18. *New York Times*, June 2, 1917.
19. *Detroit News*, June 2, 1917.
20. See Ray Tucker, *Sons of the Wild Jackass*, pp. 239–40.
21. *Detroit News*, February 25, 1918.
22. *New York Sun*, March 2, 1918.
23. *Ibid.*; also see Richards, *The Last Billionaire*, pp. 71–72.
24. *Detroit Free Press*, February 20, 1918.
25 *Detroit News*, February 20, 1918.

CHAPTER XVII. *The Odd Candidate*

1. McRae to Couzens, November 10, 1916. In Malcolm Bingay's *Of Me I Sing* (1948) there is a prejudiced but interesting sketch of McRae. See McRae's own biography, *Forty Years in Newspaperdom* (1924).
2. Couzens to McRae, November 16, 1916.
3. *Ibid.*, March 5, 1918.
4. *Detroit News*, April 1, 1918.
5. William Alden Smith to Couzens, April 5, 1918.
6. *Detroit News*, June 4, 1918. Concerning Ford's candidacy for U.S. Senator, *see* Nevins, *Ford, II*, pp. 114–124.
7. See Catlin, *op. cit.*, also Leo Donovan of the *Detroit Free Press* in *Our Fair City* (ed. by Robert S. Allen), p. 153.
8. Mrs. E. Roy Pelletier, interview, July 10, 1941.
9. *Detroit News*, December 22, 1922.
10. *Ibid.*, July 16, 1918.
11. *Detroit News*, July 9, 1918.
12. *Detroit Free Press*, December 14, 1895, quoted by O'Geran, *A History of the Detroit Street Railways*, pp. 153–55.
13. Detroit papers, August 14, 1918.
14. *Detroit News*, August 14, 1918.

CHAPTER XVIII. *The Strong Mayor*

1. Couzens to Gertrude Beeks, May 4, 1915.
2. C. H. Haberkorn, Jr., interview.
3. Couzens to Dr. Hugo A. Freund, December 3, 1924.

4. *New York Times,* December 10, 1922.

5. William Alden Smith to Couzens, September 3, 1919; Couzens to Smith, September 9, 1919.

6. William Hard, *op. cit.*

7. Mabel Ford, his secretary, interview, July 2, 1941.

8. William Hard, *op. cit.*

9. *Detroit Times,* March 30, 1921; *New York Times,* March 31, 1921.

10. *Detroit News,* January 31, 1922.

11. *Detroit News,* June 21, 1919.

12. *New York Times,* December 4 and December 8, 1921.

13. Couzens to James Schermerhorn, June 23, 1919.

14. *The Detroiter,* December 4, 1922.

15. Miss Mabel Ford, interview, July 2, 1941.

16. George W. Engel, interview.

17. H. S. Campbell, interview, February 19, 1941.

18. See *Detroit's Government, Report by the Common Council and the Mayor of the City of Detroit,* 1922, p. 73.

19. *Ibid.,* p. 74, and *Detroit News,* October 26, 1921.

20. See Leo Donovan, in *Our Fair City, op. cit.,* pp. 153ff.

21. Angus McSween to Couzens, April 19, 1920.

CHAPTER XIX. *The People's Man*

1. Lloyd Wendt and Herman Kogan, *Big Bill of Chicago,* 1953.

2. See Frederick Lewis Allen, *Since Yesterday,* and Walter Johnson, *William Allen White's America.*

3. *Detroit News,* September 19, 1922.

4. *Detroit News,* September 19, 1922.

5. *New York World,* December 3, 1922.

6. See Frederic L. Paxson, *Postwar Years, Normalcy, 1918–1923,* pp. 229 and 266.

7. Ray Lyman Wilbur and Arthur Mastick Hyde, *The Hoover Policies,* pp. 370–71.

8. Henry S. Morgan, interview.

9. Associated Press Story, Detroit, November 21, 1919.

10. *Detroit News,* November 21, 1919.

11. See F. L. Allen, *Only Yesterday,* and C. Vann Woodward, *Tom Watson, Agrarian Rebel,* for good accounts of the Palmer raids. Also Beard, *Rise of American Civilization,* II, p. 671.

12. Beard, *op. cit.,* II; p. 671.

13. *Detroit News,* January 7, 1920.

14. *Detroit Saturday Night,* January 10, 1920.

15. See Johnson, *William Allen White's America,* p. 323.

16. *Detroit Free Press,* January 15, 1919.

CHAPTER XX. *The Battle For M.O.*

1. Jay G. Hayden, Mss., *op. cit.*

2. E. T. Fitzgerald, interview, July 12, 1941.

3. Jay G. Hayden, Mss., *op. cit.;* Clarence E. Wilcox, then Detroit's Corporation Counsel, interview. The commissioners were Abner Larned, Sidney D. Waldon, and Francis C. McMath.

4. J. Hutchins, *op. cit.,* p. 274.

5. *Detroit News,* October 13, 1915.

6. Original in Couzens papers.

7. Pipp, *Henry Ford, Both Sides of Him,* p. 20.

8. *Detroit News,* April 3, 1919.

9. Hayden, *op. cit.;* see also Sorensen, *op. cit.,* p. 188–89 for Sorensen's side.

10. "Senator Couzens' Metamorphosis from Business Man to Politician," December 30, 1922.

11. *Detroit News,* April 4, 1919.

12. *New York Times,* April 8, 1919.

13. *Detroit News,* June 7, 1919.

14. *New York Times*, June 8, 1919.
15. *Detroit News* and *New York Times*, June 10, 1919.
16. *Detroit News* and *New York Times*, June 12, 1919.
17. *Detroit News*, December 26, 1919, and March 3, 1920.
18. *Ibid.*, March 14, 1920.
19. Clarence E. Wilcox, interview, *op. cit.*, also Hayden, *op. cit.*
20. *Detroit News*, January 6, 1920.
21. Hayden, *op. cit.*
22. *Ibid.*
23. *Ibid.*
24. Couzens to Clarence E. Wilcox, January 17, 1927. See also Garrett, *The Wild Wheel*, p. 120; Burlingame, *Henry Ford*, p. 98; and Quaife, *Anderson*, pp. 139ff.
25. Quaife, *Anderson*, p. 140; also Couzens to Walter H. Bennett, and *New York Times*, September 24, 1918.
26. *Detroit Saturday Night*, November 8, 1919.
27. *Detroit News*, April 7, 1920; see also Catlin, *op. cit.*, pp. 633–34; and Ross C. Schram, "How Detroit Came to Run Its Own Street Cars," a pamphlet.

CHAPTER XXI. *"The Damnable Outrage"*

1. Hayden, *op. cit.*
2. *Detroit Times*, August 17, 1920.
3. *Detroit Times*, January 10, 1921; Hayden, *op. cit.*; also Tucker, pp. 241–42.
4. *Detroit Free Press*, January 27, 1921.
5. *Detroit United Railway, Appt., v. City of Detroit, et al.*, 255 U.S. 171, 1921.
6. *Detroit News*, March 4, 1921.
7. *Ibid.*, August 5, 1921.
8. *Detroit News*, January 2, 1922.
9. *Detroit News*, December 7, 1920.
10. Henry S. Morgan, interview; also Hayden, *op. cit.*
11. *Detroit News*, April 18, 1922.
12. See Catlin, *op. cit.*, pp. 621ff.; an obviously prejudiced and antagonistic view is given by Malcolm W. Bingay in *Detroit Is My Own Home Town* (1946). Bingay and Couzens, once friendly, were engaged in an almost constant feud. With respect to Couzens, Bingay was seldom reliable.

CHAPTER XXII. *The Reward*

1. Charles W. Duke, in *Philadelphia Public Ledger*, June 18, 1922.
2. *Detroit News*, July 27, 1925.
3. *Newberry v. United States*, 256 U.S. 58, 1920; see also Spencer Ervin, *Henry Ford v. Truman Newberry* and Nevins, *Ford, II*, pp. 114–124.
4. George W. Norris, *Fighting Liberal*, pp. 216ff.
5. Spencer Ervin, *op. cit.*; also Paxson, *Postwar Years*, p. 271.
6. Hayden interview.
7. B. C. Forbes, *Forbes Magazine*, December 22, 1922.
8. Charles W. Wood, "He Had Millions, But Wanted a Job," *Collier's*, August 5, 1922.
9. *Detroit News*, June 10, 1922.
10. Forbes, *op. cit.*, December 22, 1922.
11. See Norris, *op. cit.*, p. 216; and Pat Harrison, "Keynote Address, Democratic Convention, 1924," in William A. White, *Politics the Citizen's Business*, p. 246.
12. Couzens to Fred W. Upham, May 16, 1918.
13. *Detroit Times*, November 22, 1922.
14. Ross Schram, Mss., *op. cit.*
15. Couzens to Madeleine Couzens, November 11, 1922.

CHAPTER XXIII. *The One-Man Bloc*

1. NEA News Service, December 26, 1922.
2. See Frederic L. Paxon, *Postwar Years, Normalcy, 1918–1923*, p. 319.
3. *Detroit Times*, December 9, 1922.

4. Senator Arthur Capper, interview.

5. Charles P. Stewart, NEA syndicate story, June 14, 1926.

6. Jay G. Hayden, interview, April 17, 1940.

7. See Charles A. and Mary R. Beard, *America in Midpassage;* also Paxon, *op. cit.;* and Karl Schriftgiesser, *The Gentleman from Massachusetts, Henry Cabot Lodge.*

8. Cordell Hull, *Memoirs,* p. 113. Mr. Hull was then chairman of the Democratic National Committee.

9. See Beard, *op. cit.,* II, pp. 692–93.

10. Norris, *op. cit.,* p. 215.

11. *Literary Digest,* November 23, 1929; also Tucker, *op. cit.*

12. See Samuel Hopkins Adams, *Incredible Era, The Life and Times of Warren Gamaliel Harding;* also William Allen White, *Autobiography,* and his *A Puritan in Babylon, the Story of Calvin Coolidge,* pp. 260–63.

13. *New York Tribune,* March 11, 1923.

14. *Detroit Free Press,* December 8, 1922.

15. *Detroit Times,* March 18, 1923.

16. *St. Louis Censor,* January 4, 1923.

17. Beard, *op. cit.,* II, p. 694. For a good, though colored summary of the Ship Subsidy Bill, see Senator Pat Harrison's keynote speech at the Democratic National Convention, 1924, reprinted in William Allen White, *Politics: The Citizen's Business,* p. 242. See also Paxon, *op. cit.,* pp. 351–53.

18. Norris, *op. cit.,* pp. 328ff.

19. December 12, 1922.

20. December 14, 1922.

21. Norris, *op. cit.,* p. 261; also Alfred Lief, *Democracy's Norris;* Simonds, *op. cit.,* pp. 197–98; Keith Sward, *op. cit.,* pp. 127–31, and Nevins, *Ford, II,* pp. 305–311.

22. Claudius O. Johnson, "George William Norris," in *The American Politician* (J. Salter, ed.), p. 103.

23. C. H. Haberkorn, Jr., interview.

24. *Detroit Free Press,* December 7, 1922; see also Norris, *op. cit.,* p. 249.

25. Couzens to Malcolm Stewart, June 5, 1925.

26. *Detroit Free Press,* December 7, 1922.

27. Charles P. Stewart, February 13, 1930.

28. Richard Barry, "Newberry's Successor; A Study of Senator Couzens," *The Outlook,* December 10, 1922.

29. *Congressional Record,* Vol. 64, p. 2905.

30. *Ibid.*

31. John P. Frank, *Mr. Justice Black, The Man and His Opinions,* p. 48.

32. *Congressional Record,* Vol. 64, pp. 2911–15; also newspapers, February 3, 1923.

33. *Congressional Record,* Vol. 64, pp. 2914–16.

34. February 3, 1923.

35. *Labor,* January 12, 1923; also *New York Tribune,* January 13, 1923.

36. Associated Press story, January 27, 1923.

37. *New York Times,* January 27, 1923.

38. *Kansas City Star,* January 30, 1923.

39. *Detroit Times,* March 18, 1923.

40. Senator George W. Norris, interview with author, April 12, 1940; also see La Follette, *op. cit.,* p. 1090.

41. White, *A Puritan in Babylon,* p. 230; see Samuel G. Blythe, "A Calm Review of a Calm Man," *Saturday Evening Post,* July 28, 1923; and Will Irwin, *The Making of a Reporter,* pp. 386–405.

42. Mrs. James Couzens, interview.

43. Walter L. Dunham, Detroit banker, interview, July 1941.

44. Couzens' notebook, February 7, 1923; also *Philadelphia Record,* February 5, 1923.

45. Harding to Couzens, February 26, 1923.

46. Couzens to Harding, February 27, 1923.

47. Warren G. Harding to Couzens, March 1, 1923.

48. White, *op. cit.*, p. 295.

49. *Detroit News*, March 5, 1923.

50. *Detroit News*, July 17, 1923.

51. James B. Morrow, "Couzens, Radical—and Rich," *Nation's Business*, June, 1923.

52. Anon., "Who's Who—and Why—Serious and Frivolous Facts About the Great and Near Great," *Saturday Evening Post*, April 21, 1923.

Chapter XXIV. *The Plain-Speaking Statesman*

1. Garrett, in *The Wild Wheel*, gives an interesting account of the Ford Presidential boom, pp. 159ff. See also Burlingame, *Henry Ford*, p. 123, and especially Nevins, *Ford, II*, pp. 300–305.

2. *New York Times*, October 28, 1923.

3. Norris, *op. cit.*, pp. 256ff.

4. *Detroit Times*, June 25, 1923.

5. See Mark Sullivan, *Our Times, The Twenties*, p. 246; Adams, *Incredible Era*, p. 369; Pringle, *Taft*, p. 982.

6. *Detroit News*, July 8, 1923.

7. *Detroit News*, July 25, 1923.

8. *New York Times*, July 10, 1923; *New York Herald*, July 4, 1923.

9. *Christian Science Monitor*, July 7, 1923.

10. *New York Post*, October 13, 1923.

11. *Ibid.*

12. Couzens to Calvin Coolidge, November 23, 1923.

13. See Claude Bowers, *Beveridge and the Progressive Era;* and Pringle, *op. cit.*, pp. 1012ff. and 1060.

14. *New York Evening Post*, October 13, 1923.

15. Couzens to Vandenberg, June 11, 1924.

16. Vandenberg to Couzens, June 2, 8, and 12, 1923.

17. About a year later, Couzens did drop his support of the proposed La Follette amendment, but was never happy over the old arrangement. Couzens to Vandenberg, July 22, 1924.

18. Couzens to Willis J. Abbott, November 21, 1923.

19. *Detroit Times*, November 1, 1923.

20. Couzens' notebook, October 29, 1923.

21. C. Bascom Slemp, *The Mind of the President*, p. 227, and Garrett, *The Wild Wheel*, p. 167.

22. Garrett, *op. cit.*, concerning Coolidge on Muscle Shoals and also Ford's plan; see C. Herman Pritchett, *The Tennessee Valley Authority*, pp. 8ff., and also Nevins, *Ford, II*, pp. 305–311.

Chapter XXV. *The Millionaires' War*

1. Quoted by Couzens in a letter to *New York Times*, November 13, 1923.

2. *Ibid.*

3. *Detroit News*, November 3, 1923.

4. Paul Kerns in *The American Politician* (edited by Salter), p. 10; see Thomas L. Stokes, *Chip Off My Shoulder*, p. 177.

5. White, *Politics: The Citizen's Business*, p. 36.

6. See Harvey T. O'Connor, *Mellon's Millions, a Biography of a Fortune;* also Philip Love, *Andrew Mellon*.

7. Mellon to Couzens, January 5, 1923, in *New York Times*, January 6, 1923.

8. Couzens to Vandenberg, August 1924.

9. David Lawrence, column, April 14, 1924.

10. *New York Herald Tribune*, March 19, 1925.

11. *Ibid.*

12. Couzens to Mellon, January 10, 1923.

13. Mellon to Couzens, in *New York Times*, January 9, 1923.

14. Couzens to Charles L. Brownell, May 17, 1923.

15. *Congressional Record*, May 27, 1936, p. 8005.
16. *New York Times*, January 13 and 19, 1924.
17. Couzens to Mellon, January 12, 1924, in *New York Times*, January 13, 1924.
18. Walter R. Dorsey, interview, April 1940.
19. Jay C. Hayden, interview, April 1940.
20. *Congressional Record*, February 21, 1924.
21. Frank Kent, "Couzens of Michigan," *American Mercury*, May 1927.
22. *Congressional Record*, March 12, 1924.
23. See *Congressional Record*, March 22, 1928, pp. 5148ff; and Kent, *op. cit.*, pp. 52ff.
24. Mrs. James Couzens, interview, 1943.
25. *New York Times*, April 11, 1924, *passim;* see also George H. Haynes, *The Senate of the United States, Its History and Practice*, p. 561. Concerning Heney, see La Follette, *Robert M. La Follette*.
26. Gifford Pinchot, interview with author in Washington, 1941.
27. *New York Times*, April 8, 1924.
28. *Ibid.*, April 15, 1924.
29. *Congressional Record*, April 12, 1924.
30. *Congressional Record*, April 12, 1924.
31. *Ibid.*, p. 6194; also *New York Times*, April 12, 1924; Stokes, *op. cit.*, pp. 175–77; and Tucker, *op. cit.*, pp. 231–32.
32. Pringle, *Taft, op. cit.*, p. 1020.
33. *Congressional Record*, pp. 6194–95; also George H. Haynes, *The Senate of the United States*, p. 982.
34. See Rixey Smith and Norman Beasley, *Carter Glass, a Biography*, pp. 252–57.
35. Couzens' notebook, March 25, 1924, and *passim*.
36. Syndicated column, April 16, 1924.
37. Earl Davis of Detroit was substituted for Heney.
38. Senate Report 27, 69th Congress, 1st Session, 3 parts, "*Investigation of Bureau of Internal Revenue, Pursuant to Senate Resolution 68*," 1926. See also *Congressional Record*, March 22, 1929, pp. 5149ff., for Couzens' comments on reports.
39. See *New York Times*, December 11, 1925.
40. *Ibid.*, January 13, 1925.
41. *Ibid.*, and Oliver Clarkson and Ernest Sutherland Bates, *Hearst, Lord of San Simeon*, p. 299; also see *Congressional Record*, March 22, 1928, p. 5149, concerning the case of William Boyce Thompson, Republican leader.
42. Wilbur and Hyde, *The Hoover Policies*, p. 536; see also Kent, *op. cit.*, pp. 176–77.
43. See George Haynes, *The Senate of the United States*, pp. 313–15; and Tucker, *op. cit.*, p. 234.
44. See *Congressional Record*, March 9, 1925, pp. 59ff. and Thomas L. Stokes, *op. cit.*, pp. 176–77.
45. *New York Herald Tribune*, February 11, 1927. Senator Watson denied this in a letter to author, October 11, 1940, but the facts are against him. See also Kent in *American Mercury*, May 1927, pp. 50–51, and Quaife, *Anderson*, iii, ff. and p. 137.
46. See statement by Joseph E. Davies, U.S. Board of Tax Appeals, *Transcript*, I, pp. 23–24; also *New York Herald Tribune*, February 11, 1927; and *Detroit Free Press*, February 13, 1927.
47. See *Transcript*, U.S. Board of Appeals, pp. 2662–65; pp. 2690–91.
48. See *New York Times*, May 9, 1929; *Detroit News*, May 8, 1928.
49. Tucker, *op. cit.*, pp. 232–33.

CHAPTER XXVI. *"The La Folletteite!"*

1. *Detroit News*, March 18, 1931.
2. Couzens to Alfred Sleight, Sturgis, Michigan, August 26, 1924.
3. *Saginaw News Courier*, August 4, 1924.
4. James Couzens, address, "La Follette, The Greatest American of the Age," in *Brotherhood of Locomotive Firemen and Enginemen's Magazine*, September 1925, pp.

216ff.; see also, for an estimate of La Follette, William B. Hesseltine, "Robert Marion La Follette and the Principles of Americanism," in *Wisconsin Magazine of History*, Vol. XXXI, March 1948, pp. 261ff. See also W. A. White's contemporary estimate, *Politics: The Citizen's Business*, pp. 122ff. Also Bela and Fola La Follette's biography, *op. cit.*

5. *Detroit Times*, June 5, 1924.
6. Vandenberg to Couzens, July 7, 1924; Couzens to Vandenberg, July 8, 1924.
7. *Detroit News*, July 5, 1924.
8. Norris to Couzens, July 12, 1924.
9. Johnson to Couzens, July 10, 1924.
10. Johnson to Couzens, July 12, 1924.
11. July 19, 1924.
12. Couzens to Vandenberg, July 8, 1924; *Detroit News*, July 7, 1924.
13. James H. Shideler, "The La Follette Progressive Party Campaign of 1924," *Wisconsin Magazine of History*, Vol. XXXIII, June 1950, p. 450; also White, *op. cit.*, p. 307.
14. Couzens to Vandenberg, September 5, 1924; also Couzens' notation, "Telephoned him September 5th saying not an issue and could not say now what I would do," on Vandenberg-to-Morgan telegram, September 5, 1924.
15. Vandenberg to Couzens, September 6, 1924.
16. Couzens to Vandenberg, September 5, 1924.
17. Couzens to Vandenberg, September 8, 1924.
18. *Detroit News*, August 21, 1924.
19. Couzens to Vandenberg, September 12, 1924.

Chapter XXVII. *The Critic of Coolidge*

1. Couzens to Vandenberg, August 29, 1924.
2. Text in *Brotherhood of Locomotive Firemen's and Enginemen's Magazine*, September 1925.
3. For the text of Chief Justice Warren's address on La Follette, see *Madison Capital-Times*, June 20, 1955; also story in *New York Times* and other newspapers, same date.
4. Walter Johnson, *William Allen White's America*, p. 398.
5. Norris, *Fighting Liberal*, p. 221.
6. *Congressional Record*, March 7, 1925, pp. 24–31, and pp. 79ff., see also White, *A Puritan in Babylon*, pp. 319ff., and Leif, *Democracy's Norris*, pp. 280ff.
7. *Congressional Record*, March 7, 1925, pp. 18–19.
8. White, *op. cit.*
9. Thomas Sugrue and Edmund W. Starling, *Starling of the White House*, p. 228.
10. White, *op. cit.*, p. 321.
11. *Ibid.*
12. February 21, 1925.
13. *Detroit News*, March 11, 1925.
14. For a good account, see Senator James Watson, *As I Knew Them*, pp. 242–44.
15. *Congressional Record*, March 9, 1925, p. 50.
16. *Ibid.*, pp. 59ff.
17. *Congressional Record*, March 13, 1925, pp. 215ff.
18. *Ibid.*, March 9, 1925, p. 50; also see Kent, *American Mercury*, *op. cit.*, p. 51.
19. *Detroit Times*, October 23, 1936.
20. Mark Sullivan, *Our Times, The Twenties*, p. 631.
21. *Detroit News*, October 14, 1925; Emile Gauvreau and Lester Cohen, *Billy Mitchell, a Biography*.
22. *Grand Rapids Herald*, September 27, 1925, for a good account of this.
23. Couzens to William J. Norton, December 29, 1926; also Norton interview, February 12, 1941.
24. *Detroit News*, March 21, 1928.
25. *Congressional Record*, March 22, 1928, pp. 5146–51.
26. Galbraith, *The Great Crash, 1929*, p. 114.
27. Couzens to Madeleine Yaw, December 2, 1929.

CHAPTER XXVIII. *The Restless Statesman*

1. Mss. fragment in Couzens papers.
2. Couzens to Vandenberg, July 22, 1924.
3. John P. Frazer, interview.
4. Couzens to Madeleine Yaw, January 30, 1928.
5. Charles L. McNary, Arthur A. Ballantine, etc., interviews with author.
6. See Mary Earhart Dillon, *Wendell Willkie*, concerning McNary.
7. Joseph P. Tumulty to Couzens, May 22, August 10 and 12, and September 21, 1924.
8. Couzens to Clarence Wilcox, February 22 and March 4, 1935; also *Lima Trust Company, as Trustee for Creditors of Couzens Ice Machine Company v. Charles F. Carroll, et al.*, Common Pleas Court, Auglaize County, Ohio, No. 11481.
9. Couzens, James, "The Installment Buyer Worries Me," *Nation's Business*, December 1926, p. 36.
10. Clarence Wilcox interview, February 9, 1941.
11. Couzens to Madeleine, October 1, 1929. For Frank Couzens' career, see obituary articles in *Detroit Free Press, News,* and *Times,* October 31 and November 1, 1950.
12. Frank Couzens, interview.

CHAPTER XXIX. *The Magnificent Gift*

1. Couzens to Gordon McGregor, December 23, 1915.
2. Gitchell interview, October 24–25, 1942.
3. *Ibid.*
4. Norton interview and others; also his talk, "The Saga of a Foundation Executive," before Prismatic Club of Detroit, November 6, 1954.
5. *Detroit News,* October 22, 1919.
6. Henry S. Morgan, interview.
7. Trust instrument, March 26, 1924.
8. Lacy memorandum to author, May 2, 1940.
9. Couzens to Madeleine Yaw, March 3, 1929.
10. Children's Fund of Michigan, *Reports;* also Norton to author, February 10, 1955, and Norton's Prismatic Club talk, *op. cit.* For a full report on the Children's Fund of Michigan and a good account of Couzens' philanthropies, see the book published in 1957 by the Fund—*Biography of a Foundation, The Story of the Children's Fund of Michigan,* by William C. Richards and William J. Norton.
11. Children's Fund of Michigan, *Sixth Annual Report.*
12. Dr. Stewart Hamilton to author, October 29, 1942.
13. Couzens to Ralph Stone, December 15, 1926.
14. Couzens to Martin H. Carmody, December 2, 1924.
15. Norton, Prismatic Club talk, *op. cit.,* and interviews.
16. See Children's Fund of Michigan, *Twelfth Annual Report,* 1940–41, 6.
17. Children's Fund of Michigan, *Seventh Annual Report,* 1935, 5.
18. William J. Norton, memorandum for author, 1941.
19. Couzens to Mrs. Yaw, May 14, 1929.
20. *Ibid.,* June 18, 1929.

CHAPTER XXX. *The "Dangerous Man"*

1. Herbert Hoover, address at Palo Alto, August 11, 1928, in Wilbur and Hyde, *The Hoover Policies,* p. 2.
2. Couzens to C. H. Haberkorn, Jr., June 5, 1925.
3. Couzens to Norton, November 8, 1926.
4. Couzens to Frank Couzens, February 21, 1928.
5. Couzens before Keidan grand jury, Detroit, testimony on August 18, 1933.
6. *New York Times,* June 5, 1929.
7. *The Causes of Unemployment,* U.S. Senate, 70th Congress, Senate Report No. 219, published in March 1929.
8. *Ibid.,* pp. iv–vi.

9. *Ibid.*, p. xv.

10. Couzens to Leon F. Whitney, May 13, 1929.

11. Couzens to George W. Johnson, July 23, 1929.

12. Frederick Lewis Allen, *Since Yesterday*, New York, 1939, p. 26.

13. Myers and Newton, *The Hoover Administration*, p. 23.

14. See Dixon Wecter, *The Age of the Great Depression, 1929-41*; also Charles A. and Mary R. Beard, *America in Midpassage*, pp. 55ff.; Allen, *Since Yesterday* and Galbraith, *The Great Crash, 1929*, which are among the best works on this.

15. *Literary Digest*, November 9, 1929.

16. Arthur Pound, *Detroit, Dynamic City*, New York, 1940, p. 316.

17. Galbraith, *op. cit.*, discusses the causes in an impressive way. It is interesting how close were Couzens' views at the time with those expressed by Galbraith in 1955 in his book, *The Great Crash, 1929*.

18. Arthur H. Vandenberg to author, letter, August 18, 1941.

19. *Literary Digest*, March 30, 1929.

20. Frank R. Kent, *Without Grease*, p. 274.

21. See Tucker, *Sons of the Wild Jackass*, pp. 14–17, and p. 242; also Watson, *As I Knew Them*, pp. 164–66.

22. Charles P. Stewart, Washington column, February 14, 1930.

23. Thomas L. Stokes, *Chip Off My Shoulder*, p. 79.

24. *New York Times*, January 13, 1931; see Stokes, *op. cit.*, p. 354.

25. *New York Times*, April 15, 1931.

26. Richard Hofstadter, *The American Political Tradition and the Men Who Made It*, p. 286, an incisive analysis of Herbert Hoover.

27. Leif, *Democracy's Norris*, p. 256; Couzens to Mrs. Yaw, February 13, 1929.

28. Couzens to Hoover, January 18, 1930.

29. See Stokes, *op. cit.*, pp. 257ff., 293ff.

30. *Detroit Times*, August 13, 1933.

CHAPTER XXXI. *The Crusader Again*

1. The Beards, *America in Midpassage*, pp. 42ff.; also Pritchett, *The Tennessee Valley Authority, op. cit.*, pp. 12ff.

2. Myers and Newton, *The Hoover Administration*, p. 470.

3. The Beards, *op. cit.*, p. 62.

4. Myers and Newton, p. 60.

5. *Ibid.*, and *New York Times*, January 1, 1931.

6. Myers and Newton, p. 61; see also *Literary Digest*, January 17, 1931.

7. Couzens to Mrs. Yaw, May 29, 1930.

8. *Congressional Record*, February 3, 1931, p. 3833.

9. *Ibid.*

10. *Ibid.*, Part 6, February 26, 1931, p. 6230.

11. Hoover Message to Congress, December 6, 1932, in Wilbur and Hyde, *op. cit.*, p. 463. See also Stokes, *op. cit.*, p. 326.

12. Couzens to William Timberlake, May 8, 1936.

13. *New York Times*, August 5, 1931; also Bates, *The Story of Congress*, p. 415.

14. Couzens to Arthur J. Lacy, May 23, 1932.

15. See Stokes, *op. cit.*, p. 280; *Literary Digest*, February 14, 1931; Wilbur and Hyde, *op. cit.*, pp. 399ff.

16. Ernest Sutherland Bates, *The Story of Congress*, p. 415.

17. Myers and Newton, *op. cit.*, p. 85.

18. Justice Frank Murphy, interview with author; *New York Times*, August 23, 1931.

19. Couzens radio speech, November 1, 1931, typescript.

20. Wilbur and Hyde, *op. cit.*, pp. 422ff.

21. Frederick Lewis Allen, *op. cit.*, p. 75, and Galbraith, *op. cit.*, pp. 98, 137.

22. Allen, p. 86. See also Dexter Perkins, *The New Age of Franklin Roosevelt*, p. 4ff.

23. Wilbur and Hyde, p. 434.

24. Simonds, *Henry Ford*, p. 224.

25. *Ibid.,* p. 230.
26. Lindley, *Halfway with Roosevelt,* p. 6, and *Literary Digest,* August 13, 1932.
27. Harold Nicolson, *Dwight Morrow,* p. 395.
28. The Beards, *America in Midpassage,* p. 81.
29. *Ibid.,* p. 70.
30. *Ibid.,* pp. 74–82.
31. Frederick Lewis Allen, *Since Yesterday,* p. 100; Stokes, *op. cit.,* p. 356.
32. *Ibid.*
33. The Beards, *America in Midpassage,* pp. 177–78.
34. *Congressional Record,* July 11, 1932, p. 14986; see also Watson, *op. cit.,* pp. 267ff.
35. *Literary Digest,* January 21, 1933; Frederick Lewis Allen, *op. cit.,* pp. 90–91.
36. Couzens to Sidney T. Miller, February 23, 1917.
37. Couzens to C. G. Marshall, May 23, 1934.
38. June 16, 1933, and June 20, 1933.
39. Ray Tucker, to author, May 5, 1951.
40. *Ibid.*

CHAPTER XXXII. *The End of An Era*

1. Sugrue and Starling, *Starling of the White House,* p. 299.
2. Stokes, *Chip Off My Shoulder,* p. 305.
3. *Congressional Record,* May 28, 1932; see also Ernest K. Lindley, *The Roosevelt Revolution,* p. 26.
4. See Mauritz H. Hallgren, *The Gay Reformer, Profits Before Plenty Under Franklin D. Roosevelt,* pp. 30ff., 220ff., 253ff., and 310 and Dexter Perkins, *op. cit.,* p. 5ff.
5. Louis M. Hacker, *The Triumph of American Capitalism.*
6. *Congressional Record,* March 22, 1928, p. 5148.
7. Pearson and Allen, *More Washington Merry-Go-Round,* p. 340.
8. Ray Tucker, *op. cit.,* p. 235.
9. *Detroit Times,* February 10, 1926.
10. Couzens to Mrs. Yaw, November 16, 1932.

CHAPTER XXXIII. *The Bank Crisis*

1. *America in Midpassage, op. cit.,* p. 155. In C. C. Holt and N. S. Keith, *28 Days, A History of the Banking Crisis,* will be found a good circumstantial summary of the national banking picture in connection with the "holidays." Also see, for good, though brief accounts, F. Cyril James, *The Growth of the Chicago Banks,* and Marquis James and Bessie R. James, *Biography of a Bank, The Story of the Bank of America* (1954), and Jesse H. Jones with Edward Angly, *Fifty Billion Dollars.* But to get the full story it is necessary to study, as was done for the account in this book, the thousands of pages of testimony in *Report and Hearings Before the Committee on Banking and Currency,* U.S. Senate, 73rd Congress, Second Session, 1934, among other official sources, for which see footnotes.
2. In particular in Malcolm W. Bingay, *Detroit Is My Own Home Town* (1946) and Lawrence Sullivan, *Prelude to Panic* (1936), both quite unreliable. It is a curious thing that Herbert Hoover, in his *Memoirs,* Vol. III, *The Great Depression,* includes, p. 207, a long excerpt from Bingay's account, as if this were really substantiation of his own version. The "curiousness" of this, as Alice in Wonderland might say, will become apparent as the story unfolds.
3. See *Report and Hearings Before the Committee on Banking and Currency,* U.S. Senate, 73rd Congress, Second Session, Part 10, 1934; hereafter cited as *Senate Report* or *Senate Hearings;* also Ferdinand Pecora, *Wall Street Under Oath,* and *Transcript of Hearings Before Judge Harry B. Keidan,* of Detroit, who conducted a one-man grand jury investigation, 1933. Basic is *Senate Report.*
4. Edsel B. Ford testimony, in *Senate Hearings,* pp. 4677–84; also testimony of Kanzler, Longley, and letter of A. P. Leyburn, chief federal bank examiner to the Comptroller of the Currency, June 14, 1932, in *Senate Hearings,* p. 4639. For pertinent, if biased, comments on Kanzler, concerning Edsel Ford, see Sorensen, *op. cit.,* pp. 307 and 310–11.

5. Robert O. Lord testimony, *Senate Hearings*, p. 4210.
6. Frank Couzens, interview, also letter to his father, 1931. For the connection of the Universal Credit Corporation with the Guardian Group, and also the roles of Edsel Ford and Kanzler in this respect, together with the relationship of the Ford Motor Company, see the interesting material in Nevins, *Ford, II,* 465.
7. Frank W. Blair, former president of the trust company, testimony, *Senate Hearings,* pp. 4803 and 4806.
8. Edsel B. Ford testimony, *Senate Hearings,* pp. 4677–84; also pp. 4681ff.
9. *Senate Hearings,* p. 4685.
10. *Senate Hearings,* p. 4808, testimony of Longley; also *Times Publishing Company and the Union Guardian Trust Company v. Harvey C. Emery, Liquidating Trustee, Brief for Appellees,* by Butzel, Levin and Winston, in the Supreme Court of Michigan, No. 40472, which goes into detail on the condition of the trust company.
11. *Senate Hearings,* p. 4810, minutes of the RFC, June 28, 1932, *ibid.*
12. Minutes of the RFC, July 5, 1932, *ibid.,* also Leyburn to Comptroller, June 14, 1932, *ibid.,* p. 4639.
13. *Brief of Appellees, Times Publishing Company, et al., v. Emery, op. cit.,* p. 35.
14. *Ibid.*
15. *Senate Hearings,* p. 4733.
16. *Senate Hearings,* p. 4516.
17. Leyburn testimony, *Senate Hearings,* pp. 4638–39.
18. Edsel Ford testimony, *Senate Hearings,* p. 4687.
19. *Ibid.,* p. 4692.
20. Kanzler testimony, *Senate Hearings,* p. 4755.
21. *Brief for Appellees, op. cit.,* p. 59.
22. *Senate Hearings,* p. 4725.
23. RFC minutes, February 6, 1933, in *Senate Hearings,* pp. 4562–63.
24. *Harper's Magazine,* January 1933.
25. Leyburn testimony, *Senate Hearings,* p. 4627; also Pecora, *Wall Street Under Oath, op. cit.,* p. 256.
26. Minutes of the RFC, February 6, 1933, in *Senate Hearings,* p. 4693.
27. McKee testimony, *Senate Hearings,* pp. 4728 and 4735.
28. Minutes of the RFC, February 6, 1933, *op. cit.*
29. For example, Hoover, *Memoirs,* III, pp. 206–07.

CHAPTER XXXIV. *The White House Conference*

1. Charles A. Miller, memorandum, March 27, 1942.
2. Burlingame, *Henry Ford, op. cit.,* p. 158; and see Edsel Ford testimony, *Senate Hearings.*
3. See Leyburn testimony, *Senate Hearings,* p. 4627.
4. Miller memorandum, p. 4; also Longley testimony, *Senate Hearings,* p. 4627. Hoover did call Ford *after* the bank holiday. C. C. Holt and N. S. Keith, *28 Days, A History of the Banking Crisis,* p. 8. In correspondence with the author, Hoover stated that he asked Ford's assistance and that Ford was always willing. But this clearly referred to a later time. In his *Memoirs,* p. 207, Mr. Hoover says: "Together with Secretary Mills and Under-Secretary Ballantine, I made great efforts to secure local support to that key bank which would make it eligible for RFC loans even on any definition of legal security. Henry Ford has $7,000,000 on deposit in this bank. I persuaded him to subordinate to the RFC loan any claim he might have on its assets. . . ." This was true, *except* that this occurred at a later time, after the crisis had gotten out of hand, as will be seen. Perhaps the explanation pertinent is that matters developed so rapidly and hectically, as will be seen, that Mr. Hoover is not to be blamed for getting some things mixed up in recollection, especially as he continued to be angry with Couzens, as his *Memoirs,* published almost thirty years after the events, show.

Incidentally, Henry Ford was not the only wealthy person Hoover had called for campaign funds in 1932, and found himself turned down. Another such call was made to A. P. Giannini of the Bank of America in California, as told in Marquis and Bessie R. James, *Biography of a Bank, op. cit.,* pp. 361–62.

5. *Literary Digest,* November 5, 1932.

6. Wilson Mills, chairman of the First National Bank, Detroit, interview, 1941.

7. James Couzens, "Michigan Banking Events," a memorandum prepared for the Keidan one-man grand jury, 1933. Also his notebook, February 7, 1933; *Detroit News,* June 20, 1933.

8. *Senate Hearings,* p. 4627.

9. See *Unemployment Relief Act (Public No. 5, S. 598),* approved March 1933, described in Beard and Smith, *The Future Comes,* p. 123; also *Detroit News,* February 14, 1933; *Congressional Record,* February 9, 1933, p. 3706.

10. John Carson to author, October 25, 1931; Longley testimony, Keidan grand jury.

11. Couzens memorandum, "Michigan Banking Events," *op. cit.*

12. C. C. Colt and N. S. Keith, *op. cit.,* p. 24. For an account of the Dawes bank matter (the $90,000,000 loan was repaid), from Dawes' view, see Timmons, *Portrait of an American; Charles G. Dawes* (1952), p. 316.

13. Carson to author, October 25, 1941.

14. Miller memorandum for author, *op. cit.,* p. 9.

15. Hoover telegram to Harry S. Toy, Prosecuting Attorney of Wayne County, Michigan, in *Detroit News,* August 23, 1933. Mr. Hoover does not make all this so clear in his *Memoirs, op. cit.,* in 1952. His statements there must be read very carefully, though they are true as far as they go in most frames of reference.

16. Charles A. Miller to author, March 27, 1942.

17. Miller memorandum, p. 6. Vandenberg corroborated this in public statements, see *infra.*

18. For examples, see Bingay, *op. cit.,* and Hoover, *op. cit.,* as well as Arthur Ballantine, "When All the Banks Closed," in *Harvard Business Review,* March 1948, pp. 129ff. The article by Mr. Ballantine, who was in a position to know the facts and who testified objectively in the Senate investigation, is strangely unsatisfactory as a piece of history, though presented as such. While valuable as an eyewitness account, for its facts, this article is likely to mislead students of the Detroit bank crisis when Mr. Ballantine expresses some subjective conclusions that incorporate several myths, such as the myth that Couzens and Ford were then feuding and also that Couzens' "rooftops" remark and his attitude toward RFC loans were factors in the closing of the banks. Mr. Ballantine, of course, was then a member of the Hoover administration.

19. *New York Times,* November 5, 1932.

20. *Detroit News,* June 20, 1933; see also Sward, *Legend of Henry Ford,* p. 249.

21. Herbert Hoover, to author, September 14, 1941.

22. *Ibid.*

23. *Ibid.* See also Hoover, *Memoirs,* p. 207, substantially the same, but with the added comment: "As Senator Vandenberg was a witness to this scene, it rankled in Couzens' mind until he died. The Detroit banks closed."

24. Miller, memorandum, p. 7.

CHAPTER XXXV. *The Climax*

1. Ballantine testimony, *Senate Hearings,* p. 5793.

2. Miller memorandum, p. 10.

3. Ballantine testimony, *Senate Hearings,* p. 5793.

4. This and other data in this section is based on Miller's memorandum, testimony of Edsel Ford and Arthur A. Ballantine in *Senate Hearings,* and conversation between the author and Mr. Ballantine, July 30, 1946.

5. Simonds, *op. cit.,* p. 233.

6. Henry Ford's threat to draw out all Ford deposits was fully corroborated later at the Senate hearing by Edsel Ford. "Mr. Henry Ford made that statement." (p. 4695) Also by Arthur Ballantine in his testimony, (p. 5796) and in personal interview, July 30, 1946. It was also recorded in the minutes of the RFC for February 13, 1933, *Senate Hearings,* p. 4695. The quotes in the text are from Mr. Miller's memorandum, but in almost identical language they are also in the record of the Senate hearings. Mr. Ballantine also tells of Ford's threat in his article in the *Harvard Business Review, op. cit.* But his conclusions as to the causes of the Detroit crisis and why the original RFC

loan was not made should be read with great caution. He accepts the scapegoat role for Couzens. See note 18, Chapter XXXIV.

7. Edwin Wildman, *Famous Leaders of Industry*, p. 131. Concerning Henry Ford's way of thinking, see also Nevins, *Ford*, for example pp. 576 and 582; also Coghlan in *Life* Magazine.

8. Carson memorandum to Couzens.

9. *Detroit News*, June 17, 1933.

10. Arthur Ballantine testimony, *Senate Hearings*, p. 5796.

11. *Senate Hearings*, p. 5797.

12. Wills testimony, *Senate Hearings*, p. 5511.

13. Couzens to Henry Ford, December 5, 1927; also to Edsel B. Ford, December 7, 1927.

14. Miller Memorandum, pp. 16–17.

15. Couzens testimony, Keidan grand jury, August 17, 1933.

16. Couzens memorandum; also testimony before Keidan grand jury, August 17, 1933. Mr. Longley confirmed this in his testimony before the Keidan grand jury, September 15, 1933; see *Detroit Free Press*, September 16, 1933; also letter of Wilson W. Mills to Couzens, August 3, 1933. Mills confirmed this in an interview with author, February 11, 1941.

17. Couzens testimony, Keidan grand jury, *op. cit.*

18. Huddleston interview, February 11, 1941.

19. See *Senate Hearings*, Part 12, Leyburn testimony, p. 5762.

20. *Ibid.*

21. Lacy testimony, Keidan grand jury, August 29, 1933; *Detroit Times*, August 29.

22. Comstock proclamation in Detroit papers, February 14, 1933.

23. Wilkin testimony, Keidan grand jury, June 25, 1933.

CHAPTER XXXVI. *"The Hell of a Mess"*

1. Leyburn testimony, *Senate Hearings*, p. 5656.

2. *Ibid.*, and *Detroit Free Press*, August 16, 1933; see also Frederick L. Allen, *Since Yesterday*, pp. 99–100; and Lindley, *The Roosevelt Revolution*, p. 73.

3. Hoover to Harry S. Toy, telegram, August 23, 1933, in *Detroit News*, same date.

4. Joslin, Theodore G., *Hoover Off the Record*.

5. Sullivan, p. 86.

6. Wilbur and Hyde, *The Hoover Policies*, p. 530.

7. F. Cyril James, *The Growth of Chicago Banks*, II, p. 1054. This book contains one of the best published accounts of the general banking crisis of 1933.

8. Lindley, *op. cit.*, p. 73.

9. *Literary Digest*, February 25, 1933; see also Simonds, *op. cit.*, p. 232. On the bank crisis, this book by a Ford publicist is almost completely unreliable. Cf. Colt and Keith, p. 8, and Sward, pp. 242ff.

10. Among others, Wilson Mills was told by Hoover that Couzens was to blame, interview, July 11, 1941.

11. *Detroit Free Press*, February 15, 1933. On the morning before, Bingay printed a similar, but less "pepped up" version. This same story, almost without change, was reproduced thirteen years later in *Detroit Is My Own Home Town*, by Bingay, even though the *Free Press* in the interim had carried much corrective material. See Hoover, *op. cit.*

12. See *Detroit News*, March 3, 1933.

13. Keidan grand jury testimony, August 22, 1933; in *Detroit Times*, same date.

14. *Detroit News*, February 13, 1933.

15. See Pearson and Allen, *More Washington Merry-Go-Round*, p. 147.

16. *Ibid.*, pp. 147–48 and 479.

17. *Detroit News*, March 3, 1933.

18. See *Annual Report of the Secretary of the Treasury on the State of Finances for Fiscal Year Ended June 30, 1933*, pp. 23 and 187ff.; also Beard and Smith, *The Future Comes*, pp. 17ff.; and *Literary Digest*, March 11, 1933, p. 9.

19. Sullivan, *Prelude to Panic, op. cit.*, p. 98; see also Colt and Keith, pp. 18 and 29.

20. Statement issued by the Ford Motor Company, *Detroit Times,* February 27, 1933.

21. Roy D. Chapin to Couzens, February 25, 1933.

22. *Detroit Times,* February 27, 1933.

23. *New York Times,* February 27, 1933.

24. Sward, *op. cit.,* p. 252; also *Literary Digest,* March 11, 1933, p. 10.

25. Miller memorandum, *op. cit.;* Couzens' statement, "Michigan Banking Events"; also Detroit papers, March 3, 1933.

26. Couzens' statement, *op. cit.*

27. See RFC minutes for February 22, 1933, *Senate Hearings,* Part 10, p. 4748.

28. Couzens telegram to Charles A. Miller, February 25, 1933; in *Detroit Times,* February 27, 1933; Jesse H. Jones to author, April 30, 1946.

29. Couzens to Don R. Carrigan, letter, February 23, 1933.

30. RFC minutes of February 26, 1933, in *Senate Hearings,* p. 4752.

31. Miller memorandum, *op. cit.,* and Sullivan, p. 102.

32. Miller memorandum, *op. cit.*

33. See Wilson Mills testimony, Keidan grand jury, August 17, 1933.

34. *Senate Hearings,* Part 10, p. 4753.

35. Couzens testimony, Keidan grand jury, August 18, 1933.

36. Mills testimony, Keidan grand jury, August 17, 1933.

37. Mills to the RFC, telegram, *op. cit.*

38. Eugene Meyer to Herbert Hoover, February 25, 1933, in Myers and Newton, *op. cit.,* p. 357.

39. Couzens notebook, February 28, 1933.

40. E. D. Stair to Couzens, February 28, 1933.

CHAPTER XXXVII. *The Mission That Failed*

1. Vandenberg to Couzens, memorandum, "Memo to Senator Couzens from Senator Vandenberg," in Couzens papers.

2. *Detroit Times,* March 2, 1933.

3. *Detroit Times,* March 1, 1933.

4. *Detroit Free Press,* March 3, 1933.

5. Couzens to C. L. Cardwell, March 4, 1933.

6. See Beard and Smith, *The Future Comes,* pp. 1–3; Wecter, *The Age of the Great Depression,* pp. 62–63; and C. F. James, *op. cit.*

7. Hoover to Roosevelt, February 17, 1933, in Myers and Newton, p. 340.

8. Grace Tully, *F.D.R., My Boss,* p. 63.

9. Roosevelt to Hoover, February 28, 1933, *ibid.*

10. Franklin D. Roosevelt, *Public Papers and Addresses,* I, p. 871.

11. Myers and Newton, p. 361.

12. Roosevelt, *Public Papers and Addresses,* I, p. 871.

13. Myers and Newton, p. 359.

14. *Ibid.,* p. 362.

15. Myers and Newton, pp. 365–66.

16. *Ibid.,* p. 364.

17. Raymond Moley, *After Seven Years,* p. 144.

18. *Ibid.,* p. 146; also Roosevelt, *Public Papers, op. cit.,* p. 870; also Ernest K. Lindley, *The Roosevelt Revolution,* p. 74.

19. Grace Tully, p. 64.

20. See Myers and Newton, p. 366; Roosevelt, *Public Papers,* p. 870; Raymond Moley, *After Seven Years,* p. 147; and Smith and Beasley, *Carter Glass,* pp. 340–42.

21. See Roosevelt, *On Our Way,* p. 24; also *Public Papers, op. cit.,* pp. 868–71; also for all texts, *Annual Report of the Secretary of the Treasury on the State of the Finances for Fiscal Year Ended June 30, 1933,* pp. 187–202.

22. See Jesse Jones' version in his *Fifty Billion Dollars,* pp. 66ff.

23. Couzens' testimony, Keidan grand jury, September 18, 1833; see also Ballantine testimony, *Senate Hearings,* p. 5803.

24. See Lindley, *The Roosevelt Revolution,* pp. 56 and 285ff; and the Beards, *America in Midpassage,* p. 146.

25. *Congressional Record,* March 5, 1933, pp. 6–7. See Rexford G. Tugwell, *The Democratic Roosevelt,* p. 264, for a sympathetic portrait of Secretary Woodin.

26. Couzens to Woodin, March 27, 1933.

27. Detroit papers, March 21, 1933; also statement by Jesse Jones, July 13, 1933.

28. Couzens to Madeleine Yaw, March 23, 1933.

29. Detroit papers, July 14, 1933.

Chapter XXXVIII. *The New Deal Onlooker*

1. Karl Schriftgiesser, *This Was Normalcy,* p. 296.

2. *Literary Digest,* March 18, 1933, quoting Ray Tucker.

3. *Ibid.,* also Lindley, *The Roosevelt Revolution,* p. 80.

4. John Carson to W. R. Yaw, April 1940.

5. Couzens to Madeleine Yaw, March 23, 1933.

6. Couzens to Clarence E. Wilcox, May 1, 1933.

7. Harold Nicolson, *Dwight Morrow,* p. 378.

8. *Congressional Record,* May 17, 1933.

9. John Carter Franklin, *The New Dealers,* p. 121; Grace Tully, *F.D.R., My Boss,* pp. 177–78.

10. Lindley, *The Roosevelt Revolution,* pp. 88–91.

11. See *Literary Digest,* March 18 and 25, 1933.

12. *Congressional Record,* March 14, 1933, p. 347.

13. *Congressional Record,* March 14, 1933, p. 346; *Literary Digest,* March 25, 1933, p. 6.

14. *Congressional Record,* March 15, 1933; *Literary Digest,* March 25, 1933.

15. Franklin D. Roosevelt, *op. cit.,* pp. 53–54, 219–21; also Lindley, p. 163.

16. *Congressional Record,* February 11, 1933, p. 3858.

17. *Ibid.,* p. 3841.

18. *Congressional Record,* February 11, 1933, pp. 3841 and 3858.

19. Lindley, p. 91.

20. *Ibid.,* p. 100.

21. McNary interview, April 15, 1940.

22. See Beard and Smith, *The Future Comes, A Study of The New Deal,* viii; also pp. 42ff. and 165; Stokes, *op. cit.,* pp. 369ff.; Saul Alinsky, *John L. Lewis;* cf. Mauritz A. Hallgren, *The Gay Reformer* and Dexter Perkins, *op. cit.,* pp. 15ff. and pp. 71ff.

23. See Frank Kent, *Without Gloves,* p. 25, and *Without Grease,* pp. 10–11. See also James E. Watson, *op. cit.,* p. 297; and Stokes, *op. cit.,* pp. 457–58.

24. See Pearson and Allen, *Washington Merry-Go-Round,* pp. 184ff. for an incisive analysis of the Progressives' inherent weaknesses.

25. *Men Around the President,* pp. 69–70; see also Lindley, *The Roosevelt Revolution,* pp. 105ff.

26. Johnson, interview, April 22, 1940.

27. Couzens to Albert Couzens, May 26, 1933.

Chapter XXXIX. *The Investigator Again*

1. The Beards, *America in Midpassage,* p. 161.

2. Lindley, *The Roosevelt Revolution,* p. 139.

3. Stokes, p. 348; see also Kent, *Without Gloves,* pp. 70–72; and Rodney Dutcher column, June 1, 1933.

4. Frank R. Kent, *Without Gloves,* p. 22; also Lindley, p. 143.

5. Kent, p. 24.

6. *New York Times,* May 27, 1933.

7. *Literary Digest,* June 10, 1933.

8. *Senate Hearings, op. cit.,* part 2, pp. 150–52; also the Beards, *America in Midpassage,* pp. 166–67, and Galbraith, *The Great Crash, 1929,* p. 56.

9. Rodney Dutcher, syndicated column, June 1, 1933.

10. Beards, *op. cit.,* pp. 167–68.

11. *Senate Hearings, Stock Market Practices,* Part 1, pp. 172–73.

12. *Ibid.,* p. 254; also Part 2, pp. 882–84.

13. *Ibid.,* Part 1, pp. 172–73; also *Literary Digest,* June 10, 1933.
14. *Senate Report, Stock Market Practices,* pp. 109–10.
15. *Senate Report, Stock Exchange Practices,* pp. 331.
16. *Senate Report, op. cit.,* p. 321.
17. *Congressional Record,* March 22, 1928, p. 5151.
18. *Senate Report, op. cit.,* pp. 380–81.
19. James M. Cox to author, November 13, 1945.

CHAPTER XL. *The Delegate to London*

1. Senator McNary, interview, April 11, 1940; also Rodney Dutcher, column, June 6, 1933. Concerning the conference, see Jeannette P. Nichols, "Roosevelt's Monetary Diplomacy in 1933," *American Historical Review,* Vol. LVI, No. 2 (January 1951), p. 308.
2. Daniel Hackett, interview.
3. Mrs. Couzens, interview.
4. Frank Couzens died October 31, 1950. Ford's son, Edsel, died in 1943.
5. White, *Puritan in Babylon, op. cit.,* p. 431ff.
6. Angell, James W., *Program for the World Economic Conference,* 15.
7. Herbert Feis, letter to author.
8. Cordell Hull, *Memoirs,* p. 256.
9. *Detroit News,* July 29, 1933.
10. Mrs. James Couzens to Madeleine Yaw, June 22, 1933.
11. *Times* of London, June 20, 1933.
12. Warburg, *The Money Muddle,* p. 114.
13. *Detroit News,* June 20, 1933.
14. Raymond Moley, *After Seven Years,* p. 239.
15. Moley, *op. cit.,* p. 239n.
16. *Ibid.,* p. 267.
17. Hull, *op. cit.,* p. 256.
18. Couzens notebook, June 22, 1933; also Moley, *op. cit.,* p. 254.
19. Mrs. James Couzens to Madeleine Yaw, June 24, 1933.
20. Associated Press, June 26, 1933.
21. Moley, *op. cit.,* pp. 249 and 253–54.
22. Couzens notebook, July 2, 1933.
23. June 30, 1933.
24. Roosevelt, *Public Papers and Addresses,* II, pp. 264–65.
25. See Lindley, *Half Way with Roosevelt,* p. 493.
26. Lindley, *The Roosevelt Revolution,* p. 216.
27. *New York Times,* July 8, 1933.
28. Mrs. Couzens to Madeleine Yaw, July 4 and 7, 1933.
29. John Franklin Carter (The Unofficial Observer), *The New Dealers,* p. 263.
30. Moley, *After Seven Years, op. cit.,* p. 217. Concerning the confusion at monetary conference, see also Tugwell, *The Democratic Roosevelt,* pp. 314–318 and 323–325, for a discussion from the Roosevelt point of view, and Dexter Perkins, *op. cit.,* pp. 92–94, 165.

CHAPTER XLI. *The Smear*

1. Jay G. Hayden, interview.
2. *Detroit News,* June 20, 1933.
3. *Ibid.*
4. *Detroit News,* June 20, 1933.
5. Couzens to Payne, June 22, 1933.
6. *Detroit Times,* June 26, 1933.
7. Statement by Arthur J. Lacy, in behalf of Mrs. Couzens, to Keidan grand jury, June 29, 1933; Couzens testimony, August 18, 1933.
8. *Detroit Free Press,* September 28, 1933.
9. Couzens memorandum, "Michigan Banking Events," and C. J. Huddleston, interview.
10. *Detroit News,* August 21, 1933.
11. *Senate Hearings,* pp. 4494–95.

12. August 19, 1933.

13. Keidan grand jury, transcript, August 23, 1933.

14. Keidan grand jury, transcript, September 18, 1933.

15. *Senate Hearings*, Part 10, p. 4641.

16. *Ibid.*, p. 4644.

17. *Ibid.*

18. Testimony, Keidan grand jury, August 18, 1933.

19. *Ibid.*

20. Hoover to Couzens, September 5, 1933.

21. Keidan grand jury testimony, August 18, 1933.

22. Ray B. Westerfield, "National Versus State Banks," *Annals of the American Academy*, January 1934, "Banking and Transportation Problems," p. 21.

23. *Detroit News*, September 18, 1933.

24. Frederic L. Smith, to Couzens, January 14, 1934.

25. Wilson W. Mills, interview, July 11, 1941.

26. December 29, 1914.

27. Frederic L. Smith to Couzens, *op. cit.*

28. *Detroit Free Press*, September 28, 1933.

29. Couzens to Keidan, letter, in *Detroit News*, September 20, 1933.

30. Couzens' statement, *Detroit News*, September 20, 1933.

31. Findings of Judge Harry B. Keidan, September 18, 1933; in *Detroit Free Press*, September 19, 1933.

32. Associated Press, September 26, 1933.

33. September 28, 1933.

34. Mrs. Couzens, interview.

35. Couzens to Payne, January 4, 1934.

36. *Detroit Free Press*, June 7, 1933.

37. See *Detroit News*, June 5, 1933.

38. Couzens notebook, October 2, 1933.

39. *Senate Hearings, Stock Market Practices*, Parts 9, 10, 11, and 12.

40. *Senate Report, op. cit.*, p. 231.

41. *Senate Hearings*, Part 10, pp. 4677–99 and Part 12, pp. 5791 and 5807.

42. *Detroit Free Press*, October 23, 1936.

43. Couzens to Payne, February 9, 1933.

44. Frederic L. Smith to Couzens, January 16, 1934; Couzens to Smith, January 22, 1934.

45. *Detroit News*, August 1, 1934.

46. *Detroit News*, June 9, 1937.

47. *Senate Report, op. cit.*, pp. 266–68.

CHAPTER XLII. *The New Deal Republican*

1. *New York Times*, August 26, 1934.

2. *Ibid.*

3. See Lindley, *The Roosevelt Revolution*, pp. 305–07; also Stokes, p. 384.

4. Couzens to Madeleine Yaw, January 31, 1935.

5. Letter, January 2, 1934.

6. Couzens notebook, November 20, 1933.

7. *The New Dealers, op. cit.*, p. 118. See also Galbraith, *The Great Crash, 1929*, p. 186.

8. *Congressional Record*, June 16, 1936, p. 9565.

9. Couzens to Mary Kingsbury Simkhovitch, January 4, 1936.

10. *Congressional Record*, June 15, 1936, p. 9346.

11. William R. Yaw to author, February 26, 1940.

12. W. J. Norton, interview, June 22, 1941.

13. *New York Times*, June 20, 1935.

14. *Ibid.*

15. Lindley, *op. cit.*, p. 280.

16. Couzens to George R. Averill, February 20, 1936; and Jay G. Hayden, interview, April 17, 1940.

17. Couzens to Dr. Freund, December 28, 1934.
18. Couzens to Lord Ashfield, May 10, 1935.
19. Carlson and Bates, *Hearst, Lord of San Simeon*, p. 247.
20. B. C. Forbes column, April 10, 1934.
21. *Congressional Record*, May 3, 1934, p. 7977.
22. Carlson and Bates, *Hearst*, pp. 220ff.; Norris, *Fighting Liberal*, p. 375; Leif, *Democracy's Norris*, pp. 297ff.
23. *Congressional Record*, May 3, 1934, p. 7977.
24. *Ibid.*
25. Couzens to W. S. Gilmore, March 13, 1935.
26. Couzens to C. T. Bach, December 18, 1934.
27. *Detroit Free Press*, April 7, 1935.
28. *Chicago Tribune*, June 2, 1935.
29. *Detroit News*, August 23, 1933.
30. See *Literary Digest*, August 3, 1935.
31. Stokes, *op. cit.*, p. 456.
32. Couzens to Walter L. Bouve, Jr., December 4, 1934.
33. Couzens to Howard C. Lawrence, February 23, 1935.
34. *Detroit Free Press*, March 2, 1935.

CHAPTER XLIII. *The Unbowed Head*

1. *Congressional Record*, February 18, 1935, pp. 2075–76.
2. *Ibid.*
3. *Ibid.*, pp. 2284–85.
4. *Literary Digest*, August 31, 1935.
5. Couzens to George R. Averill, February 20, 1936.
6. *Literary Digest*, February 9, 1935.
7. *Ibid.*, June 1, 1935.
8. Homer Couzens to Couzens, April 24, 1934.
9. *Congressional Record*, May 14, 1934.
10. *Ibid.*
11. *New York Times*, August 26, 1934.
12. Carlson and Bates, *Hearst*, pp. 268–69; *Literary Digest*, June 29, July 13, and September 28, 1935.
13. Couzens to Madeleine Yaw, March 23, 1935.
14. Couzens to Rosetta Hauss, March 30, 1935.
15. *Detroit News*, June 11, 1935.
16. Dr. Freund to Carson, July 4, 1935.
17. Dr. Freund, interview, February 14, 1941.
18. Couzens to Madeleine, December 10, 1935.
19. Franklin D. Roosevelt, *op. cit.*, 1936, p. 17.
20. Jay G. Hayden, interview.

CHAPTER XLIV. *The Political Dilemma*

1. Couzens to John C. Manning, January 31, 1936.
2. Couzens to W. R. Yaw, January 21, 1936.
3. Couzens to Chairman Jesse H. Jones of the RFC, April 2, 1935; also *New York Times*, February 25, 1936.
4. March 8, 1936.
5. *Congressional Record*, February 24, 1936.
6. George Averill to Couzens, February 15, 1936; Couzens to Averill, February 20, 1936.
7. May 5, 1936.
8. Couzens to John C. Manning, January 31, 1936.
9. Couzens to *ibid.*, March 30, 1935.
10. Manning to Couzens, February 23, 1935.
11. *Ibid.*
12. Manning to Couzens, February 23, 1935.

13. Justice Frank Murphy, interview, April 19, 1940.
14. Couzens to Manning, March 5, 1935.
15. Justice Frank Murphy, interview, April 19, 1940.
16. *Ibid.*
17. Attorney General Harry S. Toy to Vandenberg, June 4, 1935.
18. Frank Couzens to James Couzens, November 29, 1935.
19. Couzens to Frank Couzens, December 20, 1935.
20. February 1, 1936, p. 45.
21. Couzens to Payne, January 8, 1936.
22. Couzens to Frank D. Fitzgerald, February 4, 1936.
23. Averill to Couzens, May 21, 1936.
24. Couzens to Payne, May 21 and 28, 1936.
25. Prentiss M. Brown, letter to author, September 6, 1941.
26. John Carson, letter-memorandum to William R. Yaw, August 26, 1943; Prentiss Brown to author, September 6, 1941, and interview, June 1946.
27. Justice Murphy, interview, *op. cit.*
28. Prentiss M. Brown, interview, *op. cit.*
29. *Detroit News*, June 16, 1936.
30. Prentiss Brown confirmed this in interview, June 1946.
31. Carson memorandum to Yaw, *op. cit.* In Couzens' notebook for June 19, 1936, the day he entrained for Detroit, there appears this: "Carson at train—talked about Farley leaving PMG." Mr. Farley has commented: "Certainly it was never discussed with me by President Roosevelt. . . . I'm inclined to think there wasn't anything to it. It might have been some other place in the Cabinet, but not the Postmaster General." Letter to author, January 29, 1946.

Chapter XLV. *The Independent Man*

1. Couzens to Vandenberg, September 1, 1936.
2. John P. Frazer, interview.
3. W. J. Norton, interview, February 12, 1941.
4. *Detroit News*, August 5 and 7, 1936.
5. Radio address, Station WJR, August 21, 1936.
6. Couzens to W. R. Yaw, radiogram from yacht *Buccaneer*, August 12, 1936.
7. John P. Frazer, interview, September 26, 1943.
8. Ray Tucker, *Sons of the Wild Jackass, op. cit.*, p. 365.
9. Madeleine C. Yaw, interview, June 1946.

Chapter XLVI. *The Triumphant Defeat*

1. Couzens to McNary, August 24, 1936.
2. W. J. Norton to author, interview, *op. cit.*
3. Couzens to Vandenberg, September 24, 1936.
4. Senator McNary, interview, *op. cit.*
5. In Couzens papers; also in Grace Tully, *F.D.R., My Boss*, pp. 215–16.
6. August 27, 1936.
7. *Detroit News*, October 23, 1936.
8. In Couzens papers. The text, in part, of this letter was released by the White House on October 16, 1936, *New York Times*, October 27, 1936.
9. Couzens to Roosevelt, September 25, 1936.
10. Vandenberg to Couzens, September 16, 1936, dated "Wednesday afternoon, Lakewood Farm."
11. Couzens to Vandenberg, September 24, 1936.
12. Couzens' notebook, September 19, 1936.
13. *Ibid.*, September 24.
14. *Ibid.*, October 7, 1936.
15. Roosevelt to Couzens, October 7, 1936.
16. Couzens' notebook, October 11, 1936.
17. Arthur Krock, letter to author, February 26, 1946.
18. Justice Murphy, interview, *op. cit.*

19. *Detroit News,* October 23, 1936.
20. *Ibid.,* October 16.
21. Roosevelt, *Public Papers,* 1936, pp. 495-99.
22. W. R. Yaw, interview, June 1946.

CHAPTER XLVII. *"The End of the Road"*

1. Dr. Freund, interview, June 1946; see also Children's Fund *Report,* 1942-43, p. 3.
2. Madeleine C. Yaw, interview, June 1946.
3. In Couzens papers.
4. *Detroit News,* October 21, 1936.
5. *Ibid.,* October 23, 1936.
6. Madeleine C. Yaw, interview, June 1946.
7. *New Republic,* September 30, 1936.
8. *Detroit News,* October 23, 1936.
9. Roosevelt, *Public Papers, op. cit.,* 1936, p. 531.

BIBLIOGRAPHY

Adams, Samuel Hopkins, *Incredible Era, The Life and Times of Warren Gamaliel Harding,* Boston, 1939.
Alinsky, Saul, *John L. Lewis,* New York, 1949.
Allen, Frederick Lewis, *Lords of Creation,* New York, 1939.
———, *Only Yesterday,* New York, 1931.
———, *Since Yesterday,* New York, 1940.
Allen, Robert S., ed., *Our Fair City,* New York, 1947.
Alsop, Joseph, and Catledge, Turner, *The 168 Days,* New York, 1938.
———, and Kintner, Robert, *Men Around the President,* New York, 1939.
American Encyclopedia of the Automobile.
American Mercury.
Angell, James W., *Program for the World Economic Conference,* Boston, 1933.
Annals of the American Academy of Political and Social Science.
Anon., "Who's Who and Why—Serious and Frivolous Facts About the Great and the Near Great," *Saturday Evening Post,* April 21, 1923.
Appel, Joseph H., *The Business Biography of John Wanamaker,* New York, 1930.
Arnold, Thurman, "Must 1929 Repeat Itself," *Harvard Business Review,* January, 1949.
Automobile Magazine.
Automobile Review and Automobile News.
Ballantine, Arthur A., "When All The Banks Closed," *Harvard Business Review,* March, 1948.
Baltimore Sun.
Barber, H. L., *The Story of the Automobile, Its History and Development from 1760 to 1917,* Chicago, 1917.
Barkley, Alben W., *That Reminds Me,* New York, 1954.
Barron, Clarence W., *They Told Barron,* ed. by Arthur Pound and S. T. Moore, New York, 1930.
Barron's Magazine.
Barry, Richard, "Newberry's Successor: A Study of Senator Couzens," *The Outlook,* December 20, 1923.
Bates, Ernest Sutherland, *The Story of Congress, 1789–1935,* New York, 1936.
Beals, Carleton, *The Story of Huey P. Long,* Philadelphia, 1935.
Beard, Charles A. and Mary R., *The Rise of American Civilization,* New York, 1930, 1939.
———, and Smith, George E. H., *The Future Comes, A Study of the New Deal,* New York, 1933.
Beasley, Norman, *Knudsen, a Biography,* New York, 1947.
Bennett, Harry, as told to Paul Marcus, *We Never Called Him Henry,* New York, 1951.
Benson, Allan, "The Bombshell That Henry Ford Fired," *Pearson's Magazine,* April 1915.
———, *The New Henry Ford,* New York, 1923.
Bingay, Malcolm, *Detroit Is My Own Home Town,* Indianapolis, 1946.
———, "Get A Horse," *Saturday Evening Post,* June 29, 1940.
———, "The Motor Boys in Action," *Saturday Evening Post,* July 6, 1940.

Bingay, Malcolm, obituary article on James Couzens, *Detroit Free Press,* October 22, 1936.

——, *Of Me I Sing,* Indianapolis, 1948.

Blythe, Samuel G., "A Calm Review of a Calm Man" [Warren G. Harding], *Saturday Evening Post,* July 18, 1923.

Borth, Christy, *Masters of Mass Production,* Indianapolis, 1945.

Bowers, Claude, *Beveridge and the Progressive Era,* Boston, 1932.

Bradford, Gamaliel, *The Quick and the Dead,* Boston, 1929.

Briscoe, Benjamin, "The Inside Story of General Motors," *Detroit Saturday Night,* June 22, 1927.

Burck, Gilbert, and Silberman, Charles E., "Why the Depression Lasted So Long," *Fortune,* March 1955.

Burlingame, Roger, *Backgrounds of Power,* New York, 1949.

——, *Henry Ford,* New York, 1954.

Burns, James M., *The Lion and the Fox—Roosevelt,* New York, 1956.

Busch, Niven, Jr., *21 Americans,* New York, 1930.

Bushnell, Sarah T., *The Truth About Henry Ford,* Chicago, 1922.

Butler, Nicholas Murray, *Across the Busy Years,* New York, 1936.

Byers, George, "The Selden Patent Case," *Patent Office Journal,* October 1940.

Carlson, Oliver, and Bates, Ernest Sutherland, *Hearst, Lord of San Simeon,* New York, 1936.

Carter, John Franklin (The Unofficial Observer), *The New Dealers,* New York, 1934.

Catlin, George B., *The Story of Detroit,* Detroit, 1926.

"Causes of Employment," Hearings Before the Committee on Education and Labor, United States Senate, 70th Congress, 2nd Session, United States Senate Investigation, 1928.

Chatham (Ontario) *Planet.*

Chicago Tribune.

Children's Fund of Michigan, *Reports.*

Coghlan, Robert, "Co-Captains in Ford's Battle for Supremacy," *Life,* February 28, 1955.

Cohn, David L., *Combustion on Wheels, An Informal History of the Automobile Age,* Boston, 1944.

Colt, C. C., and Keith, N. S., *28 Days, A History of the Banking Crisis,* New York, 1933.

Columbia Motor Car Co., et al., v. C. A. Duerr and Co., et al. 184 Fed. 893, 1911. The second Selden patent case.

Commercial and Financial Chronicle.

Congressional Digest.

Congressional Record.

Connally, Tom, *My Name Is Tom Connally,* New York, 1954.

Couzens, James, "American Industry and the Social Good," *Printer's Ink,* July 1934.

——, "The Installment Buyer Worries Me," *Nation's Business,* December 1926.

——, "Why I Believe in High Wages," *World's Work,* April 1916.

——, "Providing for the Depreciation of Human Earning Power," *Michigan Manufacturer and Financial Record,* October 26, 1918.

——, Report of Detroit Police Department, Detroit, 1918.

——, "Senator La Follette—The Greatest American of Our Age," *Brotherhood of Locomotive Firemen and Enginemen's Magazine,* September 1925.

——, "Wages," *Survey,* April 11, 1930.

——, "What I Learned About Business from Ford," *System,* September 1921.

Cox, James M., *Journey Through My Years, An Autobiography,* New York, 1946.

Crowell, Merle, "Would You Be Happier If You Were Worth Millions?," *American Magazine,* February 1923.

Cuncannon, Paul M., "Arthur H. Vandenberg," in *The American Politician,* ed. by J. T. Salter, New York, 1938.

Cycle and Automobile Trade Journal.

Current History.

Davies, Joseph E., *Mission to Moscow,* New York, 1941.

Dearborn Independent.

Detroit Common Council Proceedings.
Detroit Free Press.
Detroit Journal.
Detroit Labor News.
Detroit News.
Detroit News Tribune, "The Wonder Plant and the Man Who Guides It," August 29, 1915.
Detroit Saturday Night.
Detroit Times.
Detroit Times and Tribune.
Detroit United Railway Appt. v. City of Detroit, et al., 255 U.S. 171, 1920.
Detroiter.
"Detroit's Government," Report by the Common Council and the Mayor of the City of Detroit, Detroit, 1922.
Dillon, Mary Earhart, *Wendell Willkie,* Philadelphia and New York, 1952.
Dodge, John and Horace, v. Ford Motor Co., Michigan Supreme Court, 1919, 170 Northwestern Reporter, 669.
Donovan, Leo, "Detroit," in *Our Fair City,* ed. by Robert S. Allen, New York, 1947.
Doolittle, James F., *Romance of the Automobile Industry,* Chicago, 1916.
Electric Vehicle Co., et al., v. C. A. Duerr & Co., et al., 172 Fed. 923, 1909.
Engineering Magazine.
Epstein, Ralph, *The Automobile Industry,* Chicago and New York, 1927.
Ervin, Spencer, *Henry Ford vs. Truman H. Newberry,* New York, 1935.
Everybody's Magazine.
Farley, James A., *Behind the Ballots,* New York, 1938.
———, with Walter Trohan, *Jim Farley's Story,* New York, 1948.
Faurote, Fay Leone, "The New Ford Line-up," *Engineering Magazine,* January 16, 1916.
———, and Arnold, H. L., *Ford Methods and the Ford Shops,* New York, 1915.
Fay, Charles Norman, *Social Justice, The Moral of the Henry Ford Fortune,* Cambridge, Mass., 1926.
Filler, Louis, *Crusaders for American Liberalism,* New York, 1939.
Flynn, John T., "Detroit Business Men Cheer Couzens' Defeat," *New Republic,* September 30, 1936.
———, "Inside the RFC," *Harpers,* January 1933.
———, "Michigan Magic—The Detroit Bank Scandal," *Harpers,* December 1933.
Forbes, B. C., "Why Multimillionaire Couzens Quit Business," *Forbes Magazine,* December 1922.
———, and Foster, O. D., *Automotive Giants of America,* New York, 1926.
Forbes Magazine.
Ford, Henry, *My Life and Work,* New York, 1922.
———, with Samuel Crowther, *Today and Tomorrow,* New York, 1926.
———, with Samuel Crowther, *Moving Forward,* New York, 1931.
Ford Times.
Foreign Policy Reports.
Fortune.
Frank, John P., *Mr. Justice Black, The Man and His Opinions,* New York, 1949.
Freidel, Frank, *Franklin D. Roosevelt,* 3 vols., Boston, 1952, 1954, 1956.
Fuess, Claude M., *Calvin Coolidge, The Man from Vermont,* New York, 1940.
Galbraith, John Kenneth, *The Great Crash, 1929,* Boston, 1955.
Garrett, Garet, "Henry Ford's Experiment in Good Will," *Everybody's,* April 1914.
———, *The Wild Wheel,* New York, 1952.
———, "A World That Was," *Saturday Evening Post,* June 8, 1940.
Gauvreau, Emile, and Cohen, Lester, *Billy Mitchell, a Biography,* New York, 1942.
Gibbons, Herbert Adams, *John Wanamaker,* New York, 1926.
Gilbert, Clinton W., *Mirrors of Washington,* New York, 1921.
Ginger, Ray, *The Bending Cross, a Biography of Eugene Victor Debs,* New Brunswick, 1949.
Glasscock, G. B., *The Gasoline Age, The Story of the Men Who Made It,* Indianapolis, 1937.

Grand Rapids [Michigan] *News.*

Graves, Ralph H., *The Triumph of an Idea*, New York, 1935.

Green, James F., "Great Britain's Foreign Trade Policy," *Foreign Policy Reports*, January 15, 1938.

Gunther, John, *Inside U.S.A.*, New York, 1948.

Hacker, Louis M., *The Triumph of American Capitalism*, New York, 1940.

Hallgren, Mauritz A., *The Gay Reformer, Profits Before Plenty under Franklin D. Roosevelt*, New York, 1935.

Hamilton, James de Roulhac, *Henry Ford, the Man, the Worker, the Citizen*, New York, 1927.

Hard, William, "Coming: Couzens of Detroit," *Hearst's International*, May 1922.

Harpers.

Harrod, R. F., *The Life of John Maynard Keynes*, New York, 1951.

Hatch, Louis C., and Shoup, Earl, *A History of the Vice Presidency of the United States*, New York, 1943.

Hayden, Jay G., "A History of the Detroit Railway Commission" in manuscript.

Haynes, George H., *The Senate of the United States, Its History and Practice*, Boston, 1938.

Hendrick, Burton J., *Age of Big Business*, Cambridge, 1927.

Hesseltine, William B., "Robert Marion La Follette and the Principles of Americanism," *Wisconsin Magazine of History*, Vol. XXXI, No. 261, March 1948.

Hewitt, Oscar, articles in the *Chicago Herald*, October 1923.

High, Low Washington, anonymous, New York, 1932.

Hinshaw, David, *Herbert Hoover, American Quaker*, New York, 1950.

Hinton, Harold B., *Cordell Hull, A Biography*, New York, 1942.

"Historical Chatham," *Chatham Planet Souvenir*, Chatham, Ontario, 1904.

Hofstadter, Richard, *The Age of Reform, from Bryan to F.D.R.*, New York, 1955.

———, *The American Political Tradition and the Men Who Made It*, New York, 1948.

Hoover, Herbert, *Memoirs*, New York, 1951 and 1952.

Howe, Irving, and Widick, B. J., *The UAW and Walter Reuther*, New York, 1949.

Hull, Cordell, *Memoirs*, New York, 1948.

Hutchins, Jere C., *A Personal Story*, Detroit, 1938.

Hutchinson, William T., *Lowden of Illinois*, Chicago, 1957.

Ickes, Harold L., *Autobiography of a Curmudgeon*, New York, 1943.

———, *The Secret Diary of Harold L. Ickes, The First Thousand Days, 1933–36*, New York, 1953.

Irwin, Will, *The Making of a Reporter*, New York, 1942.

James, F. Cyril, *The Growth of Chicago Banks*, New York, 1938.

———, ed., "Reforming the American Banking System," *The Annals of the American Academy of Political and Social Science*, January 1934.

James, Marquis and Bessie R., *Biography of a Bank, The Story of the Bank of America*, New York, 1954.

Johnson, Claudius O., *Borah of Idaho*, New York, 1934.

———, "George William Norris," in *The American Politician*, ed. by J. T. Salter, New York, 1938.

Johnson, Walter, *William Allen White's America*, New York, 1947.

Jones, Jesse H., with Edward Angly, *Fifty Billion Dollars, My Thirteen Years with the RFC 1932–1945*, New York, 1951.

Kennedy, E. D., *The Automobile Industry*, New York, 1941.

Kennedy, John F., *Profiles in Courage*, New York, 1956.

Kent, Frank R., "Couzens of Michigan," *American Mercury*, May 1927.

———, *Without Gloves*, New York, 1934.

———, *Without Grease*, New York, 1936.

Kern, Paul J., "Fiorello H. La Guardia," in *The American Politician*, ed. by J. T. Salter, New York, 1938.

King, Charles B., *Psychic Remembrances*, New York, 1939.

Labor.

La Follette, Bella Case and Fola, *Robert M. La Follette*, New York, 1953.

La Follette's Magazine.
Lane, Rosa Wilder, *Henry Ford's Own Story*, New York, 1917.
Lansing [Michigan] *News.*
Laski, Harold J., *The American Democracy*, New York, 1948.
Lauriston, Victor, *Arthur Stringer, An Appreciation*, Indianapolis, 1940.
――――, *Postscript to a Poet, Off the Record Tales About Arthur Stringer*, Chatham, Ontario, 1941.
Leach, Paul R., *That Man Dawes*, Chicago, 1930.
League of Nations, *Journal of the Monetary and Economic Conference*, No. 4, London, 1933.
Lee, John R., "The So-called Profit-Sharing System in the Ford Plant," *The Annals of the American Academy of Political and Social Science*, May 1916.
Leonard, Jonathan Norton, *Tragedy of Henry Ford*, New York, 1932.
Levine, Isaac Don, *Mitchell, Apostle of Air Power*, New York, 1943.
Lief, Alfred, *Democracy's Norris*, New York, 1939.
Life.
Lindley, Ernest K., *Half Way with Roosevelt*, New York, 1936.
――――, *The Roosevelt Revolution*, New York, 1933.
Lippmann, Walter, *Interpretations*, selected and edited by Allan Nevins, New York, 1936.
Literary Digest.
Littell, Robert, *Read America First*, New York, 1926.
Lochner, Louis P., *Henry Ford*, New York, 1925.
Lodge, John C., with Milo Quaife, *I Remember Detroit*, Detroit, 1949.
London Daily Herald.
Long, Huey P., *Every Man a King*, New Orleans, 1933.
Long, J. C., *Roy D. Chapin*, Detroit, 1945.
Love, Philip, *Andrew W. Mellon*, New York, 1930.
Lyons, Eugene, *Our Unknown President, A Portrait of Herbert Hoover*, New York, 1949.
Mackay, Kenneth Campbell, *The Progressive Movement of 1924*, New York, 1947.
Madison (Wisconsin) *Capital-Times.*
McManus, Theodore F., *The Sword Arm of Business*, New York, 1927.
――――, *They Told Barron*, New York, 1927.
――――, with Norman Beasley, *Men, Money, and Motors, The Drama of the Automobile*, New York, 1929.
McRae, Milton A., *Forty Years in Newspaperdom*, New York, 1924.
Marquis, S. S., *Henry Ford, An Interpretation*, Boston, 1923.
Marshall, Margaret Mooers, interview, *New York World*, December 1, 1922.
Mason, Alpheus Thomas, *Harlan Fiske Stone, Pillar of the Law*, New York, 1956.
Mertz, Charles, *And Then Came Ford*, New York, 1929.
Michigan, A Guide to the Wolverine State, compiled by WPA writers of the State of Michigan, 1941.
Michigan Manufacturer & Financial Record.
Miller, James M., *The Amazing Story of Henry Ford*, Chicago, 1922.
Moley, Raymond, *After Seven Years*, New York, 1939.
Morrow, James B., "Couzens, Radical—and Rich," *Nation's Business*, June 1923.
Motor World.
Myers, William Starr, and Newton, Walter H., *The Hoover Administration*, New York, 1936.
Nadler, Marcus, and Bogen, Jules I., *The Banking Crisis*, New York, 1933.
Nation.
National Magazine.
Nation's Business.
Neil, Judge Henry, "Senator Couzens Tells Why He Broke With Henry Ford," *Real America Magazine*, April 1934.
Neuberger, Richard L., "A Politician Unafraid" [George W. Norris], *Harpers*, October 1936.

Neuberger, Richard L., and Kahn, George, *Integrity—George W. Norris,* New York, 1936.

Nevins, Allan, *John D. Rockefeller,* New York, 1932.

——, with Hill, Frank Ernest, *Ford, The Times, The Man, The Company,* New York, 1954.

——, and Frank Ernest Hill, *Ford, Expansion and Challenge,* New York, 1957.

Newberry v. United States, 256 U.S. 58, 1920.

New Republic.

New York Herald Tribune.

New York Post.

New York Sun.

New York Times.

New York World.

Nichols, Jeannette P., "Roosevelt's Monetary Diplomacy in 1933," *American Historical Review,* Vol. LVI, No. 2, January 1951.

Nicolson, Harold, *Dwight Morrow,* New York, 1935.

Norris, George W., *Fighting Liberal,* New York, 1945.

Norton, William J., address at memorial services for James Couzens, Traverse City, Michigan, November 1, 1936, published by the Kiwanis Club of Traverse City.

——, "The Saga of a Foundation Executive," address before Prismatic Club, 1954.

Norwood, Edwin P., *Ford Men and Methods,* New York, 1931.

O'Connor, Harvey, *Mellon's Millions, The Biography of a Fortune,* New York, 1933.

O'Geran, Graeme, *A History of the Detroit Street Railways,* Detroit, 1931.

Outlook.

Parker, Read L., article in *Fort Wayne* [Indiana] *Journal,* November 15, 1914.

Paxson, Frederic L., *Postwar Years, Normalcy, 1918–23,* Berkeley and Los Angeles, 1948.

Pearson, Drew, and Allen, Robert S., *More Washington Merry Go Round,* New York, 1932.

——, and Allen, Robert S., *Washington Merry Go Round,* New York, 1931.

——, and Brown, Constantine, *The American Political Game,* New York, 1935.

Pecora, Ferdinand, *Wall Street Under Oath,* New York, 1939.

Pepper, George Wharton, *Men and Issues,* New York, 1924.

——, *Philadelphia Lawyer,* New York, 1924.

Perkins, Dexter, *Charles Evans Hughes and American Statesmanship,* Boston, 1956.

——, *The New Age of Franklin Roosevelt, 1932–1945,* Chicago, 1957.

Perkins, Frances, *The Roosevelt I Knew,* New York, 1946.

Philadelphia Public Ledger.

Pipp, E. G., *Henry Ford, Both Sides of Him,* Detroit, 1926.

Pipp's Weekly.

Pound, Arthur, *Detroit, Dynamic City,* New York, 1940.

——, "The Ford Myth," *Atlantic Monthly,* January 1924.

——, *The Iron Man in Industry,* Boston, 1922.

——, *The Turning Wheel,* New York, 1934.

Pringle, Henry F., *Life and Times of William Howard Taft,* New York, 1939.

——, *Theodore Roosevelt,* New York, 1931.

Pritchett, C. Herman, *The Tennessee Valley Authority, A Study in Public Administration,* Chapel Hill, 1943.

Pusey, Merlo J., *Charles Evans Hughes,* 2 vols., New York, 1950.

Quaife, Milo M., *The Life of John Wendell Anderson,* Detroit, 1950.

Report on Motor Vehicle Industry, House Document No. 468, Federal Trade Commission, Government Printing Office, Washington, D.C.

Richards, William C., *The Last Billionaire,* New York, 1948.

——, and Norton, William J., *Biography of a Foundation, The Story of the Children's Fund of Michigan,* Detroit, 1957.

Rogers, Lindsay, *The American Senate,* New York, 1926.

Roosevelt, Elliott, ed., *F.D.R., His Personal Letters,* 2 vols., New York, 1950.

Roosevelt, Franklin Delano, *On Our Way,* New York, 1934.

——, *Public Papers and Addresses,* New York, 1938.

Roosevelt, Theodore, *Autobiography,* New York, 1926.

Ross, Martin, *Shipstead of Minnesota*, Chicago, 1940.
Saginaw [Michigan] *News Courier.*
Salter, J. T., ed., *The American Politician*, Chapel Hill, 1938.
Saturday Evening Post.
Schlesinger, Arthur, Jr., *The Age of Roosevelt*, Boston, 1957.
Schram, Ross C., "How Detroit Came to Run Its Own Street Cars," pamphlet, City of Detroit, 1922.
Schriftgiesser, Karl, *The Gentleman from Massachusetts, Henry Cabot Lodge*, Boston, 1944.
———, *This Was Normalcy*, Boston, 1948.
Schuman, Frederick L., *Europe on the Eve*, New York, 1939.
Secretary of the Treasury, *Annual Report, 1933*, Washington, 1933.
Selden, George D., "The Selden Patent," *Rochester Alumni-Alumnae Review*, February–March 1940.
Seltzer, L. H., *A Financial History of the American Automobile Industry*, Boston, 1928.
Sherwood, Robert E., *Roosevelt and Hopkins, An Intimate History*, New York, 1948.
Shideler, James H., "The La Follete Progressive Party Campaign of 1924," *Wisconsin Magazine of History*, June 1950.
Simonds, William A., *Henry Ford, His Life, His Work, His Genius*, Indianapolis, 1943.
———, *Henry Ford, Motor Genius*, New York, 1929.
Sinsabaugh, Chris, *Who Me?*, Detroit, 1940.
Slemp, C. Bascom, *The Mind of the President* [Calvin Coolidge], New York, 1926.
Sloan, Alfred P., "Adventures of a White Collar Man," New York, 1941.
Smith, Rixey, and Beasley, Norman, *Carter Glass, A Biography*, New York, 1939.
Sorensen, Charles E., *My Forty Years with Ford*, New York, 1956.
Steffens, Lincoln, *Autobiography*, New York, 1931.
Stern, Philip Van Doren, *The Tin Lizzie*, New York, 1954.
Stewart, Maxwell S., "The Work of the London Economic Conference," *Foreign Policy Reports*, November 8, 1933.
Stidger, William L., *Henry Ford, the Man and His Motives*, New York, 1923.
———, *The Human Side of Greatness*, New York, 1940.
Stiles, Lela, *The Man Behind Roosevelt, The Story of Lewis McHenry Howe*, Cleveland and New York, 1954.
"Stock Exchange Practices," United States Senate Report No. 1455, Report of the Committee on Banking and Currency, 73rd Congress, 2d Session, Washington, 1934.
Stokes, Thomas L., *Chip Off My Shoulder*, Princeton, 1940.
Stone, Irving, *Clarence Darrow for the Defense*, New York, 1941.
———, *They Also Ran*, New York, 1944.
Street, Julian, "Dynamic Detroit," *Colliers*, July 4, 1914.
Stringer, Arthur, *Lonely O'Malley*, Indianapolis, 1920. A novel about Chatham, Ontario.
Sullivan, Lawrence, *Prelude to Panic*, Washington, 1936.
Sullivan, Mark, *The Education of an American*, New York, 1938.
———, *Our Times—the 20's*, New York, 1936.
Sward, Keith, *The Legend of Henry Ford*, New York, 1948.
Time.
Times, The (London).
Timmons, Bascom N., *Jesse H. Jones, The Man and the Statesman*, New York, 1956.
———, *Portrait of an American, Charles G. Dawes*, New York, 1953.
Toronto Border Cities Star.
Toronto Daily News.
Tucker, Ray, and Barkley, Frederick R., *Sons of the Wild Jackass*, Boston, 1932.
Tugwell, Rexford G., *The Democratic Roosevelt*, New York, 1957.
Tully, Grace, *FDR, My Boss*, New York, 1949.
Upham, Cyril B., and Lanke, Edwin, *Closed and Distressed Banks*, Washington, 1934.
Upson, Lent D., *A Quarter-Century of Citizen Concern with Government*, a preface and a bibliography of the Detroit Bureau of Governmental Research, 1916–1941.
Vandenberg, Arthur H., Jr., and Morris, Joe Alex, eds., *The Private Papers of Senator Vandenberg*, Boston, 1952.

"Vanishing Millions, The Story of the Detroit Bank Crash," a series in *Detroit Times*, March–April 1933.

Viereck, George Sylvester, *Glimpses of the Great*, New York, 1930.

Villard, Oswald Garrison, "The Unique Millionaire—A Weak Heart Made James Couzens Great," *Forum Magazine*, January 1937.

Wallis, J. H., *The Politician*, New York, 1935.

Warburg, J. P., "Monetary Policy of the United States," *The Annals of the American Academy of Political and Social Science*, January 1934.

———, *The Money Muddle*, New York, 1934.

Watson, James, *As I Knew Them*, Indianapolis, 1936.

Wayne, Flynn, "A Master Builder of Efficiency," *National Magazine*, September 1915.

Wecter, Dixon, *The Age of the Great Depression*, New York, 1949.

Wendt, Lloyd, and Kogan, Herman, *Big Bill of Chicago*, Indianapolis, 1953.

White, William Allen, *Autobiography*, New York, 1946.

———, *Calvin Coolidge*, New York, 1925.

———, *Masks in a Pageant*, New York, 1928.

———, *Politics: The Citizen's Business*, New York, 1924.

———, *Puritan in Babylon*, New York, 1939.

White, William S., *Citadel, The Story of the U.S. Senate*, New York, 1956.

Wilbur, Ray Lyman, and Hyde, Arthur Mastic, *The Hoover Policies*, New York, 1937.

Wildman, Edwin, *Famous Leaders of Industry*, Boston, 1920.

Wood, Charles W., "He Had Millions But Wanted a Job," *Colliers*, August 5, 1922.

Woodward, C. Vann, *Tom Watson, Agrarian Rebel*, New York, 1938.

World's Work.

Young, William P., *A Ford Dealer's Thirty Year Ride*, Pittsburgh, 1932.

U.S. Senate Report 27, "Investigation of Bureau of Internal Revenue Pursuant to Senate Resolution 68," 69th Congress, 1st session, Washington, 1926.

U.S. Department of State, *Foreign Relations of United States, 1933*, I, Washington, 1950.

UNPUBLISHED SOURCE MATERIAL

Couzens, James, general letters, notebooks, addresses, and clippings, 1903–1936, Library of Congress.

Couzens, James, "The Michigan Banking Crisis," a memorandum, 1933.

Detroit Board of Commerce, Minute Books, 1911–1914.

Durant, W. C., Memoirs, a manuscript extract.

Ford, Henry vs. The Chicago Tribune, Transcript of Testimony.

Hayden, Jay G., a history of Detroit politics.

Hoover, Herbert, a memorandum on the Detroit bank crisis.

Jones, Edgar Dewitt, radio address on anniversary of James Couzens' death.

Lauriston, Victor, "When Senator Jim Couzens Peddled Soap in Chatham," unpublished article on James Couzens in Chatham.

League of Nations mimeographed bulletins on the World Monetary and Economic Conference, London, 1933.

Miller, Charles A., memorandum on the Detroit bank case, 1942.

Neil, J. H., notes on interview with James Couzens, 1924.

Pratt, John S., special assistant to the U.S. Attorney General, Memorandum to Assistant Attorney General Keenan, "Re: Detroit Banking Situation," March 22, 1934.

INTERVIEWS AND CORRESPONDENCE

Among others:

Herbert Hoover, Charles G. Dawes, John N. Garner, Hiram Johnson, Charles L. McNary, Robert M. La Follette, Jr., George W. Norris, Frederic W. Hale, Pat Harrison, James E. Watson, Key Pittman, Arthur H. Vandenberg, Prentiss M. Brown, Arthur W. Capper, Cordell Hull, William C. Bullitt, William Comstock, Alex J. Groesbeck, James M. Cox, Gifford Pinchot, Frank Murphy, Henry Morgenthau, Jr., James A. Farley, Bernard M. Baruch, Herbert Bayard Swope, James P. Warburg, Samuel S. Marquis, Samuel Crowther, Jay G. Hayden, Charles A. Miller, Arthur A. Ballantine, Edward Keating, Thomas L. Stokes, Ray Tucker, John Carson, Frank L. Klingensmith,

Harry B. Harper, Edward G. Liebold, Herbert Feis, Raymond Moley, Edward T. Fitzgerald, Theodore C. Joslin, Charles T. Bennett, Ida M. Tarbell, Arthur J. Lacy, Clarence Wilcox, C. J. Huddleston, Ross C. Schram, Henry A. Morgan, Joseph E. Davies, Abner Larned, Wilson W. Mills, W. L. Dunham, Daniel J. Hackett, Mrs. Roy Pelletier, Dorothy Dunn, Walter R. Dorsey, Garet Garrett, Victor Lauriston, Arthur Stringer, William Mann, Charles Donovan, A. E. Couzens, Homer Couzens, Frank Couzens, Mrs. Alice Couzens Lund, Mrs. Rosetta Couzens Hauss, Mrs. James Couzens, Mrs. Madeleine Couzens Yaw, William R. Yaw, William J. Norton, MacPherson Browning, A. R. Malcomson, William C. Durant, Charles B. King, Charles T. Bennett, Vernon Fry, Herbert L. Satterlee, John C. Lodge, John P. Frazier, Harvey Campbell, Byers H. Gitchell, C. H. Haberkorn Jr., Henry T. Ewald, Dr. Hugo A. Freund, Mabel Ford, George W. Engel, A. C. Studer, Dr. Miles Griffin, Thomas W. Payne, William J. Twohey, John C. Manning, Helen Malcomson Gore, George Judson.

PERSONAL ACKNOWLEDGMENTS

To a number of persons, in addition to those named, gratitude is felt for various helps and encouragements in the fruition of this work, in particular, though not all-exclusively, to Wayne Andrews, for much valued guidance as well as a colleague's inspiration; to Allan Nevins, for having suggested that this work be done; to Judith B. Papier, for the index and other aids; to Stephen A. Mitchell and Bertram B. Moss, for crucial advice; and, foremost, though last here, to Ruth E. Barnard, my wife, who, through it all, was what God doubtless intended a wife to be in all respects—strong, comforting, and endlessly patient.

H. B.

INDEX

369

Books by Rosalind Laker

THE SMUGGLER'S BRIDE

RIDE THE BLUE RIBAND

WARWYCK'S WOMAN

CLAUDINE'S DAUGHTER

WARWYCK'S CHOICE

BANNERS OF SILK

GILDED SPLENDOUR

JEWELLED PATH

WHAT THE HEART KEEPS

THIS SHINING LAND

TREE OF GOLD

THE SILVER TOUCH

TO DANCE WITH KINGS

CIRCLE OF PEARLS

THE GOLDEN TULIP

THE VENETIAN MASK

The
Venetian
Mask

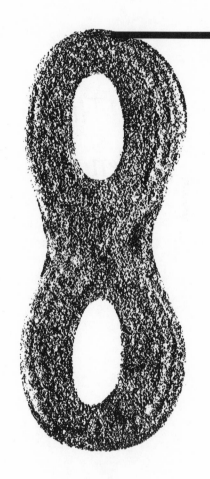

D o u b l e d a y

NEW YORK   LONDON
TORONTO   SYDNEY
AUCKLAND

The
Venetian
Mask

ROSALIND
LAKER

PUBLISHED BY DOUBLEDAY
a division of Bantam Doubleday Dell Publishing Group, Inc.
666 Fifth Avenue, New York, New York 10103

DOUBLEDAY and the portrayal of an anchor with a dolphin
are registered trademarks of Doubleday,
a division of Bantam Doubleday Dell Publishing Group, Inc.

Library of Congress Cataloging-in-Publication Data

Laker, Rosalind.
The Venetian mask / by Rosalind Laker.
p. cm.
I. Venice (Italy)—History—Fiction.   I. Title.
PR6065.E9V46   1993
823'.914—dc20   92-12488
CIP

ISBN 0-385-42190-7

BOOK DESIGN & ORNAMENTATION BY SIGNET M DESIGN, INC.

Printed in the United States of America
JANUARY 1993
FIRST EDITION
I   3   5   7   9   10   8   6   4   2

To
Paul, Nancy, and Jenny
for the Venice Carnival
in the snow.

The
Venetian
Mask

Chapter 1

Marietta raised the velvet-covered lid of the box. Immediately her green eyes widened at the sight of the full-faced golden mask that shone from its bed of black satin. A strange shiver passed down her spine.

"Who has ordered this mask, Mama?" she asked almost warily, recalling that a few days ago she had seen her widowed mother, an outworker for a shop in distant Venice, give it a second coat of a certain rust-red paint in preparation for its gilding. Then it had been just another mask among so many in the workroom, but now, newly returned from the gilder, it had somehow leapt into life. Its strong male features showed a forceful nose, deeply indented chin, wide planes across the brow and cheekbones, and a well-cut mouth.

"I know nothing about the purchaser, except that the base was molded from a sculpture of his face." Cattina Fontana looked up slowly from stitching sequins to a mask, every movement an effort in her poor state of health, and her gaze lingered fondly on her twelve-year-old daughter.

"Why would anyone want his own likeness in a mask?" Marietta continued to be uneasily intrigued. Masks were to conceal, not to reveal the wearer's identity.

"It will be for fashionable occasions, when everyone knows the young man, not a mask for disguise. I expect he has a host of those and wanted an exclusive one with which to impress his friends."

"How do you know he's young?"

"I don't," Cattina admitted, "but it's the kind of novelty that would appeal to a youth in Venice. Now add the tie-ribbons to it as I asked you."

Cattina returned to her sewing, her hands trembling with weakness. A persistent cough had drained all her energy over the past several months. Although her illness had given her a greyish pallor and hollowed her eyes it could not change the facial bone structure that had made her a fine-looking woman. It was from her that her only child had inherited an unusual beauty destined to fascinate.

The sequins winked little flashes of light as Cattina stitched. It was the last mask on which she would ever work. Even with Marietta's skillful help her mask-making days had come to an end. She was full of dread. For far too long she had postponed telling Marietta what was to happen on the morrow.

With care Marietta took the golden mask out of its box and set it down on the table in front of her. Then she measured two lengths of black silk tie-ribbon from a roll, snipping them off with her scissors. Her fingers seemed to tingle as she threaded a ribbon through the small hole at each side and fastened them into place.

"This Venetian must be rich to have such a costly mask made at a whim," she remarked as she closed the lid on it again. She had the eerie feeling that it was continuing to stare through the box at her.

"If he's a member of one of the wealthy patrician families it will be a mere bagatelle to him. Yet it's an investment, because he'll be able to wear it all his life."

"As I shall wear mine!" With a swirl of her long red-gold hair Marietta pulled open a drawer, took from it the *moretta* mask her mother had made her some while ago, and held it to her face. It was black and oval as these charming masks commonly were.

"May it always be a pleasure to you, child." Cattina had enjoyed making it as a Christmas surprise. The *moretta* mask was worn by all social classes of women in Venice, according to Iseppo Marcello, the bargeman who plied his trade between the heart of the Most Serene Republic and Padua. It was

Iseppo who delivered the work to Cattina and then collected the finished masks from her. He had given his promise of transport for the day that had come far sooner than Cattina expected.

Marietta began packing the finished masks in boxes ready for Iseppo. Once the workroom had been her late father's carpentry shop, but his tools had been sold long since and the walls were now covered with the pegged-up brilliant and exotic results of her and her mother's mask-making skills. Ranged on the shelves were boxes of twinkling spangled trimmings, soft plumes that wafted in the slightest draft, glass gems that flashed ruby, sapphire, and emerald; there were swathes of cobwebby Burano lace, dawn-hued gauzes, and the tangled sheen of rainbow ribbons. Less colorful were the masks still to be trimmed, made of papier-mâché, leather, or waxed canvas; something about the empty eye-sockets gave them a sinister air, but then every mask had an aura of mystery about it.

As she worked, Marietta hummed a few bars and then began to sing a favorite old song that her father had taught her when she was three. It was about Columbina, a serving wench loved by Harlequin, who was driven to distraction by her flirtatious ways. The song told of her capricousness as she danced through Carnival-time, evading him here and there in the arcades of St. Mark's Square, on the Rialto Bridge, along the Merceria, and even in a gondola where she closed the shutters of the *felze,* the black wooden hood, in order that he should not see her. But he always found her—only to lose her again.

On the surface it was a merry song, but Marietta never failed to be touched by its bittersweet theme. When her mother gave a little clap of applause, Marietta looked over her shoulder with a smile. Cattina nodded.

"You sang that very well today."

"Did I?" Marietta was pleased. It was as natural for her to sing as it was to breathe. Her earliest memories were of her late father's splendid tenor voice, but then it was said that there was not a Venetian born who did not sing or play a musical instrument. She was proud that she had inherited his musical gift and that his blood ran in her veins like the water in the canals of his native city, which she had never seen.

As Marietta began another old song, a violent spasm of coughing seized Cattina by the throat. Marietta rushed to fetch a bottle of herbal syrup and poured some into a cup, but there was no question of Cattina being able to drink as yet. As the cloth Cattina kept pressed to her mouth became stained with blood, Marietta was terrified that her mother would hemorrhage to death. When at last the coughing ceased the girl held the cup to her exhausted mother's lips.

"I'll help you to bed, Mama."

It was a slow process, Marietta supporting Cattina from the workroom and up the stone staircase from the kitchen. When at last Cattina was in bed, Marietta sat beside her.

"I have something to tell you," Cattina said, clasping her daughter's hand. "When Iseppo collects the boxes of masks in the morning, you and I must be ready to travel with him to Venice."

"You're not well enough to go anywhere! You must rest."

"In the morning I'll be better again. You know how my strength waxes and wanes."

"But why should you be thinking of such a journey? Let's wait until you're better."

"We have to go, child. You remember how I've talked about those four conservatories of music in Venice for girls unable to pay for their keep or their training? They are renowned for their choirs that sing like angels and for their superb orchestras. A tradition of music has been built up almost from their beginnings and the fame of these *ospedali* is known throughout Europe." Cattina smiled over what she was telling, unaware that she was plucking nervously at the coverlet. "It's no wonder that visitors to Venice—whether they be from neighboring Italian states or foreigners on the Grand Tour—consider it an essential part of their sojourn to hear these young singers and musicians. Iseppo says noble folk wait in long lines to buy tickets whenever an *ospedali* concert is to be performed."

"Do they?" A growing dread had stiffened Marietta's spine and she dared not anticipate what she was to hear next.

"At the best of these places, the Ospedale della Pietà, your father once made all the music stands for the orchestra. That was before I knew him. So it is to the Pietà that I'll be taking you. There you will live and be educated while your voice, which is so sweet and clear, is trained."

Marietta began to tremble with shock and dismay. "No!" she burst out frantically. "I don't want to leave you!" She leaned forward to throw her arms about her mother, the words tumbling from her. "Please don't make me go! You couldn't manage the work alone and there'd be nobody with you when you coughed. All I want is to be with you!"

Cattina cradled her daughter close, struggling to keep back her own tears. "But I'll be leaving here too. You see, once I know you are safely looked after I shall go to the convent in Padua where the nuns will nurse me."

"I'll come with you!"

"That's not possible. Only the sick are admitted."

"I'll join the convent as a novice and then the nuns will be bound to let me look after you."

"No, Marietta. You're too much your father's daughter to be confined forever within convent walls. I've decided what is best for you."

Marietta sat up and spoke on a gulping sob. "I long for you to be well again. More than anything else in the whole world."

"I know you do. But let us think of what lies ahead for you. You will get to know the City of the Sea. Your father never tired of talking about it. Tomorrow you and I will be seeing it for the first time."

"Why did he never take you there?"

"He couldn't. The Most Serene Republic has very strict laws and your father broke away before his indentures were fulfilled."

"What was the reason?"

"He had a cunning master who didn't want to lose a good craftsman and played several underhanded tricks to extend the apprenticeship. At twenty-one your father couldn't tolerate being under the man's thumb any longer and broke the law by leaving. I met my dear Giorgio when he came through the village on his way to find work. Even a small offense can be severely punished in Venice." Cattina saw her daughter shiver and became reassuring again. "You will never be involved with anything that brings retribution."

"What if I should run away from the Pietà?"

Cattina uttered such a gasp that it brought on another attack. When it finally subsided she caught Marietta's wrist. "Promise me that you will never run off! I want your word that you will stay until you are a grown young woman with a fully trained voice."

"I promise!" Marietta was frantic with distress at the attack she had caused.

"You'll make the best of everything and work hard?"

"I will!"

Cattina closed her eyes thankfully. The girl would keep a vow given.

Then she looked again at her daughter and cupped a hand against her face. "You'll be happy at the Pietà, I feel sure of it. It has such generous patrons and charges such high fees for its concerts that the girls live in comfort, with good food to eat and fine clothes to wear. Your father told me that whenever the choir and orchestra perform the girls all wear a spray of fresh or silk pomegranate blossoms in their hair."

Marietta did not think such a vivid flower would look well with her red hair, but she dared not raise any more opposition to the plan that had been made for her lest her mother start crying and coughing again. "You will come to see me at the Pietà when the convent has restored you to health again, won't you?"

Cattina held out her arms and folded her daughter close to her, pressing the girl's face against her neck. She was fearful that her anguished expression would reveal more than she wished at the moment. It would be too cruel to tell Marietta as yet that the four musical *ospedali* were only for orphaned and abandoned female children. Marietta was not being cast out, but it would be only a short time before she was alone in the world. "Whether that is possible or not, my love will always be with you."

Downstairs somebody entered the house and called out. Marietta drew away from her mother's embrace and went to the head of the stairs, recognizing the voice.

"We're up here," she answered.

Signora Tiepo, large and good-natured, was one of several women in the village who did what they could for their sick friend. When she reached the upper room she was concerned to see Cattina in such an exhausted state. Marietta left them to go down to the workroom and finish packing the masks. She was out of earshot when Cattina spoke of what was to happen the next day.

"I've told you before and I tell you again," Signora Tiepo said, sitting at the bedside, "you're without any family and I'm willing to foster Marietta. I'll take care of her as if she were my own."

"I know you would," Cattina said huskily, "and I'm grateful for your offer, but I've nothing to bequeath Marietta except this chance for her to be a trained singer."

"I agree she has a sweet voice, but Venice—" The woman left the sentence unfinished. She shook her head grimly. Venetian-born, she knew more about the Most Serene Republic than her sick friend. Ruled over by a succession of Doges, each elected for life, and great councils of noblemen, Venice had once been the supreme sea-power in the Mediterranean and the richest of all trading centers. Again Signora Tiepo gave a shake of the head. Over the years, set-backs in war, coinciding with political decline, had brought about many changes. Now in this August of 1775, Venice still owned colonies along the coast, but much of its empire was lost, its former strength weakened and undermined by hedonism and vice. Venice had become as wicked as it was beautiful, tainted by thousands of courtesans and known far and wide as the Brothel of Europe. As for the annual Carnival, which lasted from October to the eve of Lent—suspended only for the pious observance of Christmas Day—the merry disguises eliminated all social distinctions and allowed every kind of licentious behavior.

"Marietta will be well protected at the Pietà," Cattina insisted. She knew what was running through her neighbor's mind. "The girls are chaperoned at every step. They sing to the public behind grilles or from high, tiered galleries."

"But how do you know Marietta will be taken in when you get there?" Signora Tiepo questioned, feeling it was her duty to be blunt. "These *ospedali* were founded for the waifs of Venice. Not for children from anywhere else."

"I have a good case," Cattina answered firmly.

Signora Tiepo shifted her weight to a more comfortable position and sighed to herself. Those music stands! Just because they had been ordered by the late priest-composer, Antonio Vivaldi, who had been the Pietà's maestro at the time. For all this sick woman knew those music stands might have been thrown away and replaced long ago. Reaching out a work-worn hand, she took hold of her friend's fingers.

"Promise me one thing, Cattina," she urged. "If Marietta is turned away by the Pietà you'll bring her back here to me and let the rest of your days pass in peace without regrets."

"You're very kind, but all will be well."

"When are you going to let the child know how ill you really are?"

"As soon as she has been accepted by the Pietà. I shall ask those in authority for a little while alone with her. Marietta has a stout heart. She and I will be brave together."

Signora Tiepo's broad peasant face softened with compassion. "May God's blessing be on you both."

The next day, when Cattina opened the door to Iseppo, she and Marietta were both in their best shawls and ready for travel. The obvious deterioration in her state of health since his previous visit disturbed the bargeman greatly. He thought she looked as if she had not the strength to stand, much less to embark on a journey.

"So it is to be today, is it?" he said with sympathetic understanding. He would willingly have delivered the girl to the Pietà, but ever since Cattina first asked him for transport, she had been adamant about taking Marietta herself.

"Yes, Iseppo," she answered bravely, "we are ready to leave with you now."

"So be it." With a deliberate change of attitude he grinned cheerily at Marietta. "So you're off to Venice, are you?" he said to her, setting his hands on his hips with his elbows jutting. "Well, you sing like a lark already and you'll soon put the rest of the pupils at the Pietà in the shade."

His tone pierced the wretchedness that had settled on Marietta since yesterday. It reminded her to look on the brighter side. Her mother was going to be properly nursed to recovery, and the training she was to receive would enable her to become a professional singer or a teacher of music. She would be able to provide a good life for her mother and herself.

"It will be more than singing, Signor Iseppo," she answered. "I'm to be educated too."

"Is that so?" he exclaimed with feigned surprise, bushy eyebrows lifting. "I wouldn't be surprised if you ended up marrying the Doge of Venice!"

His jest had coaxed a smile to Marietta's face. "The Doge is married already and is far too old for me!"

"I dare say you're right," he said with mock regret, "but the next one might not be, and I would like an invitation to drink a glass of wine at the Ducal Palace. Will you remember that?"

"I will, but it won't make any difference."

Cattina looked gratefully at Iseppo. He was helping her and her daughter through one of the worst moments of their lives. She obeyed him when he advised her to wait on the bench outside until all was ready. Speedily he collected the boxes of finished masks from the workshop as well as the surplus bases and other materials no longer needed. Marietta, who carried the specially commissioned mask in its own container, accompanied him down to where his barge was moored. It was well loaded already, not only with goods brought from Padua but also with large baskets of melons, grapes, and peaches that local growers had brought for delivery. Iseppo's stepson, Giovanni, who had been stowing the baskets away, called a greeting to Marietta. She went down the wooden steps in the bank to go aboard and handed him the box with the special mask.

"Take extra care with this one, Giovanni. It's gilded."

"Is it indeed!"

He found a safe ledge for it within the canopy that covered certain of the goods and she waited while he and his stepfather placed the rest of the mask consignment under cover. Then she helped Giovanni arrange some old blankets and sun-faded cushions to make a comfortable place for her mother.

"Signora Fontana will be sheltered by the canopy here," the youth said reassuringly.

Satisfied, Marietta left the barge and ran back up the steps after Iseppo, who had gone to fetch her mother.

By now Signora Tiepo was with Cattina, who sat surrounded by neighbors and their children. It seemed that the whole village had come to bid Marietta farewell. All the adults knew what this departure meant for the two of them and there was not a woman who did not have tears in her eyes. Iseppo offered his arm to Cattina, but she had been coughing and when he saw what an effort it was for her even to rise from the bench, he lifted her up in his arms.

Glancing over his shoulder, he called out to Marietta, who was receiving small gifts of cakes and sweetmeats for the journey. "Come along, little lark!"

Marietta broke away from Signora Tiepo's tearful embrace and ran to catch up, her bundle of possessions bobbing on her arm. So much sadness shown by the women had reawakened terrible misgivings in her. It was almost as though they thought she would never be coming home again.

Cattina was made comfortable with cushions propped on the makeshift bed and Marietta knelt to tuck a shawl about her. On the bank Giovanni sprang onto the back of the large barge-horse waiting to tow the vessel, a switch in his hand. At a shout from his stepfather he flicked the horse and it began to plod forward. Marietta watched the tow rope tighten and the barge began to move. The children had gathered on the bank to wave to her. She waved back sadly until she could see them no more.

Cattina had closed her eyes. She had never felt so weak, and the pain in her chest was acute as it always was in an aftermath of coughing. The voices of Iseppo and Marietta came and went, making everything seem slightly unreal. She supposed some time had passed when she was offered food, which she refused, although she took a few sips of Iseppo's wine.

"There's so much to see, Mama," Marietta said once.

"I'm enjoying the rest," Cattina answered in a faint whisper. "Wake me when we get to Venice." Already the comfort of sleep was drawing her away again.

Marietta hoped her mother would be able to keep awake on the return journey, because Iseppo was full of amusing stories about various sights along the way. Whether they were true or not did not matter, for when she laughed it eased the dread that lodged like a heavy stone in the pit of her stomach. They were passing farms and vineyards and at one point the ruined remains of a Roman palace. All along the way, located for convenience close to the river banks, were the grand villas, many Palladian, that were the country seats of rich Venetians. These were pink or cream, yellow, peach, or white, their shutters in contrasting colors, and some were as ornate and spectacular as others were starkly plain. Many families were in residence and there were glimpses of well-dressed children, ladies with parasols, and a coming and going of riding parties. At one of the most palatial villas a gaily painted passenger barge was disgorging a noisy group of young people in a swirl of coat-tails and the flutter of fans. The door of the villa stood open and a young man was on his way to receive them.

"That's the Torrisi villa," Iseppo said drily. "It looks as if all is well there today."

"Why shouldn't it be?" Marietta questioned, thinking this to be one of the finest of the villas she had seen along the banks of the river.

"The Torrisi family and the Celano family have been at one another's throats for centuries and have no civilized contact. The origins of the vendetta go back to the fourteenth century when a Torrisi bride was snatched from the altar by a Celano, who married her before a rescue could be effected. Only last week there was a sword fight between a Torrisi and a Celano on a bridge where each demanded priority in passing."

Marietta regarded the villa with renewed interest. There had been quarrels between temperamental families in her village and fisticuffs between men on occasions, but these clashes never lasted long. How was it possible to sustain ill feelings over hundreds of years?

For a while Marietta was allowed to ride the barge-horse while Giovanni walked alongside. Her mother continued to sleep, only occasionally disturbed by coughing, and then Marietta flew to attend to her. As the river voyage drew to its end and the barge passed through the gates into the Maranzini lock, Marietta realized with a renewed pang of almost unbearable anguish how little time she had left with her mother.

When the final lap of the journey began across the Lagoon to Venice, the barge towed now by a *remulico* with strong men at the oars, Iseppo saw that Marietta had tucked up beside her mother, holding the sleeping woman's hand.

By the time they reached the custom house, the sun was setting. Iseppo went through the formalities while Giovanni supervised the unloading of the cargo. Then Iseppo stepped back on board and stood looking for a moment at the sleeping woman and the young girl who had fallen asleep at her side.

"This is a sorrowful business," he said in a heavy voice to his stepson, who agreed.

It seemed to Iseppo that some change had come over Cattina during the journey, but maybe it was a trick of light. He was glad that sleep had spared her mulling over the ordeal of parting that awaited her.

"Cattina," he said, giving her shoulder a gentle shake, "we're in Venice."

She stirred and her movement awoke Marietta, who sat up sharply, rubbing her eyes, then gasping in amazement at the sight before her. The sun was setting over a gilded city that appeared to be floating on liquid gold.

"This is a magic place!" she exclaimed in wonderment, having forgotten momentarily why she was there. Then the painful realization dawned with equal suddenness and with a cry she turned to throw her arms about her mother's neck.

Cattina patted her gently and looked up inquiringly at Iseppo. "Is this the *ospedale?*"

He shook his head. "No. This is the custom house. I have a gondola waiting to take us to the Pietà."

Iseppo had to lift her to her feet, and she swayed against him as they stepped from the barge onto the quayside. Giovanni, left in charge, said farewell to Marietta as she followed her mother. Iseppo needed the gondolier's help to get Cattina safely into the gondola. Then, when Marietta had taken the place beside her, Iseppo settled himself on a side seat as the gondola set off at its graceful pace across the water, heading for the broad parade that ran eastward from the Doge's Palace and was known as the Riva degli Schiavoni. Marietta saw nothing of where they were going. Her face was buried against her mother, whose arms were wound around her. She started as if struck when, after a while, Iseppo's voice rang out.

"There's the Ospedale della Pietà."

She forced herself to look. It was still a short distance away, a large mansion with a plain façade, its windows grilled with inner shutters. "It's a grand house," she murmured.

The ornamental entrance faced the parade, its recessed doorway guarded by iron gates. On the building's east side was a narrow canal and on its west it adjoined a sizable church. Iseppo gave its name.

"That's the church of Santa Maria della Pietà, one of the places where the choir and orchestra of the *ospedale* give concerts."

Cattina whispered fondly to her daughter, "That's where you will sing one day."

Marietta's only acknowledgement was to press closer to her. Cattina stroked her daughter's hair. The gondola was drawing nearer the Riva degli Schiavoni and she could see by the light of a single lantern illuminating the main doorway that the gates in front had an opening at the bottom just large enough for the anonymous abandoning of a small offspring. A sudden wave of doubt swept over her, chilling her through. In her weak and helpless state she began to fear for the first time that her daughter might not be taken in. It was the little ones who still had priority here, not a child already old enough to work. As the gondola left St. Mark's Basin to glide under a bridge into the side canal, Cattina saw that at the water entrance of the *ospedale* the gates had the same opening. The gondola came alongside the steps.

Iseppo told Marietta to alight first, and her hand hovered twice before she forced herself to jerk the iron bell-pull. Then she reached out to support Cattina as the two men propelled her up onto the steps. As for Cattina herself, she felt drained of all strength, her knees threatening to buckle at any moment. Then the door opened, releasing a flood of candlelight. A white-robed nun stepped forward to the gates.

"Yes?" she said inquiringly.

Cattina clutched frantically at the bars between them, feeling as if everything, even life itself, were falling away from her. All she was going to say, the appeal she had rehearsed, deserted her. She cried out a single desperate plea: "For mercy's sake give my child a home!"

As her mother collapsed, Marietta shrieked in alarm. If Iseppo had not tightened his hold on Cattina, she would have slipped from his grasp and vanished into the dark water.

Afterward Marietta had no clear recollection of the events of the next few hours. All she could remember was Iseppo carrying her mother into the building. People scurried around and the faces of some young girls appeared behind a gilded latticework grille, only to be shooed away again.

Cattina was put to bed by the nuns in attendance. A priest from the church of La Pietà performed the last rites. Marietta sat holding her mother's hand, leaning her cheek against it when tearful exhaustion overcame her. Iseppo, who had been allowed by the nuns to stay with the child, woke her at their grave nods just before the end came at dawn. Cattina, who had not spoken since the moment of her collapse, opened her eyes and looked at her daughter with the faintest of smiles. Then it was all over.

Iseppo gave a full report on Marietta to a senior nun, Sister Sylvia, who wrote everything down for the governors. He wanted to take Marietta home to his wife and even hastened her with him into the entrance hall to get her away, but the nuns stopped him. His offer to bring her back in a month or two was similarly turned down. Sister Sylvia put an authoritative hand on Marietta's shoulder.

"This child is in our care now, signore. A dying woman's wishes cannot be refused. This is a well-named house of pity."

He had no option but to leave. As the door opened to the full light of day on the parade outside, he paused to look back at the child standing bleakly in the nun's charge. Her arms hung limply at her sides, her red hair was tousled about her pale, tear-blotched face, and her drab peasant clothes contrasted with the nun's composed and snowy appearance.

"I'll come back to see you, Marietta," he promised.

"No visitors," the nun stated, signaling for a servant to close the door and the gates after him, "except by appointment."

Marietta said nothing. Grief had choked her to silence.

Chapter 2

*B*y the time Marietta had been three years at the Pietà, her earlier life had faded to poignant memories. It could not be said that she had really settled into the *ospedale*, although the joy of singing and having her voice trained had given her a dedicated outlook. She discussed her feelings with her friend, Elena Baccini, on the morning they were to be auditioned by the Maestro di Coro for possible inclusion in the Pietà's premier choir. Until then they had both been in a secondary choir, which meant that they had sung only behind grilles during services at the adjoining church of Santa Maria della Pietà, and then only when the premier choir was singing at the Basilica, the vast edifice that was the Doge's own chapel, or in the cathedral.

"I wish I weren't so nervous," Marietta confided, buttoning the bodice of her red gown, which was the uniform of the girls of the Pietà, "but so much depends on how we sing today. It's more than the honor of getting into the premier choir that's at stake. Getting accepted means the chance to enter the outside world again at public performances. That will be like inhaling the breath of freedom once more."

She frowned slightly, seeming to hear again the echoing slam of the door that had shut her away forever from all she had known in the past. Yet she was not unhappy at the Pietà. Her nature was too lively and resilient for her not to have made the best of everything, but she had never fully accustomed herself to institutional life. Discipline at the Pietà was strict, as it had to be with some hundreds of girls of all ages under its roof, but otherwise there was a relaxed and pleasant atmosphere conducive to the study of music.

"I'm scared I'll sing a false note," Elena wailed despairingly as she brushed her soft fair hair. She was still in her petticoats with the pads over her hips to hold out her skirts at the sides in keeping with fashion. The governors encouraged an interest in all things stylish. Most of the other girls in the dormitory were already dressed and leaving to go downstairs. "I think I'll die if I have to endure another carnival without getting beyond the Pietà walls."

After her parents died while she was still a baby, Elena had been raised by her great-aunt. With that lady's demise, Elena had been placed at the *ospedale* by a lawyer-guardian, which made her one of the few fee-paying orphans there. She had arrived some weeks after Marietta and the two newcomers had become close friends.

Marietta fastened the final button and gave her friend a twinkling glance. "Tell me again what it was like when you and your great-aunt took part in the fun."

Elena uttered a happy little laugh. "You're indulging me, because you know how I love to talk about it. Did I tell you about the year when I went to the Carnival dressed in yellow, red, and gold? The costume was refashioned from a wonderful chest of old carnival robes that Great-Aunt Lucia had hoarded since girlhood. You should have seen us, Marietta!" She stopped brushing her hair and flung her arms wide. "We were both masked and she was wearing an ancient purple domino that swirled dramatically about her. We sang and danced and dodged the egg-shells full of rose-water that the young bloods threw into the crowd. And oh! the marvelous fireworks! No creeping out of bed to try to watch them from the windows as we do now, but standing in St. Mark's Square under a canopy of colored stars. All this I shall see again, albeit at a chaperoned distance, if only I'm chosen by the Maestro today!"

"I'm sure you will be, but do hurry or we'll be late for breakfast."

Marietta took up a silver medallion stamped with a *P* for Pietà and slipped its chain around her neck. Back in the fourteenth century when the

Pietà was founded, its orphans had been branded with a P on the foot upon entry, but mercifully that custom had been replaced in these more enlightened times with the wearing of a medallion.

Elena heeded Marietta's advice and began to put on her red gown, but she was still brimming with anticipatory excitement. "When I become one of the two prima donnas with the premier choir—you will be the other—I think I'll be known as the Rose of the Pietà."

It was not unusual for the public to find a descriptive title for a favorite Pietà singer. The *ospedale*'s present prima donna, a young woman named Adrianna, was known throughout Europe as the Venus of the Pietà. Marietta did not doubt that Elena would gain that acclaim for her appearance. With her pale gold hair, her pink and white porcelain complexion and slightly uptilted nose, a mouth of extraordinary sweetness and eyes of an astonishingly deep blue, Elena was indeed rose-like and the very epitome of the Venetian ideal of beauty. Throughout the Republic of Venetia many women of fashion resorted to dyes in an attempt to achieve hair of that ravishing hue.

"What shall I call myself?" Marietta pondered with a wide smile, willing enough to share the embellishment of their mutual dream of Pietà success. "I can't think of any title that would suit me."

Elena raised an eyebrow, incredulous that her friend had not given thought to the matter when they had discussed so often the honor paid to Adrianna as the Venus of the Pietà. "That's easy. You'll be the Flame of the Pietà!"

Marietta was dismayed. "Is my hair so orange?"

"No!" With a laugh Elena took Marietta by the shoulders and thrust her in front of a silver-framed mirror. "It's a marvelous color—red as copper in the sunlight and dark bronze in candleglow. It's just the same beautiful hue as the great painter Titian loved to use. But that's only a part of it. It's you yourself. Can't you see?"

Marietta studied her reflection critically. Her well-brushed hair had a fine gloss and her longish neck was slender. She supposed her eyes and her even white teeth were her best features and the other girls expressed envy of her long dark lashes, but she saw nothing else to favor. Picking up a handglass she turned sideways to reassess her profile in the reflection of the wall mirror. Her nose seemed longer and thinner than ever and her chin far too determined to suit her idealized notion of beauty. Even her cheeks had little hollows under high bones.

"More like the Dandelion of the Pietà," she jested ruefully, never minding a joke against herself.

"Tiger-lily," Elena corrected, amused. "That's more flattering." She found it comical, having astutely judged her own good looks, that Marietta should fail to see reflected in her own face the beauty of another age. She had the same thin-nosed, smoldering looks that gazed out from medieval frames. One knew instinctively that those women of a much earlier century, for all their docile poses, were full of fire and tempestuous passion. It was Marietta herself who had made this observation when they were taken to view some early works of secular art. Elena watched her friend closely. Was Marietta really seeing herself at last?

Marietta had glanced down into the hand mirror. Then quickly she put it aside. She had seen rising in her eyes a certain brilliance that she had come to recognize as an expression of all the forceful, mixed-up yearnings that assailed her at times, making her want to break out of the Pietà to discover what awaited her in the outside world. But she had to be patient. It was fortunate that she had music to fill all her waking hours. Her love of singing was all-consuming and would be her mainstay throughout her life. Maybe Elena was right and such passions did make a living flame of her.

After breakfast the two friends went their separate ways until they should meet again for the audition at noon. Each had a singing class to teach between practice sessions of their own, Marietta on the harpsichord and Elena on the flute. A pyramidal system of teaching in music existed at the *ospedale*, with older girls passing on their musical knowledge to those a year younger. When they reached a certain standard the pupils passed into the classes of the *maestri*, male and female, who were highly accomplished and considered the best teachers to be found anywhere. Pupils with no apparent gift for music could, with diligent training and much hard work, become good instrumentalists. For those without the will or the inclination, there was always the domestic side of the Pietà.

When Marietta entered the audition room at the end of the morning, she found Elena had arrived before her. She was peeping cautiously out of the window, but turned to beckon as Marietta approached.

"Come and look," she whispered merrily. "But don't let them see you."

Marietta joined her to peer down through the outer ornamental grille. The Riva degli Schiavoni was a favorite promenade for Venetians and foreign visitors alike, the Pietà always an object of curiosity. The two well-dressed young men below had followed the pattern of many visitors by putting all manners aside in trying to see through one of the ground floor windows. In a city where sexual pleasures came easily, the virginal mystique of the closely guarded Pietà girls was often an irresistible incitement. Marietta, who was able to see only the tops of the young men's tricorne hats, was as amused as Elena to hear their remarks. They were Italian, their accent not Venetian.

"This wretched grille casts shadows. What can you see, Roberto?"

"No girls unfortunately."

"It's a salon. There's furniture."

"And a door, Guido. Maybe if we wait a while some of the beauties will enter."

The two girls clapped hands over their mouths to control their laughter. The salon below was an anteroom to the governors' boardroom and since there was no meeting it would be deserted at this time of day. But the young man addressed as Guido had sharp hearing and looked up quickly before the girls could draw back. He gave his companion a nudge with his elbow, a broad grin lighting up his exceptionally handsome face. His friend was no less personable and beamed his delight. "What good fortune! Two beautiful Pietà girls on our first day in Venice!"

Laughing, Marietta and Elena fled to the other side of the music room as if the windows were not grilled and the two strangers might come leaping in from the parade below. It was one of the strictest rules of the Pietà that no communication from the windows ever take place. To their dismay the young men began shouting.

"Come back! Don't go! Tell us your names!"

Marietta rushed back to the window, followed by Elena, and leaned out to call down through the grille. "We're not supposed to talk to anyone! Please go away!"

But the two Italians were too excited by this unexpected turn of good fortune to let the adventure come to nothing. "Your names! We want to know!"

"Marietta and Elena! Now please go away!"

Guido blew a kiss to Marietta and Roberto did the same to Elena, as though each were laying claim to his choice. "Get out of that nunnery and we'll all have a wonderful time!" Guido called.

"Take pity on us!" Roberto urged, laughing. "Two strangers in your city."

Passers-by had begun to stop and stare. Marietta slammed the window shut. Both she and Elena knew how dire would be the consequences if anyone in authority at the Pietà should receive a report of the incident. They both jumped in alarm as a handful of small stones rattled against the windowpanes. Then another handful followed, showing that the young men had no intention of going away.

"It's no good!" Elena's hands were clenched in panic. "The Maestro di Coro will be here any minute. Speak to them again, Marietta. Say anything to make them go away."

Marietta opened the window again and both Guido and Roberto cheered. "Do leave us alone," she implored. "We'll be severely punished if you continue to make an uproar."

Elena at Marietta's side endorsed the request. "Be kind and do as Marietta says!"

Neither of them heard Sister Sylvia enter the room in her soft-soled shoes. She had heard the commotion outside and had come to investigate the source. Her shriek of outrage impaled the girls where they stood. "You wanton creatures!"

The punishment that followed was the hardest that either had ever had to endure. The Maestro di Coro canceled their auditions and the two girls were separated, forbidden to communicate for three months. Should they break this restriction they would both be turned out of the Pietà, Marietta to be placed in a household as a domestic servant and Elena returned to her guardian. Their musical prospects would be at an end.

Occasionally from a distance they exchanged commiserating glances, but neither dared even to pass a message through someone else. The authorities would not hesitate to carry out their threat. But it was apparent to both that they had not been suspended from singing lessons, and individually they took this to mean that nobody wanted their progress interrupted.

Neither were they barred from educational outings with their gentlewomen teachers, the art and architecture of Venice having such close links with its music. Closely chaperoned, often by Sisters Sylvia and Giaccomina, the latter as round and plump and amiable as the former was thin and strict and sharp-tongued, the Pietà girls set out in groups, their faces covered by compulsory white veils. The girls all thoroughly enjoyed these expeditions, which took them into the streets and squares as well as onto the canals. Until the ban, Marietta and Elena had always walked side by side, but now they were in separate groups. Marietta missed her friend's lively chatter and comments on the young men who eyed them.

Whether they were viewing great art such as Titian's Assumption of the Virgin in the Frari Church, or gazing at the golden mosaics in the Basilica, there were always plenty of well-dressed young men close by. Venice teemed with young male visitors on the Grand Tour, and fashion had never been more favorable to the male sex. Velvet or silk waisted coats swung out over well-fitting knee breeches, lace frothed at the neck and wrists, and topping all else were the high-sided tricorne hats, the highest of all favored by the Venetians and set firmly on white wigs or powdered hair tied back with a black bow.

Men always stopped or turned their heads to watch the veiled Pietà girls go by. They would bow, pay compliments, or even try to make advances, much to the annoyance of the chaperones, who would then gather their charges closer under their protection. More than one love-note or poem had been passed quickly into a girl's hand, and there was much giggling under the white veils.

Thus hurried along, the girls caught only tantalizing glimpses of plays being enacted by strolling players on stages set up in the squares. They had no chance to linger and watch the tumblers, clad in gaudy pink and yellow costumes, forming human pyramids, or to applaud the jugglers or the dancing dogs or one of the many dancing troupes. But they could look their fill at ladies of fashion in their wide panniered gowns and plumed hats, who vied with one another as they promenaded in the arcades. Many would be escorted by their *cavalieri servanti,* young gentlemen who carried their jewel-collared lap-dogs and who attended and protected the ladies and— according to Elena, who professed to know from her great-aunt's gossip— pleasured them in every way. The most grandly established courtesans were indistinguishable from the patrician ladies, although Elena could pick them out, and there were hundreds of their less fortunate sisters who flaunted themselves in gowns so low-cut that the aureoles of their nipples were revealed.

Marietta was always glad when the educational venue necessitated an early-morning ride in a gondola along the Grand Canal. Then she could sit enthralled by the sight of the beautiful palaces that rose up from their own reflections, elegant with balconies, colonnaded loggias, ornamental stone-work, statuary, and an occasional mosaic mural that sparkled like gold-set jewels. By their ornate water porticoes the mooring posts were striped in the heraldic colors of the particular partrician family who lived within. If there was also decay, evident in crumbling brickwork, sodden wood, and rotting doorways, it only symbolized the decadence that afflicted *La Serenissima.*

The Palace of the Doges had a beauty all its own, a double tier of columns and arches delicate as lacework. The lovely, ever-changing light of Venice constantly played its marble into opal or ivory, amber or pearl or deepest rose, like an artist ever seeking a result more perfect than the last.

Twisting and turning in her seat, Marietta would watch all that was happening in the shops and stalls on the parades flanking the Grand Canal. The hostelries had customers coming and going even at such an early hour, and some were still dressed in evening splendor, having called in for break-fast after a night of revelry before hailing a gondola to take them home. The shouts of the water-carriers mingled with those of vendors selling every-thing from fruit to exotic spices. Thrifty housewives darted about for the freshest fish and vegetables, some buying direct from boats lying alongside the parades. Rafts and barges came with supplies such as creels of seafood for the Rialto market and wine that was awaited at the Fondemento del Vin.

And dominating everything was the music of Venice. The gondoliers sang and others took up the refrain. There always seemed to be somebody about with a lute or a violin, often in a gondola, and bands of musicians strolled the streets and performed in the squares. But it was at night, when the girls were settling in to sleep, that music came into its own. To Marietta it was like a siren call. As she lay in bed watching the flickering patterns on the ceiling caused by the reflected light from the water, it was as though she were gazing at fingers beckoning her out to all the city held in wait for her.

At the end of their three months of punishment, Marietta and Elena were summoned by the governor from whom they received the strictest lecture. They were reminded once more that the Pietà prided itself on the impeccable reputation of all the girls in its charge. Never again must they commit such an indiscretion, for they would not get a second chance. On this note they were dismissed. They went docilely from the room, but as soon as they were out of earshot they embraced hilariously.

"At last! It's been so boring. What a tedious time! I had so much to tell you and yet I had to hold my tongue."

They talked at the same time, each with laughter not far from tears of relief that they could pick up the threads again. When they had calmed down Marietta spoke more soberly.

"We must never let silence be imposed on us again."

"I agree. And I've thought of a way we could have communicated."

Marietta set hands on her waist and threw back her head in renewed merriment. "I know what you're going to say. I thought of it too. A series of signals with a glove, a sheet of music, or even a false note. Just like the language of fans or of beauty patches on the face!"

"That's it!" Elena clapped in her delight that they should both have hit upon the same idea. "I've made a list."

"So have I!"

"Then let's compare notes."

It was not long before they had devised a series of signals to convey the time of a meeting, where it should be, and so forth. They practiced until they could communicate in class and during the hours of silence, as well as on other occasions. Gradually they brought their communicating to a fine art, so that even the tap of a finger against chin or cheek, on lace or paper, and on hand or sleeve was used to convey a letter of the alphabet. More than once they had to struggle against laughter when they shared a joke from opposite sides of the room.

Their postponed auditions with the Maestro di Coro finally took place, and close to their sixteenth birthdays, Marietta and Elena both became full-fledged members of the Pietà's renowned choir. With this honor came the privilege of a bedchamber each. Their days of sharing with others were over.

"Only one more step up the ladder to lead solo singers, and then we'll have an apartment each!" Marietta declared.

They were well pleased with their new accommodations. The rooms were small but had fine furnishings and draped brocade curtains that concealed a bed in an alcove.

Another cause for high spirits was their splendid new wardrobes made by the Pietà girls training to be dressmakers. For singing in church and at other ecclesiastical occasions there was a simple silk gown in Pietà red with a diaphanous white cowl that could be looped over the head. For concert appearances, fashion held sway in panniered evening gowns with low dé-colletage, either in white silk or black velvet. Marietta and Elena each received a spray of vermilion silk pomegranate blossoms, to be worn at concerts only when no fresh sprays could be found. The two girls tried wearing the silk sprays in many ways, although they would be required to wear them in their hair, at the right of the face and toward the back of the head.

Their first public appearance was to be at a great service in the Basilica. Excitedly Marietta and Elena donned their scarlet gowns and matching cloaks and hoods. Then they proceeded two by two with the rest of the choir out of the Pietà and along the Riva degli Schiavoni to St. Mark's Square. There they passed through the great doors into the heart of Vene-tian sacred music.

From the gallery Marietta could just see the Doge seated far below in his robe made of gold cloth, as was his corno, the horned cap of his office. His senators, the elite and legislative body of the government, made a scarlet silken spread in their robes, a vivid contrast to the bat-like hue of the civic attire worn by the many hundreds of members of the Great Council who were also present.

As the service commenced Marietta thought there could be no better place in all the world in which to sing. Such were the marvelous acoustics that the organ seemed to be expanding the golden mosaic walls with its music, and the voices of her fellow choristers might have been those of the angels to whom they were so often compared. As for the paeans of the silver trumpets, it was as if the Archangel Gabrieli himself had passed on his gift to the trumpeters.

From then on Marietta and Elena entered a whole new world of music. They sang at many important festivals and in the Doge's Palace. At concerts they were arranged in rows along specially constructed, velvet-draped galleries, as if, Elena said, they were slotted into the wide, tiered pockets of a giant's coat. They performed in sumptuous public halls and glittering palace ballrooms, allowing the two friends an insight into the luxurious life of the rich nobility, who sat on gilded chairs to listen to them. Sometimes ten or twelve choristers, hidden and protected behind grilles set in the wall, would provide background singing at private ridottos where high-stakes play took place at the gaming tables. This in turn showed Marietta and Elena another side of life, where fortunes changed hands continually.

Yet all these grand people, whether Venetian or foreign, considered it an honor to be invited to one of the exclusive Pietà receptions where the choristers and lead musicians were presented to the guests. Women were as curious as men to see the angels of song at close quarters. Adrianna, the prima donna of the Pietà, gave Marietta and Elena advice on how to conduct themselves at these receptions. In her mid-twenties, she was tall and deep-bosomed, with smooth blue-black hair and a flawless olive complexion, her demure face enhanced by handsome black eyes and a smiling mouth. The title she had gained as the Venus of the Pietà was an embarrassment to her, for she had none of the fiery temperament and lust for fame usually associated with singers of her stature. Warm-hearted and maternal, she was always ready to rock a fretful baby to sleep in the nursery quarters or listen sympathetically to the troubles of others. It was she who had done much to ease the first few weeks at the Pietà for both Marietta and Elena by drawing them slowly into the daily routine.

"Now remember all I've told you," she said to them as they lined up with the other choristers in readiness for their first reception. No one knew better than she how to speak charmingly while avoiding the groping hand or turning aside the lascivious compliment. She had already found the man of her choice, but for reasons of her own she was keeping it a secret.

Marietta and Elena soon became as expert as Adrianna at avoiding unwanted and unwelcome attentions. The pleasant and interesting people they met usually outnumbered the rest. But the most objectionable visitors of all were often those newly arrived in Venice, who had not yet attended a concert and knew the choir only by its fame and through hearing the girls singing unseen in church. Their discovery that, with a few exceptions, the girls were not as beautiful as their voices immediately destroyed cherished illusions. It was not unusual for someone to make a disparaging remark, with no thought for the unfortunate girl who might overhear it.

It was on such occasions that Elena showed the deep warmth of her nature. She would comfort and encourage, often managing to get a girl's tears dried in laughter.

"Here am I," she once remarked wryly to Marietta, "cheering everybody else up when I'm far from being betrothed myself. I shall probably end up with the baker's apprentice. He is good-looking and likes me! If ever I happen to be downstairs on my own when he is making the first deliveries he wants to talk. He has started bringing me a cake to have with the cup of hot chocolate I always collect from the senior cook to take to the music room."

Marietta was amused. "You would never go hungry married to a baker!"

Elena threw back her head to laugh. "No! But I would be sure to end up round as a barrel! Those cakes are extremely good."

Chapter 3

Early in January in the New Year of 1780, the seventeenth birthdays of Marietta and Elena slipped by. Iseppo and his wife brought Marietta a home-baked cake, as was their custom on her birthday. They sat on one side of the gilded grille in the visitors' room and she sat on the other, chatting eagerly. Afterward the cake was shared around, but a section with some of the sugar flowers was saved for Marietta to take to the orphans in the nursery section. Among them was five-year-old Bianca, the god-daughter Marietta had acquired soon after her arrival at the Pietà. Adrianna, wanting to help her through the anguish of her recent bereavement, had taken her to see the day-old infant who had been left nameless on the doorstep. Marietta had been drawn immediately to the newborn baby bereft of a mother as she was herself, and had found comfort in holding her.

"Would you like to be her godmother?" Adrianna had asked. When Marietta had nodded eagerly Adrianna told her to chose the baby's name.

"Bianca," Marietta had replied without hesitation. "It's such a pretty name and it suits her."

When Elena became Marietta's friend, it was natural that she should share Bianca as they shared a common interest in everything else. When

Bianca was old enough, Elena had begun teaching her to play the recorder. Now she and Marietta went together to take the little girl her piece of cake.

"It's pink! And for me!" Bianca cried out with glee when she saw them.

The two girls stayed to play with her and the other little ones and, before leaving, Marietta sang "Columbina," getting them all to join in.

At this time of year, evening performances gave Elena her long-awaited chance to see something of the colorful costumes, the music and the laughter of Carnival, and for Marietta to see every kind of mask she had ever worked on in her mother's workroom.

Since early childhood she had known all the legends that surrounded the traditional masks. Many were based on characters from the Commedia dell' Arte, but there were others much older in origin. To her, the most frightening had always been the white *bauta* mask with its spectral connotations. It took its name from the black mantilla of silk or lace that covered the wearer's head completely, being fastened under the chin and worn with a tricorne hat by both men and women. She still thought there nothing more eerie than to see people thus clad looming out of the darkness like harbingers of death, or sitting in gondolas illumined by small swinging lanterns. Beneath that useful disguise could be sweethearts who had slipped away together, errant husbands or wives, a criminal leaving the scene of his crime, a senator on a secret mission, a spy, or any other person who wanted to keep his or her identity a secret.

One particularly cold Carnival night when frost added its own glitter to the city, Marietta and her fellow choristers arrived shivering with the orchestra at the water portico of the Palazzo Manunta on the Grand Canal. Colored lanterns celebrating Carnival shone on them as they entered the great flagged hallway known as the *andron*. As was usual in these palaces, it was decorated with ancient armor and weapons, many tapestries hanging on the walls, and chandeliers of glittering Murano glass lighting the way to the ornate main staircase. The girls were directed away from the flow of arriving guests and shown into a bedchamber where they could leave their cloaks and tidy themselves. There were also useful chamber pots behind screens set across one corner.

The girls were all in their black velvet gowns, Marietta's suiting her coloring particularly well. She finished adjusting the scarlet silk pomegranate spray in her hair and took her place with the other choristers to file into the ballroom where tiered galleries had been erected along one wall specially for them. As the line of girls began to move forward behind the musicians with their instruments, Elena whispered in Marietta's ear.

"Another step toward our becoming the Rose and the Flame of the Pietà!"

Marietta threw her a laughing glance. It was true that they were being called upon to sing solo more than anyone except Adrianna. The Maestro di Coro had completely taken over their training and now personally rehearsed them on a regular basis.

Thunderous applause greeted the musicians and then the choir as they entered the ballroom. The façades of the galleries were looped this evening in green velvet with clusters of silver braided tassels, and a tall candle, as was customary, stood at each girl's place. The musicians settled on the lower tiered platform. Huge chandeliers suspended from the gilded ceiling held hundreds of candles whose glittering light enhanced the dazzling masks and rich evening clothes of the audience below. A potpourri of fragrances wafted from both men and women—musk, verbena, lavender, and jasmine. Marietta had never been in a perfumer's shop, but she knew now how it must be to enter one.

Even louder applause greeted Adrianna's entrance, and then an equally warm welcome was given to the Maestro di Coro as he took his place on a podium. When he had bowed acknowledgement of his reception, he faced the tiers of his orchestra and choir, raising his baton. Then the orchestra entered into the joyous first movement of Vivaldi's "Four Seasons." Marietta, who had seen the original score, which was written in the priest-composer's own hand, knew every note. The music seemed to run gloriously through her veins as she let her gaze travel over those faces in the audience that were unmasked. There was a striking-looking young man in his twenties, clad in oyster silk and silver lace, at the right-hand end of the first row. It was obvious that his curly straw-colored hair defied the efforts of any hairdresser to mold it even with pomade into the conventional style of rolled curls over each ear, and it was drawn back into a *bow solitaire* at the nape of his neck. He was oddly attractive although not in the least handsome, but he had dangerously hooded eyes and he exuded the conceit of the confident charmer. The quick, spontaneous smile that he turned on the woman at his side had the desired effect each time, for she leaned meltingly toward him, whispering behind her fan.

Marietta summed him up as a man with whom any female should be wary. Then her gaze moved on. An exceptionally beautiful woman had just lowered her silver mask on its ivory stick. At first glance her marvelous rubies and sumptuous gown might suggest she was from the highest ranks of the nobility, but she was as likely to be a nobleman's courtesan. A few seats further on a portly, florid-looking gentleman was already nodding. No doubt he had dined and wined well before coming. But how could anyone sleep through such lovely music?

Now and again the double doors opened to admit an occasional late-comer. After the concert was fully under way, the footman in attendance did not take them to their host but conducted them straight to vacant seats. The latest arrivals held Marietta's attention. The woman was dainty and dimin-utive, her half-mask sewn with pink pearls, her panniered gown of match-ing lace, her movements graceful; there was the look of a porcelain figurine about her. The man accompanying her was well over six feet tall, broad-shouldered and straight-backed, dressed handsomely in dove-grey silk. Marietta stiffened in her chair as if she had been turned to ice. He was wearing a golden mask that seemed extraordinarily familiar.

Reason told her it was highly unlikely to be the one she remembered from her mother's workshop, for she had seen many other golden masks since coming to Venice, but there was something about this one that struck a distinctive chord of memory in her. The wearer, courteously attentive to the woman, led her by the hand in the wake of the footman, who was showing them to two vacant seats at the left-hand end of the front row. Even from a distance there was something magnetic about this masked man that compelled Marietta to observe him. It could only be that he had revived poignant memories in her. Whether he was dark or fair it was impossible to tell, for he wore his hair formally powdered with a roll over each ear and tied back with a black bow at the nape of his neck like almost every other man present. The charming femininity of the woman, comple-menting his intense masculinity, made them a perfect pair.

By now the orchestra was into the allegro of summer and Marietta's concentration on the new arrivals was broken as she realized that nobody in the audience was listening any more. The arrival of the golden-masked man and his lady had had the effect of a stone thrown violently into a quiet pond. Everyone in the room stirred in their seats, craning their necks and murmuring to one another. Faustina, the soprano at Marietta's side, whispered while staring straight ahead: "A Torrisi in the same room as a Celano! What a disaster!"

It had taken half a minute longer for the reaction of the audience to reach the front row where the couple had arrived at their seats. But they did not sit. A loud clatter at the opposite end of the row had resounded like a warning. A chair had shot back and overturned as the young man of the dangerous charm leapt to his feet to face them, his hand flying to the hilt of his dress sword, his whole stance aggressive and alert. Marietta, watching with widening eyes, recalled how she had first heard of this deadly vendetta on Iseppo's barge, and it was like watching silent actors in a drama set to the music of the Pietà orchestra. The woman had drawn close to her golden-masked escort in fear, but very calmly he was guiding her to a seat, his eyes never leaving his enemy.

Marietta, overcome by curiosity, broke one of the strictest rules of the choir by turning her head to whisper to Faustina.

"Who is in the golden mask?"

Faustina raised her song sheet and replied in a hiss, almost without moving her lips. "That is Signor Domenico Torrisi. He is said to be the only man in Venice in love with his own wife. That is she with him. The other man is Marco Celano and the better-looking in my opinion. But they are well matched. Both the same age, both splendid swordsmen, and if we are in luck we shall see a fine flash of rapier blades. Even a killing!"

Marietta shuddered. All the time Faustina had been whispering the drama had continued. Both men had stepped into the space that separated the first row from the podium, where the maestro of the Pietà continued to conduct his orchestra. Domenico Torrisi's hand had gone to the hilt of his sword, and he and Marco Celano faced each other warily. The high-pitched tension in the room had become almost palpable. All but those in the first rows were on their feet and people at the back had clambered onto their chairs to get a better view. Their host, Signor Manunta, had sprung up from his seat to come forward and hover uncertainly, not knowing to which man he should advise caution, being fearful that such interference might act as a spark to tinder.

Then Signora Torrisi, seeing her husband's knuckles stand out as his grip tightened for the whipping out of the rapier from its scabbard, snatched off her mask. Her classically beautiful face was torn with anxiety. "No, Domenico!" she cried out in a desperate plea. "No!"

It was as if all the spectators held their breath. Then slowly his grip relaxed and his hand fell away from the hilt. A kind of sigh went up from all around as people expressed either relief or disappointment. Marietta, held spellbound by the whole scene, watched as Domenico Torrisi turned toward his wife and sat down almost casually in the seat next to her. She leaned her forehead against his shoulder and he ran a hand reassuringly down her arm. Marco Celano was left standing in furious astonishment. Then he shook his head and angrily resumed his seat, the set of his jaw and the tightness of his mouth showing he did not consider the matter settled yet. Marietta saw that Signor Manunta was mopping his brow. She pitied the man who had planned such a splendid occasion for his guests, only to have such a crisis arise. Somehow the guest lists must have been muddled. She guessed he was thinking that the evening was far from over and there was the supper hour still to come.

The Maestro was puzzled when the last notes of the "Four Seasons" did not bring forth the thunderous applause to which he was accustomed, but as he acknowledged the uneven clapping his sharp glance took in the gilded mask and the presence of a member of the Celano family. He saw their joint presence as a challenge to himself. He would gain mastery over the audience in spite of the unwelcome distraction in the front row. As he raised his baton again, Adrianna stood up in readiness to sing. To him it was like playing a trump card. Not even the dual presence of a Torrisi and a Celano could divert attention from her.

While Adrianna's lovely voice captivated the audience, Marietta studied Domenico Torrisi. What was he like behind the gleaming golden shield that covered his face? She could gaze at him freely, for he had eyes only for his wife, who was still obviously distressed. It was five years now since he had ordered that mask—if indeed it was the same one—and she herself had traveled to Venice with it. Her mother had been so certain that it was a conceit fancied by a young man, but that theory was belied by his age, if he was now about twenty-eight, as she judged his enemy also to be. There must have been a reason other than youthful whim for such a specialized order.

She noted that he had well-shaped hands, a jewelled ring on each, the lace of his cuffs cascading about them. What would it be like to feel such a hand traveling fondly down her arm? Or cupping her face? Or even caressing her in those as yet unexplored realms of love? These speculative thoughts disturbed the regularity of her breathing and she was thankful that Adrianna's song was giving her some respite before she and her fellow choristers had to sing.

Then, as Adrianna ended her song, the Torrisis, although applauding, stood to leave. It was clear that Signora Torrisi was in no state to remain any longer. Her husband had made his point in any case, refusing to be intimidated by Celano's threat. There had even been something taunting in the way he had dismissed the challenge, reminding his enemy, even as his wife had reminded him, that the hospitality of their host was as sacrosanct as that of a church when it came to their vendetta. Still applauding, he came forward, looking up at Adrianna.

"Well done!" he exclaimed in a strong, deep voice. "Magnificent!"

His tribute paid, he led his wife to where Signor Manunta was hurrying toward them. Marietta saw that explanations were being given and apologies exchanged as the host escorted the departing guests from the ballroom. It was then that a strange thing happened. In the second or two before the door closed after them Domenico Torrisi looked back over his shoulder. Marietta supposed that it was to ensure that Marco Celano was not following them, but curiously, through a trick of light on his mask, it was as if he looked straight at her.

With the Torrisis gone, the audience settled down to enjoy the rest of the performance. Even Marco Celano's expression became amiable again as he took pleasure in letting his gaze dwell on the prettiest among the performers. He passed over Marietta, whose unusual beauty he acknowledged, but when his eyes reached Elena he looked long and hard. She had fine features and full young breasts, round as apples, filling out the black velvet of her bodice, and her hair was the palest gold, a color he much admired on a woman. What a waste that this appealing little virgin should be shut up within the Pietà walls. The seemingly unobtainable was always the most desirable. Who was she? It might be of interest to find out more about her. Why had he not noticed her before?

During the applause for this song and the following music he conversed with his female companion, but as soon as the choir rose to their feet again he fixed his stare on Elena, who had by now become aware of him. He had seen when she felt his gaze earlier, for without turning her head her eyes had moved to meet his stare with a shock of surprise and then look quickly away again. Since then she had become a little bolder, meeting and holding his gaze enticingly. When he smiled at her, she allowed the corners of her inviting mouth to twitch slightly. It amused him to have this flirtatious exchange with an innocent of the Pietà, who was ripe for far more than a few glances.

Elena, who knew that the Maestro saw everything within his range of vision, even if disturbances in the audience had no effect on his concentration, was careful to limit the number of times her eyes strayed in Celano's direction. She knew his gaze never shifted from her. All the time she and the choir were singing a madrigal he continued to play the same trick on her. It made her feel curiously exposed and caused her heart to hammer with excitement while her cheeks seemed to be permanently on fire. Then suddenly she had something else to think about. When the time came for her friend's solo, the Maestro shook his head at Marietta and signaled it was not to take place. Instead he took the orchestra into the final piece before the interval. Elena was bewildered, but she was too far from her friend to be able to use their sign language to make an inquiry.

Marietta had guessed immediately the reason for this cancellation. She felt a sickening sense of dismay. He must have seen her whispering. It was foolish of her to have taken such a risk and she dreaded to think what the consequences might be.

During the interval, fruit juices were provided for the Pietà girls in an anteroom. But before Marietta could reach the table where the refreshments were being served in crystal goblets, Sister Sylvia came hurrying up to hand her cloak to her.

"There's been a message from the Maestro, Marietta. I'm to take you back to the *ospedale* at once."

Marietta did not have to ask why. Elena came darting over to her.

"Where are you going? Are you not well?"

"Yes, I am, but I'll explain later." Marietta's voice caught in her throat.

Elena was anxious. "What is wrong? I must know." She turned impatiently to the nun. "Why is Marietta so upset?"

Sister Sylvia shrugged primly. "I'm only obeying the Maestro's orders. So come along now, Marietta."

Faustina watched her leave with a sense of relief that she herself had escaped the Maestro's eagle eye. Marietta had not yet learned the trick of holding a song sheet in such a way that he could not see when lips were moving other than in song. She herself was getting established as a soloist and considered her own voice equal to Adrianna's. Sooner or later, she was sure, the Maestro would realize this. Then, as she turned to take a goblet of juice from a footman, she saw Sister Sylvia returning and knew that she had not escaped after all.

"Get your cloak, Faustina," the nun ordered.

A gondola took the nun and the erring singers back to the Pietà. The girls had to wait outside the Maestro's office until he returned. He was not in a good temper. The audience had not been fully appreciative, the early confrontation between the two enemies having left them unsettled. It was not unusual for people to walk about and converse during a performance, but never when he was on the podium. His pride was offended and his bad humor was exacerbated by the lack of self-discipline exhibited by the two singers. As they stood before him he upbraided them scathingly.

"The Pietà choir has a long tradition of being perfectly composed in all situations and tonight you both failed me dismally."

Marietta spoke up. "I am the one you should blame. It was I who asked Faustina a question and my fault that she answered me."

"Bah! She whispered to you first," he snapped. "Do you think I'm a fool, Marietta?"

"No, Maestro. But it is only fair that whatever punishment we are to receive should be in proportion to what was done."

Faustina faced him defiantly. "Marietta is right. She is more guilty than

I. And there were extenuating circumstances for me. It seemed as if blood-shed between a Torrisi and a Celano was about to occur and I was nervous."

"Silence!" he roared so loudly that she started violently. "Nobody else in the choir lost her head and not an instrumentalist in the orchestra faltered. I have suspected you of whispering many times, but it was not until this evening I knew for certain that I was not mistaken. You are suspended from the principal choir until further notice. Now go!"

Faustina flew from the room on a sob. The Maestro turned his glare on Marietta. "How do you think it looks to an audience when a chorister cannot stop whispering? Bad, eh? You disappoint me, Marietta."

"I apologize, Maestro." She had never been one to excuse herself from any misdemeanor and she did not intend to start now. Her innate dignity and self-respect would not allow it.

He became calmer. "For the next three weeks you will be suspended from the choir and you will give up your leisure time to practice. Have you anything to say?"

"No, Maestro. Not about that, but may I ask a question about this evening?"

"Yes, what is it?"

"How did it happen that a Torrisi and a Celano were invited to the same private function?"

"Signor Manunta explained it to me with the most profuse apologies. Domenico Torrisi travels a great deal on diplomatic affairs and sometimes his wife goes with him. It happened that an invitation was sent to them, but when it was learned that they were expected to be away for another two months, an invitation was sent to Signor Celano. Unfortunately for Signor Manunta things did not go according to plan. Signor and Signora Torrisi arrived home unexpectedly today, saw the invitation and decided to avail themselves at the last minute of a chance to hear the Pietà performance. Unfortunately it created a distressing turn of events."

"I fear it was for all concerned."

He knew she included herself and Faustina. "I agree. Good night, Marietta."

She went slowly upstairs to her room. The lack of leisure time did not trouble her, except that she would have no opportunity to be with Bianca. Elena would have to explain to the child. But the suspension was shattering. She was furious with herself for having allowed some tenuous link with the gilded mask to get her into such trouble.

As soon as Elena arrived home, she went straight to see Marietta, who explained what had happened. Elena was genuinely sympathetic, although it was easy to see she had something of her own to tell.

"Did your solo go well?" Marietta encouraged.

"Yes!" Elena clasped her hands together excitedly. "More than well, I dare to hope. The Maestro showed such faith in me. After you left he came to the anteroom and told me I was to take Faustina's place and sing the love song!"

"What a wonderful chance for you!" Marietta was delighted that some good had come out of the catastrophe. They had both sung that song many times and she knew how Elena could convey its tenderness and passion, which expressed her own yearning for love. "Was the applause exciting?"

"It was!" Elena hugged herself with joy. "Marco Celano himself rose to his feet and came forward to applaud me! Did you have a good look at him? He is handsome, isn't he? How quick he was to face Torrisi's hostility!"

"I couldn't see there was anything to choose between them," Marietta said frankly.

"Oh, but you're wrong," Elena argued quickly. "Everything about the Torrisi was menacing until he backed down before the threat of Marco's sword."

Marietta refrained from causing further argument. "So it is Marco, is it?" she teased playfully.

Elena laughed happily. "That's how I think of him. I'm sure he wanted to speak to me, but there was no chance." Her eyes were sparkling. "I asked Adrianna about him and what do you think? He is the son who is permitted to marry and is not betrothed to anyone as yet."

"Oh, isn't he?" Marietta knew, as did everyone else, of the harsh rule about marriage upheld by the Venetian nobility. Since the eldest son did not inherit automatically, one male offspring was chosen to succeed to everything and he alone was permitted to marry and carry on the family name. It was a practical way of ensuring that great fortunes and the power that such wealth controlled should not be dispersed and weakened. As a result it was the licentious behavior of countless bachelor noblemen in Venice that added to its reputation as a city of debauchery and vice. It was no wonder that the high class courtesan enjoyed a social position that was all her own. This rule, loathed by women of noble birth, reduced their chances of marriage and propelled hundreds of them unwillingly into convents.

"Tomorrow Adrianna is going to tell me all she knows about the Celano family," Elena continued blissfully. "Do come with me and hear everything too."

"Yes, I will." Marietta wondered if she should offer a word of caution and then decided against it. Elena was so innocently joyous over the attention she had received from Marco Celano that it would be heartless to try to dampen her spirits, especially as it seemed unlikely that anything would come of this.

"As for the young woman with him," Elena declared with a snap of her fingers, "her yellow hair was dyed and a crude color compared with mine." She shook her beautiful hair proudly and ran her fingers through it, wandering about the room as she talked, almost on tiptoe, as if it were difficult to contain without dancing the excitement the evening had induced in her. "I think I'm going to fall so deeply in love with Marco Celano that it will cast a spell over him and he will never be able to desire another woman again."

Marietta felt bound to speak out. "Elena! Please! Don't build up such hopes yet. Wait and see what happens next time he is in an audience."

Elena paused, her face radiant. "Tomorrow he will send me flowers. You'll see!"

The flowers did not come. Elena waited in vain for several days, blaming the laxness of deliveries, the forgetfulness of family clerks entrusted with the ordering of bouquets, and even the temporary flooding of the Schiavoni parade and St. Mark's Square. Eventually she ran out of excuses and for a few days was unusually subdued and quiet. Then her spirits revived and she made no more mention of Marco Celano. Marietta, in spite of knowing her so well, assumed mistakenly that she had put him out of her mind.

In the meantime both girls had learned a lot about the Torrisi and the Celano families from Adrianna.

"So the Celanos come here sometimes?" Elena queried for confirmation.

"Yes, but never with a Torrisi."

Adrianna went on to tell them all she knew about the two great families. Throughout the centuries the Torrisis and the Celanos had been warriors and merchants, tax collectors for the Doge, bankers to foreign royalty, scholars, musicians, and poets. They had been suspected of murder and treason, been excommunicated with the whole of Venice on two occasions by an irate Pope, been exiled, lost vast fortunes and made them again. They had always been represented on the Great Council of thirteen hundred nobles, who governed the Most Serene Republic under the statesmanship of the Doge, and had sat many times on the Upper Council of Ten. Far more sinister was the ruthlessness they had shown on the still more exclusive Council of Three in condemning those suspected of crimes against the state to the dungeons and torture chambers of the prison attached to the Doge's Palace by an ornate bridge. Throughout the city there were ancient stone letter-boxes with lions' faces set into the walls. Secret accusations against fellow citizens of disloyalty to the state could be slipped into the lions' gaping mouths. These were investigated and placed before the Council of Three, who were feared to this day as they were in the past. Having heard all this, Marietta thought how fortunate it was that neither she nor Elena was destined to be involved in any way with either family. She hoped that Elena would come to see that the failure of Marco Celano to send a posy was a blessing in disguise.

During the three weeks of Marietta's suspension from the choir Elena sang solo in public many times. Since Elena did not mention Marco Celano once, Marietta assumed that either he had not been present or Elena had failed to recognize him in a full mask.

It was a relief to both girls when Marietta was reinstated in the choir. She had been back in routine practice for just a day when Adrianna sought out her and Elena with an invitation.

"I would like you to come to the green reception room this evening at eight o'clock. The governors are holding a small party there for me." An enigmatic little smile danced on her lips as she forestalled the question she knew was about to come. "Don't ask me anything now. You will know why when you get there."

That evening when Marietta and Elena arrived at the green reception room, Adrianna, wearing a panniered gown of pale lemon silk, welcomed them in. Their fellow choristers and the lead musicians were there as was the Maestro di Coro, the maestri, the governors with their wives, and some people the girls did not recognize but assumed to be patrons of the Pietà. Glasses of wine were being served and slices of melon handed around. The room was noisy with conversation until eventually the head of the governors came forward and officially welcomed all present. Then he stepped back and bowed for Adrianna to take the place he had vacated in the middle of the room.

"It makes me so happy," she began, "to be surrounded by so many friends on this special evening when I have to tell you that I shall soon be leaving the Pietà, which has been my home for almost twenty-seven years. I know many people have wondered why I stayed so long, but I suppose I have always known that I would recognize the right moment to leave. Now that time has come and I have discussed my decision with our Maestro di Coro. I have every reason to be grateful to him, not only for his training but for his constant guidance and advice. I've always been proud to sing for the Pietà." She turned to him. "If you please, Maestro, speak for me now."

He nodded and came forward to stand beside her. "It is no secret that I consider Maestra Adrianna's voice to be the most glorious I have ever heard. The fact that she stayed with us at the Pietà, enhancing the reputation of our establishment to the far corners of the globe, is to be counted as the greatest good fortune for us. Now fame has been turned aside and Adrianna has followed instead the dictates of her heart. I have pleasure in announcing the betrothal of Maestra Adrianna to Signor Leonardo Savoni of Venice!"

There was a moment of stunned silence before there came a chorus of congratulations, surprised comment, and general amazement at a secret so well kept. Then this gave way to applause as a square and solid middle-aged man with a portly girth, whom most of those present had thought to be a patron invited by the governors, came forward to take Adrianna's hand. Somewhat thick-necked with a beaked nose and fierce black brows that did not seem intended for such mild brown eyes, he was a singularly ugly man, but Adrianna was gazing at him in utter adoration as he was at her.

"I am the most fortunate man in all Venice," he declared in a voice choked with emotion, and he kissed her hand.

Elena, approving his elegant clothes of cinnamon-hued satin and his clocked hose, turned to Marietta almost defiantly. "You see! Adrianna has chosen an eligible nobleman before all else!"

Since titles were never used in Venice, except in written matters, there was no telling yet whether Signor Savoni was a count or if he held some other high rank. Marietta and Elena joined those clustering around Adrianna to wish her happiness. When their turn came she accepted their felicitations with special pleasure.

"Do tell us," Elena implored, overcome by curiosity, "whereabouts is the Savoni Palace? Is it on the Grand Canal?"

Adrianna shook her head merrily. "I'll not be living in a palace, Elena. Whatever gave you that idea? Signor Savoni is a mask-maker. His house is on the Calle della Madonna. After our marriage I shall ask that you and Marietta are both allowed to visit us sometimes."

Elena was staring at her incredulously. A mask-maker! Then a sharp dig from Marietta's elbow prompted her into covering up her astonishment. "Whereabouts are Signor Savoni's business premises?"

"His shop is only two or three doors away from Florian's coffee house in the arcade on the south side of St. Mark's Square."

"May we know how you met him?"

Adrianna was delighted to tell them. "I have had a number of letters from would-be suitors, which I have disregarded, but there was something about Signor Savoni's letter that touched a chord in me and I told the governors that although I could not consider his proposal of marriage I should like him to write to me again. We began to correspond regularly and his letters won me even before I met him. Then, when at last I did agree to a meeting, I knew I had found all I have ever wanted in his good heart."

"Then I could not be more glad for you!" Elena declared so fervently that Adrianna looked at her with understanding and put a hand on her arm.

"May such love be yours too one day."

Elena's eyes swam with tears. "I thank you for that wish."

Marietta realized with sudden insight that Elena had been affected by that brief moment of attention from Marco Celano even more than she had first supposed. Her friend was pining to a degree she had not even guessed. In compassion she thrust her arm through Elena's. "Could we be presented to Signor Savoni now?" she asked Adrianna. And they went off to find him in the crowd.

He greeted both girls most courteously, and during their conversation Marietta brought up the subject of mask-making, which gave Elena the chance to rejoin Adrianna, who had moved on again.

"I used to help my mother in her workshop until I was twelve. She was an outworker for Signor Carpinelli."

"I knew him well. He has retired away from Venice and his son has taken over the business. What exactly did you do?"

She told him of her skills. "I could take up that work again if ever the need should arise," she said, not wholly in jest.

"Ah." He wagged a finger. "From what I have heard from Adrianna you have a delightful voice and your future as a singer is assured. But I agree about mask-making skills. Once properly trained one never loses them. My father took me into his workshop when I was young and gave me a grounding in the whole trade. I will tell you a secret." He lowered his voice confidentially, although it was unlikely that anyone could overhear them. "In my workshop Adrianna's first mask is being made. It will be silver tissue over white satin and sewn with pearls."

"Who is to sew on the pearls?" she asked at once.

He eyed her quizzically. "Do I hear an offer?"

"Indeed you do! Maestra Adrianna has shown me nothing but kindness ever since I came here. Nobody would object to my attaching the pearls in my spare time. I could carry out the task in my room and she would never know. It would give me so much pleasure to play a small part in the making of your gift."

"Then I accept." He had no qualms about entrusting her with this delicate work. All the girls at the Pietà, whether in the musical section or not, were taught to sew well and Marietta was already experienced in his particular field. Yet it was more than this that made him agree to her request. There was a bond between mask-makers and he recognized it in her. She knew, as he did, that through such hands as theirs passed the disguises that could make or break lives, bring romance to some and venery to others, cast aside social barriers and create a dangerous freedom. Masks also created the pure joy of Carnival as well as its darker shades, and the one he would be giving the woman he was to marry symbolized his own committed faithfulness and love.

"Is there to be a veil to cover the lower half of her face?" Marietta asked.

"Yes. I have some of the finest Burano lace, delicate as a cobweb."

She sighed in sheer delight at the thought of the beauty of such a mask. "Adrianna will be overwhelmed by such a gift. How she will treasure it! You will be able to take her to her first Carnival when she wears it, because, as she once said to me, those of us at the Pietà are ever on the outside of it all."

"She has spoken of that to me too. As soon as the mask is ready for the pearls I will have it delivered to you. Shall you have to explain the work to anyone?"

"Only to Sister Sylvia. She will respect a good reason for innocent secrecy."

"Then all is well."

Sister Sylvia made no objection to Marietta receiving the mask, which came in a box from Leonardo Savoni. On the contrary, she was pleased to be in on the secret and studied with interest the design for the pearls that was sketched on a piece of paper. She was an excellent needlewoman herself, the most beautiful altar cloth in the Santa Maria della Pietà being an example of her superb craftsmanship, but never had she had any dealings with stitching a mask.

"Would you like me to help with the little veil?" she questioned hopefully as she ran the exquisite lace over her spread hand.

Marietta saw how eager she was. "That's very kind. I'll show you exactly how it has to be gathered."

Sewing on the pearls was intricate work with the finest of needles, but Marietta took delight in the painstaking task. She had only about ten more pearls to attach when she laid the mask aside to get ready to sing at a ridotto one evening. These events were run by noblemen at great houses throughout Venice, known more generally as casinos. They were extremely popular and because they were private affairs, no matter that few strangers or foreigners were turned away, they were exempt from the law that had closed down public ridottos in a move against gaming. In fact, many of those very councillors who had helped to pass the law were among the keenest patrons. The governors had no objection to the Pietà girls singing on the premises since they had no contact with the gamblers. These places were also respectably run, and although assignations did take place there were special houses far more suitable and much less public where such liaisons could be fulfilled.

It had been snowing all day, giving the city a new and pure beauty. The girls with Sister Sylvia, and the bludgeon-carrying guards who accompanied them on such outings and in Carnival, had to keep their heads down against the driving flakes as they left their gondolas. But the room that awaited the girls was warm with a good fire blazing. It also had two grilles set like windows in the walls, but of so intricate a design that the girls could peep through like the inmates of a harem while they were invisible to those on the other side. Elena had stayed behind with a slight cold, and Sister Sylvia, who thought she might be coming down with the same malady, took a comfortable seat by the fireplace. Two violinists, a celloist, and a girl at the harpsichord were the only musicians. Marietta and two fellow choristers would sing solo and in duet in turn.

When Marietta had finished her first song she went to look through one of the grilles at the gaming room below. Every table was ringed with players, all of whom were masked. Here as elsewhere the white *bauta* was popular, men and women in full evening splendor but completing their disguise with a tricorne hat and black mantilla fastened under the chin. Although those wandering about chatted with one another, the players at the tables maintained the complete silence that was traditional.

Having looked her fill at this scene, Marietta moved to another grille to look out on the reception area. All who came up the stairs from the entrance hall had snow covering their hats or hoods and clinging to their outer garments. Footmen and waiting maids took cloaks and mantles from them, brushed snow from their hats and even took their *bauta* masks to wipe away the snow that had gathered on the protruding lip. One of the screens provided for those who wished to conceal their identity while their masks were being cleaned stood at a slight angle to the grille. Marietta found that if she stood on tiptoe she could see behind it.

When three tall men in *bauta* masks came up the stairs, all snow-covered in their long swinging mantles, Marietta's attention was drawn immediately to the one in the middle. There was something familiar about the authoritative way in which he moved. Any last doubt as to his identity was swept away when one of the others addressed him.

"What a night, Domenico! Your wife did well to stay at home with mine for their own game of cards."

"I agree, Sebastiano. I wouldn't have wanted her to come out in these bitter conditions under any circumstances."

Marietta held her breath. Was there a chance that she was about to see the face of the man who owned the gilded mask? She felt she was willing him to go behind the nearest screen. To her relief he did, his two companions with him. A footman, respecting their wish for privacy, reached a hand around it to take their *bauta* masks. Without the least compunction Marietta boldly gripped the grille and raised herself high enough to see the features of Domenico Torrisi.

His face was just as that special mask had shown. There was the wide brow and cheekbones, the large and well-formed nose with the strongly carved nostrils, the deeply indented chin with its arrogant jaw, and the mouth handsome and worldly with its sensual lower lip. She was able to see at closer quarters that his eyes were a remarkably clear grey. It was easy to judge that in repose he would look stern and fierce, but this evening he was sharing the good humor of his companions, one of whom bore such a striking likeness to him that she could only conclude he was a younger brother. Although all three wore their hair powdered, she was able to tell by Domenico's straight black brows the color beneath the powder.

"I'm for a game of Faro this evening," he remarked, smoothing the lace of his cravat. "What's your choice, Antonio?" He was addressing his apparent brother.

"The dice are calling me." Antonio shook a half-closed fist in the air as if he was already coaxing the dice in his favor, a keen glint in his dark eyes. "What of you, Sebastiano?"

"I'll take the cards with Domenico," was the reply. Then, as the footman's hand reappeared with the masks, "I see our *bautas* are ready."

Masked once more, the three men sauntered into the first of the gaming rooms—unaware that a Pietà girl, having noted that Sister Sylvia had fallen asleep by the fire, rushed from one grille to the other in order to follow their progress. The candlelight of the great chandeliers played across their wine satin coats. Two women holding half-masks on ivory sticks smiled in invitation, but were to be disappointed. The trio split up, Antonio going on to the dice board and Domenico and his friend turning away to the Faro table out of Marietta's sight.

She did not see Domenico again until she was singing for the last time just before dawn. When she was halfway through the song he emerged from the gaming room to leave on his own. She could see him quite clearly from where she was standing. His mantle was put about his shoulders and his gloves handed to him. Yet he waited, glancing in the direction of the grille as he listened attentively. Only after she had reached the final note did he set off down the stairs.

After sleeping until noon, a privilege granted after such engagements, Marietta told Elena all that had happened at the ridotto. "The coincidence of the gilded mask has gone full circle," she declared lightly. "The spell is broken and my curiosity satisfied. I know what its wearer looks like and he has heard me sing, even though he will never know the connection."

Elena, who knew her so well, thought that for all her casual bravado Marietta sounded like someone not entirely sure that a ghost had been exorcised.

Chapter 4

Every day the Maestro di Coro received letters with requests to engage the Pietà choir and orchestra for various events, sometimes for great occasions and others for less formal gatherings. When a request came one day for a soloist and a quartet to provide a musical interlude at a betrothal dinner, the Maestro decided to let Elena have this chance. Marietta helped her decide what she should sing and he approved the selection.

What Elena had not expected was that Marco Celano should be among the guests. Her heart began to hammer as soon as she saw him and all the romantic feelings she had tried to suppress came to the surface again.

There were no galleries for such an informal evening. She and the musicians performed in full view of the audience of thirty people seated in a semi-circle. It was on such occasions that, under chaperonage, the Pietà girls had most social contact with their audience, who would converse with them when coffee was served during the interval. Elena, who had met Marco's smiling eyes all too often while she was singing at such close range, was fully prepared when she and the musicians were drawn into the company to find him leading her to a sofa.

"This is a good seat away from everybody," he said as they sat down together. "It is an honor to meet you at last. I admired your voice the very first time I heard you sing."

She felt almost overwhelmed by his close presence. He seemed to be invading not only her eyes and her ears but her racing blood as well. Somehow she kept her head.

"When was that?" she challenged, certain he would not remember.

"I recall the occasion extremely well. There was a slight contretemps at the beginning of the evening between a Torrisi and myself, but afterward I was able to enjoy the concert and, in particular, your singing."

So he had remembered! A footman was pouring coffee for her and she hoped her hand would not shake with excitement and rattle the cup on its saucer. Fortunately this did not happen. She heard herself making conversation and then he said something that cut her short.

"I know all about you, Maestra Elena," he said quietly.

She caught her breath. "What do you mean?"

"Your seventeen years are now an open book to me. I know where you were born in Venice, how you were raised by your late great-aunt, who your guardian is, and the very day when you were entered at the Pietà."

"Why should all that interest you?" She was amazed that she could remain outwardly composed while her mind had been set awhirl. Her Pietà training now stood her in good stead.

"Surely you can guess? Why do you think I came here this evening? My late father's friendship with the head of this house goes back to their childhood but this betrothal is of no consequence to me. I'm here because I learned you would be singing and I could not stay away. I have heard you sing more often than you realize. I deeply regret I didn't send you flowers after that first evening, but I shall make amends tomorrow. Will you accept whatever comes?"

She began to feel more in command of this encounter. "If I do?"

"Then I shall know that a further step might be taken and then another. Unless," he added, pausing for a telling second or two, "your music is everything to you and you have set your plans for the future."

"Music will always be an integral part of my life."

"I would not wish it otherwise, but there are other pleasures that it can enhance."

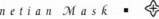

"I agree," she said. "One only has to think of dancing and of Carnival and of theatrical drama and—"

"And love?"

She gave him a long slow look under her lashes. "And love," she repeated. With an instinctive sense of timing she rose to her feet, which was a signal to the quartet to return to their chairs for the rest of the performance.

As soon as she was back at the Pietà she gave a full account to Marietta, who was prepared to sweep away any doubts she had had about Marco Celano if he should keep his word. Then in the morning a posy of violets in a lace frill tied with silver ribbons was duly delivered to Elena at the Pietà. Blissfully she inhaled the scent of the little blooms. Amid the stems she found a hidden love note.

From then on Elena continued to receive flowers and notes from Marco. She conversed again with him during a supper following a private concert for selected guests at the Pietà and again at a reception. He was now to be seen wherever she sang. Her happiness was apparent to all, although only Marietta knew the reason.

When Marietta had finished sewing on the pearls of the Savoni mask she attached the veil, which Sister Sylvia had prepared. The result was a little masterpiece. As it had to be handed back to Leonardo before the wedding, and without Adrianna's knowledge, she asked the nun to inform the mask-maker on her behalf that the work was done.

"There's no need for a message," Sister Sylvia replied. "I'll deliver it myself tomorrow afternoon. Sister Giaccomina and I are accompanying Adrianna to Signor Savoni's mask-shop. She has never been there. I'll carry the box in the inside pocket of my cloak and pass it to him at the first chance."

Alone in her room Marietta packed the mask in its box, her mind racing. If only she could go too! The sewing of the pearls had created a nostalgic yearning in her to experience again the sights and sounds and textures of her childhood. After slipping the box into a drawer she hurried off to find Adrianna.

"I understand how you feel," Adrianna said after hearing what Marietta had to say. "I intended to wait until after my marriage to ask that you and

Elena might visit me at home with the nuns, but perhaps I could make a special request to the Maestro on this occasion, which is so important to me."

"Elena would like to come too," Marietta said, for she had not made the request just for herself.

"Leave the matter with me, but don't raise your hopes too high. Go now to your choir practice and I will see you at noon."

Marietta told Elena what she had requested and they agreed reluctantly that there was not much hope. But when they met Adrianna at noon she had both good and bad news. Elena could not go on the expedition, but Marietta had been granted the privilege.

"Why has he made the difference between us?" Marietta asked, dismayed on her friend's behalf.

"Only because Elena has a lesson with him tomorrow afternoon, but," Adrianna added to Elena, "he said you could come another time after my marriage." Her eyes danced. "I was lucky enough to find him in good temper with you both. He had on his desk the new pieces you each composed last week and was very pleased with them. He intends that you shall both have the chance to sing your own work in the near future."

These good tidings, although welcome, did nothing to ease the acute disappointment that Elena felt at not being included, simply because she might have caught sight of Marco somewhere on the way. From a window she watched Marietta and Adrianna set off in their veils with the two nuns in the direction of St. Mark's Square. Then with a sigh she went to her lesson.

Marietta felt invigorated by the crisp, cold air. Snow had fallen during the night and the sky was still leaden, promising more to come. Icicles glittered over windows and doors as if jewels from the Pala d'Oro had been borrowed to bedeck the city. Near the Piazzetta a triple row of gondolas, snow thick on the covers and the roofs of their felzes, slapped the water at their moorings. Later, toward the hour when evening festivities drew near, transport would be in demand and in the meantime the gondoliers watched out in vain for hirings and stamped their feet to keep warm.

People had made paths in the snow like trails across the Piazzetta. Sister Sylvia led the way as they went in single file with Sister Giaccomina, who was round as a ball in her thick cloak, bringing up the rear. They passed the tall tower of the Campanile just as its giant bell began its daily toll to summon councillors to meetings at the Doge's Palace; and, as if to rival it, the two Moors on the clock across the square began striking the hour of two o'clock.

Sister Sylvia stopped as soon as she had stepped into the colonnaded arcade for Adrianna to come to her side while Marietta took her place beside Sister Giaccomina. Two by two they went along past little shops full of fine wares and Florian's coffeehouse, from which wafted the most delicious aroma of coffee. A few steps farther on they reached the Savoni mask-shop. Marietta, whose first chance this was to linger and gaze at the masks on display, did not follow Adrianna and Sister Sylvia into the shop, but remained outside to study all that lay in front of her while Sister Giaccomina waited impatiently. In every rainbow hue, as well as in silver, bronze, and gold, the masks tempted and dazzled. Such patterns! Such strange designs with sequins! On some tragic masks drop-pearls hung like tears from the eye-holes. Others represented the Lion of St. Mark, the elements, and similar fantasies, some new to her but many that were endearingly familiar.

"Come along, Marietta," Sister Giaccomina urged, wanting to get inside out of the cold.

Marietta obeyed, throwing off her veil upon entry as Adrianna had done. In the shop, where seemingly every inch was covered by masks, Leonardo stood with his arms wide as if he would embrace them both.

"Welcome to my shop!" he declared, smiling broadly and kissing their hands, giving Sister Giaccomina cause to experience her own sense of nostalgia. Like Sister Sylvia she was a noblewoman who had moved in high social circles until circumstances forced her to take the veil instead of becoming a wife and mother as she would have wished. Antique books were her interest and food was her consolation. Having glanced at the cakes in Florian's she could only hope that the mask-maker would have equally delicious refreshment to offer his guests today.

"Do you have anyone to assist you in the shop, Signor Savoni?" Sister Sylvia was asking.

"Yes, I have assistants, but they have gone to pack goods in the workshop this afternoon because I am shutting the shop while you are here. I don't want any interruptions while I'm showing my guests around the premises. I'll bolt the door now."

The shop was so crammed with displays that the large man had difficulty in getting past Sister Giaccomina. Marietta tactfully offered to do it for him and continued to let her gaze travel around the shop as she slipped the bolt home. How contentedly she and her mother would have settled into a little mask-shop of their own if ever such an opportunity had come their way!

Leonardo, chatting with Adrianna and the nuns, stood aside to let them go ahead through the curtained archway that separated the shop from the workshops at the rear. Marietta, being last, was able to take the mask-box from the pocket of her cloak and hand it to him.

"You have created a beautiful mask," she whispered. "The loveliest I have ever seen and I wanted to bring it to you myself."

Quickly he thanked her and placed the box out of sight in a drawer.

As Marietta entered the first of the workrooms she was met by the familiar aromas of glue and paint, canvas and wax and fine fabrics. A craftsman was seated at a workbench sculpting a mask in clay from which a mold would be made for the shaping of a special mask. At another table four women were making papier-mâché masks, using a mold and alternating layers of handmade paper and glue. An apprentice was dipping canvas shapes into wax until they were sufficiently coated. Marietta spoke to everyone, as did Adrianna, who wanted to know all the staff by name. Sister Giaccomina was as fascinated as a child by all there was to see, and pretended not to hear when Sister Sylvia tugged on her sleeve with a fiercely whispered reminder that Carnival and all that went with it made up the Devil's playground.

Marietta asked Leonardo about his outworkers, and he told her that he employed quite a number, but none from her village. While the nuns were out of earshot she told him of the circumstances surrounding the golden mask. She did not want her chaperones to think her interest more attached to the wearer than to the mask itself.

"I've reason to believe," she said, "that I've seen that golden mask from my mother's workshop on Signor Domenico Torrisi."

"The head of the House of Torrisi himself?" Leonardo shook his head doubtfully. "I can't think it is the same. I have always made his masks, and I don't remember making such a one for him."

"Then I was mistaken." She was aware of being disappointed.

"Wait a moment!" Leonardo wagged a finger in the air to stir his memory. "When would this mask have been made?"

"In the late summer of 1775."

"It was around that time I was laid low with a fever, one of those unpleasant illnesses that are said to come to the city like the plague itself from foreign ships, when a special Torrisi order came in. My chief craftsman was also stricken by the fever and I didn't want to trust such fine work to any other man in my employ, so I handed it on to someone who would do it well."

"Who was that?"

"Your employer at that time, Signor Carpinelli."

"So it could be the same mask after all."

"Indeed it could." He opened a cupboard to reveal stacks of old ledgers. After finding the one he wanted, Leonardo turned to the month of August and ran his finger down the names. When he found what he was looking for he punched his forefinger on the entry. "There we are! 'One mask to be molded and gilded from the sculpted face of Signor Domenico Torrisi. Work carried out by the Carpinelli workshop.' "

"So I was right?"

As he closed the ledger he looked puzzled. "How strange that you should have remembered that mask. It must be because it was the last piece of work you did at home."

"I suppose that might be so," she replied noncommittally. There was no way of explaining how it had fascinated her.

The tour of the workshop over, Leonardo escorted his guests back to a private room where refreshments had been delivered by a serving man from Florian's and set out on a marble-topped table. There were dishes of sweetmeats and cakes, together with a steaming pot of hot chocolate; the cups and plates were of Chinese porcelain. When they were all seated, Leonardo watched proudly as Adrianna poured the chocolate. His happiness, as on the evening of the reception, was so apparent that he endeared himself anew to Marietta. She hoped that one day she might count him as a friend even as she did Adrianna.

After the refreshments, while everyone was still talking, Marietta asked if she might return to the shop itself to look around more closely. The nuns gave their permission, content to try another cake or two, and Leonardo was able to move into Marietta's vacant seat next to Adrianna.

In the shop without her veil, which she had left on the back of her chair, she was free to try on any mask she fancied. It was like being back in her mother's workshop, the whole atmosphere imbued with the symbolic meanings, mysteries, and secrets of the many faces of Carnival.

For fun she picked up a grotesque olive green mask and held it to her face in front of the mirror. It was that of the character Brighella, a wily, impudent servant who would assist his master in any kind of debauched intrigue. It was not a suitable mask for a Pietà girl, and if either of the nuns had chosen to look into the shop at that moment they would have shrieked their shock. Amused, she exchanged the Brighella for the mask of a lawyer character, who was played in Carnival as portly and learned and a true know-it-all. This mask covered only the forehead and gave the wearer a bulbous nose.

She laughed at the effect and was returning the mask to the shelf when she became aware of being watched. It made her realize for the first time that with the gloom of the snowy afternoon deepening toward darkness outside, she was as fully illumined by the chandelier suspended above her as if she were on a stage. But who would loiter to stare at her when the weather was so bitterly cold? Slowly she turned her head to look in the direction of the shop window.

In the dusk the young man looking in at her was silhouetted against the blanket of snow lying in St. Mark's Square, and she could just see that he was smiling.

Her sense of humor gained the upper hand. He must have found the effect of these grotesque masks as funny as she did. Safe in the knowledge that the shop door was securely fastened and Sister Giaccomina unlikely to resist yet another cake before allowing Sister Sylvia to move from the table, she took up a *moretta* mask. Putting the button behind its mouth between her lips, she took her hands away as if she were a conjuror to show it had no visible support. She heard the applause of his gloved hands through the glass of the window. He applauded again when she took the gilded stick of a half-mask and held it to her eyes. But when she clamped on Pulcinella with its clown's beak of a nose she saw him shake his head, although he laughed.

She changed it for a papier-mâché one that Columbina might have worn, a half-mask that prettily covered the nose. Marietta tied the ribbons behind her head, but when she turned from her reflection to the shop window again he had gone. Her immediate disappointment turned to panic as the door burst open and he entered, shutting it again quickly to keep out the cold. Too late she realized she must have failed to shoot the bolt right home.

"Good day, mademoiselle. Do you speak French?" he asked in what she took to be his native language.

"Only enough to understand what I'm singing and pronounce the words correctly," she replied in his tongue, "but I'm not fluent."

"So far you have spoken the best French I have heard since leaving France," he praised. "I happen to have some Italian and so between us we should manage very well. How splendid that you should be a singer as well as an entertainer with masks!"

"I had no idea at first that a spectator was outside." With a soft little laugh she removed the Columbina mask and returned it to its shelf. She knew she should call Leonardo and then retreat to the nuns' chaperonage, but she was enjoying this unexpected encounter too much to let it end so soon. This stranger seemed to have set the whole atmosphere of the shop to vibrating. He had classic good looks—a thin straight nose, wide cheekbones, and a bony jaw; his complexion was olive, his eyes dark and bright and good-humored, set romantically in lashes as dark a brown as his unpowdered hair.

"Allow me to present myself," he said, switching to strongly accented Italian. "I am Alix Desgrange of Lyon. I arrived in Venice yesterday from Padua on the Grand Tour in the company of a friend, Henri Chicot, and the Comte de Marquet, our tutor, whose duty is to instruct us in the wonders of the art and architecture of all the countries we are visiting. He also advises us on the purchase of works of art to take home. Your servant, signorina." He swept off his tricorne and bowed to her.

"It is as well you came yesterday," she said, thinking that this young Frenchman, who was surely no more than nineteen or twenty, had such a carefree attitude that he must be extracting the maximum fun out of what would otherwise be a most tedious test of cultural endurance. "I heard today that the lagoon is beginning to freeze where the River Brenta flows into it."

"It is certainly cold enough. I had never expected to see Venice in the snow."

"How long are you staying?"

"As long as possible. My friend Henri and I have had a surfeit of vistas and views, statuary and picturesque ruins and handsome paintings. Now we intend to enjoy the carnival. For that I need a mask. Would you advise me?"

She did not hesitate. "With pleasure." Her encompassing gesture indicated the full shelves and mask-covered walls. "What is your preference? Comical? Grotesque? Mysterious? Dashing?"

"A mask that will take me anywhere."

"That is easily settled. It has to be a *bauta* mask for you." She took one from a peg and held it out to him. "This is the most popular mask for regular use with men and women because the prominent upper lip juts out over the mouth allowing unimpeded speech as well as eating and drinking."

"Let me try it on."

She handed it to him. "You can turn the *bauta* up against the side of your tricorne if you want to be free of it for any reason. I always think it looks like a curious ornament, but it is constantly done."

He held the *bauta* to his face while she tied its ribbons for him. When he turned to face her again her heart seemed to miss a beat. For the first time the *bauta* mask did not convey a sinister graveyard look, for his eyes through the aperture were so merry.

"How do I look?" he asked.

"Splendid! You are now wearing the official mask of Venice, because it is the only one permitted to be worn out of Carnival, although not before the hour of noon."

"What an odd rule. I had heard that Venetian law is full of them. Is it true that gondolas must always be black?"

"Yes, it dates back to an old law intended to curb the Venetian love of extravagance and flamboyance, although there is plenty of color on the canals on festival and regatta days. You'll see! But tell me, is the mask comfortable?"

"Extremely so, but it's an odd shape." He felt the base that stuck out over his mouth in the shape of a monkey's upper lip. "This must make me look like an ape!"

"No!" she protested. "See for yourself in the mirror."

He looked at his reflection and laughed. "The Comte de Marquet will never recognize me in this!"

"You can be doubly sure of that," she suggested mischievously, "if you wear a traditional mantilla with it."

"I've seen them on people everywhere I've been in the city." He was enthusiastic. "Show me the best you have."

She looked behind the counter and found a drawer full of mantillas. Quickly selecting one of the best, she unfolded it and handed it to him. He removed his tricorne and she draped the mantilla over his head before fastening it under his chin. While he replaced his hat she smoothed the cape of the mantilla over his shoulders.

"There!" she exclaimed with satisfaction, stepping back a couple of paces to study his appearance. "Remember it is accepted by all that in a *bauta* you need never raise your hat or bow to any man, because it eliminates all social distinctions just like the carnival itself."

"Another curious rule," he joked, "but a most useful one."

"If you buy yourself a long black mantle with its own deep shoulder-cape to go with it you'll look like a native Venetian. You mentioned that your tutor is a comte. If you are a nobleman too, then you should buy a silk mantle with a fur lining, because silk is the only fabric that the law allows the nobility to wear. At least"—she added—"if you aim to look as if you belonged to the city while you are here."

He laughed, shaking his head. "I've no blue blood in my veins. A black wool mantle will suffice." He regarded his reflection in the mirror again with renewed mirth. "I know I'm going to have a splendid time in Venice!" Swiftly he turned to face her again. "Would you share it with me?"

"I?" Astonishment arched her brows. "That is impossible!"

"Nothing is impossible! Didn't you know that? Tell me your name."

She hesitated only briefly, swept along by the intoxicating experience of flirting freely for the first time in her life. "Marietta Fontana."

"So, Signorina Fontana, let us arrange where we should meet."

"That, Monsieur Desgrange," she replied in amusement, "is far too difficult a problem for either of us to solve."

"I can't believe that. What time do you finish work here? Until I have a chance to get my bearings beyond the immediate vicinity of St. Mark's Square perhaps I could meet you here at the shop? Where would you like to go? To a performance of Commedia dell'Arte—I've heard the plays are enormous fun and full of laughter. Or would you prefer to dance? I have had a good supper-place recommended to me by someone I met who was in Venice last year."

She was filled with a yearning to spend an evening with him. To go to the theater was one of her ambitions. To dance would be wonderful. She and Elena knew all the latest dances, for when the orchestra played at balls, note was taken of the new steps and the information passed around. Never before had she experienced such fierce longing to break loose and go her own way for a brief spell. She felt almost angry with the Frenchman for making such a dazzling offer she could not accept.

"I'm not free to dance or sup or go anywhere with you," she said sharply. Then, overcome with remorse for speaking so harshly, she softened her tone. "Not that I wouldn't have enjoyed such entertainment, but it's out of the question."

"Why?"

"This is a pointless discussion." She threw up her hands in exasperation. "Let us concentrate on your purchases. Would you like to try on any other masks?"

He was not to be turned aside so easily. "Are you betrothed?"

"No!" Surprise made her laugh at the unlikely reason he had surmised for her refusal. "Far from it."

"Then are you the daughter of the mask-maker? Have I been presumptuous in thinking you to be his assistant?"

Smilingly she shook her head at his persistence. "It's nothing like that. If you made a thousand guesses I don't believe you would ever reach the truth of the matter. I will explain. Have you heard of the Ospedale della Pietà?"

"Certainly I have. All Europe has. The Comte de Marquet is presently trying to obtain tickets for a concert by the choir tomorrow evening."

"I shall be singing at that concert. I am a Pietà girl."

He pushed up his mask. His expression had become serious and he narrowed his eyes incredulously. "What are you doing here then? I heard that those girls never go anywhere on their own."

"We don't," she said, and explained how she came to be on the premises. "The shop was supposed to be closed for the afternoon and the door bolted. But when you came in unexpectedly I saw no reason not to help you choose a mask."

"I'm glad you did." He smiled at her. "Shall you be visiting here again soon?"

"That's most unlikely."

"Then where am I to see you next?"

She pursed her lips ruefully. "Only from a seat in the audience."

"That won't do at all!" He was adamant. "Let us plan another meeting in the face of all odds."

She felt quite light-headed. His determination to see her again was intoxicating. "If there is any way to meet you I will find it," she promised half in jest, wanting to prolong his keen pursuit for the sheer novelty of the experience.

"Good. You have only to tell me the time and the place. I will await you."

She studied him under her lashes. He had not taken her remark as a joke. She supposed it to be one of those nuances of translation one missed when not entirely at home in a foreign language. Although she was inexperienced in such matters, she sensed the strength of his attraction. The inner guard that she had been keeping up against him, and even against herself, began to melt away. But she was still unsure whether it was Alix himself or the tantalizing glimpse he had given her of a joyous liberty beyond the walls of the Pietà that was drawing her into dangerous waters.

"I would need to think how it might be managed," she heard herself say.

Her thoughts were racing. Could she slip the net of the Pietà for an hour or two? Perhaps with Elena's help she'd be able to find a loophole.

"We are staying in a house on Campo Morosini," he said. "You could always send me a message."

"A message!" she exclaimed with gentle mockery. "You might as well be on the moon for all the chance I would have of sending one. Also, most of us at the Pietà have no one to write to us, which means any letter that does come is placed before one of the governors first."

"Then tell me where you expect to sing again after the concert tomorrow."

She told herself that he could find out easily enough even if she refused to tell him. Crossing to the counter, she took a sheet of paper and wrote down a list of forthcoming performances and venues.

"You will need a map of Venice to find some of these places," she warned.

"I have one already," he said, putting the list away in his pocket. Then voices were heard in the corridor and there came the sound of footsteps approaching.

"Quick!" she exclaimed in alarm. "I must not be found alone with you! Please get behind that display figure!"

It was a wicker frame draped in a long mantle with a wig and a high-sided tricorne, the face represented by a mask painted with green and white diamond shapes. Alix stepped swiftly behind it, and Marietta swung away just as Sister Sylvia pushed aside the curtain in the archway and entered.

"Go along and get your cloak now, Marietta," she instructed, dressed ready to leave. "We are about to go."

Marietta went past her into the corridor where she had left her outdoor garments. She was anxious to get back into the shop before the nun's sharp gaze detected Alix's presence, but Leonardo was prolonging these final minutes with Adrianna, reluctant to see her go. Marietta had to join in the conversation courteously while every second seemed as long as an hour.

Sister Sylvia, believing herself alone in the shop, dropped her pious attitude toward the masks. She touched the gauzes and lace that trimmed the most feminine of them and picked up one on a stick with curling feathers, which she laid sensuously against her cheek. Secretly she would have loved the chance to join in the revels of Carnival. Was it any wonder that she had grown sharp-tongued and bitter during the years of celibacy that had been so cruelly imposed on her?

Wandering on, she came to a mantle-draped figure in a harlequin mask. On a flight of fancy she imagined how she might take part in the Carnival, unknown and unrecognized in such a costume. Her hand, almost of its own volition, reached for the tricorne. In the same instant a man in a white *bauta* mask loomed out at her from behind the figure. She shrieked involuntarily as much from her own guilt as from his sudden appearance.

"Your pardon, signorina, for alarming you," he said in French-accented Italian. "You did not hear me enter the shop."

"The door is locked," she gasped.

"You are mistaken." He went across to the door to open and close it in demonstration. "The bolt appears to be almost home, but that is all."

Leonardo, who had come running, burst through the curtained archway. "What is amiss?" he demanded, looking fiercely from the nun to the man in the mask and back again. Marietta, her face anxious, followed close behind.

"Everything is in order," Sister Sylvia informed Leonardo hastily. "I was passing the time by looking at the masks and failed to hear this gentleman enter." She knew well enough she was not in the least deaf, but such was her absorption in her own thoughts that she could have been in another world. "I was taken by surprise to suddenly see him there. It was as if one of your display figures had come to life."

Calm was restored, and Leonardo assured the stranger that he would attend him shortly. Alix stood back and his gaze through the mask followed Marietta as she and another young woman, both veiled, left with the two nuns. He felt he had quite deftly saved the situation for her. Nobody suspected they had spent time on their own together.

He went nearer the window, and when Marietta turned to glance one last time in his direction, he dipped his head slightly to her. As she went away with her companions, he thought to himself that all he had heard of this city of intrigue was true. He had been in Venice for less than twenty-four hours and already he was involved in a game of hide-and-seek with a beautiful Venetian girl. His first sight of her had been between masks. Her beauty had caught him by the throat. The pale oval of her face amid that mass of deep red hair blazing in the overhead candlelight! Her eyes, her inviting mouth, and the subtle sexuality that emanated from her had drawn him like a magnet. The fact that she was a Pietà girl simply added zest to the adventure.

The mask-maker had come back into the shop. "Now, signore, how may I serve you?"

Alix untied the *bauta* mask and removed the silk mantilla. "I will purchase these two items."

Leonardo thought to himself that this young foreigner had certainly made free with the contents of the shop, but these young bloods on the Grand Tour were all the same, wild and undisciplined away from home. In his opinion the Grand Tour was less for the gaining of cultural polish and far more for the sowing of wild oats away from their own territory.

He pitied the unfortunate tutors who always accompanied them. He had heard many express their despair at trying to keep track of their charges, especially in Venice where the disguise of a mask gave the young devils free rein.

"Have you arrived recently in Venice, signore?"

"Yes, yours is the first mask-shop I have entered."

"I am honored." Leonardo thought to himself that the first purchase these young men made was always a mask, and their second the book published specially for travelers that listed the best of the thousands of courtesans in the city together with their addresses and specialities. "Have you traveled far?"

"From France originally, but there have been months of journeying since then."

Leonardo noted he did not say he was from Paris. Parisians never failed to let it be known where they were from. This Frenchman was probably from one of the wealthy noble families who lived in the country and had little contact with the social life of Paris or Versailles. From what he had heard, there was little to choose between the morals of Versailles and those of Venice.

"After so much traveling I am sure you would like all paths smoothed for you here," he said obligingly. "I could arrange a selection of carnival costumes for you." He and a costumier on the Merceria recommended each other whenever possible and afterward shared their profits. "Delivery would be made to your place of sojourn where you could consider the various costumes at your leisure. Have you any preference?"

Until that moment, Alix had not given the matter any thought, but what his costume should be was an immediate decision. "I have Harlequin in mind."

"An excellent choice."

"You may arrange for several other costumes to be sent. My fellow traveler, who is about my height and build, will also need an outfit or two."

"It shall be done."

Measurements were taken and Alix's address written down. Leonardo then bowed his customer to the door. Good business had been done. He prided himself on being a good salesman. From lowly beginnings and a hard apprenticeship to a merciless master, who had beaten him for the smallest error, he had worked himself up slowly and surely from a peddler's tray to a stall and then a hovel of a shop that he had transformed through his own imagination and initiative into a place where people of all ranks began to come for well-made masks of original design. By then he had apprentices of his own who he treated fairly, and now he owned these present premises in the most prestigious of all sites in Venice. By the same perseverance and patience, he had won a bride for himself who was above all other women in Venice. It had taken two years of correspondence, and when eventually she had accepted him he wept with joy.

With everything tidy again he glanced proudly about his shop. It was small, which gave a sense of intimacy that Venetians liked, but he had the best stock in all Venice and served most of the nobility. How odd it was that Sister Sylvia should not have seen the young Frenchman rigging himself out in mask and mantilla. Admittedly the shop was crammed with wares and there were several display figures, but nothing that would have hidden him from view. Unless the nun was extremely short-sighted? That must be the explanation. Deciding that he had solved the mystery, Leonardo gave it no more thought.

Not far away Jules, Comte de Marquet, was on his way back to the apartment he had rented for himself and his two charges on the Campo Morosini. He strode purposefully over the snowy ground, a tall thin man in a white wig with a hawkish face weathered by his sixty years, his eyes sharp and observant. In the pocket of his greatcoat were three tickets for the Pietà concert, which he had obtained by standing in line for twenty minutes. The Pietà choir was as popular now as it had been on his previous visit to Venice years ago when he was newly married. He and his bride had heard the girls sing more than once and had attended a concert conducted by Vivaldi, who had been the Maestro then. The whole city was full of pleasing associations for him.

How different his financial position had been in those days, Jules recalled with a slight shake of his head. His name was an old and distinguished one in France, but the extravagances of his forebears and their weakness for the gaming tables had frittered away the family fortune. He had lived on a virtual pittance at Versailles until his marriage to Adelaide. They had lived happily and fecklessly on her dowry until her father's death revealed he had been penniless and in debt. Settlement of the estate had forced the sale of all his possessions.

For a while they had struggled to remain at Versailles by selling Adelaide's jewels until there were no more to sell. The blackest day of their lives was when they left Versailles for the last time. One of her uncles took pity on them and loaned them a country house near Lyon with a small allowance to keep them in modest comfort, but Adelaide had never been able to adjust to country life and had pined for the old days, becoming bitter and bad-tempered. If they had had children that might have helped her, but it was not to be. When eventually she died it was a relief to him, for she was no longer the woman he had married. He had been reduced to two miserable rooms in Lyon where he had taught private pupils until Messieurs Desgrange and Chicot, both wealthy and successful silk-mill owners, had asked him to complete the education of their sons.

Jules, by reason of his noble birth, had faced verbal attacks from thirteen-year-old Alix on his first morning in the schoolroom of the Desgrange mansion.

"Monsieur le Comte, why don't the aristocrats at Versailles get off their backsides and visit their country estates?"

"What are you talking about?" Jules was offended.

"The land everywhere is in desperate need of good husbandry. It is going to waste! They take everything from it and leave nothing for those who work in the fields."

"Some noblemen do oversee their estates once every other year or two," Jules answered in a lordly manner. "But there is too much happening at court for them to be spared more often."

"I can't believe that! They would be quick enough to come if their bailiffs did not send the monies that the land produces for them. Our former tutor told us the aristocrats do not even pay taxes like everyone else."

"It strikes me," Jules said coldly, "that he talked a deal too much about matters above his head. In future you will refrain from coarse terms and speak with the politeness expected of a gentleman."

Alix sprang up from where he was sitting. "Politeness be damned. Does the King not care that every winter hundreds of peasants die from hunger while the aristocrats debauch themselves at Versailles?"

"Silence!" Jules was angry, taken aback by such vehemence, and his old loyalties came to the fore. "Versailles is the King and he is France herself! I will not allow such treasonable sentiments to be uttered in my classroom! Apologize this instant!"

The boy drew himself up. "I meant no disrespect to His Majesty. When I am grown my sword will always be ready to serve France even at the cost of my life."

Jules found it impossible not to like the boy, however much he disagreed with his inflammatory accusations. "I trust it never comes to that, Alix," he said more calmly. "Your parents have high hopes for your future and in time to come heavy responsibilities will rest on your shoulders." Then he glanced at Henri, sitting with elbows sprawled across the table. "And yours too, Henri. Sit up straight, boy!"

While both boys were intelligent, Henri was by far the more easy-going of the two. Alix, on the other hand, only grew more fiery in support of his ideas. By the time he was sixteen and being trained for management, he had outraged his parents by trying to improve conditions for the workers at the Desgrange silk mill.

Jules was no longer needed now as a teacher, except to continue instruction in Italian, Greek and English, but he had adapted by doing a great deal of clerical work for Monsieur Desgrange and thus ensuring permanent employment.

When Alix was eighteen and had roused the workers to stopping their looms for an hour in protest at their low wages, it evoked such a quarrel between father and son that only Jules's intervention averted a permanent rift between them. When peace was restored, Jules took the opportunity to make a suggestion.

"In my opinion," he said, "it is high time your son's education was rounded off as a gentleman's should be. Let me take him away for a couple of years on the Grand Tour. It will give him the chance to get matters here in perspective by seeing something of the culture of other lands. I feel sure it would inspire him with a new understanding of design and art, which can only be beneficial to your business when he returns."

Monsieur Desgrange eyed Jules astutely. He was no fool and could see that the comte was offering to do everything in his power to change Alix from a hot-headed idealist into a man of sophistication and logic. Travel could do that. The lad would see how well weavers did in Lyon in comparison with workers in other lands. Alix had good sense when he chose to use it.

"I am in agreement should my son wish to avail himself of the opportunity. Well, Alix? What do you say?"

Alix's eyes gave his answer before he spoke. His whole face lit up. It would give his father time to come around to his way of thinking. For months now sparks had flown almost every time they spoke to each other. That would have changed by the time he returned. In the meantime he would travel!

"I should like to go, Father."

"Good. I daresay Monsieur Chicot might be persuaded to let Henri go with you."

So the journey had begun. They had traveled by coach and on horseback, been tossed about on stormy seas, rattled along in village carts, and ridden mules along precipitous mountain paths. Twice they had been attacked by bandits, but all three of them could handle a rapier to good effect, and on another occasion Jules himself had winged a thief with his pistol.

There had been comfortable and clean accommodations as well as filthy hovels and bedbugs. Splendid meals and meager peasant fare had alternated according to where they had put up for the night. And everywhere, much as Jules had expected, the two lustful young bloods in his charge found women eagerly attracted to them. Before leaving on the journey he had given them plenty of good advice and this morning he had handed each young man a copy of a refined list of Venetian courtesans, which was more selective than the usual book purchased by male visitors to Venice. Nothing could shake his determination to return the two youths in his charge to Lyon as healthy and unemcumbered as they had been when they left home.

He reached the Campo Morosini, unlocked a door into a small court-yard and went up the snow-covered steps to the apartment he had rented for their sojourn. Alix had not yet returned from a solitary exploratory walk, but Henri was writing one of the obligatory letters home. He glanced up as Jules entered the well-appointed room, a bored expression on his face. He had a kind of foxy handsomeness and a way of looking at women under hooded lids that they seemed to find irresistible.

"I thought I would get this letter over and done with," he said, looking down again to sign his name.

"But you have nothing to tell your parents and sisters about Venice as yet!"

"Yes, I have. I described our arrival yesterday and how we dined afterward at the Hotel Louvre—my mother always wants to know that I have eaten well. Then after midday we climbed those hundreds of steps up the Campanile to view the city and were nearly deafened forever when that giant bell chimed."

"We have not visited the Basilica yet!" Jules handed his outdoor garments to the manservant, who was hired with the apartment.

"We viewed the façade and the four bronze horses. I have described the splendid sight. Now I need not write again until we reach Vienna." Cheerfully Henri sprinkled sand over the ink and shook it off, and when he was sure it was dry he sealed the letter with a grunt of satisfaction. "Did you see Alix while you were out?"

"No, but I have tickets for the concert. That sounds like Alix now."

Boots were being clumped against the doorstep to shake off the snow. Then Alix came in briskly, clearly in high good humor with a large box under his arm. Henri grinned, getting up from the desk.

"You are looking very pleased with yourself, Alix. What have you bought?"

"A mask, a mantilla, and a black wool mantle. Carnival costumes for you, Henri, and myself will be delivered shortly."

"You have had a successful outing," Jules remarked.

"Extremely so." Alix lifted the lid of the box and raised an eyebrow at Henri to indicate that he had more to tell him later when their tutor was out of the way.

Elena was enthralled by Marietta's account of her meeting with the Frenchman.

"How opportune that you failed to bolt the door properly!"

"I agree." Marietta spoke almost triumphantly. "The Frenchman came into the shop like a breath of the outside world—not just the world of Venice or Italy or his own France, but the whole universe. I have never felt more like turning my back on the Pietà than when he invited me out for the evening. Just an evening, and yet it was as if he had flung doors wide open for me!" She moved about the room as she spoke, pacing like a caged animal. "I'm tired of grilles and constant chaperonage and, although I know we are not prisoners here, locks on doors for our own well-being. It is too safe here. Sometimes I feel I can't breathe!"

Elena sprang up from where she was sitting and put a restraining hand on Marietta's arm. "Calm down. I've never seen you like this before."

"It's been slowly building up in me, although I've never experienced so much envy of those to whom we sing in public. I still want the future the Pietà can give me as a singer. But I also want the liberty to come and go as I please!" She looked quite frightened, as if realizing that all her self-discipline had suddenly been cast into an abyss. "I'm sure it has nothing to do with Alix Desgrange himself. It was what he offered. Maybe just being in the mask-shop reminded me of the freedom I once knew at home. Do you suppose that those shut up in the Doge's prison get moments of such madness when they do not know how to endure the bars and locks a minute longer?"

"I'm sure they do." Elena felt unsettled herself. This mood of Marietta's was alarming. A chance meeting had created as much change in her friend as disillusionment had wreaked in her. Such trivial events by comparison with the great happenings of life, but she and Marietta had both been indelibly marked by them. Maybe it was always such small matters that exerted the most influence.

Marietta paused by the window and gazed blindly at the twinkling lights of the ships at anchor. The music of a sailors' orchestra drifted from one of the Venetian warships. Not even at sea could a Venetian be parted from his music. "I must get out of this place for a little while. An hour or two in which to be with Alix would be enough." She spoke vehemently as if to convince herself as much as her listener. "After that I will think of nothing else but work again."

Elena felt obliged to advise caution. "Don't think of doing anything rash. Not yet. Wait until he seeks you out again. If he is really determined he will find a way. Then we can make plans."

Marietta became calmer but turned swiftly to her. "I have one!"

"Already?"

"I began thinking it out on my way back from the shop. But I would need you to cover for my absence."

"I will do that gladly. You don't have to ask. What have you in mind?"

"There is that ancient door in the wall of the loggia that encloses the garden. It can only lead into the *calle* that lies between this building and the church."

"But that key could have been lost or thrown away long ago since the door is never used."

"I doubt it. There must have been a reason for that door. Perhaps it offered a route of escape in case of fire. Remember Venice has seen plenty of fires. Even the Doge's Palace burnt down once."

"Then the key must be in Sister Sylvia's possession."

"But she would not have the only one to any door. Hers duplicate those that hang in a cupboard in the governors' boardroom. I know where they are, because the cupboard door was ajar on the day we were reprimanded and forbidden to speak to each other for three months. Didn't you notice?"

"I was too upset to notice anything except my own feet. I knew that if the Pietà threw me out my guardian would simply marry me off to anybody that came along. How would you know which key to take?"

"There were plenty of old tattered labels attached."

"What if the cupboard should be locked?"

"Then I shall pick the lock."

Elena was suddenly nervous in the face of such determination. Some force was driving Marietta and there would be no stopping her. "I'll keep guard for you," she promised, thinking that all their previous escapades faded to nothing beside this dangerous venture. "But how will you let the Frenchman know when—or if—you manage to get this key?"

"He will be at the concert tomorrow evening. I know that somehow he will find a way to speak to me."

"You're very sure."

Marietta had a clear, bright look in her eyes. "I have never been more certain of anything. That is why I have to get the key tonight."

In the early hours of the morning, when Marietta expected the night watchman to be asleep, both girls crept from their rooms as arranged. Elena kept guard at the head of the stairs while Marietta went slowly down to a point where she could see through the latticework grille that divided the hall where visitors were admitted from the rest of the building. To her dismay the watchman was awake and on his feet, shining his lantern around him. As its rays struck the grille she dodged down just in time. The Schiavoni parade was often noisy during Carnival-time and no doubt something untoward had set him on the alert.

She heard him open a door. Cautiously she peeped through the grille. Judging by the way the glow of the lantern light had faded, he had gone into the governors' anteroom and thence into the boardroom beyond. Then he reappeared and looked into another room. Satisfied that all was well there, he advanced toward the door that led into the grilled area. Swiftly Marietta slipped out of sight beside a large bookcase and held her breath as he went past her hiding-place and into one of the corridors on a full inspection of the ground floor.

As his footsteps faded she darted into the hall and across the gleaming marble floor to the governors' rooms. She went straight through to the boardroom where she lit the candle she had brought with her. Then she went to the cupboard where she knew the keys were housed. Fortunately it did not need the knife she had concealed in a pocket, for it opened at a touch. Immediately she took a ring of the oldest-looking keys from a shelf. The labels were yellow with age and the ink somewhat faded, but the writing in a variety of hands was still legible. Failing to find one for the door out to the *calle*, and hoping it was not among those unlabeled, she tried another bunch of keys.

The task took her far longer than she had anticipated. It was not until she was on the seventh bunch of keys that she found what she was looking for. Even as she took it from its ring, she heard the watchman returning. In a matter of seconds she had pocketed the key, returned the rest of the bunch to the cupboard, and blown out the candle. Anxiously she crept to the open anteroom door and listened. She heard a metallic clank as the watchman put his lantern on a marble-topped side table and a scraping of chair legs as he seated himself. There was no way she could go past him without being seen. She would have to wait until he snored. But that was not to be. There was the rasp of a tinderbox and then the puffing of a pipe. She sat down on a cushioned bench to wait. One hour and then another ticked slowly by. She hoped that the governors realized what a good watch they had in their man.

Eventually she herself dozed, only to wake with a dreadful start to the first glimmer of day and a hand clamped over her mouth to prevent her crying out. It was Elena.

"Hush! It is all right. The watchman has gone off duty. I knew something must have happened, but I could not come down to you until Sister Sylvia, who was up before the rest of the household as usual, gave him leave to go home. Let's get back upstairs while she is dealing with the baker's delivery."

That evening Marietta was extraordinarily calm as she dressed in her white silk gown for the concert. Since becoming a soloist she was able to wear panniers that held her skirt out fashionably over her hips. Deftly she pinned the spray of pomegranate blossom to her luxuriant mass of hair.

This evening was about to alter the course of her life. She knew it with every nerve and fiber of her being.

The key was in her trinket box. After an hour or two spent with Alix, whenever that should be, the key would be returned to its cupboard. By then the fire that burned for freedom in her heart, her mind, and her body would have been quelled and she would be able to pick up the normal threads of her life. An hour ago, when the loggia was deserted, she had tried the key in the door to the *calle*. She had expected to have to struggle with the old lock, but with a little oil, it opened easily.

Chapter 5

*W*hen the concert ended there was, as always, a standing ovation for Adrianna. Alix, who was seated in the second row, took advantage of the moment to signal to Marietta by pointing to the door. The message was clear. He would be waiting outside.

When she and the other girls emerged from the building it was snowing hard again. Alix stood alone, watching for her. She raised her hand so that he would know her in her veil. Fortunately the escort of nuns was less observant than usual in the swirling snowflakes, and when she drew level with him he took a posy quickly from under his cloak and handed it swiftly to her.

"When?" he asked.

"Later tonight. Wait in the *calle* between the Pietà and the church."

He swept away at once, his long mantle billowing around him. Only Elena had witnessed the swift exchange.

"Well done!" she whispered to Marietta. "Flowers too. What are they?"

"Winter roses, I think." Marietta was holding the posy under her cloak. "I only had time for a glimpse."

"They will look beautiful in your room." It was typical of Elena not to be envious but to delight in her friend's good fortune.

The winter roses were pale as porcelain and tinted green around their golden stamens. Marietta arranged them in a vase of deep blue Venetian glass where they shimmered like snowflakes against a wood-paneled corner of her room. She had changed into a simple dark gown in readiness for going out and she touched the open petals with her fingertips, admiring their delicacy. Then she chose one blossom, snapped the stem, and tucked it into a ribbon bow on her bodice. She longed to fly to the *calle* door at once, but knew she had to wait for the whole community to settle down for the night and the watchman to finish his first extensive round.

In the heavily falling snow Alix had lost his way and found himself following the twists and turns of the narrow *calli* like the paths of a maze. He was afraid he might miss Marietta, and it was with immense relief that he finally came out into St. Mark's Square, for he knew his way from there.

The flakes swirled about his lantern as he waited by the door through which he guessed Marietta would appear. Time slid by. He began to wonder if he had arrived too late, but he had no intention of leaving. The lantern illumined a carved sign from the fifteenth century on the church wall. To pass the time he brushed the snow away to read it. In old Venetian spelling it warned that dire punishments and curses awaited any person who tried to place unlawfully at the Ospedale della Pietà any female child who was neither an orphan nor a bastard.

He looked again at his watch, getting more anxious as time passed.

In her room Marietta went to her trinket box and lifted out the top tray. At the bottom lay the *moretta* mask that she had brought from home. How long she had waited for this chance to wear it! Now the time had come in a way she had never anticipated.

She held it to her face in front of the mirror. Nobody expected a woman in a *moretta* mask to speak, for it was feather-light and kept in place by a button on the inside held between the lips. It was a mask with a special allure, and Marietta had seen how men's eyes always followed any woman who wore it. She held up a hand-glass and turned her head one way and then the other, noting with pleasure that the black velvet oval accentuated the alabaster smoothness of her brow, chin, and the sides of her cheeks.

But now at last it was safe to leave. She put on her cloak and gloves before drawing the hood over her hair. Elena appeared in the hallway just as Marietta emerged from her room.

"I'm going to time the watchman's rounds," Elena whispered. "He may only check again if he hears anything unusual, but it is a risk to leave the door to the garden unbolted. I shall slide the bolt back at the right time for you to come in again."

Marietta paused to look at Elena in the glow of the sconce that lighted the stairs. Briefly she removed the mask to speak. "You are the best friend anyone could have," she whispered appreciatively.

"Never fear! I shall demand return from you a thousandfold one day," Elena joked in reply. "That is if I ever have need of it."

"You shall have it!"

Downstairs Elena watched as her friend sped along the loggia. At the ancient door Marietta ran her fingers down the old woodwork in the darkness to locate the lock and insert the key. Then she was outside in the *calle*.

"Marietta!" Alix exclaimed with relief, looming out of the falling flakes like a specter in his *bauta*. Then he drew in his breath as she turned after relocking the door and he saw her masked face in the lantern light.

She lowered her *moretta*, her eyes merry with laughter. "It is I," she reassured him. "I didn't dare to come before. Have you been waiting long?"

Mentally he dismissed all his previous anxiety. She was here, he had not missed her after all, and that was what mattered. He told a lover's lie to put her mind at rest.

"Time flew by. Come! Let's get away from here."

He took her hand and they passed under the wing of the Pietà that joined the church, hastening out of the narrow way toward the Calle Cannonica. There he led her through the door of a brightly lit coffeehouse.

The welcome warmth hit them like a wave as Alix handed his lantern to a page. The gilded and muraled rococo salon was crowded, every table occupied with merrymakers, many of them in masks and fantastic costumes. There was a whole party in rich Renaissance garments. An orchestra was playing, white-wigged and in blue satin coats and breeches. Such places were often at their busiest after midnight, when members of the leisured class of Venetian society liked to turn night into day.

A waiter showed them the way, amid the chatter and laughter, to the alcoved table Alix had reserved. Several people glanced in the direction of the new arrivals in case they should be acquaintances, but Marietta in her mask and hood was confident of being fully disguised. Their outer garments were whisked away, and when Alix had given his order, the waiter released the brocade curtains, which swung closed to ensure their privacy.

Neither Alix nor Marietta realized that during those few minutes their reflections had been observed in a wall mirror by a man whose back was toward them. He was a member of the Renaissance-clad party, his costume of sapphire and emerald-green velvet, his mask studded with jewels. In the moment before the curtains of the nearby alcove were released, his wife at his right hand had spoken to him chidingly. Scented, masked, and richly gowned, with her luxuriant hair caught up in a cap of pearls, she had plucked at his full-cut sleeve.

"You're not listening to me, Domenico! What are you staring at?" Angela Torrisi followed the direction of her husband's gaze, but was too late to detect the source of his interest.

He turned to her with a lazy smile. "I thought for a moment I had recognized someone, but I must have been mistaken. Forgive me, my love. What was it you were saying?"

Although he did not allow his attention to be noticeably distracted again, Domenico Torrisi could not shake off the conviction that it was the red-haired chorister from the Ospedale whom he had seen. But a Pietà girl in here? It was impossible! Yet surely that marvelous hair, which had been fully revealed when she let her hood fall back, was unmistakable. He had seen her only once before, on the evening of his confrontation with the Celano, but the beauties of the Pietà were often talked about in male company and since that night he had heard her name. Marietta. Some of her admirers had been concerned when she was missing from the choir for three weeks, apparently through some indisposition. He himself was as quick as any other man to look at a beautiful woman. Yet that was not why he had been drawn to glance back at her when leaving that concert. It had been a strange moment. The pull on his gaze had been as strong as if she had called his name.

He saw in the mirror that the waiter had returned to the alcove with a coffeepot and dishes of sweetmeats and small cakes on a tray. The brocade curtains parted, but not enough to allow another glimpse of the girl. Domenico's curiosity remained unsatisfied. Could she be the Pietà girl? He had heard vague rumors of nocturnal visits to the Pietà, but never of a girl coming out. Business and diplomatic missions on behalf of the Doge, which took him away from home more frequently than he would have wished, and the longstanding vendetta between his family and the Celanos, had taught him never to ignore anything that was even slightly mysterious or unusual. This alertness had served him well on more than one occasion, but tonight he feared his suspicions would have to remain unresolved.

Then Angela spoke to him again. "Why not let us all remain here for the rest of the night's pleasure? I have no wish to go in and out of the snow twice more before going home." She had always loathed cold weather and had come out this evening against her better judgement.

Everybody at the table chorused agreement, content to talk the hours away. Domenico smiled as much to himself as to the company. "I think that is an excellent suggestion." So he was to have the chance to see the girl again.

In the alcove Marietta and Alix sat on soft and comfortable seats, their masks laid aside as they smiled triumphantly at one another in the candleglow. Now that the waiter had gone, the buzz of conversation beyond the brocade curtains seemed very far away. With the walls of their alcove painted in a design of birds and flowers, it was as if she and Alix were seated in a secret arbor, and Marietta was bursting to tell him all about her escape from the Pietà.

"Getting out was far easier than I had imagined possible!" she exclaimed joyfully, "although getting the key to the *calle* door was hardest." Briefly and amusingly she described her adventure while he approved her daring and was thoroughly entertained. She was unaware that in her plain gown with no adornment other than the pale winter rose tucked in her bodice, she scintillated, her eyes sparkling, the excited little gestures she made quick and twinkling, her hair full of coppery lights. Alix had been infatuated once or twice or maybe thrice on this Grand Tour, but never had he been so affected as by this powerfully alluring young girl.

"Here's to your success, which is my good fortune," he said, raising his coffee cup to her.

"My good friend Elena played her part."

He was not interested in anyone but her. "Is there any danger of the key being missed before you return it?" he asked, holding out a silver platter of cakes for her.

She helped herself to a ring-shaped one before replying. "I hope not. I'll have to put it back as soon as possible."

"How shall you manage that? Will it be by night again?"

"No. The governors meet only once a month unless there is some special reason, although one or another of them makes an appearance quite often to discuss affairs with the Maestro. In any case, it will only take a second to pop the key back on its hook." She smiled encouragingly at him. "Tell me about your travels. Where did you start?"

"In Holland." His first purchase on the Grand Tour, a Hals painting, was made there and she wanted to hear about it. She was equally interested when he spoke of traveling on through some of the German states to sail down the Rhine. Her eyes widened as he told of the precipitous paths they had followed through the Swiss mountains down to the states of Italy. With her fingers linked under her chin, she absorbed all he had to say about the marvels of Florence and Rome as well as the extraordinary ruins being excavated at Pompeii.

"After those two months in Greece," he concluded, "we arrived back on Italian soil about six weeks ago."

"And where do you go from here?"

"Vienna and Paris. Then it's home again." Alix laughed as he told her how he and Henri tried to get away from their tutor as often as possible. "We have had a surfeit of paintings and sculpture and mosaics and murals for the time being. Now we want to enjoy the pleasures of the Venetian Carnival."

He went on to say that he and his friend were beginning to get their bearings in the city, although he had not managed well that night. She was amused to hear how he had become lost.

"Did you think you might have missed me when you arrived?" she probed mischievously.

"I was beginning to wonder."

"So you were about to go home again?" Her eyes were dancing.

"No!" His protest was vehement. "I would have waited until dawn!"

She was not sure whether this could be true and hoped that it was. She knew how to deal with flirtatious talk at the Pietà receptions, but this was a new situation altogether. Never before had she been alone with a young man, and Alix was well used to the ways of this outside world in which she suddenly found herself again.

"It was clever of you to have found such a pleasant and private place for us to talk," she commented lightly. "As you may have guessed, this is the very first time I've ever been in a coffeehouse. Whenever I'm out with the nuns and the choir I look in the windows as we go by, and I've always wondered what it would be like to sit at one of the tables and chat the time away. When I still lived at home there was no money for treats of any kind, and in any case the nearest coffeehouse was far away."

"Tell me about your life."

He sounded very serious, and she looked at him curiously. His eyes were intent, although his well-shaped mouth still held the hint of a smile as if to show his reason for asking was not to pry. Nevertheless she felt as if he had caught her with a silken ribbon such as those people used to take others captive in Carnival. If she talked too much about her own life she would find herself bound by a second ribbon, and should she begin confiding hopes and dreams she would become too entangled to enjoy the very freedom she had come to find.

"What is it you want to know?" she asked warily.

"Everything right up to the present day. To this very moment!"

"Since you know something about me already," she said carefully, taking a sip of coffee, "you should be the one to talk about yourself first."

"All I know of you is that you are a Pietà girl and that you sing like a lark."

She jerked her head back involuntarily, feeling the ribbon tighten. "Nobody has used that comparison since I was a little girl."

"Who said it? Your mother? Or your father? Maybe a brother or sister?"

"No. It was an old friend of the family. His name is Iseppo. He and his wife still call to see me on my birthday. It was he who brought me with my mother to Venice."

"Tell me about that day. Was it summer or winter? Spring or autumn?"

A whirlwind of invisible ribbons, so vivid in her mind's eye, were twirling all about her. It was no longer possible to escape them. Maybe he had begun to cast them in the mask-maker's shop, ensnaring her from the moment of their first encounter. Why else should she have been so mad as to risk her whole future for this short tryst that had no past and no future.

"It was late summer." She felt as if her will had melted away and her voice had taken over of its own accord. "We came down the River Brenta in Iseppo's barge and I saw Venice first at sunset—it seemed a golden city floating on the water." She paused and he saw by the pain in her eyes that the memory evoked nothing but distress.

"And then?" he said gently.

She took a deep breath and continued her story. He listened without interruption, his gaze never leaving her face as he observed the subtle changes in her expression, fleeting as the drift of clouds across the sky on a windy day. Neither did he miss the slightest nuance in her voice. She kept strictly to events and did not mention feelings until she had concluded the account of her years at home and at the Pietà. "It was only after a long time that I began to realize how merciful it was that my mother's death came when it did. It spared us having to part in the knowledge that we would never see each other again. I don't know how either of us could have borne it."

"She must have been a most courageous woman," he said with respect.

"That is what Iseppo said when he explained on the morning of her death that she'd never had any hope of a cure. When he had to leave and I was left alone with strangers, it was as if I had slipped down into a fathomless pit and would never emerge again. I'm haunted even as I speak of it," she said uneasily. "But then, I should never have talked about myself in the first place."

"I disagree. It is the only way I can get to know you or you to know me."

"I'm with a stranger," she countered almost accusingly.

"Not any longer." He caught her hand across the table and held it tightly. "My life has been different in every way from yours and yet I already feel a bond between us."

He leaned forward over the table. "I have to see you again!"

She sat back slightly, almost defensively. "It was to have been only this once."

"Not for me!"

Inadvertently he had reminded her of how long she had been away from the Pietà. "I must go!" she said, moving restlessly. Those ribbons could be snapped if she left now.

"No, wait. A few minutes longer." He covered her free hand with his own and this time felt her shiver at his touch. "That key! I could make an impression in one of these candles. Somehow I would get the duplicate to you. Then at least I would know there was a chance of being with you again."

She hesitated. He waited anxiously, acutely afraid that she would shake her head. Then, to his huge relief, she turned to take up the little velvet purse that lay on the seat beside her. She pulled open the strings and took out the key to give to him. As his hand closed over it she felt herself possessed, and at the same time she knew a rush of happiness at the prospect of liberty.

Quickly, he made the impression and summoned the waiter to put it in the snow for a few minutes to harden. As they awaited his return, they devised a simple plan for Alix to give her the key. That settled, he spoke softly to her.

"I understand the great risk you took tonight and that everything connected with me is danger for you. All I can say is that seeing you again has meant more to me than anything I can remember in my whole life. I have fallen in love with you, Marietta." In that moment when she made her decision about the key, he had recognized the emotion that had struck him at his first sight of her.

She did not doubt him. The truth shone in his eyes and in the timber of his voice. She did not dare to examine her own feelings in case she should discover that it was this same feeling that had seized her in the mask-shop and not simply a sudden desire for a taste of freedom.

"I do believe you," she said gently, letting herself be wise, "but it is well known that Venice casts spells over travelers."

He leaned toward her. "It is you alone who will hold me spellbound forever!" he declared passionately.

She thought to herself that as long as she lived she would never hear words more beautiful or loving. His declaration had sealed the bond between them, but she dared not let him know it yet. There were too many obstacles and too many pitfalls.

She was about to respond when the waiter coughed discreetly before parting the curtains. This coffeehouse was not a place of assignation, but when customers paid extra for a little harmless privacy the management respected their wishes.

Domenico turned in his chair to watch as the girl, again well hooded and in her mask, swept by him with her escort. Disappointingly, her identity remained a mystery.

Alix collected his lantern and then he and Marietta went back into the night. It had stopped snowing and she became anxious about leaving her footprints so clearly leading to the *calle* door, but he promised to obliterate them by scooping loose snow over the marks and stamping about himself.

"What subterfuges we are using!" He laughed quietly, setting down the lantern. Then he drew her to him and she went willingly to lean against him as his arms enfolded her. His lips, cool from the chill air, melted into warmth on hers in tenderness and desire. She clung to him. All time was suspended until with a little sigh she broke away. He unlocked the door for her and returned the key into her charge.

"Good night," she whispered. Then she disappeared through the door and it closed after her.

The next day Alix returned to the Savoni mask-maker's shop. Although Marietta looked enticing in her *moretta* mask it had its disadvantages since she could not remove it in public even to speak.

"Good day, signore," Signor Savoni greeted him warmly. "What is your pleasure today? Another mask, perhaps?"

"Yes, but not for myself. I want one of the best quality in that shape."

He pointed to the one Marietta had been wearing when he first entered the shop.

"That is a Columbina mask." Leonardo took a selection of them from pegs and shelves to lay in a multicolored array on the counter. The Frenchman's choice went unerringly to one of green velvet trimmed with minuscule golden beads. It was one of the most expensive in the shop. Leonardo nodded approvingly. "Splendid workmanship in that one. Do you wish a mantilla to go with it?"

Alix chose one of cobwebby Burano lace. Both items were packed into a beribboned box, which Alix tucked under his arm as he left. His next stop was at a locksmith's shop on the Merceria where he had earlier left the wax impression. Two new keys were waiting for him. If ever the one for Marietta should be discovered and confiscated, he would still have the means to get in to see her.

It was Sunday morning and Jules was about to leave for mass at the Santa Maria della Pietà when Alix appeared, dressed and barbered and in his cloak.

"I'm coming with you, Monsieur le Comte."

Jules reminded himself that both Henri and Alix had been out until the early hours in their carnival costumes. "Are you sober?" he inquired gravely. "Otherwise you may not come."

"Yes. I made up my mind last night to attend mass today."

"Where is Henri?"

"Still asleep."

Jules guessed that Henri had imbibed to excess whereas, somewhat surprisingly, Alix had not. They left the apartment together. No more snow had fallen and a thaw had turned what there was to slush underfoot. Church bells, so much a part of Venice's own music, were chiming all over the city. Pigeons rose with a great flapping of wings as the two men crossed St. Mark's Square, which was strewn with the jester litter of Carnival— scattered ribbons, broken egg-shells, a number of trampled masks, and a single satin shoe with a pink rosette.

"Henri and I were here about two o'clock this morning," Alix said as he

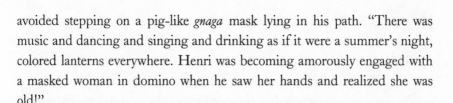

avoided stepping on a pig-like *gnaga* mask lying in his path. "There was music and dancing and singing and drinking as if it were a summer's night, colored lanterns everywhere. Henri was becoming amorously engaged with a masked woman in domino when he saw her hands and realized she was old!"

"Ah. Not all is pleasure at the Carnival," Jules remarked drily. "How did you fare?"

"Well enough." Alix let his tutor put his own interpretation on that comment. It could not be explained that everything about life lost its savor when Marietta was not with him. And in Venice of all places! He thought he must be mad. It was like being presented with the most enticing banquet in the world and having no appetite. But then love was a kind of madness. He had heard it described as a period of temporary insanity and so it had proved in the past. But although he had seen Marietta on only three occasions—in the shop, on the evening of the concert, and during their nighttime meeting—he knew that this love was different.

When they reached the Santa Maria della Pietà, Alix looked up at the *ospedale* on the other side of the *calle* where he and Marietta had met. He wondered which was her room. Then he bared his head and followed Jules into the church. While Jules's appreciative gaze took in the fine altar paint-ing and the magnificent work by Tiepolo overhead, Alix looked up at the grilled galleries encircling the interior, where a rustling indicated that the members of the Pietà choir were taking their places. Then the priest entered and mass began.

Marietta was behind one of the lower grilles set like windows on each side of the church and she could see Alix clearly as he bowed his head and knelt in prayer, his thoughts composed even if his heart, of its own volition, was seeking hers. When she sang solo he knew it was her.

When the service ended it was easy for Marietta to stay behind while the rest of the choir went back into the Pietà. She pretended to be searching for a very special sheet of music that she had mislaid, but which, in fact, she had tucked into her sash. It was Alix's good fortune that Jules expressed a wish to look closer at the treasures of the church as the rest of the congrega-tion were leaving. Casually Alix strolled to a long, high-backed wooden seat set into the wall and pushed the key behind a corner cushion as he and Marietta had arranged at the café. Not long afterward he was out of the church with his tutor. Only then did Marietta enter the main body of the church to retrieve the key.

On the Riva degli Schiavoni, as Jules and Alix ascended the steps of a bridge over a side canal, a well-dressed, white-wigged, amiable-looking gentleman was descending toward them. He and Jules recognized each other immediately as old acquaintances from Versailles in spite of the span of years since they had last seen each other.

"Can it be possible!" Jules exclaimed in astonishment. "Monsieur le Marquis de Guérard!"

"Monsieur le Comte de Marquet, I do declare!" Hearty greetings were exchanged and then the Marquis noticed Alix. "Who is this young man then? A nephew, or a son by another marriage?"

Jules had to swallow his pride. "Neither. The years have not been generous to me. Allow me to present Monsieur Desgrange, one of my two pupils whom I am escorting on the Grand Tour."

To have made such an admittance at Versailles would have brought immediate ostracism and Jules was fully prepared for the marquis to nod curtly and walk on. But that did not happen. Instead his fellow aristocrat, after greeting Alix, revealed that he and his wife were living in Venice as voluntary exiles since he had also suffered reverses at Versailles and was out of favor with the King.

You must come and dine with us this evening, messieurs," the marquis said, concluding the conversation. "Bring the other young man with you. My wife will be delighted to see you again, Monsieur le Comte. And we have a bevy of granddaughters with us now who will welcome new dancing partners in Monsieur Desgrange and his friend. You will find we have created a little Paris far from home."

The mention of dancing was the first indication to Alix that he might not be able to get away to meet Marietta that night. Perhaps if he returned to the church he would be just in time to let her know. He made a quick bow.

"Pardon me, messieurs. I seem to have left my cane in the church." He turned on his heel and went back at a run, ignoring his tutor's assurance that he had not taken one that morning. When he reached the church he whipped off his tricorne as he entered to find the place deserted and Marietta about to vanish through a side door.

"Marietta! Wait!" He hurried to her. "You have the key?"

She smiled to see him. "Yes."

"Good." He spoke quickly. "Unfortunately plans have been changed and I may not get to the *calle* tonight, but I will be there tomorrow at midnight."

"So until then!" She gave a little wave as she closed the door after her. Hurrying up the narrow staircase into the Pietà, she placed her hand over the key that had replaced the music in her sash.

The marquis and his wife were living very grandly in the Palazzo Cuccino, which they had rented on the Grand Canal. In the gondola on the way Jules assured Alix and Henri that they were about to enjoy the most civilized and elegant evening of their lives. "There will be no grotesque Venetian disguises this evening," he assured them. "No spies for the Council of Three lurking in the shadows and no vinegary wine. No black garb to ensure anonymity and no—"

"—beautiful Venetian women," Henri intercepted glumly.

"I was about to say no air of mystery and no secrets. All will be French!" Jules put the gathered fingertips of his right hand to his lips and threw a kiss of homage to France into the Venetian air.

Alix thought to himself that his tutor was wrong on one point—he did have a secret.

The evening proved to be exactly as Jules had anticipated. The great rooms and the rich furnishings were as sumptuous as anything in Paris. About fifty of their fellow countrymen and women were present and there was not a mantilla or mask to be seen. Neither was a word of Italian to be heard the whole evening. And the orchestra in the minstrel's gallery played only French music.

The Marquis and Marquise de Guérard were a welcoming host and hostess to a score of young men besides Alix and Henri who were also on the Grand Tour, a number of older travelers, and two newly married couples on nuptial journeys. Among the Guérard family staying at the palace were the granddaughters the Marquis had mentioned. There were five in all—one married and accompanied by her husband, the other four ranging in age from sixteen to nineteen, including a widow—and all were attractive young women.

Alix was allotted the widow to take into dinner. He had heard already that she had been married at the age of sixteen to a much older man, who had died a year later. Her gown and her jewels showed that she had been left well provided for, but there was nothing flamboyant in her attire. She was also serious and demure with large questing hazel eyes shaded by light brown lashes under thin arched brows, her hair formally dressed and powdered. She wore a beauty patch shaped like a star by the corner of her firm little mouth. By chance he had one of the same shape on his right cheekbone and she commented with a twitch of a smile on their mutual good taste. Her name was Louise d' Oinville.

At the long glittering table she engaged Alix in intelligent conversation. He found her to be ideal company at that time, for with his thoughts constantly drifting to Marietta he was in no mood for the foolish badinage that would have been expected of him by the other girls.

She in turn liked him precisely because he did not play up to her. So often, when they learned that she was a widow, men either considered her fair game or else—visualizing the money she had been left—immediately began to think of marriage. Her experience as a wife had not left her enamored of that state, simply because her late husband had had a closed mind, a gross body, and had treated her as if she were brainless. Why her late father, who had allowed her to be educated like a son, had arranged such a match for her, his only child, she would never comprehend, unless perhaps it was to see her financially secure. The relief of being able to talk to Alix as an equal was a treat in itself.

"So you are from Lyon, Monsieur Desgrange," she said after those within earshot at the table had looked askance at their talk of some scientific experiments they had both read about. "I know the view from Fourvière extremely well. My uncle Henri and his wife have made their home in Lyon since he retired from the army."

It emerged in the course of their conversation that she was acquainted with quite a few people Alix knew. She had a wry wit and an observant eye, several times surprising him into a grin.

Dancing and cards followed the dinner, and it was not until a buffet breakfast with champagne had been served that the guests finally departed. It was dawn and the rain in the night had finally washed away all traces of the snow, leaving a mildness in the air.

"The weather is as changeable as a young girl's heart," the marquis commented from the watergate steps of the palace as Alix and Henri left with Jules in a gondola. Louise, who had also come down to see the guests off, thought scoffingly to herself that men were far more fickle.

That night Alix unlocked the *calle* door and went into the loggia to wait for Marietta. There was no moon, but the sky was full of stars. When he heard her coming out of the building he whispered her name, not wanting to frighten her by suddenly appearing. She ran to him with her arms outstretched and he caught her hands in his.

"Such a risk!" she exclaimed in a whisper, both excited and alarmed that he should have had a second key made for himself. "If the watchman had seen you he would have had you arrested as an intruder!"

"My coming here is nothing compared with the risk you are taking to meet me. Did you return the key?"

"Yes. Nobody questioned me."

Outside in the *calle* she began to put on the *moretta* mask that she had brought, but he stayed her.

"Not that one tonight," he said, putting a beribboned box into her hands. "Wear this one instead."

By the light of his lantern she opened the box and the gold beads winked on the green velvet mask where it lay upon the lace mantilla. "Oh! it's a beautiful Columbina!" When she was arrayed in both, she leaned forward and kissed him on the lips in thanks, so quickly and lightly that she was out of his reach again before he could seize her. She went tripping and spinning and dancing ahead of him along the *calle*.

"Now I'm really free!" she called recklessly over her shoulder, not appearing to care who might hear her. He was suddenly afraid that in his gift of the Columbina mask he might have given her far more liberty than he had intended. The last thing he wanted was that she should feel free of him. He ran to catch up with her.

"Would you like to go to a ridotto?"

"I should like that immensely! What fun to be on the other side of the grilles for once. Which one have you in mind?" When he told her she nodded. It was at the house where she had glimpsed Domenico Torrisi without a mask. "That one is all right. The Pietà musicians are playing elsewhere tonight."

"Would it matter? None of them would recognize you."

She smiled to herself. Naturally a man would not think of the one clue that might have set the girls questioning even if they had not actually become suspicious. "They would have known my velvet gown, which I had made in the color, design, and fabric of my own choice."

If she had known she was to receive the Columbina mask and a mantilla she would have worn one of her very best gowns, but to date she had thought it wise to dress discreetly and thus avoid notice. But now a sense of daring was taking hold and she felt immune to danger.

Her feet still seemed not to be touching the ground as Alix escorted her into the ridotto's buffet salon for supper and wine. Knowing that she was totally unrecognizable, wearing a mask in which she could talk, eat, drink, and flirt—even sing if she disguised her voice—made Marietta feel completely light-headed. She would always treasure her dear little *moretta* mask, but having the Columbina was a lifelong dream come true. She made Alix tell her all about his home and his family, right up to the quarrel with his father that had led to the Grand Tour.

"Don't you get on with your father at all?" she asked incredulously.

"Yes, when we avoid talking politics and certain aspects of business. He cannot see that changes are needed everywhere in France. But I'm not going to talk about all that to you. Not tonight anyway."

When Alix took her into the gaming rooms, something about her poise made Domenico Torrisi, lounging between games, stare at her from behind his *bauta* mask. Leaning a shoulder leisurely against a pillar, he watched the two newcomers take seats at one of the tables. It was clear that the girl was a complete novice, for the young man with her was advising her on every move. But she was obviously quick to learn. When they went on to another table and a game that required more skill, she was soon making her own decisions and was innocently jubilant when she won.

Marietta had lost all sense of time. She was so absorbed in the play that she took no notice when a seat was vacated beside her and someone took it at once. She looked at the two cards she held, confident of winning this time, and was just about to make her wager when a male voice spoke quietly in her ear.

"How have you flown the walls of the Pietà, Maestra Marietta?"

The cards fell from her hands. On a choked gasp of fright she looked wildly at the masked man who had spoken and knew him to the depth of her being. His grey eyes pierced into hers and she realized that nothing she might say would counteract the truth that she had been discovered. On her other side, Alix was asking what the matter was but she ignored him, still looking into Domenico Torrisi's eyes.

"Don't give me away!" she said between her teeth. It was a hiss that was neither a plea nor a demand.

"Trust me," he replied and turned his attention back to the game.

Trembling violently, she hastened from the table, Alix following quickly behind. "What is wrong?" he exclaimed in bewilderment when they reached the reception hall.

She shook her head, not answering him until they were outside the building, when she almost collapsed against him. "That man! Signor Torrisi! He recognized me."

"But how?"

"It could only be the color of my hair that gave me away, but I thought it would not show through the lace."

"It only glinted a little. Nothing more. I'll buy you a silk mantilla tomorrow."

"He said I could trust him." She was still preoccupied and pulled away to start back in the direction of the Pietà. Alix fell into step and put an arm about her waist.

"Is he to be believed?"

"I think so."

When they reached the door in the *calle* Alix entered with her to hold her tight. She was still trembling and he thrust up his mask and kissed her tenderly, full of concern and yet not wanting her to put an end to their meetings.

"Don't say you will not see me any more, Marietta. We can go to quieter places where we are unlikely to meet Signor Torrisi again."

He felt her straighten in his arms. Abruptly she took his face between her hands and pulled him down fiercely to bestow a kiss that contrasted in every way with their earlier one. Breathless, she drew away again.

"I'm not afraid of a Torrisi! He shall not drive me into the shadows. I leave that to the Celano family. Let us go dancing next time. What I would like most of all would be to spend a whole night of Carnival with you, not returning here until dawn!"

"Somehow I will grant you that wish," he vowed, fervently catching her in his arms again and kissing her even more passionately than she had kissed him. She felt herself slipping out of her depth as his hand moved caressingly over her velvet-covered breasts, arousing new, painfully sweet sensations in her.

"Good night, dear Alix," she whispered, although it was less than two hours until dawn. Then she slipped away from him and ran along the loggia to re-enter the Pietà. Once inside, she paused briefly in the darkness to face a moment of truth. She could no longer deny to herself that she loved him.

In their grand bedchamber Angela Torrisi lay in her husband's arms. She was intrigued by the second installment in his account of the wayward Pietà girl.

"How has the young maestra managed it?" she pondered delightedly. "Such daring! What spirit! Love will always find a way."

Domenico smiled into her bright little face, enjoying the impish sparkle in her eyes. "Perhaps it was just an urge for adventure. She was certainly enjoying her first experience of gaming. Maybe the young man is introducing her to the pleasures of Venice."

She prodded her forefinger into his chest. "Don't spoil the romance of it for me. You know as well as I do that no Pietà girl would risk breaking all the rules without an over-riding motivation, which can only be that she is in love." Then her attitude turned playfully against him. "It was cruel of you to give her such a fright."

"On the contrary. If *I* could penetrate her disguise, so could others. It was for her own good."

"But you had the advantage of having seen her briefly without her hood."

"True. And now I hope she will be less careless in future."

She scrutinized his expression. "You mean that, don't you."

"I do."

"I'm glad. There are those who would take a fiendish delight in denouncing her." All cruelty was abhorrent to Angela. Only that morning she had chanced to see a condemned man being strung up by his thumbs between the two upper columns of the Doge's Palace, which were deliberately constructed of a deeper rose marble than the rest and where such tortures often took place. She had almost fainted with pity and horror.

Domenico cradled her to him and kissed her lovingly. She responded to his mounting desire as his hand traveled down her back and over her smooth thighs. There had been so many miscarriages, so many disappointments in the seven years of their marriage, but their passion for each other had not waned. His lips moved to her breasts and, as always when he began to make love to her, she hoped that this time she would conceive a son she would carry successfully to term.

Once Marietta had donned Alix's gift of a new silk mantle and mantilla, for which he had received an appreciative kiss, she had no second thoughts about risking an encounter with Domenico again.

"Let us go back to those same gaming rooms, Alix!" she urged, her eyes sparkling.

He did not argue. Almost from the start he had sensed that the spice of danger only added to her enjoyment of their time together. Now, with his arm about her waist, he wondered, not for the first time, how much she might dare in her relationship with him.

Once she had settled down at one of the gaming tables, Marietta took a few seconds to look around at the ring of spectators. "The Torrisi is not here tonight," she said with conviction to Alix at her side. She had brought her own money this time, and her first small stake had already increased quite handsomely.

"How can you know that?" Alix asked. "All men in *bautas* look alike."

"I would know him out of a thousand thus masked." Then her whisper rose in glee. "Oh, look! I have won again!"

By the time they left she had lost most of her gains and was almost back to her original stake, which did not depress her in the least, for she considered she had had a wonderful time. In the loggia, when Alix enfolded her in his arms, she could feel through her skirts the effect that passion had on a man's body.

While Alix's nightly excursions with Marietta continued, his days and evenings were fully occupied. He and Henri spent many hours with Jules studying the architecture of churches and secular buildings, and there was no end to the masterpieces and other treasures to be viewed. Alix appreciated all he saw, but he would have enjoyed these sessions much more with Marietta at his side. How easy it would have been elsewhere in Europe to view historical monuments and famous paintings with a pretty girl and her chaperone in tow, but the grilles of the Pietà were like prison bars.

Much of Alix's time was also taken up in finding works of art to send home. A promising young local artist was touting his paintings to those sitting at tables in the arcade outside Florian's. Alix, who had been drinking coffee there with Henri, bought this artist's domestic scene of two women sipping hot chocolate, which he particularly admired. He had been exercising his own taste since halfway through the tour and had already dispatched from Venice a small thirteenth-century painting on wood of a Madonna and Child, as well as two views of the Grand Canal by another Venetian artist known as Canaletto.

Added to these activities were evenings at the Palazzo Cuccino for cards or music. Alix spent one such evening playing billiards with the marquis and afterward they sat in the mezzanine library talking politics over good French wine. They found they held many of the same opinions, although the marquis had the wisdom and experience to temper Alix's grandiose ideas of how miracles of reform might be accomplished overnight.

"Patience and perseverance," the marquis advised. "That is the only way.

We must talk again. I know a couple of other exiles in Venice who would appreciate meeting you. That shall be arranged."

The marquis and his family had begun to take it as a matter of course that Jules, Alix, and Henri should be included in their round of entertainments. Gradually Alix had come to know Louise better than her cousins. He was not in the least attracted to her, but he continued to find her intelligent company, for she had a comprehensive knowledge of French and Venetian politics as well as a wide knowledge of music, literature, and art. If he took any note of her looks at all it was to think how pale and lusterless she was in comparison with the vibrant seventeen-year-old girl he loved and desired and longed to see again each time they were parted. When he had cupped Marietta's bare breast in his hand for the first time she had uttered a soft little cry of erotic pleasure.

It was during a musical evening at the Palazzo Manunta that Louise unwittingly offered to do him an extremely good turn.

"My grandparents have obtained an invitation to take my cousins and me to a reception at the Pietà quite shortly. As you and I have agreed, the girls' voices are quite wonderful. One of my cousins will not be coming, because her parents are returning from a visit to Verona that evening and she wants to be here to receive them. Although I do not doubt," she added drily, "that if the choir consisted of young men she would have quite forgotten her filial duty. Would you like to take her place? I know my grandparents would be agreeable."

Managing to control his glee, Alix replied soberly that he would be most pleased to accept. Marietta rejoiced with him when he told her the news, welcoming the bonus of an extra meeting. It also made up for the time he had missed seeing her through being unable to extract himself from the Guèrards' company until it was too late. More than once he had arrived with only a minute to spare.

Then there had also been the night when he waited for her in vain. Again and again he had checked his watch to make sure he was neither too early nor too late. Finally he had to leave. When she failed to appear again the next night he became anxious. Had she been discovered the last time she returned? Or had the Torrisi failed to keep his word? Several more nights went by. Two or three times Alix tried the door into the building itself only to find it securely bolted. He looked up at the windows, hoping she would throw down a written message, but although lights went on and faded away again there was no sign of her.

Marietta was at a sickbed. Bianca had fallen ill with a high fever, and since the infection could not be diagnosed, isolation had been imposed— not only on the child, who had been removed from the bedchamber she shared with other children, but also on those nursing her. Had Elena not been sharing the nursing duties, she would have delivered a note of explanation to Alix; but as it was, Marietta had to let him remain puzzled in the darkness, for she could not risk passing the infection to him by any means.

Then the morning came when Marietta and Elena were able to leave the sickroom. The fever had broken at last with no dreaded signs of either smallpox or the plague.

"It's going to be a fine day," Marietta said wearily, pausing to look out the window. Then her head drooped as she pressed a hand to her suddenly quivering mouth and her voice broke. "I was so afraid we were going to lose Bianca."

She had uttered the words that neither of them had dared even to think while sponging down the child's feverish body, giving her sips of water, and smoothing the sweat-tangled curls. Elena put an arm about her shoulders.

"It is over now. Get some rest. Bianca will want to see us again when she wakes."

Shortly after midnight, while Bianca again slept peacefully, Marietta left the sickroom briefly on the chance that she might see Alix for a few minutes. But the loggia and the *calle* were deserted. When she returned, she found Bianca awake and crying for her.

"Hush, little one. I'm here." Marietta rushed to the bed and sat down to gather the child gently in her arms.

"I was afraid," Bianca whispered, her head resting weakly against Marietta's shoulder.

"I shall not leave you again by night for a single minute until you are well and strong again," Marietta promised. It was like cradling a little bird that had fallen from the nest, for the child's fever-wasted body was all bones.

"Sing 'Columbina.'" It was a drowsy, whispered plea.

Marietta sang softly, rocking the child gently. Not until she was sure Bianca slept soundly again did she undress and lie down herself in the truckle bed alongside. Then she lay looking up at the pool of candlelight thrown across the ceiling. She did not blame Alix for not being outside, but disappointment at not seeing him, even briefly, stabbed like a knife at her heart. Rain began slashing at the window.

Alix, who had been delayed by an absorbing discussion with the marquis and his two exiled friends, reached the shelter of the loggia. He shook some of the rain from his cloak and took up his hour-long vigil.

The next day, when Alix arrived at the Palazzo Cuccino shortly before noon, he was shown into one of the lush salons to await Louise. It was a beautiful room, full of light, with a fine ceiling painting and more decoration on the gilded double doors as well as on another that led into a small oratory for solitary prayer.

There came a tap of heels and Louise entered. They greeted each other. Then she sat down on a buttercup yellow sofa and folded her hands neatly in her azure silken lap as he drew up a chair to sit facing her. He had not taken the decision lightly to speak to her about Marietta, but he was desperate, and in any case he was sure he could trust Louise to keep silent whether she agreed to help him or not.

She heard him out. "I shall go to the Pietà this afternoon," she said without the least hesitation.

He smiled broadly in his relief. "What a good friend you are, Louise."

When he had gone, she crossed to one of the windows looking down on the Grand Canal and watched as a gondola bore him away. She thought him foolish to have fallen so seriously in love when he could have enjoyed a passionate relationship with the Pietà girl without any involvement of the heart. Yet she felt grateful to Marietta—was that not the name of Tintoretto's daughter?—for showing her how strong was the bond of friendship that she, Louise d'Oinville, shared with Alix.

At the Pietà Louise had no difficulty getting the information she needed. Marietta was well. She had not been appearing in concert because she was caring for her convalescent goddaughter by night. When Alix received this report he realized it might be the evening of the reception before he saw Marietta again.

Chapter 6

As she was dressing for the reception Marietta wondered, not for the first time, how it would be when she and Alix met again. Perhaps he would be angry that she had to all intents deserted him. Maybe he would not come at all.

As soon as she and Elena were ready, they went to see Bianca. Still pale and weak, she sat propped against her pillows and smiled as soon as she saw them. Sister Giaccomina, sitting at the child's bedside, looked up with a pleased expression from the book she had been reading to her.

"See how much better our little patient is this evening," she said, indicating an empty bowl and cup on the side table.

"Did you really eat all your supper, Bianca?" Marietta exclaimed with approval.

The child nodded proudly. "Every bit!"

Elena applauded. "Well done!"

"I'm to be allowed out of bed for a little while tomorrow."

"That is good news." Marietta was about to say she would be back to spend the night as soon as the reception had ended, but the nun forestalled her.

"Bianca knows that I'll be sleeping here every night until she is able to return to her own bedchamber. It is important that you get proper rest again, Marietta."

It was a sign of the little girl's improvement that she had accepted the new arrangement without tears. Had this been Sister Sylvia it might have been another matter, but all the children liked Sister Giaccomina for her motherly ways.

At the reception, presentations were already underway when the French family group arrived. Marietta sighted Alix immediately and knew from the surge of joy in his eyes that their time apart had only increased his feelings for her. Although she longed to run straight into his arms, she kept her place in the receiving line, smiling and curtseying as the Maestro and the maestri on the staff took the visitors from one girl to the next.

Then, as Marietta rose from yet another curtsey, it was to look straight into the eyes of Angela Torrisi.

"This is a pleasure, signorina," Angela said smilingly. "I admire your lovely voice so much."

"I'm honored, signora." Marietta was thankful that Domenico's wife was alone. It would have been difficult to keep her composure under his taunting gaze. Then Angela Torrisi's next words stirred Marietta to unease.

"I should like to talk to you for a little while later," she said, inclining her head as she moved on.

Elena, who was ahead of Marietta in the line, paid the French guests the courtesy of replying in their own tongue. Then she heard the name Desgrange and realized she was curtseying to Alix.

"It is an honor to meet you," he said with a wink, aware of others within earshot.

"I hope you are enjoying your time in Venice," she answered, her smile showing she was pleased to be meeting him.

"All the highlights have been linked to the Pietà choir."

When he reached Marietta, his eyes were full of infectious merriment. She responded gaily with a deep curtsey to the exaggerated flourish of his bow.

As soon as the presentations were over Angela beckoned Marietta over to sit by her side. Somewhat uncertainly Marietta obeyed, but she soon overcame her initial disquiet as the two of them entered into conversation.

Before long Marietta found herself talking about her singing, her village days, and her hopes for the future.

"So you have your sights set on the concert stage," Angela remarked with interest. "Not an opera company?"

Marietta gave a little laugh, completely at ease now with this gracious young woman. "I've heard so many tales of how badly the impresarios treat their singers, even forcing them out of a sickbed to sing if need be, that life in an opera company doesn't appeal to me."

"I believe such merciless treatment is quite common, but not toward a prima donna as you would be."

"You compliment me most highly, signora."

"No one deserves praise more. But I've been taking up too much of your time. Others are waiting to chat with you. We shall meet again, I'm sure."

At last Marietta was free to wend her way through the gathering toward Alix. He broke away from his conversation with a group of gentlemen as she reached him. Elena, passing from one guest to another, noticed how engrossed in each other the two of them appeared. Then she saw that the young Frenchwoman, Madame d'Oinville, was also watching them observantly. Her composed expression was impossible to read, but there seemed to be a hint of exasperation beneath the bland surface.

That night when Marietta emerged from the Pietà, she and Alix ran to meet each other and he swept her up and around in jubilation at their being together again. He no longer had any doubt that he was deeply and irretrievably in love.

As their nightly meetings were resumed, Alix yearned to be alone with her, away from the coffeehouses and ridotti and public ballrooms where they spent their time together. But he could tell that she never thought of their going anywhere else. She was happy wherever they were, dancing tirelessly, light as a butterfly. Only in the loggia did passion sweep through her as she responded to his kisses, and each time he was tormented by the thought of how it would be if she were lying in his arms.

Cherishing her as he did, his whole nature balked at the idea of taking her blatantly to a place of assignation, of which there were many in Venice. He was not at all sure she would agree in any case. The apartment where he was staying would have been ideal, but although Henri rarely returned before dawn, Jules was too light a sleeper to risk taking her there. The problem remained unsolved and his intense desire for her unassuaged.

It was a night bright with moonlight when Marietta saw that Alix was attired in his Harlequin costume as he waited for her in the loggia. Outside in the *calle* she admired his appearance.

"You make a dashing Harlequin! I am sure that is one of Signor Savoni's masks that you are wearing!"

"It is." Jokingly he struck an attitude for her in the best Carnival tradition. His jacket and pantaloons were vividly diamond-patterned, his ruffle white about his neck. Bows adorned his shoes and there was a feather in his round-brimmed hat.

She gave a mock-rueful sigh. "I shall lose you to the first Columbina who comes along, even though I'm wearing my lovely green mask."

He took her hand, looking lovingly down into her upturned face. "She is already here. Tonight we shall celebrate Carnival in St. Mark's Square with everybody else, but we shall transform you first."

They ran most of the way to the costumier's shop on the Merceria. At the week's end, when the carnival gained momentum, it was worthwhile for those in any trade connected with it to keep their business premises open late. When Alix and Marietta arrived, breathless and merry, the costumier knew at once what they required.

Behind a curtain Marietta changed into the Columbina costume that had been produced for her. It was of silk, in the shimmering turquoise of the lagoon on a summer's day. The abundantly full skirt was banded with multicolored, diamond-shaped patches bordered in silver braid, and a narrow pink ruffle about her neck matched the little apron and the bows on the elbow-length sleeves with falling cuffs of lace. Lastly she tucked her hair into a white wig and topped it with a small pink frilled cap. The mirror showed her that she was Columbina. Not even Domenico Torrisi could recognize her now. Like a dancer she sprang lightly out through the curtains for Alix's inspection. His reaction was predictably enthusiastic. "Bravo!"

She left her cloak and gown with her mantilla at the costumier's shop to change into later, for he would not be closing for another three hours. Then, hand in hand, they hurried to join the revelers in the square. Music permeated the air. Fireworks spattered and rockets soared. High on the Basilica the four bronze horses changed their hue with every burst of stars. A peddler was selling roses, little short-stemmed blooms of crimson that had been shipped in from some warmer clime. Alix was in time to buy her the last one. It had no thorns.

"I love you," he said, giving it to her, "forever."

Her shimmering eyes never left his as she put the rose to her lips in acknowledgement of his words. Her whispered reply was scarcely audible in the carnival din, but he heard her, for it was as if they stood alone in the eye of a hurricane.

"This is a night I shall remember all my life."

A soft fall of gaily colored ribbons, thrown by someone nearby, fell over them by chance as they kissed. Then he helped her to tuck the rose deep between her breasts, for she was fearful of losing it, and their eyes met again as he carressed her before he withdrew to lead her into the dancing throng.

There were no formal measures here, but a skipping and spinning and prancing well laced with kisses and laughter. Once a long line of grotesquely masked revelers wove through the crowd like a snake; the last one grabbed Marietta's hand, drawing her and Alix along with them. More dancing followed, and finally it was Alix who looked up at the Moors' clock to see that it was long past the time when Marietta's garments should have been collected.

"The costumier will have closed!" he exclaimed with concern. To his surprise Marietta, intoxicated by the carnival as if by wine, was not in the least disturbed.

"No matter," she said with a radiant smile. "You can collect them for me tomorrow." She linked her fingers behind his neck. "I daren't go back by way of the *calle* now. The watchman will be plodding about as he waits to go off duty. Sister Sylvia will be about too."

"But how else—?"

"The baker's apprentice makes a delivery at the Pietà water entrance at dawn. If you bribe him for me he would keep them busy in the kitchen and I could slip in that way. Elena may well be there and she would help too." Marietta raised herself on tiptoe with joy. "Don't you see what it means? We have until dawn to be together!"

He held her tightly to him. "Did you plan all this ahead?"

Her smile was mischievous. "Not until I put on this costume and saw my reflection in the mirror. Then I knew I couldn't go home until dawn."

"Oh, Marietta," he said softly, "I promised you a whole night at the carnival, but I had intended it to be when there was no longer any danger for you."

"How would you have managed that?"

"By making you my wife."

Instantly she leaned back and placed a fingertip against his lips, shaking her head. "No talk of that! Please. Especially this night, because it cannot be." In the same instant she had the sensation of being watched and glanced up quickly at one of the lighted windows above the north arcade. Among those looking down on the roistering below was a man whose golden mask set him apart from the rest. His glittering gaze was fixed on her.

She jerked her eyes away and threw her arms around Alix as if for safety, her cheek pressed against his. He held her close, the two of them motionless amidst the brilliant, churning throng. Then, just as abruptly, she broke from him.

"Let's get away from here!" she implored.

"I know where we can go." Joyfully he led her out of the square. Soon her exuberant mood returned and she was full of laughter again.

"Where are we going?"

"The apartment where I'm staying. The comte is at an all-night card party and Henri is at the carnival." It was the chance he had long awaited.

In the apartment she moved light-heartedly about the elegant salon, looking at everything, for she was interested to see how travelers to Venice were accommodated. When she reached a mirror she removed her mask and her wig.

"Nobody to recognize me here," she declared, smiling at his reflected image as she combed up her hair with her fingers. "Do you realize that this is the first time we haven't had masses of people all around us?"

He was well aware of it. She left the mirror and went across to the glowing fire, holding out her hands automatically to the warmth, although the night was mild and she was not in the least chilled. His gaze dwelled lovingly on her. She was standing with her back toward him and in the firelight her hair was the color of glass heated to red-gold, such as he had seen at a glassmaker's on the nearby island of Murano.

He stood behind her and put his lips to the nape of her neck. She leaned back contentedly against his chest, letting her hands fall lightly clasped in front of her while he enclosed her arms within his. He buried his face in her hair. It held the scent of summer. When he looked down he could see her shadowed cleavage.

"I wish we could have come here before," she said dreamily. "It is cozy and quiet. All our hours together have been wonderful. It's just that this is such a change."

"My darling Marietta," he breathed. "We shall have many such times as this in the future."

She chose to misunderstand. "Yes, you will be far away in Lyon and I shall be in Venice, but firelight is a pleasure everywhere."

"We need not be apart." He felt her tense at his words.

"Don't say any more, Alix." It was a kind of warning plea.

"You shall not silence me now. I love you and I believe you love me, even though you have refused to admit it. Soon I may be leaving Venice and I cannot go without you." He set his hands on her waist and turned her around to face him, but she bowed her head, refusing to look him in the eye.

"Please! No!" Her voice was choked.

"Tell me how much you care for me, Marietta. I want you to come back to France as my wife." He took her chin fondly between his finger and thumb and raised it until her eyes met his. He saw that hers were full of tears. She answered him haltingly.

"I gave you my answer when we were in the Square. Neither of us could get permission to wed. Legally you're under age and still subject to your father's will, while I'm bound by the Pietà's rules regarding marriage to foreigners. The governors would never consider you without authorized documents and the endorsement of your ambassador."

"I know all that. But do you love me? That's what I want to know." He jerked her face back to him when she would have turned away. "Tell me!"

He was not sure why he should be getting angry, but he could no longer endure her refusal to let him coax out of her the words he was desperate to hear. Unless she told him now, he could not make plans for the marriage she was so convinced could not take place. When he saw her lips tighten, as if she feared her heart might cry out what she would not say, he grabbed her by the shoulders and shook her hard.

"I'll not let you leave here until I have the truth from you! If it takes until this time tomorrow, I swear I will not release you! By then the Pietà will have dismissed you to the streets as a wanton and you'll have no choice but to stay with me."

She swung up her hand and hit him with full force across the face. As he stepped back in shock she whirled away and bolted for the door, hurling it open to dart out into the night. Instantly he was after her and caught her halfway down the *calle*.

"Forgive me! I didn't mean what I said!" he shouted. "I'm scared of losing you!"

She struggled with him, hammering his chest with her fists, her face contorted by fury and misery. "Even if I did love you, there's no future for us!"

He pulled her tightly against him, pinioning her fists. "Listen to me! We can elope!"

She became still in his arms and shook back her hair to look questioningly at him. Wariness and uncertainty showed in her expression, as if she stood at a crossroads where all paths were unknown. "The Pietà would not abandon me if I should go missing. There would be a hue and cry throughout the city to discover who had abducted me. Should it be suspected that I had run away, alone or with another person, guards would be sent in relentless pursuit until I was found."

"I know that. But I'll find a way somehow."

Suddenly she was full of hope. She loved him and she wanted to flee Venice with him. Despair melted away. As he smoothed back her hair, which had become tousled in their struggle, her eyes searched his.

"Is it possible?" she asked.

"Trust me," he urged, his embrace drawing her to him. She responded eagerly to his loving kisses. If she thought fleetingly that her happiness sprang more from relief at escaping the amorphous threat of the golden mask than from the prospect of elopement, she quickly banished it from her mind.

They did not return to the apartment. For her it had been tainted by their quarrel, and she would never want to go there again. Wandering along, they came to one of the little squares where Carnival folk in gentler mood sat on the steps of the houses as they listened to a group of singers with accompanying lutes. Marietta and Alix found seats side by side, and there they stayed until it was time for her to return to the Pietà. He hailed a gondola.

In the dawn light their gondolier waited obligingly under the bridge of the side canal leading to the water gate of the *ospedale*. A light mist lay like a spread of tulle over the lagoon. When the baker's apprentice came alongside in his boat, Marietta put her request to him. He nodded and pocketed the money Alix had produced. There was more waiting while he tied up at the water gate, sprang onto the steps, and pulled the bell. Then he took in the first basket of bread. When he reappeared for a second load he beckoned that the coast was clear.

The gondolier propelled his vessel to the steps. Marietta kissed Alix lightly. Then she alighted speedily and disappeared into the Pietà with a rustle of her skirts. She reached the safety of her room without meeting anyone, but only just in time. No sooner had she closed her door than others began to open and footsteps began pattering about. Before she changed out of her Columbina costume she put the rose in a vase of water. It kept its freshness for a week.

Louise did not want to leave Venice, but she had had three months there prior to Alix's arrival and the date of departure did not rest with her. Her uncle and aunt, with whom she and her cousins had traveled, were ready to go home. The last social event of her time in La Serenissima was to be a costumed ball for three hundred people in honor of her twentieth birthday, which by chance coincided with the last night of Carnival. The Pietà choir, including Marietta, was to give a short performance before supper and then the orchestra would take over and play for the dancing until a champagne breakfast at dawn.

Louise had never been one for flamboyant display, and a family evening with a few friends would have been much more to her taste, but her grandfather was so pleased with all he had arranged that she did not have the heart to protest. At least he had agreed to let everything be Venetian. It seemed pointless to her to have it otherwise. She would miss Venice, but so long as her grandparents were in exile she would return whenever she could.

It was the growing imminence of Louise's departure that made Alix face up to how transient was his own sojourn in Venice. It could happen without warning that Jules would decide it was time to pack and move on. The days slipped by swiftly as schemes for the elopement passed through Alix's mind and were rejected as previously unseen flaws came to light. It was when Marietta mentioned that she would be singing at Louise's birthday party that he was able to finalize a plan. It seemed fortuitous that a ship would be leaving Venice for France at the same time as the dawn champagne breakfast. But he would need Louise's help. She had proved her friendship once before, but maybe this time she would decide that he was asking too much.

Throwing on his mantle and taking up his hat and gloves, he set out from the apartment to call on her.

At the Palazzo Celano a family conference was taking place. Marco sat facing the semi-circular group much as if he were in front of the inquisitors of the Council of Three, and his annoyance was mounting. The importance of the occasion had merited his mother's presence in Venice. Signora Apollinia Celano, a small matriarchal figure of sixty, lived in the country with Marco's widowed sister Lavinia. His two other sisters were in the convent of a closed order, put there against their will by their mother when they failed to gain husbands she considered suitable. Five of his six brothers were also present, four having come from Celano palaces in the city that he permitted them to occupy. His eldest brother, who was in the priesthood as was customary for the firstborn of a noble family, had traveled from Rome to be spokesman. Three elderly uncles completed the gathering. His youngest brother, Pietro, born much to their mother's chagrin when she was forty-five, was being taught the skills of medicine in a monastery in Padua mainly devoted to the healing of the sick. He was expected to remain there and take holy orders in due course.

Marco's gaze ranged over those present. "I will not be dictated to," he stated rigidly. "It was decided by my late father that I should be his heir with the right to marry and none of you can contest that. Not you, Mother. And not even you in your cardinal's soutane, Alessandro!"

Alessandro, resplendent in his vivid red silk garments, sat in a high-backed chair at their mother's side, his elbow on the wooden arm, his chin propped by a finger and thumb. "In your case we can, Brother. When the future of a Venetian line is at stake even a priest may have special dispensation to marry and beget sons."

Another brother spoke up. Maurizio at thirty-two was next in age to Alessandro. A sharp-eyed, thin-lipped scholar of repute, who suffered from poor health as the result of a childhood illness, he had been responsible for the plans used on two occasions to outwit the Torrisis.

"You've had twelve years, Marco," he said relentlessly, "since you were sixteen in which to take a bride. You're abusing your privilege."

"I'm entitled to some bachelorhood," Marco retorted.

There was a derisive laugh from Vitale, whose handsome looks were prematurely aged by debauchery, his temper made volatile and his face bloated by drink. "Come now, brother. That is *our* lot. Yours is to take a wife." He turned to the brother beside him. "What say you, Alvise?"

"I agree." Alvise, strong and virile, considered himself to be the best swordsman in Venice. "Marco has far exceeded any allowable sowing of wild oats."

The hard tones of their mother's voice cut across their discourse. "Your brothers are right, Marco. Two years of philandering should have been more than enough. I'm entitled to grandchildren and the House of Celano to an heir!"

Her third son, Filippo, who had not spoken before, leaned forward in his chair to jeer at Marco. Broadly built and powerful, he had no liking for this brother who had inherited all he coveted for himself. "You're in a difficult position, brother. Remember you have yet to prove your manhood!"

Marco leapt to his feet, hands clenched in wrath. "If you were not my brother I would have killed you for that insult!"

"I don't doubt that you have bastards at the Pietà and other orphanages. I'm referring to legal offspring."

"That's enough!" Marco took a threatening step forward, but was checked by his mother rapping her closed fan on the arm of her chair, intent on diffusing what was clearly an inflammatory situation. It would not be the first time these two hostile sons had taken up swords against each other, but it had been some years since Marco inflicted the scar on his brother's cheek. She understood, however, that with Filippo eighteen months older than Marco, it was natural for him to be jealous of the younger man's good fortune.

"Calm yourself, Marco! Sit down and listen to what has to be said." She turned to Filippo as if he were still a boy and told him to keep quiet. Then, seeing that Marco had reseated himself, reluctant and glowering, she addressed him again. "Our patience as a family is exhausted. A few weeks ago I entrusted your Uncle Giacomo to find a suitable wife for you and he has done so, for which we thank him. She is not an heiress, but that is no cause for regret since it is offspring and not money that we need. In fact, I have noticed all too frequently that heiresses, coming as they invariably do from families lacking male heirs, are often as barren as Domenico Torrisi's wife has proved to be, or else produce nothing but daughters. Thus the dowry of the young woman chosen, such as it is, happens to be of little consequence. A pauper of breeding would have done as well. The important factor is that she comes from fecund stock."

Marco jerked forward in his chair. "Mother!" he roared. "I pardon you through your considerable age for daring to speak in such a manner to me, the head of the House of Celano!" His furious glare turned on the rest of the company. "I will not even hear the name of the female misguidedly selected for me. I am no longer a hapless youth to be married off without voice in the matter."

His mother spoke sharply. "You have me to thank for that! I interceded with your father when you were fifteen to spare you that fate!" She recalled how she had gone down on her knees to her husband, begging that their son be allowed to make his own decision when he came of age. Sentimentally she had hoped Marco would take a wife for whom he could care tenderly for as long as such feelings lasted in marriage. There had been nothing like that between his father and herself. She had not known then what her husband might well have already suspected, that Marco would most likely become a philanderer, reluctant to uphold the responsibility of marrying that had been placed upon him. Her only weakness in an otherwise strong and merciless nature was her motherly devotion to her fifth son. From the moment of his birth, he had awakened latent maternal instincts in her, which all her other babies had failed to do. She supposed she had spoiled him foolishly as a result, but she excused herself because it happened so often with one child in a family. If Marco had any fault in her eyes it was his Celano temper. It came too close to the savagery of Filippo's rages for her liking, but as always she found an excuse for him. All the blame could be placed on Filippo, for when they were boys he had led the others in tormenting Marco as the favored one. Inevitably Marco had had to find ways of getting back at them until he grew to match them in strength and height. Privately it distressed her that they should see him cornered now, for she knew they were maliciously enjoying his discomfort. Filippo was intent on taking over from Marco, and both Alessandro and her brothers-in-law had advised her to make him head of the family if Marco should fail to comply with their wishes. She would do her best to see that did not happen. Turning slightly, she signaled with her fan to her brother-in-law Giacomo. "Tell Marco our choice."

The elderly man rose from his chair to emphasize the importance of the statement he was about to make. "We have decided on Signorina Teresa Reato. You have known her since childhood, Marco. I have spoken to her father and he is willing to permit the match when the Carnival is over. Not in Lent, of course, so we have settled on the first Saturday after Easter."

Marco gave a humorless laugh. "So you would try to foist that creature on me! She has a figure like a stick and a face like a kitchen pan."

His mother blazed at him. "Shame on you! How dare you speak thus of a wholly worthy young woman!" She poked her cardinal son's arm with her fan. "Tell him now, Alessandro."

"The betrothal will be announced after the signing of the marriage contract tomorrow," Alessandro said in slow, deliberate tones, "and the marriage will take place on the day that has been set. If you refuse to accept this arrangement we shall go to law and reduce you to permanent bachelor rank. Filippo will replace you as head of the House of Celano."

Marco was stunned. His mother nodded to show her full support of this decision. It was unbelievable that she should turn against him now. How could she contemplate seeing him lose this great palace and all the wealth and power that went with it. He had known he would have to marry eventually, but Teresa Reato would have been his last choice. His only chance lay in playing for time.

"Very well," he said condescendingly, "I shall marry, but not Teresa. I insist on choosing my own bride."

"Within the allotted time?" Alessandro pressed.

"A betrothal by the end of four weeks."

"No. That is not good enough. You have come to the end of your rope. It is useless to prevaricate. The decision has to be made today. To whom do you wish to be betrothed instead of Teresa?"

Filippo drawled tauntingly from his chair, able to see, as they all were, that Marco was nonplussed. "We are waiting, Marco."

Marco knew he was trapped. Mentally he flicked through the daughters of families he knew, but not one stood out from the rest. Then enlightenment came as he suddenly recalled Filippo's mention of the Pietà. He had been planning to make Elena his courtesan. It would have been easy to arrange once he was sure of her. The Pietà would never have released her for that purpose, but since he owned one of the opera houses in Venice she could have been offered a prima donna's position and everything would have been settled from there. Now he saw her in a different light. He compressed his lips in a satisfied smile, leaning back in his chair. "Maestra Elena of the Pietà shall be my wife."

Astonished silence greeted his announcement. Then, as he had expected, they all began to talk at once. Alessandro, well used to filling a cathedral with his stentorian voice, boomed out a question, causing the others to fall silent.

"Is she a soloist in the choir or the orchestra? You forget that although I am familiar with the high moral standards of the Pietà's young women I have been away from Venice too long to know any of them by name."

"She is a singer."

"Was she a foundling bastard?"

"No. Her father was a small-scale merchant in the wine business and her mother a gentlewoman. Both died of fever within a few years of their marriage and Elena was raised by a respectable relative. She was entered as a fee-paying pupil at the Pietà by a lawyer acting as guardian when this relative fell ill and shortly afterward died."

Alessandro turned to his mother. "Well, Mother? What do you think?"

She nodded, inwardly overjoyed that Marco should have bested his brothers and Filippo in particular. "Let the governors be approached immediately, Alessandro. Go to the Pietà now and make your own thorough investigation. See the young woman for yourself. If all is well, we can proceed as originally planned. I shall stay on here for the marriage and remain until I can be sure that she knows how to manage a noble house and all that involves."

Her widowed daughter, Lavinia, who had been sitting behind her in the second row, came forward. "How can we be certain, Mother, that the young woman will agree to marry Marco? I have always heard that those holding senior positions in the choir have their wishes consulted."

Signora Celano's eyes snapped impatiently. She had always been tyrannical toward her daughters and although the other two were out of her reach in their convent Lavinia was a daily victim of her biting tongue. "Only you would ask such a stupid question! Just when we have settled the future of our family's wealth and power! There is no door that money cannot open, no path it cannot smooth. All the Pietà girls hope for good marriages. Not one with any sense would refuse this chance, and what could be better for us than a young virgin without blemish? If there should be any hesitation, which I doubt, Alessandro will offer on my authority such a large donation to the Pietà that the governors will be certain to sign the marriage contract whatever the girl might say."

Lavinia, suitably crushed, nodded meekly. Few marriageable women had control over their own fate. She had been the only one among her sisters with a true spiritual vocation and had been looking forward longingly to taking the veil with a closed order far from Venice, but then an old and lustful widower had wanted her for his fourth wife. Since he had enormous wealth her pleas and protests had gone unheeded by her parents. Yet when he died five years ago she had found herself penniless, everything going to the son of his first marriage—and she, only twenty-five, had once more come under the control of her family, who had condemned her to be her irascible mother's companion. She hoped Marco would be kind to Elena, whom she hoped to befriend, but kindness was not a noticeable virtue in the Celano family.

Not far away in the Palazzo Cuccino Louise was again seated on the yellow sofa.

"What is it this time?" she asked smilingly. When Alix gave her no answering smile, having instead a deep frown on his countenance, she felt a warning pang, every instinct telling her that events must have taken an extremely serious turn.

He sat down on the sofa beside her. "I have another favor to ask of you. Far greater than before."

"Tell me what it is, Alix."

She did not refuse the help he then requested. Her friendship with him was too important to be endangered now, but she despaired at his folly. All along she had been sure he should be seeing Marietta as much as possible in order to give the flame of love the chance to flare up and die down again. Then he would be able to leave Venice without any pain in the parting. Now she wondered if she had done right in the first place by making that inquiry on his behalf, encouraging an infatuation that might otherwise have died, although, as his friend, she could not see that it would have been possible to do otherwise. Now she dreaded her twentieth birthday celebration still more, for another cloud had formed to darken it.

When Louise set off for the Pietà again Alix accompanied her as far as the bridge on the Riva degli Schiavoni where he had first met the marquis. There he handed over to her the box he had been carrying. It was light-weight and she suspended it by its ribbons over her arm.

"Good luck," he said.

She smiled indulgently at him. If she was successful the benefit would be entirely his, something he seemed to have overlooked. "I shall do my best."

Alessandro arrived at the entrance to the Pietà at the same time as Louise. He bowed slightly to her as they waited to be admitted, but neither spoke. She thought him a man of immense presence, but he had cold eyes and a thin line of a mouth that did not suggest much tolerance or forgive-ness. There was conceit in him too, for his flowing cape was thrown back on his shoulders to display his rich robes and large jeweled cross, even though Venetian law forbade priests any outward show of splendor except for ecclesiastical processions. The door opened and Louise preceded him into the Pietà. They were received by Sister Sylvia, whom Louise had spoken to on her previous visit.

"Has Governor Tradonico arrived?" Alessandro asked haughtily. "He was to meet me here on the hour."

Louise summed him up still further: no humility either. She knew that the head of the governors was a nobleman and a close political associate of the Doge, not an inferior to come running when called. How different was this cardinal from the good monk who had founded this very *ospedale* and lived like a beggar to finance his charitable work. She noted the cardinal's displeased expression upon hearing that the governor had not arrived, and his stiff silk robes rustled as if echoing his annoyance as he was shown through an anteroom into a salon to wait.

When the nun returned, Louise explained the purpose of her visit, and Sister Sylvia lifted the lid of the box to look at the plain black half-masks that filled it.

"You have made a most unusual request," she said. "Our singers and musicians never perform masked."

"I know that, but I thought, as it is to be such a special occasion for me, with everybody in costume and the last night of Carnival, just for once the choir and the orchestra could enter into the spirit of the occasion."

Sister Sylvia could see no harm in the young woman's wish, but this was not a decision she felt able to make. "Leave the masks with me, Madame d'Oinville. I will have a word with the Maestro."

"But I must know one way or the other," Louise said firmly, able to match anyone with her imperious air. "Please ask him now."

Sister Sylvia left her for no more than five minutes before returning to say that the Maestro had given his permission. Triumphantly Louise went straight to Florian's where Alix was waiting. That night he would arrange everything with Marietta.

At the Pietà, Marietta was alone in the largest of the music rooms working on a new composition when the door flew open and Elena, flushed and excited, rushed into the room and burst into tears of joy.

"It has happened!" she cried, flinging herself at Marietta's feet. Governor Tradonico sent for me and Cardinal Celano was with him. Marco wants to marry me!"

Marietta felt a deep qualm. "What answer have you given?"

"None yet. That is to come."

"What do you mean?" Marietta took Elena's head between her hands and raised the blissful tear-stained face. "Tell me."

Elena caught hold of Marietta's wrists, jubilation in her voice. "They thought I would leap at the opportunity, but I told them I would give my answer only to Marco after a proper courtship. I will not fall into his palm like a ripe plum. This is the biggest gamble of my life!"

"The pride of such a man will not let him risk rejection by an *ospedale* girl. You may never hear any more."

"Then I should know he would never have given me the love I want from the man I marry."

"You are showing wisdom and courage," Marietta said admiringly.

"I am, am I not!" Elena sprang to her feet again and flung her arms wide. "Oh! I do hope he comes!"

When Alessandro returned to the Palazzo Celano with what he had to report, only his mother and Marco were there to listen. Lavinia had gone out on a charitable mission and the rest of the family had departed to their respective homes, all having taken for granted the result of Alessandro's visit to the Pietà. In the rooms that Signora Celano occupied when visiting her son, still furnished with many of her fine possessions, she and Marco received the news of Elena's ultimatum in entirely different ways. Marco said nothing, folding his arms and mulling over what he had heard. His mother displayed fiery outrage.

"How dare this chit of a girl behave in such a high-handed manner!" she exclaimed. It was years since she had felt so offended on her son's behalf, even allowing for clashes with the Torrisis. It was unpardonable that Elena had not accepted immediately the official proposal put to her on behalf of a nobleman who was the apple of his mother's eye. Pacing up and down, Signora Celano let forth a shrill-pitched tirade against Elena. Marco continued to keep silent while his mother's unceasing and vindictive outcry drummed discordantly in his ears, jarring his already jangled nerves. Finally she went too far.

"That settles it then, Alessandro," she declared in her most implacable voice. "The unappreciative Pietà wretch is dropped as of this instant. Teresa will be my daughter-in-law after all. There shall be no changing now."

It was then that Marco turned on her like a maddened lion. Too late she saw she had roused his temper to a pitch that had never been directed against her before.

"Be silent, woman!" With a sweep of his arm he sent her priceless collection of antique glass smashing from a cabinet to the floor. There was something close to murder in his blazing eyes. "You've been dictating to me for far too long. I've had enough! No more!"

She believed that if she had not been his mother he would have seized her by the throat at that moment. Alessandro stepped forward to stand by her protectively. "But you and the name of Celano have been slighted!" she shrieked in self-justification.

"You have taken offense where none is intended!" he roared back at her. "Elena is a Pietà girl, not a noble heiress steeped in our mercenary ways and more than ready to give herself to the highest bidder! It will surprise you to know that I have fallen in love with Elena! It took you and all the rest of my family to make me see that she is all I want in a wife. Now that she has sent this simple request, natural to any romantic-minded young woman, I realize what it would mean to me if I should lose her. I truly believe she might change me for the better. You know what they say about reformed rakes." His jaw clenched. "Do not dare to scorn or I fear I might strike you and that is something I never want to do. This is hard for you, is it not? You do not wish to see me break out of the mold you created for me. I was always to put you first, was I not? To remain the devoted son and, when I married, to have a wife for whom I cared nothing."

"That is not true! I always wanted you to share some true affection with the woman you married."

"But only because you thought she would prove to be a passing fancy like all the other women I have known. You believed that nothing would change between you and me, that I would still be the devoted son guided by you with my wife following suit to the end of your days. How satisfied you must have been that I should have named a Pietà girl to marry. You were sure she would prove as docile and malleable as Teresa would have been."

"What is wrong with those virtues?"

"Nothing when directed toward the husband, but everything if the mother-in-law is to control. But all has been turned upside down for you. You will meet your match in Elena. Never again shall you dominate this house with your bitter tongue and your savage nature! I will be proud to put a wedding band on Elena's finger on the day that has been arranged. The betrothal shall be announced tomorrow!"

With that he slammed out of the room. Alessandro took his mother by the arm to help her to a chair, but she shook him off furiously.

"Let me be! What a mess you have made of this whole affair! Why did you not keep to yourself what the young woman said and simply tell Marco she had refused him?"

"Mother, I think you are forgetting my calling."

"Bah! Get out of my sight. Go back to Rome!"

He went to order his servant to pack, thankful to be leaving. His mother would try the patience of a saint and he had not yet reached that elevated status.

At the Pietà Elena was informed that Marco had arrived to see her. As she made her way to one of the smaller reception rooms where he awaited her, the smiling faces of the other girls appeared at corners, over bannisters, and peeping through cracks in doors, accompanied by a cacophony of giggles and whispers and envious sighs.

Marco was on his feet at the sight of her. This meeting was to be far more than the first step of a courtship, as she instantly discovered. He had brought with him a betrothal ring, a rare blue sapphire to match her eyes, set in diamonds and gold. Sister Sylvia, acting as chaperone from the other side of a half-open door, overheard nothing beyond his initial greeting. Drawing the rapt girl to a seat at his side, he whispered of his undying love. Then recklessly he swept her into his arms and kissed away all her fine plans to keep him waiting for her answer. Speechless with happiness, Elena watched him slide the betrothal ring onto her finger.

Chapter 7

S*ignora Celano's request that Elena be removed* from the Pietà into her direct charge was being considered by the governors. Not until a girl of Elena's age was safely married in the adjoining church or placed in employment where her moral welfare was guaranteed did they normally surrender their responsibilities, but this was an exceptional case. In the meantime the first of the seamstresses, who were to measure and fit Elena for the extensive trousseau she would need, arrived with little fashion dolls displaying the latest styles and a selection of rich and delicate fabrics that filled her with delight. Nevertheless she was highly nervous and far less happy when Sisters Sylvia and Giaccomina came to take her to meet her future mother-in-law.

"If only Marco were going to be there too, I would not have minded, but Signora Celano wants to see me on her own."

"I'm sure she will welcome you," Marietta said encouragingly.

Elena hoped the same, and the signs seemed extremely promising when Lavinia greeted her warmly upon her arrival.

"I have been looking forward so much to meeting you, Elena. This palace has been waiting for someone like you, because I can see that all Marco has been singing in your praise is true." Then to the nuns, whom she had invited to sit down, she added, "I will return after taking Elena to my mother, who wishes to talk to her alone."

Elena, although accustomed by now to the grandeur of the palaces on the Grand Canal, could tell from all she had seen so far that her future home more than ranked with the best of those in which she had sung. She was shown into Signora Celano's own simply furnished apartment, which she guessed was in keeping with the ascetic taste of the thin-faced woman in black who was seated in a high-backed chair. Elena dipped in her most graceful curtsey. But when she rose again, no kiss nor even an invitation to sit was forthcoming. Instead there was only sarcastic abuse.

"So you are the little upstart who had the audacity to tell my eldest son, a cardinal of Rome, that the head of the House of Celano must await your pleasure before receiving an answer to the great honor he was prepared to bestow on you! You changed your mind quickly enough when you saw the ring that would be yours!"

Elena flushed angrily. "That is not true. It was Marco himself who won me over. There need not have been a ring at all."

"La! Pride and a waspish tongue do not become a young wife. Marco will be your husband and your master. The sooner you learn humility and submission the better."

"I choose to believe he will always love me as I am, whatever my faults."

Signora Celano's nostrils flared as she checked a visible sneer. Marco would never remain faithful, no matter how good his intentions were now. It was not in his nature. And what did this young girl know of love? Faults that might seem enchanting in the first flush of passion would soon become irritants, even a cause for hatred. With a flick of her wrist she indicated with her fan that Elena was permitted to sit on a nearby chair.

"So, Elena, what do you know of household management that equips you to be mistress of a palace of this size?" she questioned disdainfully.

"At no time will there be as many living here as we accommodate at the Pietà," Elena replied evenly, "and I have had my turn with the other senior girls in taking charge. Being on the musical side does not mean I was not taught every domestic task."

"Nevertheless you will need instruction from me as I have already informed the governors. This is a palace with a way of life that will be entirely new to you."

Signora Celano asked many more questions, wanting to know all that Elena could remember of her parents, her upbringing before going to the Pietà, and her late aunt. Finally, having extracted all the information she could from her future daughter-in-law, she turned to the subject of the marriage itself.

"It is traditional for Celano brides to wear an heirloom gown too precious to be allowed out of the palace except for the wedding ceremony. At all other times it is kept in a secret mezzanine room known only to the family, where all the treasures and documents of the House of Celano are kept. I have had it brought out for you to see. When the governors allow you into my care, a seamstress will come to make any necessary alterations."

All the time Signora Celano was talking, her loathing for her future daughter-in-law increased. She admitted to herself that Elena was pretty enough, clearly quick to learn and spirited enough to survive whatever she might have to face, but all this could not eliminate the stark fact that she was the cause of the first rift between a devoted mother and her cherished son.

Marietta's preparations for marriage were proceeding along lines very different from those of her friend. She would be able to take only a minimum of baggage, which she would hand to Alix the night before her flight. It distressed her to be leaving behind her lovely Columbina costume, but Elena had promised to take care of it until such time as it could be delivered to her in Lyon. It was Elena's hope that she might take it to Marietta herself on the way to Paris since Marco had spoken of such a trip sometime in the future. The love they both had for their future partners made it easier for them to face the separation that was looming before them. They had made promises to write and never to lose touch, even planning that the children they both hoped to have would visit each other and thus carry their friendship into the next generation.

"We have been like sisters all this time," Marietta said to Elena one evening when her departure was only two days away. "Whoever would have thought when you came to the Pietà that one day we should go our separate ways in this manner?"

Elena nodded, remembering. "How proud Great-Aunt Lucia would have been to know I was betrothed into the Celano family. If only she could have seen me in my wedding gown." Then her mouth began to quiver uncontrollably. She thrust the music sheets she was holding back onto a stand and pressed her hands to her eyes as a sob shook her body.

Marietta went to put a hand on her arm consolingly. "Don't cry. I'm sure I'll feel the same about my mother on my wedding day, although I'll not be gowned as you will."

"It's not that," came the tearful reply. "I'm so afraid!"

"Of what? Or should I say of whom? Is it Signora Celano?"

Elena raised her troubled face, her eyes wet. "No. She's jealous of me, but she has no power to come between Marco and me. Even my wedding gown is beautiful beyond my wildest dreams. As for Marco himself, he loves me so much."

"Then what is the problem?"

"Everything seems too good to be true!"

Marietta's face cleared with relief and she gave a little laugh. "But it is true and all is going to be well."

Her cheerful reassurance had some effect. After a few more words of encouragement, Elena's naturally buoyant spirits began to revive. She wiped her eyes and smiled again.

"You're right, Marietta. I'm being foolish. Everything is going to be splendid for both of us."

"From now on we'll only look forward to all that the future holds!" Marietta declared. And Elena happily agreed.

On the evening when Marietta was to leave the Pietà forever, she looked once more around the room that had been hers. Earlier she had spent half an hour with Bianca, playing simple games. There was no way Marietta could let the child know this was a farewell visit, but she had left a letter for her with Elena and also the gifts of a necklace of pink beads and a thimble, which were from her own childhood. Elena had promised to explain Marietta's departure to Bianca and, after her own marriage, to see her regularly.

Marietta drew together the cords of the drawstring bag she would carry under her cloak. In it she had a few necessary toiletries and nightwear as well as her *moretta* mask which, she thought, would be a better disguise than the one she would be wearing in common with the rest of the choir. The Columbina mask had gone in the piece of hand-baggage already given to Alix, who would have transferred it by now to the cabin on board the ship with his own. Like her, he was having to leave most of his possessions behind, to avoid arousing his tutor's suspicions.

"I have kept my promise, Mama," Marietta whispered to the silent room. "I have stayed here until I was grown, just as you wished."

Then she went down to the entrance hall where the choir had gathered to leave for the performance. Elena gave Marietta a little nod of encouragement. They had already said their tearful farewells, for there would be no chance from now on.

The great ballroom of the Palazzo Cuccino was crowded with guests in a multitude of splendid and exotic costumes, beaded, sequined, and bejeweled. Alix was one of several Harlequins, but Marietta would have picked him out even if he had not waved to her. At the end of her song she saw him slip from the room. She knew he would change out of his costume into traveling clothes and await her in the courtyard that led into a *calle* at the rear of the palace.

The final applause was thunderous. After taking their bows, the choir passed from the salon into a side room where the usual refreshments awaited them. Marietta forced herself to eat and drink a little. When still in their masks, they had all donned their cloaks, the girls began to move toward a narrow staircase normally used by servants, which was well away from the festivities in the rest of the palace. Elena and Marietta managed to be the last to leave the room. As the rest of the choir went tripping down the stairs, laughing and chattering, a door in the wall of a landing was opened and Louise beckoned to Marietta. As she disappeared through the door, Louise's Venetian maid, masked and hooded and of similar height, emerged to take her place at Elena's side. The exchange had been made without a hitch.

In the light of a single candle Marietta and Louise faced each other as they listened to the choir's footsteps fading away down the stairs. When the girls were counted into the gondolas none would be missing. Later, as soon as it was safe, Elena would unlock the door into the *calle* with the key Marietta had left, and the imposter would leave the Pietà. With the extra hour in bed that the girls were allowed after a late performance, Marietta's disappearance would not be discovered until she and Alix were on board ship, sailing out of the lagoon and away from Venice.

"I can't thank you enough, Madame d'Oinville," Marietta said gratefully.

"Everything I've done has been for Alix," Louise replied coolly. She opened the door again and looked out. "It's safe for you to leave now. Don't go through the archway into the *andron,* but follow the passageway that will take you to the hall leading to the courtyard. Now go! I must return to my guests before I'm missed."

In the courtyard Alix waited impatiently, eager to get Marietta to the ship with the least possible delay. He had a dual purpose now in wishing to get home as quickly as possible. Just that day he had received a letter from his mother that had been following him across Europe for almost three months. His father, she wrote, had been gradually deteriorating in his mind over a considerable period, which had resulted in business misjudgements that had only recently come to light. There was a financial crisis and the silk mill was under threat of foreclosure. She urged him to return to Lyon at once.

Alix thought thankfully of Louise. He had confided in her during the evening, relating the troubles at home, and had given her the letter to keep for twenty-four hours before handing it to the comte. Fireworks exploded overhead, jerking Alix from his reverie. The noise of Carnival was everywhere. Outside the double gates costumed figures holding colored lanterns were dancing and cavorting on their way past, their raucous singing rising in the night air.

When the gates suddenly swung open three broadly built *pulcinellas* entered with invitations in their hands. They talked together as they came across the courtyard, the huge beaked noses of their masks catching the fireworks' glow. Alix stood aside to let them go past, nodding a greeting as they drew level. Then, catching him completely off guard, one shot a fist like a battering ram into his ribs. He gasped, doubling over as he staggered back. His hand flew to his sword, but he had no chance to draw. The invitations went fluttering away as all three threw themselves upon him. He fought fiercely, landing punches and even kneeing one of his attackers, who fell back in pain. But the other two only redoubled their efforts.

As Marietta was coming from the lighted vestibule onto the scene she was in time to see Alix, pinioned by the arms in the grip of two *pulcinellas,* being dragged, struggling and kicking, toward the gates, which were held open by a third. She screamed and ran to his aid.

"Alix!"

He saw her and shouted anxiously. "Don't get hurt, Marietta! I'll come back to you! I'll return!" Then a savage punch to the point of his jaw jerked his head backward and he sagged senseless in his captors' arms.

The gates slammed in her face as she reached them, and it was Jules, dressed for travel in tricorne and cloak, who held them fast from the opposite side. His face was cold and hostile.

"Let me through!" she shrieked, rattling the gates and trying to claw his gloved hands away.

"This is the end of your elopement, signorina," he stated mercilessly. "Young gentlemen abroad get sentimental notions that they soon forget when they're home again. It is fortunate that the arrangements made for this night were overheard, for had a marriage of this kind taken place it would have been annulled in France. Be thankful you have been spared that humiliation."

"You can't keep Alix a prisoner! Henri will help him get free!"

"Henri has been similarly dispatched to a waiting boat that will take us to the mainland. I would advise you to return to the Pietà as soon as possible. All is over for you here!"

Then, with all his force, he thrust the gates inward, knocking her to the ground. By the time she scrambled to her feet and gave chase he was out of sight among the revelers.

In shock, she sank down on a nearby bench. Would the comte have Alix held captive all the way to Lyon? How else could he be prevented from returning to her? If that were the case he would write as soon as he reached home. But his name would not be on the list of those whose letters she was allowed to receive. There was a growing fear in her that could not be dismissed. It was that she and Alix had been parted irretrievably. She recalled her fanciful notion, when Alix first showed himself to be falling in love with her, that an imaginary Carnival ribbon was binding her fast. Maybe it had been an illusion in more ways than one. It was Venice itself that had been taking her in thrall, never to set her free.

She had no idea how long she sat on that bench. The final fierce glory of many exploding rockets went unnoticed. Neither did she hear the bells of the Basilica ring in Lent and the end of Carnival. Not until dawn did she lift her head in sudden realization that the night had gone.

Springing up, her lashes still wet with tears, she ran to hire a gondola. The litter of Carnival was like a multicolored carpet underfoot and exotically clad revelers were making their way toward home. Those too drunk to move sat by walls and colonnades or lay among the debris like puppets released from their strings. As before, the gondolier took her to meet the baker's apprentice under the bridge. With his help she was able to get into the Pietà undetected and flew unseen to her room.

When Marietta reappeared for breakfast she was ashen-faced and swollen-lidded. Even as she saw Elena staring at her in disbelief, Sister Giaccomina came hurrying forward, throwing up her plump hands in dismay.

"How ill you look, Marietta! You must be sickening for something. I can tell you haven't slept a wink. Go back to your room and rest for a while. I'll have a light meal sent up to you."

Elena spoke up quickly. "I'll fetch it."

Marietta was grateful for the nun's consideration, and for the opportunity to tell Elena all that had happened.

Louise had not enjoyed her birthday celebration. To her the whole occasion had been a nightmare that had started when Alix first enlisted her help in his unwise romance. She could hear the servants still putting the ballroom to rights as she wandered into the salon to sit on the yellow sofa where she had listened to Alix, his face full of love for another woman. Looking at her right hand, she placed it lightly over her left. This was exactly as it had been after Alix had kissed her in gratitude for her support of his plan to get Marietta to France. When he had gone away down the stairs she had risen to go to the window, and it was then that the door of the adjacent oratory had opened to reveal her grandmother standing there.

"I heard everything, Louise."

Louise had shown no dismay. "I did not know you were at your prayers, Grandmère."

"I had thought you and Alix would make a match."

"A man in the first flush of love cannot always see the woods for the trees," Louise had remarked drily. She remembered painfully the bitter disappointment she had felt the first time she received Alix in this salon. She had truly believed he was about to propose to her. Not by the flicker of an eyelash had she revealed her innermost feelings when it turned out not to be the case.

The marquise had come toward her. "For his own good that foolish young man must not be allowed to run away with the Pietà girl."

Louise, straight-backed, had looked the older woman full in the eye. "I have not the least intention of letting that happen, but I cannot break his trust or all will be lost. There has to be another way."

As she had hoped, the marquise had nodded understandingly at her. "Do everything he has asked, my dear. You shall emerge blameless from the whole affair. I will speak to your grandfather at once. The Comte de Marquet shall be informed. How he nips this elopement in the bud will be his decision, but he can count on the full support of your grandfather and me."

All had gone well. Now Alix was safely on his way back to France and Marietta most certainly installed once more at the Pietà. Louise smoothed a crumpled cushion and brushed some confetti from the sofa, evidence that a tired guest had escaped from the ballroom for a doze, or perhaps two lovers had made use of the sofa to kiss and embrace. She had played her part exactly as Alix requested and had not been involved in anything else.

She glanced in the direction of the oratory. When Alix came to see her on that fateful day she had guessed immediately that he wished to speak again of the girl he loved. So why then had she received him here at an hour when her grandmother was so often in the oratory at prayer? She could have taken the precaution of receiving Alix in any number of other rooms. Had it been her intention to invite the intervention of others on her behalf?

She stood up swiftly in a rustle of amber silk to drive away the thought. It was a possibility she must never call to mind again if she were ever to face Alix with a clear conscience. Fortunately this would present no problem to her determined nature. By the time she left the room, her thoughts were already on her own departure for home. She would visit her uncle and aunt in Lyon at the first opportunity. Alix would be pleased to see her, a friend to him once more in time of trouble.

The business world had always intrigued her, although she had not yet had the opportunity to engage her sharp wits and mathematical ability in that direction. But she was a wealthy woman, capable of salvaging Alix's failing mill, and to be the director of a silk mill was enticing. Maybe even a partner in time. Suddenly the future looked decidedly promising.

Marietta, because of her own distress, took a little time to notice that Elena scarcely mentioned her forthcoming marriage these days. The dressmaker and her retinue of seamstresses came and went without her even mentioning what had been shown or if another gown had been fitted. Finally Marietta realized that her own misfortune had cast a blight over her friend's happiness. It was to spare her feelings that Elena was trying to avoid all reference to the wedding day.

"Stop this," Marietta ordered, taking Elena by the shoulders to give her a fierce but affectionate shake. "You are trying to spare me pain and you are making everything much worse! I want to be happy for you! I need to know about your gowns and the jewelry you are to have and everything else. Alix will come back as soon as he possibly can." She had managed to keep hope alive by throwing herself into work with renewed vigor.

"But so much has gone against you," Elena exclaimed sympathetically. "That courtesan-imposter even stole your Columbina costume and two of your best gowns. She must have wrapped them around herself under her cloak. I can never forgive myself for not being suspicious when I fetched her from your room and let her out into the *calle.*"

Marietta frowned with unusual sternness. "You and I had a full share of quarrels when we were younger, but those are in the past and I want it to stay that way. So do not make me cross. You are not to be blamed in any way for the theft. When Alix returns he will give me another costume and a mask to go with it. So now will you stop worrying?"

"I will try," Elena promised.

"Good. Please show me what was in the dressmaker's boxes that were delivered to you this morning."

Elena nodded, glad to display her new possessions. "Come with me."

As Marietta followed she wondered sadly where her green and gold Columbina mask was now. If it was not being tossed about by the movements of the ship in an unoccupied cabin, it might well have been thrown overboard with the rest of her possessions to blend its colors with the sea.

Elena paid the Signora another visit before permission was given for her to move into the Palazzo Celano. Her immediate joy at being able to see Marco every day was dashed when she learned that one of the governors' stipulations was that he should stay elsewhere until the wedding day. Marco had agreed, but it had only increased the rift with his mother who he suspected of spiteful intent, although she insisted it was the Pietà's ruling and not hers. Yet she made a further condition of her own that he not disrupt the instruction she would be giving Elena by calling in at the palace. He was to stay away until the ball at which Elena would be officially presented to the Celano family and friends and various important personages. Elena complained bitterly to Marietta, who sympathized, but there was nothing to be done.

On Elena's last day at the Pietà the hour of departure arrived all too quickly. There were so many who wanted to wish her well when finally she stood ready to leave. Marietta held Bianca by the hand as they waited to be the last to speak to her. Sister Sylvia, who was to hand her over to the Signora, was already seated in the Celano gondola. Elena hugged and kissed Marietta and Bianca in turn.

"After I'm married I shall come back often to see you both," she promised between smiles and tears. Then she darted away through the water gate and into the gondola.

When they had waved her on her way Bianca looked up anxiously at

Marietta, clinging tightly to her hand. "I'm glad you are still at the Pietà. I would not want to stay on here without you or Maestra Elena."

"It may come to that in a year or two," Marietta replied, seeing that this might be an opportunity to prepare the child. "None of us can stay at the Pietà forever."

"But you would not go far away, would you?" Bianca looked alarmed.

"Distance is nothing between people who care about one another. I will write and always keep in touch. It may prove possible for you to visit me and I shall always want to come back to Venice to see you and Elena whenever I can." She could not yet offer Bianca a home, but she hoped Alix would agree to it when the time came for her goddaughter to leave the Pietà.

The child pondered. "But I cannot write well enough to send a long letter to you."

"That is easily remedied. I am going to take over the extra teaching that Elena has been giving you. Shall we have half an hour with your writing, Bianca? It could be a little letter for Elena after her wedding day."

The child beamed up at her. "Oh, yes!"

Signora Celano was a hard taskmaster, finding fault with Elena at every opportunity. She was made to set tables for any number of guests, including a banquet for a hundred or more, which was to ensure that she could check if a single fork was not quite straight or a glass incorrectly placed. Often she and Lavinia would sit down with the Signora and scores of invisible guests to eat small portions of the large number of courses from a menu planned for the Doge, a visiting ambassador, or some other person of importance. It would be Elena's duty to chose the menu, and if one dish or another was not approved by the Signora there would be quite a display. The woman would utter little cries of dismay, press a napkin to her mouth and wave the delicacy away or show some other exaggerated revulsion to what had been presented. Elena, however, kept herself under tight control and did not once answer back or retaliate in any way.

Yet through these tasks and others, however unpleasant the procedure was, Elena learned quickly how things should be done. Although at first she had wanted to giggle when making conversation with an imaginary diplomat or other notable of the Signora's choosing, she soon knew what subjects could be discussed and what could not. One rule she did resent, however.

"Never mention the Pietà unless in reference to a concert," the Signora said sternly. "That life is already behind you. As far as this house is concerned your life began when you came to live here, although in an extreme emergency you may refer to your years with your great-aunt since she appears to have been a woman of some taste."

On the evening of the ball Elena was beside herself with excitement. She had not seen Marco since she came to the Palazzo Celano, and now she could hardly keep still for the hairdresser, who dressed her hair over a pad in the latest mode, topping it with flowers and ribbons. Then came her gown, wide over side panniers in pale sugar-pink silk trimmed with looped gossamer swags, matching her satin shoes exactly. When she came downstairs and found Marco waiting for her, his eyes full of love, she ran to him, oblivious to the amused stares and raised eyebrows of the other members of the Celano family who had gathered to meet her ahead of the other guests.

"Darling Elena," Marco greeted her, kissing her lovingly on the lips. Then he lowered his voice for her ears alone. "Nobody has any right to keep us apart like this. At least I should be able to call on you in my own home!"

She laughed with him. "Now that I have mastered most of what the Signora has been teaching me, perhaps that will be allowed."

"So you are progressing well?"

"I intend to be the most gracious hostess in all Venice and the best wife in all the world to you!"

"As I shall be a husband to you."

They kissed again and exchanged a secret smile. Then the Signora came bearing down on them in a rustle of wine-red silk to begin the presentations with Elena on one side of her and Marco on the other. Elena noted that collectively her relatives-to-be were all proud-faced men and women, flashing-eyed and elegant. Yet there were several male cousins, some quite distantly removed, who, although attired in their best, were shabby in comparison to the rest of their kinfolk. Despite their time-honored family connections they were among the *barnabotti*, impoverished noblemen so-named because they lived in the parish of San Barnabà where free apartments were made available to them. Forbidden by family and the State to marry and compelled by law to uphold their dignity by wearing silk like all those of patrician birth, they received moderate stipends from the Great Council and allowances for their mistresses and bastards. It was obvious that these men were even haughtier in their attitude toward her than the rest of the Celanos, their disdain for her humbler origins showing through the veneer of their smooth-tongued manners. Notoriously troublesome and radical, it was the *barnabotti* on the fringes of the Celano and Torrisi families who kept the vendetta between them in a state of constant eruption.

Yet to Elena the most fearsome of all the Celanos, including the Signora herself, was Filippo, a tall man of brutish good looks and strong physique. His face was square, with fierce brows and deepset hooded eyes that had a granite glint to them, his nose bold with arrogant nostrils and his chin handsomely shaped. Dressed in silver and blue brocade, he had the air of a man well satisfied with his own appearance; there was cruelty in the set of his mouth and she was repulsed by the way he raked her with his frankly lascivious stare when he was presented. Although she tried to avoid him throughout the evening, he kept stepping deliberately into her line of vision, as if they were engaged in some conspiratorial game. When he came to partner her in a square dance with the graceful high-armed movements that were in fashion her heart sank, but she had to let him lead her onto the floor of the great ballroom. As she had feared, he fondled her fingers, and when she had to pass under his arm in the measure he lowered his lids to look down her décolletage.

"I never thought you would survive my mother's tuition," he said with cynical amusement as they danced on, "but I have been told by Lavinia that you stood up to it all extremely well. That is not easy to do. I salute you. I shall look forward to getting to know you better."

"I also heard from Lavinia that you are not a frequent visitor unless your mother is in residence, and so I expect our acquaintanceship will always be a distant one." They had come to the end of the dance.

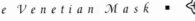

"Don't count on that, Elena."

She was thankful to get away from him. She had seen lust often enough in men's eyes, but never before spiked with such malevolence. It made her wonder just how jealous of Marco's position he might be. Fortunately Marco claimed her then, and for the rest of that gloriously dance-swirling, musical and magical night they were never apart.

The next evening they were able to talk about the ball when Marco came to dine, permitted at last by his mother to come to his own table. Elena thought he looked a little tired, but then so was she after dancing until dawn.

After hearing that Elena had not yet been into every remote nook and cranny of the palace, Marco took the excuse of a tour to get her away on his own. The Signora sent Lavinia along as chaperone, but at his persuasion, she followed along at some distance. Marco kissed and embraced Elena passionately in each alcove and behind every pillar. Now and again when they turned a corner they broke into a run, laughing as they went, to rush into a room well ahead of Lavinia and share a few intimate moments.

The tour was to end in the secret treasure room. Before reaching it Marco would have branched off in another direction if Lavinia had not intervened.

"Not there, Marco."

Before he could reply Elena raised her eyebrows inquiringly. "What is it? Some mystery?"

Marco nodded to Lavinia to show he had accepted her advice and then put his arm around Elena's waist to lead her on to the treasure room. "No mystery. It's a hidden salon that has been kept locked since a murder was committed there a long time ago."

Elena shivered. "I never want to see it. Don't ever tell me where it is."

"I won't," he promised. "Neither will my brothers nor Lavinia. Nobody else except my mother knows of it."

Elena thought uneasily that the Palazzo Celano was like the other palaces on the Grand Canal in being a blend of the beautiful and the sinister. From all she had heard, there were few, if any, that were free of dark deeds in their history.

In the treasure room Elena tried on some of the jewelry from the many caskets stored there and Marco placed on her head a bridal coronet of gold and precious stones. Lavinia, seated on a stool watching, felt a pang of apprehension. No bride-to-be should wear that coronet before her wedding day, but it was too late to say anything. In a moment she forgot her misgiving and laughed along with the happy couple. She had never seen two people more in love.

Elena felt as if she were wrapped in a cocoon of bliss as she waited the following evening to see Marco again. She went so many times to the window that the Signora ordered her to sit down and learn not to show unmannerly impatience. When footsteps finally approached, Elena sprang up from her chair in joy but it was Alvise, looking grave.

"Marco is not well," he explained. "This morning he complained of a severe headache and by midafternoon he showed signs of fever."

Elena was frantic. "I must go to him!"

The Signora snapped at her. "Don't be ridiculous! Marco's place is here in his own bed if he is unwell. Fetch him at once, Alvise."

When Marco appeared, he was swaying on his feet and supported by his brother. Elena ran to him, concerned about his high color and the sweat glistening on his temples. He managed a smile for her.

"I shall be all right tomorrow, my sweeting. You'll see."

When Alvise had helped Marco into bed the Signora tried to bar Elena from entering the bedchamber. "Marco is my son and not your husband yet," she stated with fierce possessiveness. "Keep away!"

Elena took a deep breath and defied the woman for the first time. "Step aside and let me go to him. Don't make me thrust you out of the way."

The Signora was astonished by this change from docile obedience to defiance, but realized Elena meant what she said. Turning swiftly, she entered the bedroom first.

"I've come to take care of you, my dear son," she said soothingly. But Marco was looking eagerly toward Elena.

"I want you here with me," he said, lifting his hand for Elena to take into hers, "but you might catch my fever."

"I'm immune," she reassured him, her heart contracting with fear at how ill he looked, "and I know exactly how to care for you. I've done it all before at the Pietà."

"Did the patients survive?" he jested.

She smiled. "Naturally."

"That's good." He closed his eyes, still holding her hand. His fever was rising.

At the Pietà, Marietta waited anxiously for news of Marco's recovery. There were a number of cases of the same fever at the *ospedale*, including some of the girls in the principal choir, and all engagements had been canceled. She was feeling cheered by promising signs of recovery in three of the worst cases when she met Sister Giaccomina on the landing. The nun's gentle face was crumpled with distress.

"What's happened?" Marietta demanded in alarm. "Has one of the sick children—?"

"Word has just come from the Palazzo Celano." The nun wrung her hands. "There will be no wedding for Elena. Her betrothed has died."

For a matter of seconds Marietta was speechless with shock. Then the words broke from her. "Elena needs me there! She will be out of her mind with grief."

"That's impossible. Neither Sister Sylvia nor I nor anyone else can be spared to go with you now."

"Then," Marietta said firmly, "I must ask you to look the other way for a little while. Please!"

"Oh, my!" The nun looked nervously about and then, shaking her head at her own action, hurried away, keeping her eyes down, still exclaiming as she went.

Marietta could not risk being stopped at the main door, so, taking a chance, she took the key to the *calle* door. With a swift glance to make sure there was no one at any of the windows, she slipped out and locked the door behind her.

"No visitors are being received today," she was informed when she arrived at the Palazzo Celano.

"Signorina Elena will wish to see me," she said after giving her name. "I'm from the Pietà."

She was kept waiting only a few minutes before being shown up the great staircase until eventually she entered Elena's bedchamber. Elena, already in a black gown, sat staring blindly out the window.

"I knew you would come," she said gratefully without turning her head.

Marietta rushed to her. "Oh, my dear Elena, I share your sorrow to the depths of my heart."

Elena looked at her with huge sad eyes. "But I have died too. My life went with Marco. That is why I can't weep."

Marietta had known that Elena would be stricken to utter despair, but tears would have been a natural and helpful release. She drew a chair close and took her friend's hand. "Let us sit awhile as we are. Maybe later on you would like to talk a little."

"How long can you stay?"

"As long as you wish. It can be arranged, I'm sure."

For a long time Elena did not move or speak, letting her hand rest in Marietta's comforting grasp. Then she said, "I think I should go to the Signora. The poor woman collapsed and was carried away after Marco drew his last breath. I stayed with him on my own until dawn."

"Do you want me to come with you?"

"I had better go alone. She and I have not been friends, but I should like to amend that now. I hope she will feel the same. It would be a help if she and I could console each other. Please wait for me here."

When Elena entered the Signora's salon she found that Filippo was there with Maurizio as well as Alvise. Vitale stood by his mother, a glass of wine in his hand. Lavinia was not present. Elena went forward.

"What do you want?" the Signora demanded icily. Her sons who were seated rose to their feet at Elena's approach.

"I came to see you, signora," Elena replied. "I thought we would have need of each other in our grief."

The woman's eyes narrowed. "Go back to your own quarters. You have no place in this family now. As soon as the funeral is over you shall leave!"

Filippo watched as Elena covered her face with her hands and rushed from the room. As the door closed after her, he turned to his mother with a placating gesture. "Let us not be hasty, Mother. Elena should stay on here until her future is decided."

In the ballroom, Marco was lying in state, his coffin draped in the Celano heraldic colors and set on a platform covered with a cloth of gold. Elena flung herself across it, crying out.

"Marco! Why did you leave me?" She knew then that she still lived, for nobody who had died could feel such heart-shattering grief or shed such torrential tears.

As it turned out, Marietta was not able to stay with her bereaved friend, but not because of anyone at the Pietà. She was informed by a spokesman for the Celano family that no strangers were welcome at the palace during this time of mourning, and so Elena, broken and distraught, was left to grieve without anyone close to her.

Elena's guardian came to see her the following day. After offering his condolences he told her that there was no question of her returning to the Pietà.

"No girl may go back after she has left. It could only be a disruptive influence to have one in the midst of all the rest who had sampled another kind of life. The best that can be done is that the Maestro will speak on your behalf to one of the opera companies, although he warns you never to expect to be a prima donna."

"I'm aware of my limitations," Elena replied quietly.

"Whether you would be permitted to take employment is another matter."

Elena, who had been looking down at her hands folded in the black silk of her lap, raised her head. "What do you mean?"

"You came here to live only because the governors and I signed over the responsibility for you to Signora Celano. Your future is in her hands now. Even your dowry is under her jurisdiction."

"That is monstrous! She wants me gone from here. She told me that."

"I have just spoken with her and she is no longer of that mind. The new head of the House of Celano insists that it is not seemly for one who was betrothed to his brother to be cast out upon the world. You are to remain in his mother's charge until your future can be decided."

"Have I no independent right at all?"

"None."

"Are you saying that if she wished I could be married off to whomever she might choose for me?"

"That is correct. You may count on her to do her best for you, but my personal advice is that you never go against her wishes. Such people as those among whom you are now established have absolute power, and I fear you would soon find yourself incarcerated in some harsh convent should you ever disobey Signora Celano."

"The law is very hard on women," she replied bitterly, "unless they can rise in exceptional circumstances as she has done."

"Who is to say that chance might not be yours one day?" He wanted to help her adjust to the restrictions that had been placed on her.

"If ever it should," she gave back swiftly, "I would use it with charity and compassion."

The day before the funeral Filippo spoke to his mother about Elena's future. "Since I have taken over all duties and responsibilities that were Marco's, I'm willing to put my signature to the marriage contract made with the Pietà and take Elena as my wife." He made a leisurely gesture. "She shall have time to get over her sorrow. Three or four months should be enough. She is young and resilient and will soon recover, especially if she is allowed to stay on here. From what I've seen of her she has quite a taste for the good things of life."

He fully expected some spitting-cat reaction from his mother, but he had no intention of letting her rule him as she had Marco for most of his life. It had not suited his aggressive nature to be subordinate to his favored brother, and it was virtually impossible for him to feel any grief when at last he had all that he wanted and that he had always felt should have been his in the first place. It gave him immense satisfaction to claim even the woman who Marco had chosen as a wife. To make Elena his own would finally erase any trace of his late brother's rule.

"So that's the way of things, is it?" Signora Celano saw through him. Nothing that had been Marco's was to be left unclaimed. Aware that she was surprising him, she nodded resignedly. "Very well."

"I consider it a most suitable arrangement," he emphasized.

She ignored his comment. "You mentioned a period of mourning for

Elena. I see no need for that. All the time you and she are betrothed I should have to stay on here to chaperone her and you know how much I dislike being in Venice during the hottest time of the year."

"It would suit me to marry soon."

"Then let the marriage take place ten days after my dear Marco is laid to rest. I can't mourn him here. I see him wherever I look. Only when I'm in my own house again will I be able to grieve as I should."

"I understand, Mother." He was not capable of pity, but he could comprehend why she would wish to be alone with her memories and her sorrow in the house she liked best.

"When shall you tell Elena that she is to be your wife? I suggest you go to her now."

That had been his intention, but he promptly changed his mind. If he appeared to be following her advice, he would never be free of her interference. "I shall speak to Elena in my own time," he answered irritably, "and not at anyone else's bidding."

She saw she had overstepped the mark. This son was not Marco, who had been devoted to her and had listened to her every word until that wretched girl caused a rift between them. For that, Elena should never be forgiven. Even though on his sickbed Marco had softened toward her, his loving mother, and their estrangement had been mended, the scar remained for her, never to be forgotten. Filippo would listen to her only when it suited him. Even when he was a boy she had disliked him intensely for his obduracy and his greed.

"Do whatever you wish," she said with condescension, irritating him still further by seeming to give him permission. "But leave me now. I'm tired."

He kissed her hand and went from the room.

When the day of the funeral came, Marietta and the two nuns accompanied Elena in the procession by water to the island that was the burial place of all Venetians. The gondola in which the four of them rode was relegated to a position well to the rear of those bearing the chief mourners and minor members of the Celano family. Every gondola had the traditional crimson ribbons of death wafting from its prow, and black velvet drapery trailed in the water from the ornate and beplumed funeral gondola itself in which the coffin, draped in the heraldic colors and bearing the crest of the House of Celano, was being borne to its last resting place.

Elena, veiled in black as were the other women, bore her grief with dignity. When it was all over Marietta and the nuns had to leave her at the steps of the palace as they had not been invited in. She went alone into the huge *andron*, all the rest of the mourners well ahead of her upstairs. Only the footmen bowed in sympathy as she went past.

When she had ascended the marble staircase she found Filippo waiting for her. As always, every instinct made her wary of him.

"The funeral was a hard ordeal for you, Elena," he said with unexpected consideration. "I knew what you were going through. Marco would have been proud of you."

In her highly emotional state these few kind words, the first she had received in this household since Marco's death, caught her off guard. When he took her hand she thought appreciatively that he was going to lead her to the salon where the rest of the funeral party had gathered. But when he took her instead to the door of the small salon next to it, saying he wanted to talk to her, all her fears returned. In the room she backed a few paces away from him.

"What is it you want to say to me?"

He was well aware of being a fine figure of a man, immensely attractive to women, and he smiled to put her at ease. Once Elena began to forget about his brother all would be well between them. His guess was that she, having led such a sheltered existence, had been dazzled by what Marco represented more than anything else. He would give her the same and more.

"We are to marry, Elena," he said without preamble. "It is my duty in any case to shoulder the responsibility for you in this palace that is now mine, and I also find you extremely beautiful. I'm pleased and proud to be making you my wife. You shall want for nothing. I can be generous, as you will discover."

She stood stunned. This shock, coming on the heels of her suffering, was making her whole body tremble, and she realized as if from a distance, that her teeth were chattering. One part of her mind told her that this was not

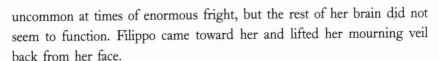

uncommon at times of enormous fright, but the rest of her brain did not seem to function. Filippo came toward her and lifted her mourning veil back from her face.

"The need for this veil is over. I shall take you with me now into the next room and announce to the company that we are to be married in a week's time."

Her eyes were enormous as she stared silently at him. As he bent to kiss her she did an extraordinary thing. She bared her teeth at him like a cornered animal. He took her hand again and crushed it painfully as a warning while he opened the door into the next room.

Elena was being dressed for her marriage. Never once since waking that morning had she spoken. The hairdresser had spent over an hour brushing and combing her hair to hang virginally down her back, and the front curls had been coaxed flatteringly across her brow. Now, perfumed and painted, she stood in the middle of the bedchamber while half a dozen women, including Lavinia, arranged and smoothed the treasured gown.

"Now for the final touch," Lavinia said as she turned to take the jeweled bridal coronet from its velvet cushion in the casket that had been brought from the treasure room only that morning. Just then the door opened and Signora Celano entered. Like the women attending the bride she was in black, for all except the bride and groom were in deep mourning. Only kinsfolk, similarly clad, would be at the marriage, including quite a number who had come for the funeral and were remaining for the wedding.

"Wait, Lavinia," the Signora ordered her daughter, who stood holding the glittering coronet in mid-air. "Since Elena has no mother to be with her today, it is my privilege to crown the bride."

Her thin beringed fingers took the coronet from her daughter. It had been given to a Celano bride in the fifteenth century by the Venetian noblewoman, Caterina Cornaro, who became Queen of Cyprus, and had been worn by family brides ever since. A single magnificent ruby, suspended from the front of it, hung in the middle of the brow. Elena, remembering when Marco had placed it on her head with love in his smiling eyes, held on mentally to that memory to give her the strength she needed. In a cruel whim, the Signora's sharp fingernails dug deliberately into the bride's skull as she set the coronet straight. Elena did not wince. She was beyond physical pain.

Signora Celano drew away as did the rest of the women to view the splendor of the bride. There was no denying Elena's beauty in a gown that was stiff with gold and a network of jewels. The substitution of delicate black Burano lace for cream at the low neckline and cuffs was to indicate that a state of family bereavement was being observed. Filippo would have a black cravat and cuffs as the same token. Elena, regarding herself in a mirror that was being held for her, saw only an unrecognizable figure in glorious array.

"That is enough self-admiration even for a bride," the Signora said sharply. "Time is pressing on."

Only Lavinia remained with Elena when Signora Celano and the others had gone from the palace to the church. In order to relieve the tension of these last few minutes, Lavinia made conversation, talking of anything that came to mind. Finally she went to the window.

"I can see it's time for you to leave." She turned back to kiss Elena's cheek and give the greeting customary at this time. In emotional tones, for she was full of pity for this girl now committed to a brother who she knew to be merciless, she said, "I wish you joy."

"I have lost joy forever," Elena answered tonelessly. Lavinia burst into tears and Elena had to help her to control herself before they could go from the room. One of the governors of the Pietà was waiting to escort Elena to the church, as was the custom when one of the musical elite made an exceptional match.

"My felicitations on your wedding day, Elena," he greeted her.

"I thank you, signore," she replied, as was expected of her.

He led her downstairs to the water gate where she saw that a fleet of gondolas occupied by Celano kin had gathered to accompany her to the waiting bridegroom. Although she could not tell who was among these people to whom she would soon be related in marriage, Lavinia had said that more than enough *barnabotti* had turned up. By right of kinship they never let slip an opportunity to join in the festivities of their richer relatives, which usually included a feast. It was a burden many noble families had to bear.

Elena's jeweled gown flashed fire back at the sun as she stepped into the bridal gondola, which was completely draped in flowers. As soon as she was settled, with Lavinia in attendance, the governor also took his place on board and the procession set off along the Grand Canal. It made a charming sight, petals drifting from the many blossoms to rise lightly in the air and dance on the water. People on the flanking parades and in other boats applauded and waved as the bride passed by. With the shutters of the *felze* slid well back, she could be seen by all in her Renaissance finery. Elena, pale and withdrawn, made automatic acknowledgement, lifting her hand or inclining her head. Her birthplace, which she had always loved, was paying her homage on what should have been the happiest day of her life.

The water traffic drew aside to let the wedding party have unhindered passage. It was an unlucky chance that a Torrisi gondolier, recognizing the Celano colors, was deliberately slow in crossing the bows of the bridal gondola, judging with skill the time needed to avoid a collision. The Celano gondolier shook his fist, prevented by the occasion from voicing the expletives he wanted to let fly. Enmity between the male servants of the two families was as fierce as that of their masters.

Although the incident went unmarked by most, it had been glimpsed by seven fiery young *barnabotti*, who were riding together in a hired gondola at the rear of the procession.

"Did you see that piece of Torrisi insolence?" one demanded heatedly. "This water needs clearing of certain unwanted flotsam!"

The rest agreed enthusiastically, already well-laced with cheap wine in honor of the day and as ever spoiling for a fight. There was no *felze* to their vessel and when one of their number stood to demand the oar, there was no protest from the gondolier, for rapiers had been drawn by those still seated and all were pointed in his direction.

The *barnabotti* in two other vessels spotted one of their number with an oar and demanded to know what was up. Within minutes their gondolas too were in their own charge, one gondolier cooperating at pistol point. Hastily the *barnabotti* took *bauta* masks from their pockets and donned them.

In the Torrisi gondola Domenico was reading through a document he had collected at the Doge's Palace and at his side Angela was watching through the open window of the *felze* as the Celano bride and her retinue went by.

"The Pietà girl looked serious and sad," she said compassionately, turning back to her husband, "but so composed and dignified."

"Did she?" Domenico asked absently.

"More than that. In that gown she could have been on her way to be painted by Titian."

He looked at her then. "But Maestra Marietta is the red-head."

"I meant that the style of her gown and the virginal flow of her hair put the bride back in time."

"Is that so?" He returned his attention to the document. "I wish her well."

She gave his arm a little shake. "It would have done no harm to show it as she went by. I waved to her and she waved back most graciously."

"Obviously she did not notice the Torrisi colors." He was still reading.

"Maybe she does not care for the vendetta any more than I do. Would it not be wonderful if the women of both families could force it to a conclusion?"

But he was not listening, absorbed again in what he was reading. Angela sighed. The vendetta had become too much a way of life for either of the families to consider ending it. She believed that the men on either side thrived on the danger and that it gave a constant spice and excitement to their lives. If only the marriage of the Pietà girl could be turned into an olive branch in some way. "Domenico," she said persuasively, "don't you think—"

She was interrupted by a warning shout from their gondolier. Her eyes widened in terror as she saw the gleaming prongs of three gondolas bearing down on them at speed. At her side Domenico leapt forward drawing his rapier, but the impact on their vessel threw him off balance. She heard the sound of splintering wood, and the whole scene before her—jeering *bauta*-masked men, palace roof tops, and the sky—seemed to turn upside-down. The cold dark water closed over her head and she was floundering, trapped within the *felze*.

The wedding party had alighted at the steps of the Molo. People gathered immediately to watch and others came to the arches of the loggia of the Doge's Palace to see the bride go by. All the way along the Riva degli Schiavoni, more people came to windows and out of doorways. All of Venice was accustomed to processions and spectacular sights, but those who saw Elena that day considered themselves fortunate. In such a gown she was a reminder of Venetian glory at its height.

At the governor's side, Elena ascended the steps of Santa Maria della Pietà, its doors open wide to her. The thundering organ, played by one of her fellow musicians, greeted her and from the gilded galleries the voices of the Pietà choir burst forth. It was comforting and familiar until she saw Filippo waiting for her where Marco should have stood and she jerked to an abrupt halt. Then, as if sleep-walking, she let the governor lead her up the aisle.

Owing to the family's state of mourning, the wedding breakfast afterward in the Palazzo Celano was a restrained occasion. Marietta and Sisters Sylvia and Giaccomina were the only representatives, with the governor, of the Pietà. When it was over the nuns wanted to leave immediately, but Marietta managed a final word with the bride.

"I'm so glad you were permitted to come," Elena said emotionally. "Soon there will be your marriage to Alix."

The two friends hugged each other. "It can't be very soon," Marietta corrected, made anxious by Elena's distracted air.

"But the time will come. Then I shall be able to rejoice in your happiness on your wedding day as I cannot on mine."

As if in a daze Elena turned away and drifted like a magnificently gowned doll back to the celebrations. Sadly Marietta watched her for a few moments and then joined her companions. Two noblemen passing on the stairs were talking of an accident linked to the name of Domenico Torrisi. Ignoring Sister Sylvia's tug on her sleeve, Marietta turned to them.

"Your pardon, gentlemen. I could not help overhearing what you said about an accident."

"Maestra Marietta!" They had recognized her. "I know you well by sight and by your remarkable singing voice," one said.

"Surely you are not departing already?" protested the other, ready to escort her back up the stairs.

"Please tell me about Signor Torrisi. Was he seriously injured?"

"No, not at all," replied the first man. "There was a collision on the Grand Canal. Nobody seems to know exactly how it happened, but three gondolas drove the prow of the Torrisi gondola against the parade wall, throwing him and his wife and gondolier into the water. Signora Torrisi was trapped in the *felze* and would have drowned if her husband had not dived to save her. So there was no fatal outcome as might easily have happened."

"Is it known who is responsible for the accident?"

The two men exchanged glances before replying. "Nobody can be sure. All except the gondoliers were masked. Suspicion has fallen on certain of the wedding guests, but since the bridal procession was far ahead when the collision took place it must have been sheer unfortunate chance."

She could tell that they were unconvinced by that theory, but since they were kinfolk under the Celano roof she suspected they were keeping their true opinion to themselves. After thanking them for their information she rejoined the waiting nuns, relieved to know that Domenico and his wife were safe. He had kept his vow made at the ridotto not to betray her nocturnal outings from the Pietà and she would always be grateful.

That night when Filippo went to his bride he found her cowering in a corner, her eyes wide with fear. When he reached for her, she darted under his arm and ran screaming for the door. He grabbed a handful of her nightshift and it tore as she was jerked off her feet. Before she could regain her balance he had gathered her up in his arms. He had heard of other men having this sort of scene with virgins on their wedding nights, but he had never expected to experience it himself. He tossed her onto the bed, intent on subduing her. She screamed again when he plowed into her, and he clapped a hand over her mouth. He was vaguely aware of trying to drive Marco out of her heart and mind with all the powerful violence of his virility.

Afterward she lay still, thinking he would sleep until morning. But she was mistaken. Her innocent belief that there would be no more that night was soon dispersed. The wanderings of his hot fleshy mouth sickened her.

At the Palazzo Torrisi Angela was making a good recovery from her near-drowning in the waters of the Grand Canal. Since she was pregnant there had been concern that she would miscarry, which was why she was spending some hours every day on a couch. She had never been robust in health, always dreading the winters and thriving in warm weather. It was Domenico's concern for how she would be in his absence, as well as her own love of travel, that had caused him to take her with him so often on his diplomatic journeys. Several times she had sailed with him to Eastern Mediterranean ports of call and once as far as India.

"Here is the new book you were searching for," Domenico said one morning. "I found it on my desk."

"So that is where it was!" She took the book from him and nestled comfortably against her cushions. She had made up her mind not to take any stairs that day, for she was feeling particularly tired. The book was welcome. It was small and easy to hold, a collection of recipes for beauty aids, which she liked to mix herself.

"Is there anything else you need?"

She shook her head smilingly. "No. Go back to your work now."

He bent down to kiss her and on impulse she caught at his sleeve, keeping him for a second kiss before he straightened up again. "What was that for?" he asked her with a grin.

"For everything."

His smile still lingered as he went from the room. They had everything except an heir, but since she was well past the period when previously she had always miscarried, he was as hopeful as she was that this time all would be well.

He remembered clearly the first time he had seen her. She had been laughing down at him from a tapestry-hung balcony as he competed in the annual September regatta. The whole of the Grand Canal was full of vividly colored racing vessels, the law of all black relaxed on this occasion, and vast crowds of spectators watched from the parades, in boats and from every window, balcony, and loggia. Such cheering! Such spectacle! He had been twenty-one and as wild for women and wine as his three brothers who were manning the oars with him. Antonio, the youngest, was seated at the tiller.

The race had been going well, the Torrisi boat well in the lead, when he had looked up from his car and seen the girl in whom all his desires were then immediately concentrated.

When the race had been won he took a small boat and rowed back on his own to call up to her. There was someone he knew among those on the balcony, and so he had been invited to join the gathering. Angela had tried to avoid him, flitting to and fro, fluttering her fan, flirting with others, but her eyes gave her away and he knew he would have her, not for one night but forever. He had left the palace only to go half a mile along the Grand Canal to his own home where he went down on his knee before his invalid father and requested that he be the son allowed to marry.

"You were always my heir," his father had answered, "but I chose to wait before announcing it until you had sown enough wild oats to be ready to accept the role as my successor."

Domenico recalled his elation and how he had returned to Angela immediately. She no longer attempted to keep him at a distance, admitting long afterward that she had sensed instinctively that the path between them was cleared. Late that night, when the party was in full swing, they had slipped away on their own to her bedchamber. There she had surrendered to him and within a month they were wed. He had given her jewels as a marriage gift, and hers to him had been a gilded mask for which he had to sit for a mask-maker's sculptor to fashion his likeness for the mold.

"There are so many occasions in Venice that call for a mask," she had said, "and I do not want your beloved features hidden from me."

There were times when she wanted him to wear the gilded mask while they made love and then she rode him ecstatically, calling him her golden steed. More than once he had snatched the mask off and hurled it away in his final passion, once causing it to crack against a wall. She had wept over the damage, clutching the mask and curled up in her nakedness, until he had coaxed it from her and spread her out to make love to her in another way.

Now, back at his desk, he attended to the papers and correspondence that his clerk had brought in during his short absence downstairs. A report from one of his spies, listing information gathered from gondoliers and other witnesses, left no doubt it was the *barnabotti* of the Celanos who had instigated the accident on the Grand Canal. Hot rage flooded through him. He could easily have had them killed, but that kind of action was not in keeping with the code of honor that both his family and the Celanos observed, whatever the behavior of those on the fringe of their respective circles. Deeds were paid in kind: duel matched against duel, ambush against ambush, battle against battle. The *barnabotti*, already on the outside, were a law unto themselves. It should be the duty of those among them who were his distant kin to equalize the affair.

There was another spy's report on Marietta, for it had been Angela's idea to discover how and why the girl had broken all the rules of the Pietà. Why Angela had taken such a notion he did not know, for she was not normally inquisitive. But over the past weeks she had taken a special interest in the Pietà, making generous donations and attending receptions, almost as if she wanted to find out more about Marietta from a personal viewpoint. He could only assume that the clandestine meetings between Marietta and her Frenchman had held some romantic appeal for his wife. He placed the report in a leather file without reading it. Angela could do so if she wished when she was well again.

As he finished putting his signature to several letters that had been drawn up for him, he lifted his head sharply, his quill pen spattering ink as he heard doors being flung open and the sound of running feet. The letters went flying as he leapt up from his desk and made for the door. As he threw it open he heard, but refused to accept, what a maidservant was crying out to him. He rushed for the stairs.

Bursting into his wife's boudoir, he saw that Angela had risen up from her cushions and then collapsed back on them, her joyous little bird-heart overly strained by all she had been through. He dashed to her bedside and was in time to catch her in his arms before the last breath went from her and her head fell back.

Chapter 8

$\mathcal{T}$he *Torrisi* BARNABOTTI *slit the throats of the*
culprits they considered responsible for Angela's death and their bodies
ended up in the Grand Canal as rough justice demanded. Their act resulted
in such violent skirmishes with the dead men's kin that all the *barnabotti*
hurled themselves eagerly into the fighting, which lasted until the Doge
sent in his own guard to restore order. He then threatened them all with
eviction from their houses and the cancellation of the allowances made for
each man's mistress if they did not keep the peace. Yet these were idle
threats, as everyone knew, for the *barnabotti* were trouble enough already
with their jealous resentment of their richer kin and the established regime
in which they themselves played no part. At the slightest provocation they
would be swift to form into a dangerous and hostile force that neither the
Doge nor the Great Council wished to unleash.

Domenico, grave-faced, received a full account of the vengeance that had
been taken. Although honor was satisfied, he thought only of how distressed Angela would have been that still more lives had been lost in what
she had always seen as a senseless quarrel.

On a Sunday in Santa Maria della Pietà the marriage of Adrianna and
Leonardo was celebrated. Afterward it was inevitable that Marietta should

wonder more than ever when her own marriage would take place. Although she had reasoned sensibly that there was little likelihood of her seeing Alix again before a year had passed, it did not stop her from looking quickly if she caught sight of a young man resembling him in height and form. Occasionally when singing in the gilded galleries of Santa Maria della Pietà she would look down on a smoothly groomed dark head, but then always an upward glance from the man revealed an unfamiliar face and disappointment would grip her once more.

She kept as busy as she could, spending many hours in practice, writing and composing her own songs, giving extra teaching to promising pupils, and spending time with Bianca. Elena kept her promise to visit, and although she always arrived in a new gown, ribbons fluttering from her hat, she was greatly changed. Her old sometimes childlike exuberance had been totally snuffed out like a candle-flame. One morning when she and Marietta had sought some shade under a tree in the garden, she said she had good news.

"The Signora is moving out of the Palazzo at last! Normally she would have retreated from the city to her country house long ago, even as we would have been at one of the villas if Filippo hadn't so much to do in his new position. Filippo thinks she stayed on to give him unwanted advice, but I think she had another reason."

"What was that?"

"I can't be sure, but she has watched me all the time. Her eyes raked my figure continuously. I've come to the conclusion she was hoping that by some faint chance I would be with child by Marco." Elena noticed Marietta's glance of surprise and sighed. "No. We had no opportunity."

"Has the Signora said anything to you about a baby?"

"Only constant hints about heirs, which she conveys to me through Lavinia, because she still avoids speaking to me directly whenever she can. If she hated me before, she must hate me twice as much now that I have disappointed her. She will hold it against me until the end of her days. I don't think there is anyone in the Celano family who knows how to forgive except good-natured Lavinia, who I shall miss very much. The Signora treats her so badly. I can understand why the vendetta with the Torrisis continues if that family is as implacable as the one I have married into."

"Have you heard any news of how Domenico Torrisi fares in his bereavement?"

"Only that he has gone on a voyage somewhere in one of his merchant ships."

They talked on undisturbed by anyone. Marietta had left a message that Bianca should join them when her lesson was finished. After a while they saw the five-year-old running across the lawn toward them and Elena sprang up to throw out her arms for an embrace.

"Here you are, Bianca! You have brought your flute. I am so pleased! Now you shall play for me."

It was the usual procedure on these visits, for Elena wanted to be sure that the child, who had begun to play quite well, should continue to make progress.

During the scorching hot weeks of summer even the stones of Venice seemed to radiate heat, and people held scented handkerchiefs or posies to their noses when near some of the canals. Marietta received relentless teaching from the Maestro. His intention was that she should be Adrianna's successor as the prima donna of the Pietà.

"But my voice cannot compare with hers!" she had exclaimed when he first informed her of his decision.

He had smiled. "Comparisons do not come into this. Not all flowers are the same hue, but each blossoms in its own way. Now let us take that last aria from the beginning again."

When autumn came, the Maestro ordered that Marietta receive the same priorities and privileges as had been granted to Adrianna. She was given the apartment that her predecessor had occupied and when going to a performance she was never crowded into a gondola with the other choristers, but traveled either with the Maestro or on her own with the two nuns. She was even allowed to visit Adrianna from time to time, either at the shop or at her home. Adrianna had become pregnant almost on her wedding night and was contentedly preparing for what she hoped would be the first of several children.

In October Filippo found that he would have to travel to one of the Venetian colonies to look after Celano interests there. When he told Elena, it seemed as if he might be thinking of going without her. The prospect of having her bed to herself and being entirely free for a little while of her humorless, demanding, and unlikeable husband was almost too wonderful to contemplate. But it was not to be.

"You shall come with me," he said. "It will interest you."

He saw it brought no response from her. Nothing did if it was connected with him in any way. Yet he could not have enough of her lovely body and mass of golden hair, which he liked to feel spread across him when she performed some marital duty for his immense pleasure. Neither in bed nor out of it could he really find fault with her, for she did all that was expected to fulfill her role as his wife. She was a delightful hostess, managed every social occasion whether large or small with attention to every detail, and he knew himself to be the envy of many men for possessing such a beauty. Yet Marco still haunted her. He himself was not a sentimentalist and whether she cared for him or not was immaterial, but he could not endure that she should be the one reminder that Marco still retained a hold over what he had inherited.

"Could I not go away with you next time?" Elena ventured. "I should like to be in Venice when Adrianna has her baby."

"No." He never argued. Several times Elena had tried to differ with him, and each time he had struck her so hard that her bruised face had kept her masked in public for some while afterward. It was a test now whether she would still persist. She did not. So he had cured that trait in her. Last time his blow had loosened one of her teeth and she was fearful of losing it, but fortunately it had settled down again. As he had supposed, she would not risk the loss of it from the force of his hand through being argumentative another time.

They were away from Venice for the whole winter. It happened that the State's representative in the Venetian colony was a weak man, not fit to be in charge in time of trouble. Filippo, as a senator, reported back to the Great Council, who in their turn appointed him in the other man's place. It was a temporary appointment, but Filippo thrived on conflict and exerting power over others. He would thoroughly enjoy his stint of office there.

While he was busy from morning to night, Elena pined for Venice. She was never without fear of Filippo's temper, which was always short when he had some difficult matter to deal with. He was not a heavy drinker, but there were times when wine made his mood worse. Since masks were not worn among the Venetian community in the colony, she often had to stay out of sight when he had blackened her eye or bruised her in his lust, making it impossible for her to reveal her cleavage in a low-cut gown. Her life was an utter misery, so her relief when they sailed for home in the early spring was overwhelming. She wept for joy when the ship anchored in the lagoon.

One of their first engagements was in response to an invitation from the Doge to a Pietà concert in the vast golden hall of the Great Council at the Ducal Palace. It was to be Marietta's first performance as the Pietà's new prima donna. The audience was seated facing the carpeted dais beneath Tintoretto's painting of Paradise, and in a high frieze the portraits of the previous Doges looked down to where thirteen hundred noblemen of Venice would assemble to discuss affairs of state. When Marietta's turn came to sing, she stepped forward with a ripple of her white silk gown to face the Doge in his splendid robes and corno. Then, without accompaniment, her rich, full tones rose and fell purely in a Vivaldi aria, all her joy of singing in her voice. When she came to the end of this first solo there was such a hush that momentarily she was gripped by panic, thinking she must have sung a wrong note or chosen a song that had given offense. Then an ovation burst forth that soared to the paintings on the ceiling overhead and to every corner of the enormous hall. She was overwhelmed, and the response proved to be the same throughout the performance whether she sang with or without accompaniment.

Soon after this evening it reached her ears that she was being talked about as the Flame of the Pietà. She did not doubt that Elena had used the phrase in the hearing of others. When challenged, Elena did not deny it.

"It describes you so well, Marietta. You sang as I have never heard you sing before. So much feeling! So much heart," she enthused. Then she added in a joke, "It is just as well that I'm not at the Pietà any more. I could never have become its Rose as I had always hoped, in the face of such competition!"

Marietta laughed. "Who can say? You must remember that the Maestro has coaxed and encouraged and bullied my voice into shape over a long time now."

Elena became serious. "I think it is more than that."

Marietta understood her meaning and gave a nod. Since that first meeting with Alix, she had experienced peaks of joy and depths of despair in entirely new dimensions. She had left her girlhood behind and her experience of life had broadened and deepened, bringing forth qualities in her voice that had been lying dormant.

"Have you heard nothing from Alix?" Elena asked.

Marietta shook her head. "When he left, he knew he could not write here. Now that I hold the position I do at the Pietà it would be possible for me to receive an unopened letter if I wished, but there is no way of letting him know."

"Why not write to him?"

"I have written." Marietta gave a sigh. "I believe my letters have been intercepted by the comte or perhaps by Alix's father. You can imagine the effect the comte's report would have had on Alix's parents. If they had shown themselves to be tolerant, Alix would have been back in Venice by now."

Elena could not disagree with this conclusion.

Unbeknownst to anyone else, a letter from Lyon had been delivered to the Savoni mask-shop. Leonardo, seeing it was addressed to his wife, supposed it to be from some persistent foreign admirer and frowned when he received it. He was a jealous and possessive man, and he disliked intensely the attention she still received from the public whenever she was recognized. With her sweet nature, she obeyed him in all matters and to please him when she went out she wore a veil as in her Pietà days or a mask.

Although he was tempted to destroy the foreign letter unread, it occurred to him that another might follow if the correspondence was not nipped in the bud. He broke the seal and unfolded it. When he had read it through he sat for a while mulling over the contents and deciding what he should do. The letter, written in passable Italian by a Frenchman, Alix Desgrange, was an urgent appeal to Adrianna, as Marietta's trusted friend, to pass on secretly letters he would send her for the girl he declared was betrothed to him. The plea would have melted Adrianna's soft heart, but he himself was made of different stuff. He did not trust any foreigners, and if this Frenchman was not free to come openly to Venice as an honest suitor, then Marietta was better off without him. On this thought Leonardo stood to light a candle and hold the letter to the flame. As it began to curl and blacken, he thought about the name Desgrange. At first it had meant nothing to him. So many foreigners came to his shop. When the letter was burnt he went to his ledger and looked back through the pages. When he found the name it still did not summon up a face and he closed the ledger impatiently. He had no time to waste on trivial matters. There were several more letters during the months that followed, and each was put to the candle-flame.

At the Pietà, notification came from the ducal palace that Maestra Marietta had been granted the honor of singing on the Bucintoro, the Doge's state barge, on Ascension Day when, as it had for the past six centuries, the ceremony of the "Marriage of the Sea" would be celebrated. Marietta's hands flew to her flushing cheeks when she was told.

"Can it be true?" she exclaimed.

It meant she was upholding the Pietà's reputation of having the best soloists as well as the prime choir. Adrianna, who had recently given birth to a son, had enjoyed the privilege of singing five times on the Bucintoro. If it had not been considered obligatory by the Doge that the singers of the other three *ospedali* should also have their chance, there was no doubt that Adrianna would have been his choice every year. Now she welcomed the chance to talk over the forthcoming ceremony with Marietta and give her whatever advice she could about the great day.

Marietta was to have a new gown of scarlet silk for the occasion, and she consulted Elena, who knew all about the latest fashions, as to the style. They were both now eighteen and leading very different lives, but they were as united in their friendship as they had always been. Elena was triumphant over her friend's success. She had long since given up asking for any news of Alix, knowing she would be the first to hear if Marietta had word of him.

Although Marietta rarely spoke of Alix, she had looked for him when Carnival came again. If there was a season above all others when he would return that was it, but Carnival gave way to Lent without a reunion. She let her singing absorb her more and more, giving herself up completely to the glory of music and the songs she had chosen for Ascension Day.

On the morning of her performance, she awoke to a feeling of tremendous excitement. Although the hour was early she flung the shutters wide and saw that it was a sapphire of a day, the facets of sky and water vying for brilliance in the sun that was already beating down on the gathering crowds.

In her vivid gown and with pomegranate blossoms in her hair Marietta left the Pietà to the applause of the girls and the maestri, who were to watch from a roped-off section of the Riva degli Schiavoni. Venice was at its most spectacular on a festival day and never more than on this special date in the calendar year. Tapestries and silken banners in vermilion, purple, emerald, and ochre, threaded through with the glitter of gilt and silver threads, hung interlaced with blossomy garlands as far as the eye could see. The great ducal barge with its red velvet canopy, looking as if it were molded out of gold and enameled in scarlet, lay at the quay by the Doge's Palace. Waiting to escort it were so many thousands of small boats that it seemed as if an embroidered spread of silken hues had been thrown across the water. People occupied every available viewing space, many high up on the Campanile where they perched perilously on ledges hundreds of feet from the ground.

Marietta, taking her place on board with the musicians, smiled to hear all the bells of Venice rejoicing in this annual celebration of a day that was both holy and imperial. More cheering rose from the crowds as the Doge and his entourage came aboard and he sat down in his gilded chair on the highest part of the deck where he could see and be seen. Cannons thundered from ships in the lagoon as the long rows of a hundred oars began to move to and fro in stately rhythm, taking the Bucintoro, the barge of state and symbol of empire, slowly across the flower-strewn water in the direction of the Lido.

Representing the voice of Venice as a bride, Marietta sang to the Adriatic, reminding it and all nations that La Serenissima with her beauty and wealth, her naval power and her military conquests, had always spread her glory across its turbulent waves. Many in the fleet of accompanying boats heard Marietta's voice carry far across the water. When the barge had passed through the Lido canal, the Doge went to the prow and cast the wedding ring with a gleam of gold into the sea.

"We wed thee, O Sea," his voice boomed out, "in token of our perpetual dominion."

Nobody listened to Marietta more attentively or watched her more closely than Domenico Torrisi, who in his senatorial red robes was on board with the ducal entourage, for he had resumed his seat on the Great Council since his return to Venice.

If his eyes appreciated the lovely sight of her in her scarlet gown with the pomegranate blossom in her brilliant hair, his expression was formed by other feelings. It was an odd blend of impatience, anger, exasperation, and —on this particular day—distaste. With her vibrant beauty set against the cloudless sky, the sea-breezes playing with her hair, and the satin of her low-cut bodice revealing clearly the full, sweet shape of her breasts, he was aware now, as he had been since she first caught his glance from a distance, of a fierce attraction that was divorced from any finer feelings. When she saddled him with an obligation not to give her away to the Pietà authorities, he could have throttled her for making him party to her nocturnal trysts. Upon returning from his voyage, he had found waiting for him the continued report on her that had been instigated by Angela and that he had forgotten to cancel. Through it he had learned that the Frenchman he had seen her with was one Alix Desgrange, the son of an elderly silk merchant from Lyon. Further information from France reported that the Desgrange mill had been near bankruptcy and despite the young man's efforts on his return, and the d'Oinville money that had been invested in the business, the mill was still in difficulty. There was little likelihood of the young man visiting Venice again in the near future, even if he should still wish it, which was not known. Nevertheless, the Frenchman's actions could not be foretold and Domenico decided that in view of a certain obligation that had been put on him by his late wife, he should make a move to settle Marietta's future.

It had been a shock to discover among Angela's papers the letter she had written to him only ten days before the *barnabotti*'s attack on the Grand Canal. The letter read:

> *I have a premonition that I shall not survive my present pregnancy. That will mean you must marry again, my beloved husband, and I beg that you will let the woman be my choice for you. I want you to have a young wife who will truly love you as I have done and give you the sons that I have failed to provide. Marry Maestra Marietta of the Pietà. I have seen for myself that she has courage and is brave when the need arises. She already trusts you completely just as I have always done, and when she sings there is so much heart in her voice that I know her feelings run deep as the sea. That has nothing to do with the young Frenchman, although she might suppose it does. Love has made her aware of herself and if you can win her with your love all will be well. I, who have had my life enriched by our marriage, want only to bequeath you happiness.*

At the time, the letter had only added to his grief. It had been terrible to him that Angela should have harbored the certainty of her own premature death, never suspecting it would come to her other than in childbirth. He blamed himself for everything that had happened—for failing to notice in time the approaching *barnabotti*, for not knowing that this pregnancy was causing her such distress of mind, and even for not having created an opportunity when she might have talked to him instead of penning the letter. There was nothing for which he did not still feel responsible, which was why he felt compelled to follow her last wish. She had always known when other women attracted him, but she had been secure in his faithfulness and in that he had not failed her. So why had she not been able to see that the sexual magnetism of Marietta had created in him no more interest than any man might feel at the sight of a particularly desirable woman, whether she should be a Pietà girl or a courtesan?

It was not so unusual that an unselfish woman who loved her husband should wish to choose her successor. His own grandmother had made such a request. Admittedly in the patrician class it was uncommon, simply because few marriages were based on anything other than material advantage, but he did not doubt that among the peasantry it happened more frequently. And it was typical of Angela with her generous little heart that even in the face of death her last consideration was for him.

But he was not ready yet for another face at Angela's place at the table, or on her pillow in his bed. His physical needs were satisfied well enough by masked and nameless married women seeking diversion and adventure for a few night hours, wanting from him only what he wanted of them. He would marry Marietta in his own good time. Meanwhile she could continue singing for the Pietà. She would only discover her destined path if the Frenchman should return in a second attempt to win her.

Marietta glimpsed Domenico on the Lido where all disembarked after the ceremony of the Marriage to the Sea to proceed into the church, but he was not looking in her direction. She saw him again at the great banquet in the Ducal Palace where she sang afterward, but he was far from her at the long horseshoe table. That old antagonism toward him, which she had never understood, stirred in her again.

It came as a surprise to all at the Pietà to hear that Domenico Torrisi had been appointed to the board of governors. Elena was concerned at first that her married name might cause her to be barred from the Pietà now that a Torrisi had a voice in its management, but the new governor did not impose any restrictions of his own. In fact he was rarely at the *ospedale*, attending only when a board meeting needed his vote to settle an important issue.

"I suppose," Elena said to Marietta, "that he considers the Pietà to be neutral territory as is the Hall of the Great Council when he and Filippo are both present on state affairs."

"We shall see if that theory holds when he learns that the choir is to sing at the Palazzo Celano next month."

To their relief Domenico did not intervene. It was a particularly happy evening for Elena to have Marietta and her other Pietà friends in her own home. Many of the girls were new to the choir since she had left, but they were equally welcome. Their angel-like voices seemed to dispel the unpleasant atmosphere that had lingered since the fierce quarrel Filippo had had with his mother.

Elena told Marietta how it had come about. The Signora, who had been used to coming to stay whenever she wished, had arrived uninvited and unannounced with Lavinia, issuing orders left and right as she came. Filippo, returning home after long hours in the Senate where he had clashed in debate with Domenico Torrisi, was looking forward to a quiet supper with Elena. He liked to talk to her about the day's happenings, and although he supposed she was sometimes bored she never showed it. So the sight of her sitting tense and strained in a salon with his mother and sister stirred his always volatile temper.

"This is a surprise," he said to his mother, his tone leaving no doubt that it was not exactly a pleasant one.

"Since you have not been to see me, I had no choice but to come."

"For what purpose?" he asked after putting a dutiful kiss on her painted cheek and greeting his sister.

"I thought you must surely have overlooked telling me that Elena is with child."

He glanced at Elena, who looked down, showing that she had been subjected already to his mother's bullying in this matter. Her lack of conception was a subject he had raised with his wife often enough, and it always ended with Elena in tears and himself in a rage. Why she did not conceive was beyond his comprehension, for she was young and healthy and strong, but he had no intention of letting his mother twist the knife in the wound that was his more than Elena's.

"There is nothing to tell yet."

"Nothing?" Signora could freeze with her voice and her expression at the same time. "You have been married well over a year. Precisely how long do you intend to keep your kin waiting for an heir?"

"You are going beyond your bounds, Mother," he said warningly.

She was too angry with him to care, remembering how he had once taunted her beloved Marco about proving his manhood. "Are *you* at fault?" she challenged bluntly. "Or is your wife failing to do her duty?"

"Silence! I am master here! You'll not speak to me in such a manner!"

"Oh, yes, you are master." Her own grief sounded in her mockery. "Had Marco still been head of this house, he would have given me a grandson in much less time."

Elena, unable to endure any more, sprang from her chair and ran in distress from the room. From a distance she could hear them shouting at each other. Then, after what seemed like an hour, all was quiet until she heard Filippo approaching. His mood would be terrible. Frightened, she trembled, hugging her arms in defense of what he might do. The door was flung wide.

"My mother and Lavinia have gone," he stated, temper still in his eyes, although mercifully not directed at her, "and I have told her never to come back."

"Where will they go?" Her trembling became more pronounced as she saw him lock the door and begin to take off his coat.

"To one or other of my brothers, I suppose. It's of no account to me. Nevertheless she is right. We must overcome this delay and have a child."

He took her by the arms and thrust her down on the floor with him. It was all over very quickly, but once more it was to be without result.

Nobody would have welcomed conception more than she. Elena was aware of a deep yearning in herself for a child, a yearning that was quite divorced from her duty to produce a Celano heir. She needed to love and be loved; the whole of her warm nature craved it. Since Filippo neither invited love nor gave it, she had begun turning more and more to finding fulfillment in other ways, and the only outlet open to her was in social pleasures. In convivial company she was able to recapture the bubbling good humor of happier days. Women liked her and men were strongly attracted to her, so invariably, with her flair for fashion, her looks, her still innocent charm, and her ability to relate gossip in an amusing way, she was the center of attention.

As long as she could dance, attend receptions at the Pietà, play games of chance, see every new play and enjoy some dazzling new entertainment in the Celano box at the opera houses, she could forget the darker side of her life at times. There was nothing she liked better than to fill the palace with people for a ball or banquet, or an old-fashioned masque. Filippo was sociable himself and an hospitable host. Since flirting was a social grace, he never minded when he saw Elena bewitching someone with her charms. He knew she would neither wish nor dare to go beyond the realms of propriety. But he had no such code for himself. It suited him to let her go out with parties of friends now and again, for there were certain places of entertainment he liked to frequent that a wife should not know about. There was a rose marble salon behind a locked door in the palace where throughout past centuries certain of his forebears had indulged themselves in a similar way, but he preferred to go elsewhere.

Chapter 9

*A*drianna *had a visitor, an art dealer from Lyon* who was in Venice to purchase paintings. Her face became increasingly grave as she heard that he was obliging Alix by making this call. Once when they were alone together, Marietta had told her of her romance with the young Frenchman.

"So, Monsieur Blanchard," she said, "you say that Alix sent letters to Marietta through my name to the Savoni mask-shop. I assure you I never received them or I would have handed them over to her immediately."

"Alix was sure of that. It's why I inquired as to where I might locate your private address, because Alix became certain the mask-shop had changed hands and that a lack of any correspondence from Marietta meant she had received none from him." Monsieur Blanchard shrugged wryly. "Since you know that Marietta has written, I can only conclude Fate has been against these two young people from the start."

Adrianna guessed that out of courtesy the Frenchman had not suggested who in Lyon had been responsible for keeping Marietta's letters from Alix. Most likely it was Madame Desgrange, since her poor husband had become, according to the visitor, almost completely senile. But Monsieur Blanchard had more to tell Adrianna about Alix. When he finished he held out a letter addressed to Marietta and a red rose that he had purchased in Venice at Alix's request.

"Would you give these to Marietta, senora?"

"I will," she said and took both from him.

As soon as he made his departure, she hastened to leave for the Pietà. On the way there she marched into the mask-shop and cornered Leonardo in his office. A stormy scene followed when he admitted burning the letters and gave the reason why. It was the first time he had ever seen her so angry.

"Such high-handed behavior and with such cruel results!" she declared furiously. "Give me your word that you will never again deceive me in any way."

He gave his promise. Peace in the house was all-important to him.

At the Pietà, Adrianna was greeted warmly. All past *ospedale* girls, except those who had been in the favored musical elite, had to speak to old friends through grilles in the visiting salon, but Adrianna was like Elena in having unrestricted access at any time. She heard Marietta's lovely voice as she approached the practice room to which she had been directed. At the door Adrianna paused, listening sadly before she drew a deep breath and entered. Marietta, accompanying herself on the harpsichord, broke off with a smile.

"This is a pleasant surprise!" Then her face fell as she noted Adrianna's drawn expression. She rose from the music stool. "What has happened?"

"I want you to prepare yourself for some ill tidings about Alix."

Marietta turned pale. "Tell me."

Adrianna held out the letter and the rose to her, speaking in a choked voice. "Alix is married, Marietta. He is never coming back."

With an almost unnatural calm Marietta took the letter and went across to the window, not for better light but to withdraw a little while she read it through. It was a defensive letter of farewell in which Alix told of his father's illness and the threat of family bankruptcy that had met him upon his return. He had written to her many times and could not understand why he had not received a single letter in return, since she had been able to write direct to him at his home. Had she deliberately forgotten him after the catastrophe of his departure? Maybe she had never forgiven him for it, in which case he would apologize for any inconvenience he had caused her. Then, as if tormented by guilt, his tone became sharper. No doubt their parting had been for the best, since their way of life, their backgrounds, their language, and even their countries were so different in every respect. By the time she read this letter he would be married to Louise d'Oinville, who had become his partner at the silk mill. In a final scrawled sentence he wished her well.

Marietta folded the letter. She was rigid with shock and pain. Her tortured gaze went to the rose that Adrianna had placed on the harpsichord. It evoked vividly that carnival night when Alix had declared his love for her. Why had he sent it? If his purpose had been to convey his remorse, it could not obliterate his broken promises and his shattering of her trust. He had abandoned her utterly! The sense of being betrayed overwhelmed her and she pressed a hand across her eyes. She scarcely heard Adrianna speak sadly to her.

"Oh, my dear Marietta! What a disappointment for you!"

Adrianna could not bring herself to reveal the rest of what Monsieur Blanchard had told her. It was his opinion that Louise d'Oinville had set her cap at Alix from the start. His desperate need to save the silk mill and keep his dependent parents and his sisters from the poorhouse must have made irresistible the young widow's offer to invest part of her fortune in the business. "As you might suppose," the art-dealer had added sagely, "one thing led to another and she was not the first bride to go to the altar with a baby on the way."

On a wave of compassion Adrianna went across to Marietta. "Draw on your courage, my dear. This agony of the heart will pass. Break cleanly from the past. Don't languish over what might have been. You have your music!"

Marietta lowered her hand and her eyes were bright. "Somehow I'll follow your advice. I must! And I'm so grateful that you broke the news to me first. Alix never received any of my letters. But what of those that should have reached me?" Then she shook her head in forgiveness. "Don't weep, Adrianna. I'm sure it was no fault of yours."

"I knew nothing about them until today." Adrianna was deeply distressed.

Marietta went to her. "There's no blame to be cast on anyone. I loved Alix dearly, but Venice always stood between us."

Adrianna wiped her eyes. "That's an odd thing to say."

"But it's true." Marietta did not elaborate and Adrianna had never been one to pry. She watched her friend hold the letter to a candle-flame.

That night Marietta put on her *moretta* mask and her domino, pulling its hood over her head before taking the key to the *calle* door from her drawer. Lastly she drew the rose from the slender vase where she had put it and took it with her as she slipped soundlessly from her room.

The velvet sky was full of stars and there were plenty of people about with lanterns or flaring flambeaux on their way to and from places of entertainment. Nobody paid her any attention as she retraced the steps she had taken with Alix. In St. Mark's Square she stood to look up at the window above the arcade where on a certain Carnival night the flash of Domenico's golden mask had been like a warning that she should leave Venice while the chance was hers.

She hastened on until she came to a quiet place by the Grand Canal. There she put the rose to her lips before stooping down to let it drop gently into the water. Straightening up, she watched it go floating away on the moon-flecked ripples.

"Farewell, Alix," she whispered, remembering his smiling eyes, his sense of fun, and the laughter they had shared. Theirs had been a bittersweet love that was doomed from the start. Back at the Pietà she returned the key to a drawer, although she would never use it again.

For the next three years Marietta went from one success to another. Her mature voice, rich and lustrous, was like a siren call, drawing people from far afield to hear her. She visited other cities, sometimes with the choir or fellow soloists, but often as the solo performer. She had a splendid apartment at the Pietà, which was furnished to her taste, and an adequate stipend. No other love had come into her life although, like Adrianna before her, she had plenty of would-be suitors.

She saw Domenico infrequently and liked best to keep out of his way. He never attended receptions at the Pietà as his wife had done, but occasionally he was in the audience when she sang, and now and again they came face to face when he was on his way to a governors' board meeting. Marietta would acknowledge his bow and passing greeting, but otherwise they had not spoken since he had given her his promise on the night of the ridotto not to betray her.

It was after Marietta returned from a concert in Padua that she found an invitation from Domenico, inviting her to dine. She had been a guest at the homes of the other governors many times, and she could only suppose that Domenico felt obliged out of courtesy to follow their example. Nevertheless she was thrown into a turmoil of agitation. Why should he decide to do this now when everything in her life was running so smoothly? She could only hope that there would be many other guests and she would need exchange only a few minutes of conventional conversation with her host.

She had exerted her authority as prima donna to gain the chaperonage of only one nun when she went out. Sister Giaccomina was her choice and they enjoyed being together without Sister Sylvia's tetchy company. When the evening of the invitation arrived they set off on their own in the Torrisi gondola, which had been sent to collect them.

Domenico was waiting to meet them under the portico of the arcaded water-gate entrance to his palace, which struck Marietta as unusual, for it meant he had withdrawn from his other guests to await their arrival. His well-groomed powdered hair set off the light tan of his skin that seemed never to have faded since his long sea-voyages.

"Welcome to my house," he said in greeting.

"It is a pleasure to be here," Marietta replied formally. She glanced about at the *andron*'s faded frescoed walls as he led her and her companion along the richly patterned Persian carpet that ran the length of the marble floor. She guessed it had been laid specially for this evening as the waters of the Grand Canal would rise into this area whenever rough winds chose to play havoc, and mostly without warning.

The three of them made conversation as they ascended a grand staircase under an arched and gilded ceiling set with blue as if the sky were being allowed to show through. At the top was an anteroom where large double doors stood open to a great ballroom exceeding in splendor any that Marietta had previously seen with the sole exception of the Ducal Palace. Using the double height of two stories with two chandeliers, each six feet in diameter and sparkling in their candlelight like waterfalls, it gained further dimension through its masterfully painted walls, which gave one the illusion of seeing far beyond into vistas of classical parks and flower gardens. The Torrisi coat of arms, set off by gilded drapery, dominated the main wall. Since this *salone de ballo* was quite deserted except for the footmen at its doors, Marietta could not resist pausing in the middle of the pink terrazzo floor to twirl around, her sea-green skirt flowing out, her pearl eardrops dancing, to gaze upward with delight at the trompe l'o eil frescoes depicting a gallery of musicians some of whom actually appeared to be leaning over into the room.

"Where are your singers, Signor Torrisi?" she asked gaily, letting her gaze rise still higher, to the ceiling that curved upward from the frescoes into a painted allegory of the virtues and achievements of the Torrisis.

"There is no one except you, Marietta. In fact you and Sister Giaccomina are my only guests this evening."

She glanced at him quickly, suddenly alert to some extraordinary situation. Sister Giaccomina also looked surprised. But there was nothing in his cool grey eyes to indicate why they should be the only guests, and he continued to converse easily, pointing out what he thought might be of interest as he led them through a tapestry-lined salon into another of coral silk. She noticed no less than three portraits of his late wife, one full-length and almost life-size depicting Angela in an oyster satin gown and a plume-trimmed hat. Then they came to what was clearly a dining-room for the gathering of a few close friends, for the table was circular and presently laid for three under an azure taffeta-silk baldachin that was draped from six fluted columns. Silver shone and goblets of blue Venetian glass glittered on the damask cloth while the scent of white tuberoses hung fragrantly in the air.

The dinner was planned to perfection. Sister Giaccomina did justice to every course, sometimes closing her eyes briefly in delight as she savored the first forkful of yet another new dish. Domenico was a relaxed host, full of good talk, but Marietta was becoming steadily more wary. She thought of the Persian carpet, the curious compliment paid her in the ballroom, the place of honor she had been given at his right hand when the nun was her senior—and, dominating all else, a conviction impossible to shake off that there was more to come. What did he want of her?

When he asked her, during the course of conversation, something about her first coming to Venice, she mentioned that she had seen the Torrisi villa from the river barge. "I remember there was a crowd of merry young people disembarking to enter the building."

"They could have been my brothers and their ladies. Only the youngest, Antonio, is left in Venice with me now. Franco is in the New World where he imports goods from Europe; Lodovico married in England without the permission of either my father or the Senate, which bars him from coming home; and Bertucci was fatally wounded in a duel with a Celano." He shook his head. "It was one of those tragic affairs when both duelists died afterward from the injuries each had inflicted on the other."

"How terrible for both families! Could not that event have brought everyone together in reconciliation?"

"You would never persuade a Celano to that view."

She thought to herself that a Torrisi would be equally implacable, but that could not be said when she was a guest at his table. If they had been on neutral ground it would have been another matter.

When eventually they rose from the table, it was to go into the book-lined library where priceless thirteenth- and fourteenth-century volumes with exquisite illustrations were laid out on tables for display. Sister Giacomina clasped her plump hands in wonder. She was a scholar of early editions, not through any training but through her own interest over the years. Her lashes became wet when he showed her and Marietta a small illustration of the founder of the *ospedale*, Brother Pietruccio d'Assisi, feeding hungry little children from a bowl.

"Such a treasure!" the nun exclaimed. "How rare! Is it of his own time?"

"I believe it to be."

"Then that must be exactly as the dear man looked! What a kind face! Do you see, Marietta?"

"I do." Marietta, studying the beautiful little painting in blues and reds and gold, thought how different her own life would have been if all those hundreds of years ago a good man had not been moved to pity by the plight of those who everybody else had cast out.

Sister Giaccomina had seated herself at the library table, prepared to peruse other pages, and Domenico moved a candelabrum nearer for her to have a better light.

"Do you know," she said, "Brother Pietruccio would cry 'Pity! Pity!' as he begged from door to door to get money for his foundlings' home. That's why the Ospedale della Pietà is so named." Her voice took on an indignant note. "It was not he who had the children's little feet branded with a *P* to make them remember all their lives what they owed the Pietà, but the rich, haughty men who financed the *ospedale* after him and wanted their charity acknowledged."

Marietta exchanged a smile with Domenico, who knew these facts as well as she. As they both expected, the nun went on to rail against the old custom, introduced by those same self-centered benefactors, of calling the children Dust or Gibbet or Stone or some other degrading name to remind them of their humble origins. Marietta spoke up.

"I, for one, am very thankful that custom was abolished along with the branding a long time ago."

Sister Giaccomina gave her a fond smile. "In your case, child, it would be as the English playwright wrote—a rose by any other name would smell as sweet." Then she turned in her chair to thank Domenico as he placed a powerful magnifying glass, which he had taken from a drawer, at her right hand. "Oh, that's just what I need!"

"If you have no objection, Sister," he said, "I'll leave you with these books while I take Marietta away with me for a little interlude."

For a moment Sister Giaccomina was uncertain. Then she reminded herself that Signor Torrisi was a governor and therefore a guardian of the virtue of the Pietà girls. She nodded. "I shall be most content here with these beautiful books."

Marietta would have preferred to stay, but she had no choice but to go with him. He took her to a corner salon facing the Grand Canal where the walls were honey-colored and there was a sensually beautiful painting of

Zephyr and Flora. Here as elsewhere the candle-glow enhanced the setting, but as it was a room of moderate size, it also created an intimate atmosphere. The windows were open to the warm May night. She took a chair where she could see the star-sprinkled sky and he drew up another. As always, the sound of music rose from various sections of the city. She listened, using her fan slowly. It was a gift from an admirer and its brilliants caught the candleglow. She was aware that in spite of Domenico's relaxed position, one arm looped over the back of his chair, long legs crossed at the ankles, he was alert and waiting. But for what? More than ever she was aware of him as a marvelously handsome man.

"There was little music in my life before I came to Venice," she remarked by way of ending the silence between them. "Only my own singing."

"I was in the village of your birth not all that long ago."

"Were you?" She realized he would have learned of her origins from the Pietà records. For the first time in many years she experienced a painful stab of nostalgia, but then all her feelings had been honed in uneasy anticipation this evening. "How did it look? I have never been back."

"Mask decoration still goes on there. Would you like to see it again?"

She smiled to herself. There was one thing about her he would not discover in the files. Maybe this was the time to tell him. "I should like to see the workshop where my mother and I spent so many hours and where I saw your gilded mask for the first time." Although she was not looking at him she could sense the impact her words had made, for there came the rustle of his silken coat as he leaned forward abruptly in his chair. He listened attentively as she listed all the evidence that had brought her to the conclusion that it was definitely the Torrisi mask that had been in her care. She did not ask the reason why he had had it made, for if he wished her to know he would tell her. "So there was a link between us," she concluded, turning her head at last to look at him, "long before you kept your word about not giving me away to the authorities."

He was too logical and reasoning a man to accept her connection with the mask as anything but coincidence, but curiously it was as though everything were falling into place. Angela, who was highly sensitive in so many ways, had been extremely accurate in her judgement of character, even warning him correctly more than once of political enmity in delicate affairs of state. "I will take you back to your village, Marietta. It can be arranged."

She shook her head. "I thank you, but no. When I do go back it must be in my own time and when I know it to be right for me."

"Some day when you are no longer at the Pietà?"

"Yes, I think so."

"Have you thought of what you want for the rest of your life?"

She gave a nod, looking back at the window. "I don't intend to stay at the Pietà longer than another two years. Then I shall take to the concert stage and travel throughout Europe."

"What of marriage?"

"That is not for me. The man I would have married did not come back for me."

"The Frenchman." It was a statement, not a question. After that night at the ridotto, because of his wife's consuming interest, Domenico had sent one of his best spies to follow Marietta and Alix wherever they went. When their failed elopement was duly reported, Angela was filled with compassion. It was then that she had insisted they attend as many concerts as possible where Marietta was singing. He had been so used to Angela's whims that he did not question her wish that they go masked on each occasion, although he wondered why it was always a *bauta* and never his gilded mask that his valet put ready for him at her instruction. After he received the report from Lyon on Desgrange's marriage he had closed the file and locked it away. But Marietta could not know any of this.

"Yes, my Frenchman," she replied, not entirely sure where this conversation was leading. "When I tire of journeying I shall settle somewhere, probably Vienna, and teach."

"What could be better than to teach children of your own to sing?"

She rested her head back on the high padded upholstery of the chair. "I can't argue with that, but as I have said, my plans do not allow for it. Several very talented new singers are coming on fast at the Pietà and it wouldn't be fair for me to rival them by continuing to perform in this city. Adrianna set a good example. She made three guest appearances for the Pietà after she left, and then slipped from public view into family life."

"Does she not sing at all now?"

She smiled. "Only lullabies to her little children."

He returned her smile. "What fortunate offspring to have such a voice to sing them to sleep. You see her quite regularly, I believe."

"I do. I have two wonderfully good friends in Adrianna Savoni and Elena Celano." Then she hesitated. "Is that name allowed to be spoken in this house?"

"You may say whatever you wish."

"In that case," she said more boldly, mischief in her eyes, "I will ask you a question that has long been in my mind. As a governor of the Pietà why haven't you had the lock of the *calle* door changed? You must realize that I came and went by that route and also that I still have a key."

"I guessed you had. Maybe I have been hoping to meet you again at a ridotto."

She closed her fan. Although she knew his remark had been a jest her face was serious. "I have never told you how much I appreciated your not giving me away to the Pietà authorities. You could still have done it when you took office there."

"I have never wished you any harm. Nor will I to my life's end."

She could see he was not jesting now. Tension filled the air. "That was a very dramatic statement to make," she said cautiously.

"I never spoke more truly." He leaned nearer and took her hand into his. "You and I have both known sadness in different spheres of lost love."

"Why do you say that?" She drew her hand from his, her eyes defensive, almost hostile.

"No Pietà girl would take the risks you took to be with a man unless he mattered to her above all else. Then suddenly he was gone. You were no longer together. I saw you from a distance more often than you realized. Once even in the midst of a Carnival throng in St. Mark's Square."

She looked down at her fan. He had mentioned a moment she would never forget. "I admit what you suppose about Alix and me. That's all I can say."

"It's not what is past in your life or mine that I wish to speak of now or in the future. I want to say to you that happiness can come again. It would not be the same for either of us, because first love is unique and nobody would wish it otherwise. But I am asking you to consider becoming my wife. I don't expect an answer now, because you need time." He would have preferred her to raise her head, for her lashes were lowered still and he could not read her eyes. "Before too long I shall ask you again to marry me. In the meantime I hope I may show you that we could have a most rewarding life together."

She was not as astonished by what he had asked as she might have expected to be. No doubt the signs she had observed of the importance of her visit this evening had prepared her. She liked him for having made no false declarations of loving her already. At least he was being honest. Since he had no heir he needed to marry again, but whereas any other woman would have been complimented by being his choice, she wanted to be much more to a husband than a bearer of children. She chose her words carefully as she finally looked up to meet his eyes.

"I can give you my answer now. As I told you, my plans are made for the future. So even though you have given me time to think matters over, I have to tell you that time will not change the decision I have already made."

"Nevertheless, the idea is new to you as yet and when you know me better you may come to feel quite differently. My wishes concerning you are known to the other governors and they have presented no barriers."

"What of the Great Council? I know a nobleman may not marry any woman not in the patrician strata or without a vast dowry. Elena learned after her marriage that Cardinal Celano had spoken to the Doge himself, who in turn had swayed those senators who would otherwise have opposed the match."

"I also have friends in high places."

She saw it was useless to say any more. He was countering every opposition she put forward. "Let us return to Sister Giaccomina now, although I am sure that with those books she has lost all sense of time." She rose to her feet and turned for the door, but he stayed her with a firm hand on her arm.

"Then we need not make haste yet, Marietta."

Too late she saw that he intended to kiss her. Then his arms were strong about her in a crushing embrace and she was almost lifted from her feet as his mouth sought hers in the most passionate of kisses. Without willing it she gave herself up to the sensual experience of the moment. Having been awakened by love but denied its fulfillment, her body seemed to yearn toward him of its own accord, her arms going without her knowledge around his neck, her mouth giving when it should only have received. When their kiss ended her heart was hammering. She rested her brow against his shoulder and a tremor went through her as he put his lips to her temple.

"Let me care for you, Marietta. I will do all in my power to ensure that you never have cause for regret."

Hastily she broke away from him, shaking her head. "Let us say no more now."

"As you wish."

As Marietta had expected, Sister Giaccomina had been so absorbed in studying Domenico's books that she looked up in surprise at what she took to be their speedy return. All the way back to the Pietà in the Torrisi gondola, Sister Giaccomina talked of the volumes, not noticing that Marietta sat in silence beside her in the felze or that Domenico, who had insisted on escorting them, gave only perfunctory answers to her questions. Behind her veil Marietta studied him in handsome silhouette against the moonlit water. The violent attraction Domenico had shown for her was dangerous and perverse. In a moment of revelation as his mouth took hers, she saw that the antagonism he had always aroused in her had its roots in a fear of falling in love with another woman's husband, a pointless love that would have wrecked her peace of mind and her work and even her life. Now that barrier was gone, but what he offered her—a marriage of convenience for both parties—that was not for her.

She spent a sleepless night. Her first appointment in the morning was with the Maestro to discuss a selection of songs for a forthcoming concert. They were seated in his office, which overlooked the enclosed garden where sunshine filtering through the trees gave a cool greenish light to the room.

"Maestro, there's something very important I should like to discuss with you," she said when the matter of her program had been settled.

"Yes, what is it?" He sat back in his chair, a white-wigged, fine-featured man in his fifties, and he linked his long, artistic fingers.

"You've always listened without comment when I've talked about my future as a singer and I've assumed that you wished me to remain at the Pietà for as long as possible."

"That is correct. There is no one ready to step into your place just yet."

"Nevertheless, something has happened that I had never envisaged and I think it would be best if I began to make preparations for leaving. I hope that, when I have explained my reasons, you will understand that I really have no choice in the matter."

He nodded his head with kindly indulgence. "You need have no fear about that. I realized it must come sooner or later."

She welcomed his attitude, which was making it all much easier for her. "I want to go on the concert stage as soon as possible."

His eyes narrowed and he frowned slightly. "The concert stage?" he repeated.

"I have always said that I did not want to be at the beck and call of the bullying director of an opera company. I would appreciate your advice as to which of the recent offers of concert tours I should accept."

He shook his head, holding the bridge of his nose briefly between finger and thumb. "Are felicitations not in order then?"

Enlightenment dawned on her. Domenico had mentioned there would be no opposition from the board to his wish to marry her. She was foolish not to have realized the Maestro would also know of it. "No, Maestro. I have yet to give Signor Torrisi my formal refusal of his offer of marriage, but my mind is already made up. And since he is a governor of the Pietà, it would be best for me to leave as soon as possible after giving him my answer."

The Maestro left his chair and paced up and down a couple of times before he halted and spoke grimly to her. "I never thought it would fall to me to have to tell you this, but your future was sealed by the governors over two years ago. I can pinpoint it to the day. It was the morning after you sang on the Bucintoro. Signor Torrisi arranged to meet with the full board here and he announced his wish to make you his wife at such time when it suited both you and himself. The contract was duly drawn up and signed within the week. Whatever he has said to you was simply a courtesy on his part."

She was appalled. "But as a principal singer I should have been consulted!" she cried out.

"I agree, and I haven't the least doubt that your wishes in the matter would have been heard if Signor Torrisi had not endowed the Pietà with what can only be described as a small fortune for the advancement of its good work. The *ospedale* had never before received a donation of such size and the governors agreed immediately to his request that nothing be said until such time as he chose to speak to you of marriage. They then gave him a coveted place on the board as a gesture of their appreciation for his generosity."

She looked at him fiercely. "So he reserved me like an item on a shop shelf! Why didn't you speak on my behalf, Maestro?"

"I did, Marietta, but mine was the only dissenting voice. I wanted other countries to have the chance to hear you sing before marriage claimed you. Adrianna was lost to the music world all too soon and I did not want that to happen to you."

Outraged, she went to the window where she gazed down into the deserted garden. A medley of sounds drifted from the various music rooms. She struggled in mental torment to adjust to her career as a singer being at an end. The concert stage had been no more than a dream that she alone had cherished. It had been destroyed by Domenico and those who had conspired with him to take away her liberty.

But how could she endure a life of idleness? Elena had adjusted to following the routine of a noblewoman, rising at noon, receiving her hairdresser while friends sat and chatted, and then turning night into day at ridottos, theaters, balls, and parties in an endless round of pleasure. For a while it would be fun, Marietta could not deny that. But she had always seen her singing and eventual teaching as a contribution to life for all she had received from it. To only take and to give nothing back was contrary to all she believed in.

"I could go away, Maestro," she said quietly, still looking down into the garden. "There is nothing to stop me from singing under another name."

"Do you suppose a Torrisi would allow you to slip the net? Or the governors either, for that matter? They would fear a demand for the return of that donation, which they are already using for the extension and expansion of the building to accommodate more waifs. Would you bring that work to a halt?"

She shook her head. "You know I cannot."

"Then you have no choice but to accept what has been arranged for you."

Another terrible consequence of her fate was dawning on her. She as a Torrisi and Elena as a Celano would be barred from seeing each other. "Maestro!" she exclaimed, swinging around to face him. "Let me visit Elena when the day's lessons are over. I have to talk to her!"

He guessed the reason. "I will take you to the Palazzo Celano myself."

It was not the first time the Maestro had been received there and while Filippo served wine to him and sat in conversation Elena took Marietta to her boudoir. Marietta explained what had happened.

"The trouble is that I'm angry about the way I have been secured by a contract, while at the same time I'm drawn to Domenico as to a magnet. I can see now that it has been the same since I first saw him in his golden mask. I find I want to be his wife as much as I wish to be free of him."

"But the Torrisi family is such a cruel one!" Elena cried out. "I've heard so much about their dreadful deeds against the Celanos down the centuries."

Marietta gave a wry smile. "In all fairness I think you should admit that it has been six of one and half a dozen of the other when it comes to responsibility for the vendetta. It was the Celano *barnabotti* who sank the Torrisi gondola four years ago on your wedding day with such tragic results."

"That haunts me still. Although most of that day is a haze to me I can remember Signora Torrisi as she waved to me. Why that should be I have no notion. Who knows? Perhaps it registered with me that she hoped the two of us might mend the blood-feud."

"Then let us have the same aim." Marietta's voice became choked. "It would help me to believe there might be some purpose to this marriage, which appeals so strongly to me in spite of myself." Her head dipped and she covered her eyes with a hand as she struggled with her feelings. "I'm so confused."

Elena flew to kneel by her chair and put a comforting arm about her. "Don't despair, Marietta! Oh, why is nothing ever as it should be!"

The comforting arm then became a clinging one. Marietta disentangled herself to take her friend by the shoulders. "Something has happened to you too. What is it?"

"You came to tell me your troubles, not to hear mine."

"Tell me!"

Elena hesitated no longer. The words burst from her. "I'm beginning to believe I might never have a child!"

"It's far too soon to draw that conclusion. It takes a few years sometimes."

"I've told Filippo that, but he is getting so impatient with me. Ever since he made up that old quarrel with his mother he has been far worse to me in every way. He listens to her now when she is spiteful about me." She clutched Marietta's arm. "I'm so afraid. I believe that if I don't eventually give him an heir she will conspire to get rid of me."

"You mustn't allow yourself to suppose such a thing!"

Elena's agonized face did not change. "You don't know her as I do. She is ruthless and unforgiving."

"Have you told anyone else of this fear? Lavinia, perhaps?"

"I dare not. She would never believe it of her mother. Sometimes I wish I had never advised Filippo to mend matters with the Signora, because it has given her an entrée back into our home and she is careful not to anger him. But she had not been well and I thought he should go to her. Now I'm sure she pretended to be at death's door for that precise purpose. She is a devious woman." Elena shook her head unhappily. "I've never needed your friendship more than at this time, when you are about to become the wife of a Torrisi."

"But we shall go on meeting after I'm married," Marietta decided determinedly. "You visit Adrianna and so do I. We can always talk safely in her house. Nobody else will ever know."

Elena brightened, her spirits always as quick to rise as to fall. "So we can. Remember the communication code we devised at the Pietà? We could use that whenever we see each other in a public place."

"I don't remember everything. It's a long time since we last used it."

"Let us go through a few of the signs. I'm sure it will all come back to us."

They practiced signals for alarm and danger first, which in the past had meant no more than Sister Sylvia's approach but which, in the realm of a bloodthirsty vendetta, might well be needed to warn of much more. The code was quickly recalled. If a sign momentarily evaded the memory of one, then a prompt from the other brought it immediately to mind.

"We must practice every time we see each other from now until your marriage," Elena said, linking her arm through Marietta's as she had done so often upon their leaving a room together. "Nobody from either side will be able to keep us from communicating."

It was a consoling thought for both of them.

Nobody at the Pietà dared to deny Domenico when he arrived to take Marietta unchaperoned to the opera. The Maestro refused to be bothered when Sister Sylvia went rushing to him, and none of the governors was available. Marietta was dressed in a gown of smoky blue satin with a velvet domino about her shoulders. She had been to the opera twice previously when away from Venice to sing, but never in La Serenissima itself. The excitement she would normally have felt was dispelled by the cloud hanging over her. In the gondola on the way to the opera house she told Domenico she knew of the marriage contract.

He frowned with displeasure. "You should not have been informed. It was my intention to win you over myself. However, since my plans have already been thwarted I see no reason why we should not marry soon." He took hold of her white-gloved hand and folded it sensuously into his own. "I shall court you after our wedding day, Marietta. It will be a great deal more convenient than having those nuns fluttering around all the time like the pigeons in the square."

She had not meant to smile, but it was such an apt description. "You must admit that Sister Giaccomina was quiet enough with those books."

"Yes, she had settled like a pigeon on a Basilica ledge."

She smiled again in spite of herself. Those white robes did billow and fold like feathers. For the first time she considered how it would be to have freedom at last from constant chaperonage. Except that she would exchange one kind of restriction for another. "I have considered running away from you," she admitted frankly.

He almost replied that she was not very good at escaping from Venice, but checked himself. "Why did you decide against such action, Marietta?" he questioned.

"You might have penalized the Pietà for my absence."

He gave her a long look from under his lids. "You must have a poor opinion of me to think I would renege on benefits donated to foundlings."

"I don't know you. How am I to judge what you would do?"

"Few couples really know each other before they are wed. Take me on trust, Marietta."

"It seems I shall have to, but does the ceremony have to be very soon?"

"I have already said it is pointless to delay."

"Are you so desperate for an heir?"

He was silent for what seemed minutes instead of seconds before answering. "I am, but I also want you, Marietta."

She swallowed and turned her eyes away from him. "Let it be a quiet wedding at Santa Maria della Pietà."

"Whatever you wish. Order everything you need and let all the bills be sent to me. I suggest we marry six weeks from now."

"I should like to invite Filippo and Elena Celano to our wedding as a gesture of goodwill."

"Impossible! Filippo Celano would not come and your friendship with his wife can't continue."

Her glance flashed at him. "We could put the invitation to the test!"

He lowered his voice to answer her, although the shutters of the *felze* were closed and the gondolier, singing a serenade, could not hear their conversation. "The last friendly overture made by some minor member of my family about forty years ago resulted in bloody slaughter on both sides. Leave well enough alone, Marietta. If you should meddle in the vendetta or misguidedly try to maintain contact with Celano's wife, you may find yourself responsible for the death of others."

"How cruel it is!"

"Cruelty thrives in Venice! When I was a boy I often saw condemned

prisoners dying in cages suspended from the Campanile. The torture chambers are less busy than they were years ago, but they have not been closed up. At times a criminal convicted of a violent crime is still slung up by his thumbs between those two deeper rose columns of the Doge's Palace. Have you never heard their screams?"

"Don't say any more!" She turned away and closed her eyes, but he seized her by the wrists and gave them a jerk that forced her to look at him.

"I've made enemies by my attempts to abolish such punishments and by exposing corruption where I have found it. So it's not just the Celanos who would rise against me if the chance appeared. For mercy's sake take note now, Marietta! Let things rest at present in the certain knowledge that good is being done even when all appears to be as black as night. Maybe one day everything will be as we wish, but in the meantime the Doge is an over-indulgent hedonist. He closes his eyes to too many things. Just as the city is being undermined by the sea so is decadence draining away its strength. It can survive, but a revival of its old strength and spirit is vital. I and others like me are working under cover toward that end, but secrecy has always been the lifeblood of Venice and that secrecy must be maintained."

She was alarmed and concerned for his safety. If it meant not meeting Elena she would have to make the sacrifice. At least they could still communicate through their sign language. She would be able to give Elena support without revealing anything concerning Domenico that her friend might inadvertently mention in an enemy's hearing.

"I shall keep your confidence always, Domenico," she promised, using his Christian name for the first time.

"So, Marietta, we have made a new beginning, have we not?" he said with a slight smile.

"Yes we have," she acknowledged. In a curious way, all he had just said had bound her to him more than any talk of love. She was extraordinarily pleased that he should have confided in her in that way. It made her hopeful that in the future she might be of help in the secret work he had undertaken, and he should have his heir. The most tender thing he had ever said to her was that it could be a joy for her to teach her own children to sing.

"I think this is an appropriate time to seal our betrothal with a ring, Marietta."

He took a ring from his pocket—a magnificent emerald set thickly in gold—and slid it onto her finger. She supposed his choice of the jewel had been guided by the color of her eyes, although he did not say so.

"It is beautiful, Domenico."

He drew her into his arms then and kissed her as passionately as before. This time he cupped her breast and through the satin felt her nipple against his palm. He could tell that, for all the unusual circumstances, he would have a responsive lover in this woman he so desired.

They had reached the opera house and the glow of many candle-lamps shone golden on the water. The Torrisi gondolier edged his way through the crush of vessels vying to land their passengers at the steps of the entrance. It was a grand assemblage in silks and satins, the women's coiffures trimmed with plumes and flowers and ribbons.

In the Torrisi box, which was in the third tier of six rising up in a great horseshoe, Marietta had a wide view of the stage and the whole animated scene. Fans fluttered, quizzing glasses winked, and people thronged about, greeting friends and acknowledging the bows of those too far away to be spoken to directly. Each box was hung with crimson drapery, and the candle-glow and the radiant jewels within made each one a little golden cave within the greater cave of the auditorium itself.

Marietta had surrendered herself completely to excitement. Her eyes sparkled as she glanced here and there. This was the largest of the six opera houses in Venice and she thought it a perfect venue for her first visit.

"I'm so glad you brought me here," she said enthusiastically to Domenico. "I have never been to the opera in Venice before."

"Have you not?" He was noticing that their box was receiving a lot of attention, because she was being recognized on all sides, but Marietta was still unaware of it. It was as well that he had ordered the footman outside the door to allow no entry to anyone except Antonio, whom he expected later. There would be time enough for friends and acquaintances to meet her after the marriage.

Suddenly Marietta saw Elena just entering a box directly across from theirs. Her hair was elaborately dressed but left golden and unpowdered with sapphire ornaments, her low-cut gown was of silver lace, and she was laughing and chatting to those in her party. Marietta turned to Domenico.

"There is my good friend, Elena!"

"That is the Celano box. I think you will find that neither she nor those in her company will look across here. It is the social protocol for Torrisis and Celanos to ignore one another in public. When others in either party are acquainted with both sides, they simply follow the behavior of the one they are with and no offense is taken. It makes life easier."

"Marco Celano once challenged you at a Pietà concert."

"I remember. Just previously there had been some contretemps between two members of our respective families and a period of high tension always follows. Sometimes it is the same for weeks beforehand. It caught Marco Celano unawares to suddenly see me there."

The orchestra had struck up the overture to the Monteverdi opera and Marietta waited eagerly for the curtain to rise. The singers were good but no one in the audience seemed to be paying attention. People went on talking and visiting one another in the boxes. Only when the prima donna sang did everyone become quiet, for she was popular in Venice and sang superbly. For the rest of the time the opera was merely a background for everything else that was going on. In several boxes, games of cards were being played; in others supper was being served. Three boxes already had their shutters closed and as there had been only one couple in each, it was not hard to guess what was going on within.

During the second act, when Domenico had ordered supper to be served, Marietta realized that Elena had seen her. She was giving a special signal sending greetings with her fan. Immediately afterward, another gesture conveyed her surprise at seeing Marietta there.

Marietta replied by lightly resting a hand at the base of her throat in one of their danger signals. Elena gave back with the same, showing that she had to be equally careful. They had no sign for "betrothed," but Marietta slid her ring up and down on her finger and knew that Elena would understand.

"Does the ring not fit well?" Domenico asked. "It can be altered."

"It fits perfectly and I'm quite dazzled by it."

Elena witnessed his questioning of her friend and neither of them risked communicating again.

During the third act, Antonio Torrisi came to his brother's box. Marietta recognized him immediately from the time she had seen him through the grille at the ridotto. He was very courteous and welcomed her into the family.

"I have heard you sing many times, Marietta," Antonio said, bowing over her hand. "Now that my brother has won you, no concert will ever be the same again." His grin was infectious. "I hope you will continue to sing for us."

"I will do that," she promised light-heartedly.

He drew up a chair and stayed a little while, talking to her. She noticed he was like Domenico in never once looking across to the Celano box.

On the way back to the Pietà, Domenico spoke of his immediate plans for after their marriage.

"I shall take you to our country villa. It will be a good time to leave Venice for the summer, and I'm sure you will like it there. It is very peaceful and the countryside should remind you of where you were born." He paused, smiling questioningly. "What is amusing you?"

"I am just thinking how astonished I would have been if I had been told long ago that one day I should stay in the villa that the barge man, Iseppo, pointed out to me on the way to Venice. Instead he predicted I should marry the Doge, and that was wrong!"

"I trust you have made the better choice."

She raised her eyebrows. "Choice!" she echoed wryly.

"That was tactless of me."

"No. It could be said that I did choose simply by not going away."

"That is gracious of you, Marietta. I believe we shall get along very well."

His warm gaze was on her and she felt ravished by it. Then he crushed her against his hard muscular body as they kissed and she felt her heart tilt as if it were more than ready to be lost to him.

They arrived at the water gate of the Pietà to be met by the mewing of an infant girl, half wrapped in a costly silk shawl, who had been left just inside the aperture under the gate. Marietta guessed she was the offspring of a courtesan, and, alighting from the gondola, she reached through the aperture to gather the babe in her arms and rock it gently.

"How fortunate it is not a cold night," Domenico said, coming to her side and ringing for admittance.

"Usually the mothers summon on the bell before they leave," Marietta explained, "but sometimes they are afraid of not getting away in time." Then she smiled. "What an unexpected ending to our evening together!"

"Everything is unexpected with you, Marietta." There was that same embracing look in his eyes. "May that never change."

The door had opened and the gates were being unlocked by the watchman. Marietta bade Domenico good night and swept indoors to meet Sister Sylvia's outraged expression with a smile.

"I have named this new arrival already," she said, placing the infant in the nun's arms. "She shall be Marietta. I have been at the Pietà so long that there should be another here when I marry Signor Torrisi."

But Sister Sylvia was not to be diverted from what she had to say. "How dare you be back so late, Marietta!"

"But I had such a marvelous time!" Marietta danced around the floor and started up the stairs.

Sister Sylvia's indignant shriek followed her. "Signor Torrisi should never have been allowed to take you off without me!"

Marietta looked back over the banisters and laughed mischievously. "You should have seen me at the opera! Without a mask! Without a veil! Half of Venice recognized me!"

There came a further shriek that made the chandelier ring. The infant, who had become quiet, began to mew again.

After that there were to be no more unchaperoned outings for Marietta and Domenico before their marriage. Sister Sylvia made sure of that. She pointed out to the rest of the board of governors that it did great harm to the Pietà's good name for one of their leading singers to be seen unchaperoned, whether she was betrothed or not. They in turn persuaded Domenico, much to his exasperation. At the age of thirty he was not prepared to endure the constant presence of a third party, particularly as that aggressive nun had declared her intention of replacing the gentler Sister Giaccomina, who would have been content to pass the time with his books.

"This means we shall not meet again until our wedding day," he said to Marietta, "but we have the rest of our lives in which to share each other's company."

She nodded. The rest of their lives. The prospect was daunting. Neither of them knew whether their marriage would be for good or ill.

Chapter 10

$\mathcal{N}$obody but Sister Giaccomina knew that Elena sang at Marietta's wedding. Between them they made secret plans. The nun let her in at the water entrance and she changed quickly into a Pietà red silk gown. With a veil over her face, she sped along to take her place behind the choristers at an upper grille where they sang for the entrance of the bride.

She thought Domenico looked particularly fine in his gold brocade coat and breeches, but it was his bride who stole the day. Following her own instinctive sense of style, Marietta was wearing a gown of gleaming cream satin in the newest silhouette, which relied solely on petticoats to give fullness to the sides and back of the skirt. Her beautiful throat and bosom rose from a fichu of lace and her luxuriant Titian hair was crowned by a chaplet of cream roses.

When the marriage ceremony was over Marietta looked up at the galleries as she and Domenico made their way down the aisle. She smiled at the girls, whom she could just glimpse through the grilles. Although she knew it was only wishful thinking, more than once during the service she had thought she heard Elena's voice among theirs. Then she went with her bridegroom out into the hot June sunshine.

Elena left the gallery immediately and ran as fast as she could to Sister Giaccomina's room, where she threw aside the Pietà veil and slipped out of the red gown into her own. Throwing on a light silk domino she sped downstairs again without meeting anyone. Those girls not in the church were at lessons or practice. The water entrance remained unlocked for her and a waiting gondola took her out of the side canal and under the bridge in time to see the flower-decked bridal gondola heading into the Grand Canal, a host of others bearing guests in its wake. As the music and love songs of the accompanying singers drifted across the water, she wished only happiness for Marietta and hoped she would find it in the Palazzo Torrisi.

The wedding feast was held in the great *sala del trono,* so named for a pair of ornate and gilded antique chairs, which had been placed side by side for the bride and groom at the head table. At the remaining tables six hundred guests were seated with ease. After the feast there was music played by the Pietà orchestra. Marietta danced tirelessly into her new life. In the weeks since her night at the opera she had had only a few words with Domenico whenever he happened to be at the Pietà, and each time she had felt herself still more bound to him by events in her own life. How could she help but associate him, however tenuously, through the golden mask to all the love and security of her earliest years. Not that she expected the same equilibrium of her married life. On the contrary, she expected to lead quite a tempestuous existence, but the thought of that appealed to her after so many years in the almost artificial peace of the Pietà.

All her partners in the dancing were graceful and full of compliments, but with Domenico it was as though her feet did not touch the floor and her happiness surfaced completely. He, worldly and experienced, saw how it was to be between them and was well satisfied.

When it was time for her to retire, a group of Torrisi women, all Domenico's cousins, assisted her out of her wedding garments. They were friendly and full of laughter, which suited her own exhilarated mood, exclaiming over the silk and lace nightshift that had been specially made for this night.

After slipping the gown over her naked body, they saw her into bed, kissed her in turn, and left her sitting against the pillows in the light of a single candle-flame. She could hear the music and the distant buzz of voices as the celebrations continued. Yet, now that she had time to reflect, she realized that since it was a second marriage for Domenico there had been a subdued note to the whole proceedings. Several times she had caught glances in the guests' eyes that told her they were wondering if she knew how great a love match it had been between Domenico and his first wife. They must have noticed, as she had, that Angela's portraits had been removed from the main salons and other paintings put in their place. She was certain that her bedchamber had been entirely redecorated and refurnished in the elegant rococo style, for everything looked brand new. The walls had flowered panels and the ceiling plasterwork was made to resemble swathed primrose silk held up by little cherubs, with garlands suspended from the cornices. The bed had hangings of floral silk, and porcelain bowls of pastel-hued roses perfumed the air.

Footsteps in the adjoining bedchamber caused her heart to thump. She heard Domenico's voice and guessed he was alone with his valet. Then the communicating door opened and Domenico appeared in a blue brocade robe with a decanter of wine and two glasses in his hands. If he had seemed handsome to her before, she found him even more so on this night. He had had his hair cropped short for the fashion of wig-wearing he had adopted that day, and it shone well-brushed in the candle-glow.

"Would you like a glass of wine, Marietta?" he asked, setting the decanter and glasses on a side table. "I could do with one myself. All that dancing has given me a thirst."

She nodded and he poured the wine into both glasses, then came across to sit on the bed beside her. "A toast is in order. I know there were plenty offered downstairs, but this is just for us to share. Let us drink to our future. May it bring us close as husband and wife."

"I can think of no better wish." She sipped from her glass.

He leaned forward, his lips moist with wine, and kissed her gently. Then as he sat back he studied her speculatively. "Your eyes are thoughtful. What is it?"

"You look different."

He grinned and ran a hand carelessly over his head. "Pomade and powder are fiendish inventions. I tolerated them long enough. That is why I have taken to a wig. Does my appearance without it displease you?"

"No. You have acted wisely."

"Then there must be something else." He reached out to stroke back a tendril of her hair and tucked it carefully behind her ear. "We are not and never have been strangers. You told me that our paths crossed long ago in a mask-maker's workshop before you came to Venice. So tell me what is in your mind."

"I was thinking that perhaps it was you I saw in the doorway of the Torrisi villa. There was someone coming out to meet those guests."

"Of course it was me!" he declared.

A smile came to her lips. "I suppose you will say next that you saw me too."

He raised an eyebrow quizzically. "Surely you saw me wave to you in the barge?"

A little laugh erupted spontaneously. "What a tale! Do you expect me to believe that?"

"Not really. But it could have happened."

"I suppose it could." She found him easy to talk to and wished she could have told him about imagining that she had heard Elena singing during their wedding, but that was impossible. Then he stroked a hand softly across her breast.

"You are a beautiful woman, Marietta. But however lovely you looked in your bridal finery, you are even lovelier to me now."

She recalled that the first time she had seen him in the golden mask she had wondered how it would be to feel caresses from such a man. The subtle skimming of his palm had set her trembling deliciously. He was still speaking.

"I know I promised to court you after we were married, but that did not mean I would leave you this night or any other."

She gave a nod. "I realized that," she said faintly.

His hand slid around to her spine and he brought her forward to take her mouth with sudden, hungry ardor in his kiss. Then he looked long at her as he took the empty glass from her fingers and left the bed to set it with his beside the decanter. Although the room was mainly in shadow, the single candle-flame flickered and highlighted him as he untied his robe and threw it carelessly across a chair. Of all the many works of art she had seen, none had prepared her for the full sight of a naked, handsomely built man

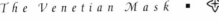

already alerted by desire. She gave a little gasp as he entered the bed and gathered her amorously into his arms.

Slowly he drew her with him into a night of sensual lovemaking. Bathed in kisses and caresses, she was borne up and down and around on crests and in valleys of passion. At times his hands were unbearably tender, touching and stroking, making her writhe sensuously, while at others he crushed her to him with a power that brought its own fierce ecstasy. As if she had been born for this night, her body seemed to cleave to his in homecoming. Once, as she tossed beneath him in ecstasy, her hair tumbling about her on the pillow, it was as though destiny had bound her to him long before this time and place.

When dawn came they lay sleeping close together in the rumpled bed, his arms about her waist. An hour later he awoke to see rays of early morning sunshine penetrating the shutters. Propping himself on an elbow, he looked down at her. He had never expected to be the first with her. Who would have thought that a love which had induced her to take such risks would have stopped short of consummation? He had always supposed that she and her Frenchman had spent time in houses of assignation, for more than once his spy had lost them in the Carnival crowds.

He smiled to himself and drew her hair back from her sleeping face. Whatever reservations she might still have held against him had been lost in the pleasure he had created for her. She was lying with the sheet barely covering her, and her limbs were in graceful repose. He would spare her waking to his presence. Had they been lovers in other than a physical sense he would have stayed, but it was his guess that when she awoke she would need time to think about all that had happened between them.

He swung himself from the bed and put on his robe. On his way to the communicating door that led to his own bedchamber he paused to look back at her. It could happen that when a long-desired woman was finally possessed her appeal soon faded, but that would not be the case with Marietta. With her unconventional looks, which held their own rare beauty, and her lovely body, she fascinated him now more than ever. He knew they had only brushed the surface of what they could experience together in that bed and already he wanted to return there. It was a narrow gulf between fascination and love, but whether he would ever carry her to the great marriage bed of the House of Torrisi in his own room, where he and Angela had always slept, was another matter.

Although he closed the door quietly behind him the unfamiliar sound disturbed Marietta's sleep. She opened her eyes with a start and then sat up abruptly, but Domenico was not at her side and the room was deserted. Memories came flooding back and she drew up her knees to rest her forehead on them and link her hands about her legs as if it were necessary to hide her face. But she was smiling.

After a while she lifted her head again and shook back her hair. She was ravenously hungry, but before she summoned a maidservant to bring a breakfast tray she must find her nightshift. Domenico had rolled it up over her head to fling it aside not long after coming to bed. She spotted it lying in a gleaming heap by the window. Swiftly she left the bed to gather it up, but before putting it on she went to the adjoining marble bathroom. There was only a ewer of cold water standing from the night before, but she bathed herself and poured the last few drops over her body to trickle down refreshingly. Wearing her nightshift she returned to the bedchamber. The windows were open and she released the clasp of the shutters to send them wide. Below was an enclosed garden of trees and flowers with antique statuary and an ornate loggia. There were roses in abundance. Suddenly, without knowing why the conviction should take hold of her, she knew that Angela Torrisi's favorite flower had been the rose.

Slowly she turned to survey the bedchamber. This had been Angela's room. The fact that it had been completely refurbished for its new occupant at least made it her own domain, but what of the rest of the palace? Much of the decor would be to her predecessor's taste. And the portraits of Angela? Where had they gone? She knew she would not rest until she found them. For the first time she realized that for a long while, perhaps to the end of her days, she would be living with the ghostly presence of another woman. It could not be easy for any woman to assert her own character and personality in a house her husband had shared with another, but it would be even harder when the woman whose place she was taking had been truly loved.

Thoughtfully Marietta returned to the bed, where she tidied the sheets and plumped up the pillows. She settled herself and then tugged on the bell-pull.

A maidservant peeped cautiously around the door before entering, as if she could not believe she had been summoned at such an early hour. Later Marietta would discover that Angela, following the routine of most Venetian noblewomen, had never risen from her bed before noon. On this first morning Marietta's early request for breakfast created as much activity as a stick stirred in an ant's nest.

No less than three maidservants brought in the meal, the first carrying a tray with the food, the second the silver chocolate pot, and the third a crystal dish of peaches. Her lady's maid, an older woman whose name was Anna, handed her a fan in case the room seemed too warm and then held forth a bowl of scented water in which to dabble her fingers before eating. Finally, she was left to enjoy her breakfast.

Afterward, Anna wanted to send for the hairdresser, but Marietta liked to follow fashion in her own way. "My hair is very manageable. I've always done it myself," she protested.

"Just show me how you like it dressed, signora. Then I can do it for you. You will find I'm very skilled."

She was true to her word, and Marietta was pleased with the result. She also found it novel to have someone in attendance to put ready petticoats and shoes and the gown of her choice. At the Pietà there had always been a friend on hand to help with lacing or the back buttons on a bodice, but that was all.

"Did you serve the late Signora Torrisi?" she asked warily.

"No, signora. I was appointed ten days ago to have your gowns pressed and ready to wear and all your new garments put away."

Marietta was relieved. She would not have wanted split loyalties in her own quarters. As for her gowns, she had restricted the number for her trousseau, wanting to choose for her needs in a more leisurely fashion. It had been difficult to concentrate on milliners' sketches and dressmakers' swatches while half her mind was on the rehearsal she should have been attending or the score of music she wanted to finish. She had enough clothes on hand to take her into July and August, when they would be at the villa on the river as Domenico had planned. When she returned to Venice there would be ample time to extend her wardrobe to meet all social obliga-tions. She intended to fulfill the role of Domenico's wife in all its aspects. It had never been her way to do anything half-heartedly and she did not intend to start now.

When she was dressed, she went down the stairs and made her way through the various salons, looking through the windows to set their loca-tion in her mind. In the *sala del trono* the steward of the palace was super-vising the setting of everything to rights after the previous day.

From there, she continued on to the kitchens where, at her unexpected appearance, some servants scattered while others stood as if frozen to the spot. A footman, shoving his arms into his coat, came forward swiftly.

"Have you lost your way, signora? I can show you back again."

"No. I am on a tour of inspection."

She had made up her mind to follow Elena's example and keep a firm finger on the pulse of the house. Now she peeped into pots and pans on the ranges and went into a cold room, where vast amounts of food left over from the wedding banquet filled the shelves. Taking one of the minor stewards in tow, she allotted what should be given generously to the poor and chose some of the still uncut cakes to be taken to the Pietà.

When she emerged, the steward of the palace had just arrived and been informed by one of the maidservants where the signora was now. He was flustered and breathing heavily from running down the stairs.

"Signora, how may I help you?"

"Come with me," she said.

During the next two hours he showed her exactly how the palace was run, and the ledgers indicated that he was an honest man. She congratu-lated him on his management of the wedding reception on the previous day, which pleased him, and she had only one criticism to make.

"At the Pietà we uphold kitchens being as spotless as those in a convent. That is not the case in this place. Please see that improvements are made at once."

"I will, signora."

When she left him, he shook his head that a bride should spend the morning after her wedding night concerning herself with such mundane matters. The late Signora Torrisi had never shown her pretty face near the kitchens, but that did not lessen his respect for the Signor's new wife. She knew what she was about. He would serve her well and make sure she did not have cause to find fault with any part of the palace again.

When Domenico returned from visiting one of the other Torrisi palaces in the early afternoon, he found Marietta sitting quietly in the salon of family portraits, studying each one in turn. Even as he entered, she moved her chair on a few paces to sit down and examine the next of his ancestors.

"You should be having a siesta in this heat," he said. It seemed to him that she had to force herself to turn and meet his eyes. He smiled to put her at her ease. In retrospect he had been extraordinarily passionate toward her in those night hours.

"Maybe I should." She folded her fan and stood up, turning automatically to set the chair back in its place, but he moved forward quickly.

"Leave that." He swung it up himself by its top rail and put it aside.

Now that she had moved she was suddenly tired, for until coming to this room she had not paused in her tour of exploration. He opened the door for her, and when she had passed through he lifted her in his arms and carried her up the stairs to her room where he laid her on a couch in the re-shuttered gloom. Her eyes were closed. He removed her shoes and left her to sleep.

She awoke two hours later and lay looking up at the plaster-swagged ceiling. There was a little gilded cherub directly overhead. Nowhere in the palace so far had she found those vanished portraits of Angela. Domenico must have had them removed to one of the other palaces, because she did not think they would be in any of the less important and smaller salons that she had yet to see. He had taken that action out of consideration for her feelings, but he might as well have left the portraits; the shadow of her predecessor was everywhere in small items and feminine touches throughout the palace. It was as if Angela had just left a room as she herself entered it. Most telling of all was a little ribboned satin cushion on a chair in one of the salons, a cushion that would have fit snugly into a pregnant woman's back. And everywhere those porcelain bowls full of roses.

Marietta sat up and put her feet on the floor. She would never want to take Angela's place in Domenico's affections, but she needed to throw off this sensation of being overshadowed if she was ever to feel at home under this or any other roof that had once sheltered her predecessor. At least she and Domenico would soon be going to the summer villa. Perhaps there she would find fewer reminders of another woman's reign.

It was a larger vessel than a gondola that with the gentle splash of oars took Marietta and Domenico across the turquoise-hued lagoon on the first stage of their journey to the summer villa. Their baggage had gone on ahead and would be unpacked before they arrived. Marietta was as enthralled as if she were a child again as the vessel entered the lock she remembered so well. When they reached the Brenta river beyond she saw barges awaiting their turn to leave, and she wondered if any of them belonged to Iseppo. He and his wife had been on her list of wedding guests, and although they had declined the invitation, they were outside the church to wave to her after the ceremony.

Now, under a green velvet canopy and on cushions of silk, Marietta looked from one bank to another as the voyage upriver continued. At the wedding she had met many of the owners of the lovely villas that Domenico pointed out to her as they drifted by. When the vessel came alongside the steps that led up the bank in front of the Torrisi villa, Marietta alighted swiftly and ran up the steps to cross the lane that lay between her and the gates, which had been opened in readiness as had the door of the villa itself. When Domenico reached her side she gave him a sparkling glance.

"Look at me!" she exclaimed playfully. "I am wearing a pretty gown and a fine plumed hat, I've a fan in my hand and jewels around my neck, and I have my ear bobs that you have given me. Nobody could tell me apart from those young women I once saw arriving here."

He was amused and threaded her arm through his to hold her hand. "There is one difference."

"What is that?"

"You are coming home. They were not."

Suddenly overcome by this unexpected kindness, she looked down to recover herself before raising her head again. He had a gift for saying just the right thing and she was emotionally vulnerable because, despite her interest in the journey and the excitement of their arrival, she had not for one moment forgotten the voyage down-river with her dying mother all those years ago. "I am indeed," she said huskily, letting him lead her up the drive.

The villa, built by Palladio in the sixteenth century, had been designed asthetically for beauty of line and practically for coolness and the ease of summer living. Marble floors, pale walls, and elegant ceilings predominated, one perfectly proportioned room leading to another. Much of the old carved furniture dated from the same period, and what had been added since kept to the soft colors of the river and the surrounding countryside in upholstery, curtains, and bedhangings.

Marietta loved it. Here she could be herself again. There was nothing to show that any one woman had had more influence on this house than another. It was as though the impossibility of exertion in the summer heat had prevented any individual stamp being set upon it. Antique statues on plinths and in niches were scattered throughout the house and the flowering garden outside. Somehow these helped to give the villa a curious timelessness, as if its foundations had been waiting in the earth for hundreds of years before Palladio had viewed the site and decided what he would raise up there.

The days passed in leisurely fashion. Domenico taught Marietta to ride horseback, and when they accepted an invitation to take supper *al fresco* some little distance away, she experienced the novelty of her first carriage ride. They entertained, held and attended summer balls, shared picnics on river trips, and enjoyed informal meals with friends whom Domenico knew well and who immediately took Marietta into their fold. She had met many of them already at Pietà receptions and concerts in their residences. Sometimes she would sing for the company, accompanying herself on the harpsichord, and this was always the highlight of the event for those present.

Only one visitor came to stay at the villa and that was her brother-in-law Antonio, who was summering at a second Torrisi villa. Marietta welcomed the chance to get to know him better, but the reason for his coming was disturbing.

"I thought I ought to warn you," he said to Domenico as the three of them sat with glasses of wine on the terrace in the warm, moonlit night. "Filippo Celano rode onto Torrisi land. I saw him from the villa but he was too far away then for me to see who it was. I thought I had a visitor and went out to the steps. Then I recognized him and was fully prepared for him to dismount and await my challenge, but he wheeled his horse about and rode away."

Marietta was puzzled. "Where is the warning in that? I see no harm in what he did. Perhaps he didn't know he was on Torrisi property until he saw you."

Antonio and Domenico exchanged glances. "It is not as simple as that," Domenico explained. "Signs are brewing that certain of the Celanos are spoiling for a fight. Their summer villas and lands are far from ours. The Celano came deliberately to warn and provoke."

"But are you and Antonio the only ones to stand against them?"

Domenico shook his head. "I can call on half the men you saw at our wedding at any time."

She leaned forward anxiously and put her hand on his arm. "Don't let it come to conflict, I beg you."

He looked at her gravely. "So long as there are trouble-makers in either family lusting for a fight, the vendetta will continue to take its toll."

She drew her hand away, knowing only too well that the feud had already cost him a much loved wife and that he and Antonio had also lost a brother and several cousins. "Must it be left to fester and destroy in the future as it has done in the past? Why not throw away your swords in the face of the enemy? None would cut down unarmed men."

Antonio looked grim. "I regret to say that once a Celano in the priest-hood did try to mediate, and it is to the shame of our house that he was slain by one of our forebears. It happened over a hundred years ago, but to the Celanos it could have been yesterday. They would show no mercy."

She thought of the goal she shared with Elena, to mend this great rift, but what she had just heard did not offer much hope. "How soon do you expect a confrontation?"

"That is impossible to say. It could be six months or a year or even longer. A volcano rumbles long before it erupts."

"Are any Torrisis making these same moves of warning?"

Antonio shook his head. "This time it is the Celanos who are throwing down the gauntlet." Then his tone became reassuring. "Don't worry, Marietta. It may come to nothing more than a duel between two men. There is no way of knowing."

She was not consoled. Surely a duel would have to be between an important member of each family to provide sufficient blood-letting for this terrible feud in its present unsettled state. She dared not think it might be Domenico and Filippo, but everything pointed that way. "Must the outcome be death?" she asked tensely.

Neither of the men answered her question. "This is too fine a night to talk of such matters any longer," Domenico said, dismissing the subject on a deliberately careless note that did not escape her ear. "Antonio has said what he had to say. That is done. Now he shall refill our glasses for us."

Antonio obliged cheerfully, switching the conversation to the grape harvest that could be expected from the extensive Torrisi vineyards that year. Then, when it seemed as if he intended to leave in the morning, Marietta invited him to stay on for a picnic that had been planned farther up-river. There were to be three boats to take the invited company and plenty of room for him.

"I accept with pleasure, Marietta."

He made the picnic very lively, flirting with the women and dancing Marietta around and around on the grass while someone played a merry tune on a lute. When the dance was over and everybody clapped, he kissed her. Surprise showed in her eyes and he grinned, giving her a wink and a squeeze about the waist. Later, as evening came, he took the lute himself and sang, with everybody joining in.

In all he stayed five days and Marietta came to know him well. Much as she liked him she thought it was fortunate that it was Domenico and not Antonio who had been chosen to head the family. The facial likeness between the two brothers was misleading, for in character they were entirely different. Antonio was totally carefree, with little sense of responsibility, his eyes rarely free of laughter. He was a keen gambler and when they played cards, whether among the three of them or when other guests were present, he was at his happiest when the stakes were high. Marietta came to the conclusion that he would gamble as easily with his life if the occasion arose. When he left, it was to go to his villa and the courtesan awaiting his return.

The rest of the summer rolled on peacefully. Now and again business or political matters took Domenico away to Venice for a day or two, and Marietta found that each time she would eagerly await his return. A good companionship had formed between them, which she saw as the rock on which their lives together would stand. Sexually they were perfectly attuned. Many times they made love with moonlight slanting across their bed and often before a siesta when the bright afternoon sun pierced the shutters. More than once he had taken her in deep grass or in a shady, secluded glade. At these times he spoke intensely loving words, but not as Alix had expressed himself, for with Domenico these words conveyed only passion and not feelings of the heart. Yet his cherishing and his praise of her were unceasing. He was also a demanding lover, taking as well as giving, and she met all his wishes generously.

It was to please Marietta that Domenico extended their stay well into September, but finally they had to return to the city for he could no longer control affairs from afar. On the morning of their departure he was at the stables, giving some last-minute instructions, while Marietta, in a cape ready to leave, took a last wander through the downstairs rooms. In a salon pale as ivory she paused by one of the windows, holding back a gauzy curtain to look out at the river on which she was soon to be borne away. The gates were open, as they had been upon her arrival and on many other occasions when company had flowed in and out.

Suddenly she stiffened. A tall, burly man in riding clothes, wig, and tricorned hat was moving into the middle of the gateway, staring toward the window where she stood, the movement of the curtain having focused his attention. He was tapping his whip across the palm of his other hand menacingly. She knew him only too well, this Celano who had come again on Torrisi land. It was Filippo Celano.

Letting the curtain drop softly back into place, she moved swiftly away with the intention of fetching Domenico, but before she could reach the door she saw through another window that the Celano had gone. She slowed to a standstill. Her hands were clenched and her heart was beating fast. There had been aggression in the man's whole stance.

When she told Domenico about the incident, he put an arm about her shoulders and walked her slowly out of the villa. "I think you will have to prepare yourself for the unexpected in that way. Don't let it frighten you."

"I wasn't frightened. I was angry."

He laughed quietly. "That is the right attitude, Marietta. I have always known you had courage."

When eventually they arrived at the water gate of the Torrisi palace, Marietta thought to herself that Domenico had no idea of the kind of courage she needed to enter this house. It was as she feared. As soon as she crossed the threshold she was instantly aware of the influence of the much loved woman who had left the country villa well alone. Then in the same instant it came to her that it was in the villa Antonio now occupied that Domenico and his first wife had spent their summers.

A stack of invitations awaited Marietta's attention and yet another was delivered as she left the house next morning to go to the Pietà where nine-year-old Bianca would be between lessons. They greeted each other joyfully. Bianca had grown a lot recently and was proud to demonstrate how she had progressed on her flute. It also pleased her that she was allowed to call Marietta by her Christian name, now that the title of 'Maestra' no longer applied. Elena had granted her the same privilege.

"Have you seen Elena?" Marietta asked.

Bianca shook her head. "Not since she went away to the country about the same time as you. She promised to come and see me as soon as she returned."

"That should be any day." Although it would have been easy for Marietta to leave a letter for Elena with Bianca, they had both agreed not to involve the child in any way. As Marietta went from the Pietà out of the parade door, she did not know that she had just missed Elena, who was alighting from her gondola at the water entrance in the side canal.

Marietta's next appointment was to visit the best dressmaker in Venice. With a full social calendar ahead of her she would need the right things to wear. It was a few days later, when she was coming from a milliner's in the colonnaded arcades of St. Mark's Square, that she saw Elena; she was the epitome of elegance in a large plumed hat and sprigged silk gown, strolling with two equally well-dressed women and several noblemen. They were crossing the square through a veil of fluttering pigeons, which rose from the stones at their leisurely approach. Filippo was not with them. Marietta moved to stand by one of the columns where she knew Elena must see her. No glance of recognition was forthcoming. Then Elena flicked her hands gracefully as she talked, spelling out a time and date. Marietta already knew the venue and continued on her way.

One of the noblemen had followed Marietta with his eyes. "That was the Flame of the Pietà. You must have known her well, Elena."

"I did," Elena replied casually. "Since then we have both changed our surnames."

When Marietta arrived at Adrianna's house at the appointed time, Elena came rushing to throw her arms around her friend.

"How are you? You look wonderful! What an eye-catching hat you were wearing that day in the square. Did you enjoy the summer? What is your villa like? They were asking more or less the same questions of each other at the same time.

Adrianna let her three little children receive the gifts that Marietta and Elena had brought them. Then she shepherded her offspring into the care of a nursemaid before returning to pour hot coffee and serve freshly baked sweet cakes to the visitors. She was very pleased that from now on they would be meeting regularly under her roof. Leonardo, being older, had so many middle-aged acquaintances with dull wives that it was refreshing to be with old friends closer to her own age.

Elena burst out the secret she had shared with Sister Giaccomina and kept from all except Adrianna. "I sang at your marriage, Marietta!"

Marietta, who had been on the point of asking her, threw back her head in delight. "So it was you! Tell me how you managed it."

They chatted over their cups, wanting news from Adrianna as well as from each other. Adrianna, who kept in close touch with her Pietà godchildren as they did with Bianca, was able to relate news about them and many other snippets of information. When it became apparent to her that neither Marietta nor Elena was going to disclose a pregnancy, Adrianna had misgivings about telling them that she herself was going to have a fourth child. Marietta was still little more than a bride, but it was a different case with

Elena, who had expressed anxiety many times about her failure to conceive. Understandably, it was becoming an obsession with her. The importance of an heir to a patrician family came before all else, and Elena had to endure her mother-in-law's hurtful and cutting remarks.

Just as Adrianna had made up her mind to wait until another time with her news, Elena, who had been studying her keenly, asked her a direct question. "Are you expecting another baby?"

Adrianna could not hold back the happiness in her eyes. "You have guessed correctly."

Elena, unselfish as ever, congratulated her warmly. "How proud Leonardo must be!"

Marietta, after giving her good wishes, turned to Elena. "How did you know about Adrianna? Her figure is not giving her away in those full skirts."

"There is something in the face," Elena explained. "Since we never saw it at the Pietà it is not surprising you have not learned to spot it yet. It is a slight change. A kind of bloom sometimes. I can see it instantly in other women now. I search for it in my own mirror every morning." She smoothed her fingertips back over her cheek. "It so often comes before there is any other definite certainty." Then her voice changed to a desperate note of appeal that startled both her listeners as she flung out her hands to them. "Promise to tell me instantly if either of you ever see it in my face! I shall want to know at once and I may not be able to see it myself through too much looking!"

"We will," Adrianna said compassionately, taking one of Elena's hands and patting it as if comforting one of her own children.

"May it be soon," Marietta added gently.

Both she and Adrianna knew that Elena still feared the Signora as much as ever. They pointed out to her that Lavinia's constant presence was a protection, for she had proved a good friend to Elena during the four years and four months of her marriage to date. Yet, when they were on their own, Marietta confided to Adrianna that knowing the ruthlessness of the Celanos, she could believe they would not hesitate to get rid of a barren and encumbering wife. Fortunately, according to what Elena had told them, Filippo, for all his harsh ways, had not tired of her, although it was well known that he spent time with a notorious courtesan. In a way his cruel obsession with Elena was in itself a guard against her enemies. Nevertheless Marietta and Adrianna were determined to see Elena as often as possible in order to keep a check on her well-being.

Marietta had taken to the social whirl of Venice with enthusiasm. Trying to find some way to mend the vendetta between the Torissis and the Celanos, and also an aim to help Domenico in his secret work, had given purpose to her marriage and alleviated any doubts she might have had about coping with this new life. Domenico, unlike Leonardo with Adrianna, did not resent the attention his wife received as the former prima donna of the Pietà. Rather, he enjoyed entering a room and seeing all heads turn toward her. She wore her fine new clothes with a dash, and her instinctive choice of colors not normally worn by those with Titian hair gave her a jewel-like beauty. Even when masked she was recognized by her graceful carriage and her hair, which she dressed high according to fashion but never powdered.

The Carnival of that first winter of their marriage set a precedent for those to follow. It was a time of lavish masked balls and extravagant suppers eaten by the tinted glow of candle-lamps on private gondolas, while the gondoliers in their liveries sang with voices that would have done credit to the stage of La Scala. Sometimes a whole orchestra played, hired to provide accompanying music on vessels alongside a fleet of merrymakers. There were gala occasions at the opera houses and the theaters, elaborately staged masques at the palaces in which all the guests took part, and always grand banquets hosted by the Doge in the gilded Hall of the Great Council.

Marietta had a variety of flattering carnival costumes. Some of the hoods of her dominoes were supported by stiffening in the traditional style to frame her face with filmy lace frills and ruffles or with satin camellias. Many of her masks were studded with jewels, but she still kept the *moretta* mask her mother had made in its own velvet box among the rest.

No evening was ever without some entertainment and the days were always busy. Marietta still paid regular visits to the Pietà to see Bianca and attended many a Pietà performance. Whenever she and Elena happened to see each other in any public place other than the Pietà they conversed as much as they could in their sign language. If sometimes other people

wondered why one or the other would suddenly smile or look amused, nobody suspected their secret.

By chance they met unexpectedly one evening at a Pietà reception after a concert in the church. Both Domenico and Filippo were sitting late at different meetings of the senate and the two young wives were jubilant at having an unhampered evening together with the added enjoyment of seeing other old friends. As always on these occasions there were foreign guests, a few brought by the Venetian hosts with whom they were staying. Elena, engaged in conversation with the Maestro, became aware of a young man's eyes on her. It was a common enough occurrence, but in spite of herself she was unable to resist a quick little glance in his direction, for his gaze seemed to be boring into her.

It was one of those moments when a man and woman experience the sensation of rebirth and the past fades away as, for a few wonderful moments, each beholds a new world in the other. He was fair-haired and of average height, not particularly handsome but with an engaging, energetic face, a thin, chiseled nose, and a wide mouth. Yet it was his eyes, somewhere between amber and brown, kind and admiring and smiling all at once, that made her forget completely what she had been saying to the Maestro.

"Well, Elena? You mentioned Bianca, didn't you?" the Maestro prompted her.

"Yes." She was flustered. "I was about to ask how she is progressing."

But she did not hear a word of what he said in reply. Every nerve in her body was attuned to the stranger on the other side of the room. It was as if she could hear the soft whisper of his lace cuffs, the velvet sigh of his coat, and even his breathing. She sensed rather than saw him approaching her, and for a few wild seconds she thought her legs would give way. Then he was close by, presenting himself to the Maestro, who in turn presented him to her and left them together. His name was Nicolò Contarini. Had it been set to music by Vivaldi it could not have sounded more beautiful to her ears.

"So you were a former Pietà singer, Signora Celano," he said. "I wish you had been singing this evening in the church. This is my first visit to Venice and naturally I wanted to hear the Pietà angels for myself."

"Where are you from?" she asked, praying it was not from far away.

"Florence. Have you been there?"

"No, but I've always heard it is a beautiful city. Tell me about it."

He gave her a good description. It turned out he was visiting an uncle on his mother's side among the Celano *barnabotti*, which meant she could not invite him to her home. Filippo never willingly associated with his poorer relatives and saw them only when commanding their assistance in the vendetta. Although Nicolò himself was clearly in comfortable circumstances, his association with the *barnabotti* kinsman would blacklist him immediately in Filippo's eyes. But it really didn't matter, since she had no wish to share Nicolò's company with anyone, least of all with the man who made her days a trial and her nights a misery.

She and Nicolò were saying more to each other with their eyes and their smiles than their conversation expressed. It was for them both as if they were alone in the room. Neither knew exactly when they drew into a corner on their own while everybody else moved about them. Marietta saw what was happening but did not intrude. It did not matter that Elena had forgotten all about her. To see her friend looking so happy was enough in itself. As for the Florentine, an educated gentleman of leisure who she had met earlier herself, he was obviously enthralled.

The other guests were beginning to leave. Nicolò noticed and spoke urgently to Elena. "When may I see you again?"

"I dare not, Nicolò. I'm married," she explained unnecessarily.

He smiled regretfully. "To my sorrow you are. But let us meet again. Tomorrow!"

She hesitated only briefly, lost to the plea in his eyes. "Florian's at four o'clock. I shall be masked."

He watched as she darted away to slip an arm through that of the red-haired young woman, Signora Torrisi, as they left the room together. Elena had failed to say how he might recognize her, and to have chosen a place as popular as Florian's betrayed her inexperience in secret arrangements. But he would discover her. Never in all his twenty-seven years had any woman awakened such a response in him. He knew himself to be head over heels in love with her.

There began for Elena the most deliriously happy time she had ever known. *Bauta*-masked in a black silk mantilla and cape, she was totally anonymous among others similarly clad, as he was, when they met. She taught him the same signal of greeting that she and Marietta used in their code, and in this way they found each other immediately in places where people were similarly disguised. As they were passionately in love, it was a short step for them to a house of assignation, where they made love in a room of discreet and elegant splendor. For Elena it was an entirely new experience to be loved with tenderness and adoring passion. At times the tears ran from her eyes in the intense joy of their coming together and at the words of love he spoke to her.

They never wanted to be apart from one another, and Elena bitterly resented the time she spent with friends who might otherwise have wondered what had become of her. Although Filippo's nights out on his own followed a regular pattern, and she always knew when he would be late at the Senate, she was still taking enormous risks in meeting Nicolò, but she did not care. If Filippo should discover her secret affair he could kill her if he wished, for her life would be nothing without Nicolò.

"I love you," they said to each other over and over again. Whenever they were in a gondola or strolling hand in hand by night along the Grand Canal, or anywhere else they were unlikely to be noticed, they would lift their *bauta* masks slightly to kiss and to speak their love once more. Several times they went to the opera, taking a box in a tier above the Celano's, and inevitably desire overcame them. Nicolò would draw the shutters closed, and with the door locked they would strip off their clothes and make love on a satin couch to the sound of some of the most beautiful music ever written.

Their agonized parting took place in the same elegant room in the house of assignation where they had first made love. Elena was absolutely distraught.

"I can't bear it!" she wept.

"My dearest love, try to be brave." He had postponed his departure far longer than he should have done, but now family obligations forced him to leave. "We shall meet again, I swear it! Somehow and somewhere it will happen. You are in my heart forever. If there should ever be a time when you are in danger, you have my address and can send for me. Oh, my darling, don't cry so. You are and always will be everything to me."

From the time of their first meeting, Elena had always insisted on going home by herself. So, for the last time, they kissed on the steps of the Molo before she tore herself from his arms and stepped into a gondola. He remained where he was, watching it until it was lost from sight. This love affair, he believed, would last the rest of their lives. Venice would always draw him back again to her, however many years might pass between their meetings.

Throughout the winter the vendetta kept flaring up in minor incidents. Sometimes it was a skirmish between Torrisi and Celano *barnabotti.* Then there was a clash between the young men of both families. Inexplicably, since none of them ever went without a sword, it had become instantaneously a whirlwind of fisticuffs and lunging kicks. It was as if only by inflicting damage on an even more personal level than by the point of a blade could there be any outlet for the poisonous hatred that had been boiling up. Later, there was a far more serious incident when a Torrisi was found dying of stab wounds on the Rialto Bridge. Nobody knew who the murderer was, but all were certain it was a Celano.

Domenico held a conference with his brother and their other male relatives. None had any doubt that Filippo was at the root of the recurring incidents.

"I never thought I would ever have cause to regret the absence from Venice of Alessandro Celano," Domenico remarked wryly, "but when he was still a priest at the San Zaccaria he kept the more dangerous elements of his family in check. As for us, we will not retaliate for the stabbing." There were murmurs of dissent, but he emphasized his order with a thump of his fist on the table. "That is just what Filippo Celano and his confederates want from us. It could be like setting a flame to gunpowder since he would say there was no proof as to the identity of the murderer. Justice will take its course eventually. In the meantime every Torrisi blade is to remain sheathed unless our own lives are threatened."

Some sighed pointedly, but all would obey him. No nobleman went against the head of his house except in the case of extreme provocation. Domenico's word was law.

Marietta thrived on her relationship with Domenico, even though at times it was somewhat tempestuous, for she was as strong-willed as he and never held back from stating her opinion when it differed from his. She guessed that in this she was a complete contrast to Angela, for he frequently looked surprised when she continued an argument he thought he had settled. Their quarrels were fierce and fiery, but never of long duration and always healed in intense lovemaking.

Finally, as summer turned to another autumn and Elena still had not conceived, it was the suggestion of the Marquise de Guérard, who had become acquainted with Elena's problem through the friendship of their husbands, that she seek medical treatment in Paris. She knew of a doctor there who was gaining wide renown for helping many previously childless women to start a family.

Elena had little faith in doctors. All the foul-tasting concoctions and pills the Venetian physicians had given her had had no effect beyond interrupting her monthly cycle and raising false hopes. Most of all she hated their embarrassing cross-questioning. But Filippo had seized on the idea of her receiving this new treatment. He went to see the Marquise for further information and came away convinced that his wife should go to Paris. There was no question of his being there with her, for the doctor ruled that husbands must stay away from their wives during the treatment, which lasted several months. To Filippo's annoyance, his mother stubbornly refused to spare Lavinia to be Elena's traveling companion, which meant he had to find someone else of impeccable character who could be trusted to watch over her during her absence.

Finally he informed Elena that everything had been arranged satisfactorily. "I have had a meeting with the governors of the Pietà. Sister Sylvia cannot be spared, but Sister Giaccomina may accompany you. She is equally conscientious and can be trusted implicitly never to leave your side. The Marquise de Guérard is letting you have her lady's maid instead of your own, because the woman wishes to return to Paris for family reasons and will also help you to practice and improve your knowledge of the

French language on the way. She will have to leave you in Paris, but the convent where you will lodge can find you another maid who is honest and skilled."

"Nothing appears to have been overlooked," Elena said without expression. She had learned never to voice an opinion that differed from his out of fear of reprisal, but he had not crushed her inwardly and in her thoughts she railed against his domination.

"You should know that I'm thorough in all details," he replied complaisantly. "When you reach the mainland the Celano coach will be waiting with an armed escort. The coach cannot take you all the way and you will have to travel by various means of transport, but the escort will be with you until you are safely at the convent. I wish I could have been there to travel part of the way with you but as you know, I must leave for the colony on the Doge's business eight weeks before your own departure could be arranged." He took hold of Elena's arms then, jerking her forward against him as he looked down into her upturned face. "I shall be awaiting your return with high hopes. Don't disappoint me." He raised her on tiptoe and his mouth crushed down on hers in threat as well as in passion.

At his request the Signora and Lavinia came to keep Elena company in his absence prior to her departure. For the first time she did not fear her mother-in-law, because she guessed the Signora was as eager as Filippo that the treatment in Paris bear results.

Although she had to spend a certain amount of time with her two visitors, Elena continued to meet her friends and carry on with her normal social routine. And, once again, she was meeting Nicolò, who had returned to Venice.

With Filippo safely abroad, Marietta and Adrianna were able to see Elena off on her journey with Sister Giaccomina. They wished her well and she promised to write. She and the nun waved to them as the craft set off to cross the lagoon.

It was customary for travelers on their own, or in a small party, to keep close to an armed escort for safety along the road. Therefore, a score of people on horseback and in two carriages followed after the Celano coach. Nobody but Elena took any notice of the young man on a black horse who rode in their midst. Sometimes Nicolò spent the night in the same hostelry, and it was an easy matter for Elena to leave the nun snoring in their room while she went to his.

"Don't go on to Paris," he urged her once after their lovemaking. "Come to Florence with me. Leave that monster of cruelty, who doesn't deserve to be your husband. Let us live the rest of our lives together." He saw her as the other half of himself, loving her almost on a spiritual as well as a physical plane.

"If that were possible," she answered sadly, tracing the features of his beloved face with gentle fingertips, "I would have gone from Venice with you when you tried to persuade me last time. But responsibilities compel you to reside in Florence and eventually Filippo would hunt me down there. Had we been able to go far away it might have been different. Accept that what you ask can never be."

"Don't say that! I would defend you against the whole world."

She smiled sweetly, deeply touched by his devotion. "Darling Nicolò, let us not think of the future beyond the hours and days and weeks ahead of us before we have to part again."

It was Sister Giaccomina who struck up a conversation with him one day when it seemed to her he must be lonely traveling on his own. "He is such a pleasant young man and comes from Florence," she said afterward to Elena. "It's a city I know so well from my youth. I should like to talk to him about the places I remember, so please be agreeable to him."

"Naturally I will," Elena replied with a little laugh of pleasure, "but how is it you know his city? I thought you were Venetian-born."

"No, my home was near the Ponte Vecchio in Florence when I was young. I fell in love with a man who shared my interest in antique books, but since he was a librarian of humble birth my father would not allow the match. He was about to confine me in the convent of a closed order, but through my mother's intervention he was persuaded to send me to a more lenient convent in Venice, where I could continue my studies. However, access to the great libraries of Venice was restricted and when the abbess offered me the chance to come to the Pietà, where I would have more freedom, I accepted instantly."

How often, Elena thought, do the young take adults for granted, never suspecting what their lives might have been. "How you must have missed your birthplace!"

"I did, but the Lord has been good to me." She patted Elena's hand. "Just think of all the children I have mothered at the Pietà. I have loved every one as if each child was my own."

Elena hugged her. "We've loved you too."

That evening at dinner Sister Giaccomina talked so much to Nicolò, whom she had invited to join their table, that Elena scarcely spoke. But she did not mind. It was enough to watch and listen to him as he answered the nun's questions. When he promised to get Sister Giaccomina an entrée to some of the renowned libraries of ancient volumes in Paris, the nun struck her hands together in delight.

"How will you manage that, signore?" she asked in happy bewilderment.

"Our ambassador in Paris was acquainted with my late father and I intend to call on him. I am sure he will oblige me for you."

Elena kept her eyes fixed on her plate. When Sister Giaccomina was with books she forgot time completely. Nicolò was unaware that he had opened the way for the two of them to be together for hours. It troubled her that she could not be honest with Sister Giaccomina, but one day, maybe sooner than later, she would confess and ask her pardon.

By the time Elena reached Paris, she knew beyond the shadow of a doubt that the travel and the foreign food had not been to blame for the queasiness and occasional vomiting she had experienced on the latter part of the long journey. She was both thrilled and terrified to know she was carrying Nicolò's child. As yet it was possible to keep her secret even from Nicolò, who could stay no longer than three weeks in Paris before leaving for home. He had spoken of returning to accompany her back to Venice, but despite all her longing for him she could not let that happen. It would complicate everything still further if he should find out she was with child. Somehow she must work out her own future and that of the new life growing within her.

Marietta and Adrianna missed Elena. Her first letter from Paris went to Adrianna's house in the Calle della Madonna and was addressed to both of them. She wrote that Dr. de Bois was a portly little man, whose treatment program required mainly that his patients drink champagne, eat rich food, and enjoy the delights of Paris under suitable guardianship. All his patients were Frenchwomen except for herself and three Englishwomen.

Dr. de Bois, Elena continued, *says too many women become so desperate about not having children that they are taut and nervous and cannot relax, but getting them away from all home commitments does wonders for them, and I believe he extends his treatment for as long as his patients wish to stay! He has correspondence from grateful husbands stating that conception took place immediately upon their wives' return. Everybody takes the doctor very seriously and it is rumored that once the Queen herself consulted him. He never fails to mention the royal children whenever he talks to a new patient. As the meager fare at the convent does not match what he wants me to eat, Sister Giaccomina and I have all our meals other than breakfast at the best places in Paris, which suits her perfectly. I think sometimes that she agreed to come with me because of all she had heard about French food!*

She went on to describe Paris as a mainly medieval city with the great avenue of the Champs Elysées sweeping impressively through its center. There were hundreds of shops and the milliners made delectable hats like spun sugar, but there was terrible poverty as well. Starving beggars appeared every day at the door of the convent and were fed from the kitchen. At a nearby village the soldiery had put down most brutally a peaceful demonstration by peasants protesting exorbitant taxes, and there was an air of unrest among the poor that was ignored by the nobility. How different it was from her dear Venice where in Carnival time those from all walks of life could mingle merrily together as could never happen on French soil.

"Perhaps there is some sense in the treatment Elena is following," Adrianna commented as she folded the letter.

"The doctor sounds like something of a charlatan to me," Marietta remarked drily.

"Maybe he is," Adrianna agreed, "but if there are good results for some of his patients, then he can be pardoned. When we send a reply you must tell her your good news. Elena, with her kind heart, would never begrudge your being with child before her."

Marietta nodded her agreement. Except for wishing the same for Elena, she rejoiced absolutely in her pregnancy. The morning sickness had passed and she knew herself to be securely on the way to producing an heir. She did not have the least doubt that she was going to have a boy. Domenico teased her about being so sure, but he could not disguise the hope that she was right. She was aware that his anticipation was moderated by the disappointments he had suffered with Angela, which in turn explained his concern and constant anxiety that she not become too tired or overwrought.

Finally, one day when he wanted to lift her light needlework box to another table to save her the effort, she laughed, pressing her healthy and swelling young body into his arms.

"Look at me! Can't you see how strong and fit I am? All will be well. This I promise you."

He rested his hands on her hips through the layers of her skirts. There was a breadth to them that contrasted with Angela's well-remembered narrow, small-boned form, and he found himself convinced that this dazzling young wife of his would complete their union with a healthy son.

When he had gone from the room Marietta took from her needlework box the baby garment she was making. Although she threaded a needle she did not begin sewing, but let her hand rest with it in her lap as she meditated. Domenico's anxiety had revealed only too clearly that Angela was still very much in his mind.

Her thoughts drifted back over the past months to her continued exploration of the palace. She had opened a door one morning into a room that the house-plan had failed to mark as his office. Here was an inlaid Boulle desk, walnut bookcases, and chests of documents and papers. She had not crossed the threshold of the deserted room, but had drawn back swiftly. It was as if she had been slapped unexpectedly across the face. She had found the three missing portraits of Angela. Together with one other she had not seen before, they adorned the walls of the office where Domenico could look at them every day while he worked. She had not gone back there again.

Chapter 11

When Marietta was in her seventh month, Domenico had to leave Venice on an important diplomatic mission to St. Petersburg and could not hope to return before the birth of their child. He was uneasy about having to leave her, but he had no choice. Arrangements had been made for her to have the best of medical care, and Adrianna had promised to be with her at the birth. Domenico had also charged Antonio with the protection of his wife.

When Domenico left, he was still frowning and anxious. Marietta linked her fingers behind his neck. "Stop worrying about me. All I want is for you to finish your diplomatic affairs as soon as possible and return to me with all speed."

"That is already my intent." Tenderly he cupped her face in his hands. "I love you, Marietta."

It was the first time he had spoken those words except in the heat of passion. "I love you too," she whispered.

Their declaration to each other gave a new meaning to their parting kiss. She wished he had spoken from the heart a bit sooner, for there was much she wanted to say to him. Now it would have to wait until his return.

"Farewell, my love." He kissed her again. "Take care of yourself at all times."

She went out onto the colonnaded balcony to watch until his gondola was barely a speck on the horizon. She rested her brow against the cold marble of a column. Domenico had finally discovered that a second love, while not negating the first, can establish itself in its own right.

The pattern of Marietta's days changed with Domenico away. She curtailed much of her social activity except for meeting informally with friends. Antonio was attentive and visited her daily, often dining with her. Elena's return to Venice was expected shortly and Filippo was already back. Two more letters had followed the first that Marietta and Adrianna received from Elena, and these were far more subdued, with homesickness easily discerned between the lines.

Antonio, who could not himself contemplate an evening without some diversion, often tried to persuade Marietta to accompany him on his outings. "Don't stay here by yourself," he urged one night when Domenico had been away almost a month. "Just for once come out and enjoy yourself."

She smiled at the way he ignored the houseful of servants. "I'm not exactly alone in the palace. I shall go to bed early with a book."

"How dull of you!" he teased, his eyes dancing. "I thought you were about to say with a lover."

She laughed at his jesting. "You'd better be on your way."

"You'll be missing a fine time if you don't come. A party of us is going to a casino."

It would have been easy enough for her to hide her figure in the swirl of a short satin cape, but the company he kept was often a little wild and that did not appeal to her at the present time.

Antonio set off and met his friends as arranged. At the casino they chatted over a bottle or two of wine and then split up, going to the gaming tables of their choice for *bassetta* or *zechinetta* or some other game of chance. Antonio, at a high-stakes table, was winning steadily from one opposing player, whom he realized after a while was Filippo Celano. Although they were both *bauta*-masked and obeyed the rule of complete silence at the tables, he became aware that somehow his enemy knew him too, which was why the play was so fierce.

Deliberately Antonio made the stakes higher and still he won. People had begun gathering around to watch this phenomenal streak of luck, and he could tell by the restlessness of his opponent that the notorious Celano temper was soaring. Financially it did not matter in the least to Filippo that he had already lost a small fortune, but the principle of losing in any way to a Torrisi was humiliating and more than he was able to endure. He had been spoiling for another confrontation with the Torrisis, but had not envisioned such a minor conflict or known that it would inflame him as much as a blow across the face.

Once more the cards turned in Antonio's favor. His eyes danced triumphantly through the eye-holes of his mask as he read the malevolent fury in the glare across the table. By now even the onlookers had guessed who they were, and word flew around that a Torrisi and a Celano were fighting it out over cards. Other tables were deserted as the crowd grew denser around the two antagonists.

When the last of the Celano gold ducats had been passed across the table to Antonio, he pushed the money into one of the leather bags provided by the establishment, then stood up and bowed to his opponent. In a final act of contempt, he tossed back a single gold piece to the Celano.

With a roar Filippo leapt to his feet, knocking his chair aside, and strode out of the gaming salon and out of the casino. Antonio had been left the victor in the field. People applauded, his male friends clapped him on the back, and the women kissed him. Waving his bag of gold triumphantly, he left with his arm round his courtesan's waist to go with her to her apartment.

Later that night she awoke and stretched lazily like a sleek cat to see him standing by her bed, dressed and ready to leave again. He pulled open the leather bag of his winnings and as he poured all the coins around her where she lay, creating a bed of gold, she sat up with a shriek of greedy delight, scooping the shining money to her bare breasts.

Laughing, he went from her apartment and set off for home. It was still dark, but the candles of the wall-shrines and the occasional flicker of a suspended lamp showed him the way through the maze of *calli*. Now and again a rat scuttled across his path. He had no fear of attack by thieves. Petty crime was more likely to be committed in crowds. It was graft and fraud and treachery that abounded on the higher social levels.

The last *calle* had opened ahead of him into a square when, without warning, he was momentarily blinded by the glare of flaring flambeaux and heard the unmistakable hiss of rapiers being drawn. As his hand flew to draw his own rapier and his vision cleared, he knew by the height and breadth of the masked man at the front of the group that it was Filippo Celano.

"What's this?" Antonio demanded fiercely.

"You cheated me at the cards, Torrisi!"

It was a deadly insult that only the swords already drawn could settle. Antonio felt the warning dig of another enemy rapier between his shoulder-blades. It told him he had no chance of setting his back to a wall the better to defend himself. Glancing quickly over his shoulder he saw it was Alvise Celano who had him trapped, his lean face grim with satisfaction.

"We have you now, Torrisi!"

Wild with anger, Antonio turned to shout back at Filippo, his voice echoing hollowly against the stone walls of the *calle*. "Come on then!" He brandished his rapier threateningly. "All try to run me through at once if that is your cowardly aim!"

His own intention was to rush forward at their joint approach and hope to slash his way through to a better position of defense, but Filippo, further inflamed by this slight, gestured for those with him to stand back.

"This matter is to be settled between the two of us! Nobody else is going to shed your blood! That pleasure is to be mine alone!"

He moved backward into the square, taking off his damask coat and throwing it with his tricorne to one of the others while keeping on his mask. People had heard the raised voices and lights began to flicker at windows. Some late-night revelers appeared, and excitement rose at the prospect of a duel. Four men, with fans of cards still in their hands, appeared in a lighted doorway. Seeing that Antonio had nobody to attend him, they pocketed their cards and hurried forward. Antonio knew the eldest man and greeted him.

"Dr. Gaulo! Your services will be needed here."

"Is it you in the *bauta*, Signor Torrisi?" the doctor replied, recognizing Antonio's voice. "Two of my friends here will act as your seconds."

One of these took Antonio's hat and mantle. The two masked duelists faced each other by the well in the middle of the square. The glow of the flaring torches illumined them eerily in a circle of reddish light. Both knew they would be fighting to the death.

Grimly they saluted each other with their rapiers. Then, with the first ring of steel against steel the duel began. With both men in a high rage they fought with a fierceness that drew gasps from the fast-gathering crowd, most of whom were in evening finery. Within the first few passes Filippo had a nicked shoulder and Antonio's shirtsleeve was slit and blood-stained. With speed and agility they thrust and parried, moving lithely about the square as one and then the other gained a slight advantage. Once Antonio stumbled back against the well and Filippo almost had him, but he twisted away in time. Blood began to spatter the flagstones and the crowd grew noisier, cheering and shouting as if they were at a cock-fight instead of witnessing an event that in normal circumstances would have been held in a quiet place with only selected witnesses. Still the slender blades flashed and the ornate hilts clashed as the two duelists became locked, grappling together before one or the other leapt free. Sweat was pouring into their eyes, their shirts clung soaked and bloodied to their bodies. Antonio had lost his *bow solitaire* and his shoulder-length hair swirled about his face.

Inevitably they began to tire and the wounds that each had inflicted on the other were taking a toll. From the start they had been so evenly matched that wagers were still being placed among the crowd as to which would be the winner. Some women screamed when Filippo's blade went right through Antonio's left shoulder. Then it was withdrawn and Antonio staggered, seeing his opponent preparing to lunge for his throat. He parried the thrust and, summoning his strength, plunged his own blade into Filippo's ribs. Blood spurted and as Antonio reeled back he saw Filippo fold and fall sprawling at his feet.

Antonio stood swaying where he stood, too exhausted for the moment to move. The doctor rushed to the fallen man. Then, out of the corner of his eye, Antonio saw the glint of a stiletto and realized that one of the Celanos intended there to be no survivor of this duel. Knowing that his life depended on escape, he ignored the shouts of his seconds wanting to attend to him and pushed his way through the crowd. Women cried out and men protested as he thrust his way through, soiling their garments with his blood as he went. Then the crowd closed against his pursuers, determined to have no more bloodshed. He would never have believed he still had the power to run, but although he staggered sometimes it was not long before he came to a side canal where he saw the lantern of an approaching gondola. He hailed it and almost tumbled aboard.

Marietta was fast asleep when there came a tapping at her door. Dragging herself to wakefulness, she saw her personal maid with a candle beside her bed.

"What is it, Anna?" she asked, pushing back the fall of her hair, but before the maid could answer Marietta happened to glance in the direction of the open door. Instantly she sat up with a piercing scream at the sight of the blood-stained figure of Antonio. For a moment she had thought it was Domenico in the shadowed doorway.

"Merciful heaven! What has happened to you, Antonio?" She pressed a hand to her chest. Her heart was thumping and she was trembling with shock. Yet she threw back the bedclothes and put her feet shakily to the floor. He had stepped forward and presented a still more gruesome sight at close quarters, with blood running down his face from a cut across his brow.

"I didn't mean to alarm you. I suppose I look worse than I realized, but my wounds are not as bad as they probably appear. My left shoulder is the worst. I can't use that arm."

"You've been dueling!" she accused, thrusting her feet into satin slippers. Anna was holding a robe for her and she stood to slip her arms into it. "With whom?"

"I have killed Filippo Celano."

She fought against this second shock. Already ashen, she was unaware that her lips had become quite colorless. "You shall tell me what happened while I dress your wounds. Anna will fetch clean linen and warm water and anything else I may need."

Anna eyed her anxiously. "Are you sure you are all right, signora?"

She nodded, getting a firm grip on herself. "Yes, Anna. Make haste."

"Wait!" He checked the maid. "I'll need a boat too. Let the footman on night duty see to that." Then, as Anna went hurrying off, he explained the reason to Marietta. "I have to get away from Venice immediately. The Celanos will be out to kill me. That's why I didn't dare go back to my own home."

She led him, dripping blood, to the marble room with the bath. "What else do you need?" she asked practically as she tore off his sodden shirt to examine his wounds and stem the blood temporarily with towels until Anna returned.

"Clothes. Money. A *bauta* mask."

Anna assisted Marietta as she dressed his wounds, putting a wad on the back and front of his shoulder and binding him up. The cut on his brow was less serious and there were minor nicks and scratches that presented no difficulty. "You will have to go to a doctor at the first opportunity," she advised, "because I have only done the best I could."

She found him the clothes he needed and packed some extra garments and a razor in a saddle-bag. While this was being done, Anna carried out her instructions to summon two strong footmen, who occasionally acted as armed escorts. A third came to help Antonio dress. When he reappeared in Marietta's bedchamber he was resting a hand for support on the footman's shoulder. His weakness now was such that he could no longer walk un-aided. His shoulder wound prevented him from wearing a coat and under his cloak his left arm was in a sling.

"I shall always be in your debt, Marietta," he said, his lips thin with pain. He was more grave than she had ever seen him before, but then there was no greater punishment for any Venetian than banishment from Venice, whether it was self-imposed or ordered by the state. "I owe my life to you." He kissed her on both cheeks and smiled with some show of his old humor. "Make sure you produce a strong nephew for me. I only hope the boy won't be full grown before I see him. I bid you farewell, sister-in-law."

"Take care!" she urged.

He nodded and was thankful that his two traveling companions were waiting to make him a bandy-chair and carry him down to the boat.

As soon as he was gone she sank down into a chair, enervated by shock and all she had done in the past hour. She felt nauseous and ill. Anna came to help her back into bed, and it was with profound relief that she lay back on her pillows. There was no need to warn Anna, or anyone else in the household, that no word should be said about Antonio's visit. There was not one Torrisi servant who would aid a Celano in tracing him.

When Marietta heard the next day that Filippo had not been killed outright, but was still hovering between life and death, it was no comfort to her as far as Antonio was concerned. A duel needed a fatal wound for one of the opponents if honor was to be truly satisfied, and if Filippo survived, the matter would continue to fester like a sore awaiting the surgeon's knife. She had sent a special messenger with word to Domenico, but if he had already left St. Petersburg her letter might miss him along the way.

She told no one of how ill she felt for days after the shock of that terrible night, not even Adrianna, who came regularly to visit her and often brought the children. The duel was three weeks in the past when she and Adrianna sat drinking coffee together while the children played with the toys that Marietta kept for them. Adrianna's eldest son particularly liked the little fleet of Venetian ships that Domenico and his brothers had played with as boys.

"Every day that goes by without news of Antonio is good," Marietta said. "It means that the Celanos haven't been successful in finding him yet, although we can't be certain that he has escaped until they return to Venice."

"Filippo continues to hold his own, I hear," Adrianna commented. "At least when Elena returns, which should be any day now, she will be spared her husband's attentions and his vicious attacks for some while to come. I was told yesterday that he is unlikely to walk again."

Marietta shook her head. "There are so many tales, it's impossible to know which are right."

Occasionally there were disturbing rumors that Antonio had been caught and was being dragged back to Venice; others claimed that he had been killed in a duel with Alvise. But when the two Celano brothers returned, shaking their heads at having lost their prey, those fears were dispersed. Marietta wished that Domenico could have been at home to share her relief, but he was still far away. Her time was drawing near, with only a few more days to wait. She passed two or three hours every day at the harpsichord, playing some of her favorite music, and had just played the last

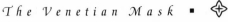

note of a piece one afternoon when Domenico's clerk came to her with a file in his hand.

"Your pardon, signora. I don't know if you wish to keep this file. I've been sorting out papers no longer wanted in Signor Torrisi's office and this came to light with your name on it."

She smiled, thinking that Domenico had planned a little surprise for her. "Put it on the table. I will go through it there."

He did as she wished. Once on her own, she drew up a chair to the leather file with *Signora Torrisi* stamped in gilt on the cover. She unfastened it, opening the clasp and expecting to find a letter from Domenico. Puzzled, she found there were many sheets, and the writing was in a hand she did not recognize. The first appeared to be a report on herself, and her smile faded as she saw that the date on the top sheet went back five years to the Carnival time of 1780 when she and Alix had first fallen in love.

She began to read and found it was an accurate account, not only of her early years but also of how she had come to Venice, her progress at the Pietà, and then her meetings with Alix. There were more reports, each presented at a different time. As she read on, it gradually dawned on her that she had been spied on when she was with Alix. Finally she came to Angela's letter. The words of advice to Domenico, that he should marry the Pietà girl if ever he became a widower, leapt out at her before she could slam the file shut. She pounded her palm on the smooth leather surface and pressed on it with force, as if she feared it might spring open again of its own accord.

Resting her elbow on the table, she held her brow in her hand; her thoughts were in agonized turmoil. Domenico had married her only as an obligation to his late wife's memory. She felt torn apart by the discovery that she had been watched by a spy even when she sat weeping after Alix had been dragged away from her. It was not enough that she had to live with the knowledge that her predecessor was still uppermost in Domenico's mind, but now Angela had reached from the grave to take away the intense joy she had been cherishing in the belief that Domenico was returning her love in full at last. How glad she was now of the distance between them! Anger began to surge up from her hurt and anguish.

She snatched up the file and paced back and forth with it clutched to her breast. The clerk could not have read the contents or he would not have brought it to her, but she would not have it destroyed. One day she would demand an explanation!

She summoned the clerk. "Return this file to wherever it was kept," she said.

"Certainly, signora." He bowed and took it away.

The whole incident had left her furious and restless. She continued pacing about the room, scarcely knowing where she was, possessed by an inexplicable surge of frenzied energy that she could not subdue. Suddenly she had to get away from the palace and everything in it, but there was something she had to do first. She sent for the steward.

"Collect up everything about the palace that belonged personally to the late Signora Torrisi. Pack it all carefully and put it in one of the attics."

"There are a few of her books on the shelves in the Signor's office." He was reminding her that nothing in that office was ever to be touched by the other servants and that he himself supervised the dusting and cleaning.

"You may leave those."

When Marietta had put on her cape she left the palace by way of the gates that led into a *calle*. She walked all the way to Adrianna's house, exulting fiercely in the exercise. A backache, which had been niggling since morning, had become more noticeable, but she blamed that on the lengthy walk. A maidservant answered her knock.

"Signora Savoni is next door," the girl said.

Recently Leonardo had bought the adjoining property as an additional mask-shop with a workshop at the back and accommodation above for a manager. So far the alterations had not been started, but Adrianna had seized on the chance to furnish the upper floor as accommodation for Leonardo's kinfolk when they came to visit. Marietta thanked the servant and went to knock on the door. A window flew open above and Adrianna, her expression anxious, looked out. Her relief was obvious when she saw Marietta.

"Thank heavens it's you! I'll come down and let you in."

She disappeared and in a few moments Marietta heard a bolt being drawn and a key turning in the lock. As Adrianna opened the door Marietta stepped inside with a little laugh.

"Why such security? Have you moved valuables into this place?"

Adrianna gave no answering smile, but twisted her hands together. "Elena is here. She's in labor! The father is Nicolò Contarini. He was even with her in Venice before she left. I'm so thankful you've come. She is very frightened."

Marietta, who had been momentarily stunned by what had been said, moved swiftly to the stairs. "I'll go to her!" Halfway up she felt a stab of decisive pain that made her realize there had been more to her backache than she had supposed. Her own baby was making a move, but there was no time to think of that at this moment. "Where is Sister Giaccomina?"

"She arrived with Elena late last night," Adrianna said as she followed. "Only Leonardo knows they are back, and he helped me move them in here after we had given them supper. He doesn't approve but he will hold his tongue for my sake. Sister Giaccomina has also committed herself to keeping silent about this birth, because she understands what Elena's future would be with Filippo Celano if ever he learned the truth. But she is alarmed and extremely nervous that I'm going to deliver Elena's baby myself. I would never have asked you to come, but could you help me at the bedside?"

Marietta paused to look at her friend. She knew that Adrianna had assisted midwives when friends and neighbors had given birth, but that she had never delivered a baby on her own before. "Aren't you calling in any professional help?"

"That's impossible. Elena is too well known in Venice for her identity to be kept a secret. But maybe I shouldn't have asked for your assistance when you're so near your own time. The nun will have to help me."

"No. I'll be with you. Sister Giaccomina can boil the water and see to anything else we might need."

The nun had heard Marietta's voice and came hastening from the salon to embrace her on the landing with arms that had grown plumper during the Paris sojourn. "Such trouble, Marietta! I didn't suspect! Who would have thought? A nice young man, but he should never have—! Neither should Elena. All my fault for not realizing—"

Marietta led her gently back to where she had been sitting. "Don't upset yourself. It happened through two people loving each other more than was wise. Now it is up to us to do our best for Elena and her baby. You have already promised silence and that is a merciful gift in itself."

The nun's face was full of compassion. "How could I do otherwise for one of my Pietà girls? Did not our Lord show mercy to the woman taken in adultery? And Elena will sin no more. She has written to tell Nicolò that what was between them is at an end."

Marietta knew that such a decision must have been heartbreaking for Elena, even though sooner or later it would have had to be made. As she entered the bedchamber Elena uttered a cry of welcome.

"You're here! Adrianna said we couldn't send for you as you're expecting a baby soon too!"

"I'm glad I came." Marietta was concerned by Elena's appearance. The journey must have been hard on her. As Marietta sat down on the edge of the bed Elena clutched her hand in a rush of pain that made beads of sweat start on her brow. Adrianna wiped them away with a soft cloth scented with rosewater.

"Don't be afraid of shrieking out," she advised. "Nobody except the three of us in this house will hear you. The walls are thick and this room backs onto an empty warehouse. Make all the noise you want. We don't mind. Marietta is going to help me with the birth. I'll leave you on your own with her for a while."

As she went, Elena managed a little smile. "Adrianna took me in as if she were my mother. She's been so good to me. I knew she would never turn me away." Then her eyes grew wide. "But I'm so afraid! Not for myself but for my baby. I wrote you a letter last night in case I should die in childbirth, because you are the only one to whom I can turn. Adrianna would take the baby if she could, but Leonardo would never allow it. He thinks I'm wanton as it is." There was a pause as the pain started again. "I love Nicolò as he loves me. If my marriage could have been annulled we would have married instantly. As it is, he is as trapped by obligations and responsibilities in Florence as I am by being Filippo's chattel."

"Leaving aside the fact that you are going to come through this birth and so is your baby, tell me what you wrote. Will Nicolò be taking the child? Is giving the infant to him what you want me to do for you?"

"He doesn't know about the baby. I managed to keep my pregnancy from him. If I should have a girl, I want you to place her at the Pietà. I shall arrange to act as her godmother, which will give me more access to her as we have to Bianca. When she is grown I will be able to tell her the truth." Another wave of agony took possession of her and this time she shrieked at the force of it. Marietta wiped her face with the rosewater.

"And if you have a boy?" Marietta asked when Elena's pain had subsided again. "Surely then he should be with his father?"

Elena spoke emotionally. "Nicolò shall have his son. I couldn't deny a boy all the advantages he would have growing up with a good father."

"I will do whatever you wish."

All the time Marietta sat at the bedside her own pains grew stronger, but she was determined to hide them as long as she could. As soon as Elena gave birth, she would return home. It would not be easy getting into a gondola, but somehow she would have to manage it.

In the end, Sister Giaccomina had to help, for shortly before the birth Marietta's own waters broke and she was pierced through by knife-like pains that caused her to collapse. Adrianna left Elena briefly to half-carry Marietta through to the neighboring bedchamber. After getting her out of her clothes and into one of Elena's spare nightshifts, she saw Marietta into bed and hurried back to Elena.

For Marietta there was only torture. Sister Giaccomina did what she could, and Marietta was unaware that her own screams echoed those of Elena. Time ceased to exist for Adrianna, who was fighting to save one woman's baby while fearing for the other. Elena's daughter was born only minutes before Marietta, who had been left temporarily alone, gave birth to a stillborn son. Even as Adrianna ran to her across the landing, Marietta was trying to reach for the flawlessly formed infant.

Twice in the night Elena woke to the sound of her friend's harrowing cries. Leonardo had informed the Torrisi servants that their mistress was a guest of himself and his wife, but gave no reason. Marietta would not want to face the well-meaning sympathy calls from friends and acquaintances as soon as she returned home. Elena wanted to go to her, but Adrianna had forbidden either of them to move from their beds.

At dawn Elena lay suckling her daughter, whom she had named Elizabetta after her own mother, stroking the dark down on the baby's head with a loving caress. Adrianna, who with Sister Giaccomina had been watching over the two friends all night, looked tired and in need of rest.

"How is Marietta now?" Elena asked.

"She is inconsolable," Adrianna said sadly. "Had she not seen the baby it would have been easier. I fear for her. I've seen women develop melancholia after losing a baby at birth."

"Is she sleeping at all?"

"She dozed for a little while in the night. For the rest of the time she either sobbed or lay silent as she is now, looking up at the ceiling with tears running from the corner of her eyes."

"How soon can I go to her?"

"Wait a while longer." Adrianna paused. "Don't take Elizabetta with you. It could rub salt into the wound."

Elena did not answer, but had made her decision during the night hours. When Adrianna went downstairs to join Sister Giaccomina, who was preparing breakfast, Elena kissed her baby devotedly.

"I had hoped to keep you with me a little longer," she whispered, "but you will be loved and cared for."

Leaving the bed, she went on bare feet into the next room. Marietta stirred and looked yearningly toward the baby in Elena's arms.

"You've brought Elizabetta to see me. I asked about her and heard she is a fine baby."

"I've done more than bring her," Elena said upon reaching the bedside. "I'm giving her to you."

She placed her daughter in Marietta's arms. As if Elizabetta sensed that some vast change had been made in her destiny, she opened her eyes and seemed to turn her unfocused blue gaze on her foster mother. Marietta's face became Madonna-like with tenderness and love as she gazed down at this priceless gift she had received. All that her own child had left hollow and bereft in her seemed to flood with warmth. It was as if his spirit had returned to settle in her heart and give her peace, enabling her always to love him as she had done in those few brief seconds before Adrianna had covered her eyes and forced her to lie down again. She was having difficulty adjusting her thoughts. "But you said she should go to the Pietà," she said falteringly.

"With you Elizabetta will have much more."

This was a matter between the two of them, and as yet neither one had given a thought to Domenico. When Adrianna came back upstairs with a breakfast tray she paused on the threshold of the room, dismayed to see that Marietta had the infant at her breast and Elena sat watching, both with the same look of devotion directed at Elizabetta. No explanation was needed. Distraught, Adrianna went to the foot of the bed.

"What have you done?" she cried to Elena. Then to Marietta, "What of your husband? He will never accept a child with Celano blood in her veins."

Marietta's expression changed to one of defiance as she gathered the baby closer in a protective attitude. "Domenico shall have a son in time to come, but I will have this child to love and care for as Elena would have done. Since he has kept secrets from me, so will I hold this secret from him!"

It seemed to Adrianna that giving birth had left neither of these two young women quite sane. Marietta was preparing to undertake a great deceit and Elena was condemning herself to heartache for years to come. At least if Elizabetta had been placed in the Pietà, Elena would have been able to visit her frequently. Yet it was impossible not to see that the solution they had chosen was the best for the child herself.

After five days Marietta went home with Elizabetta, escorted by Leonardo. During those days she and Elena had cared for the infant together. They had arranged for future meetings at Adrianna's, when Marietta would bring the child. As yet they did not look to the time when Elizabetta would be old enough to talk about these visits, deciding to meet that hurdle when they came to it. Elena showed courage when she kissed her daughter for the last time, yet no sooner was the door closed after Marietta and the baby than suddenly Elena fainted. There followed many heartrending scenes when she would rock in distress with her arms thrown over her head. She dared not return home until her milk had dried up, but at last the time came when she had to prepare to leave for the Palazzo Celano. This required even more deceit and considerable planning, for she and Sister Giaccomina had returned to Venice by sea. Leonardo organized the release of their baggage from the custom house and saw to its delivery to coincide with Elena's home-coming, as well as with the arrival that day of a ship from France. She did not let Sister Giaccomina accompany her to the palace, for fear that Filippo might question her. But as it turned out, Elena's arrival itself caused quite a stir. Servants came running to bow or bob. "Where is the Signor?" she asked.

"In the library, signora."

As she entered the large book-lined room she saw Filippo in a chair by one of the windows, a gold-topped cane propped within reach, his feet resting on a footstool.

"How are you, Filippo?"

He looked up with a jerk of surprise, and it was all she could do not to gasp at his disfigurement. Adrianna had warned her that it was said he had suffered facial injuries, but she had not been prepared for the deep rapier scar down the whole left side of his face.

"So you're back! It's about time. You've put on weight and it suits you. Don't be alarmed by this." He indicated his scar. "I fought a duel with Antonio Torrisi and neither of us was the victor. Why are you standing so far away? Does my appearance frighten you?"

"No." She believed that in spite of his terrible scar many women would still find him attractive, for with the other side of his face unflawed he had the look of a returned warrior. She went forward to give him the kiss he expected, inwardly repelled by having to suffer his lips on hers again. When she leaned down to him he clamped her head in his hands and burrowed into her mouth as if he might swallow half her face. When he released her he would have caught her about the waist, but he winced, going white about the lips, and rested a hand gingerly on his side.

"That damnable duel. If only I had killed the Torrisi it would have been worth what I've had to endure. The doctors say I'll mend with time, but I have to be patient. That was never my strong point. But I've passed a deal of my time working out how to settle the score with Domenico Torrisi in his brother's absence. He shall pay! In full!"

"What have you planned?"

"That's not for you to worry about, and nothing is decided yet. It will take time. You have other matters to concern you on a lighter plane. Now you are home we can entertain again. I haven't felt well enough before. You can sing and play for me too. Everything will be more agreeable with you back in the palace."

"Is your mother here?"

"Not at the present time. She came at once to nurse me after the duel and fought for my life." He grinned cynically. "Odd, isn't it? Considering that she never liked me or any of my siblings except Marco. I suppose she felt the House of Celano would go to pieces if drunken Vitale, or extravagant Alvise, or even Maurizio with his brains and weak heart, had to succeed me. As for Pietro at the monastery, he would be last on her list. Incidentally he has been here. You've missed seeing him."

She was surprised, recalling that Pietro had purposely not been notified of Marco's death until after the funeral.

"Why was he in Venice?"

"When it seemed I was going to die, Maurizio sent to the monastery as a last resort and Pietro came. He saved the sight of my eye. So between the efforts of my mother and Pietro I survived."

"Has the Signora softened toward him as a result?"

"Not she! He committed the crime in her eyes of arriving when she thought her days of childbearing were over. My mother never forgives. You should know that by now."

"Is Lavinia well?"

"She's well enough, but I daresay she is fit to drop. My mother suffered a slight seizure when she went home after nursing me, which has made her a semi-invalid for the time being. Lavinia is more at her beck and call than ever."

Filippo's elbow was resting on the arm of his chair, and he raised his hand to receive hers. She placed it into his clasp with inward reluctance. He fondled it, rubbing her palm with his thumb. "I'll not be able to husband you as I would wish until I'm free of the pain in my ribs, but you will be able to pleasure me in the ways I have taught you."

She felt no shame in wishing that Antonio Torrisi's rapier had pierced his heart.

———

When Elizabetta was eight weeks old, Domenico returned. Marietta had gone to a Pietà concert with friends and found him waiting for her when she returned. Her heart leapt at the sight of him, leaner from his travels and more handsome for it, but his first joyful words reminded her of the true situation and checked her from running to him.

"So I have a beautiful daughter, Marietta!"

As he swept her into his arms and kissed her she could almost have forgiven him for having deceived her. But the fact that she had equalized matters gave her no satisfaction.

He had never been more tender and loving than he was that night. Noticing a slight change in her manner, he mistook the reason, assuring her that he was not in the least disappointed to have such a daughter.

"If we should be destined to have only daughters," he said generously, "instead of a son to inherit, Elizabetta shall have everything and be head of the House of Torrisi even if I have to fight for a change in the law to accomplish it."

"No!" Alarmed that he should even consider such a move, she pressed her fingertips against his smiling mouth. "That must never be! Don't think of it again. We shall have sons. Sooner or later there will be a male Torrisi heir!"

"There's no need to get upset, my love." He had become very serious, pondering her agitation. "I only wished to relieve your mind."

She stayed awake long after he fell asleep with his arm still around her. Even if she had wished to tell him the truth, it was impossible, for she was bound to silence forever by Elena's trust. At all costs she must have a son, and soon. To let Elizabetta—of Celano descent, however removed—inherit all that Domenico upheld would be the ultimate betrayal.

Elizabetta was christened at the Santa Maria della Pietà. Adrianna and Sister Giaccomina were a natural choice of godmothers, but the nun thought otherwise about herself.

"It's not that I wouldn't gladly accept the duty," she explained to Marietta, "but in this case, who could be more suitable than Bianca? She has always been so fond of you and Elena, and both of you have always been extremely good to her. Although she is only ten she has a strong sense of responsibility toward the little children, as you know, and a kind, sweet nature. She would never harm anybody or anything. I think she deserves the honor."

Marietta welcomed the suggestion and the nun's unselfishness. Domenico was in agreement. He liked the child, who had come to visit them with the nuns several times since his marriage to Marietta.

Bianca's reaction was one of total delight. "Yes, please! How wonderful! May I hold Elizabetta during the christening?"

Marietta, who had made a special visit to the Pietà to see her, nodded smilingly. "I'm sure Adrianna will agree to that."

As at Marietta's wedding, Elena watched from behind a grille as her daughter was christened. She was pleased that Bianca was a godmother and holding Elizabetta in her arms. It was the first time Elena had seen her daughter since giving her away. In spite of the plans they had made, Elena realized after the initial parting that her agony would be renewed each time she had to see her child leave. Yet she could not have missed this special occasion in her daughter's life, whatever the cost in anguish afterward.

She was glad to discuss the christening at her next meeting with Marietta, who always gave her an eagerly awaited report on the child's progress and well-being. It pleased her that Elizabetta bore a likeness to her across the eyes, even though they were not the same violet-blue. Providentially a coppery tint was beginning to show in Elizabetta's hair, which echoed Marietta's. It was only when Marietta was with Elena that she remembered the child she loved was not of her own flesh.

To Domenico and Marietta's great relief Antonio eventually wrote to say he had settled in Geneva. Not only was it an independent state, but he had friends there, a family to whom he had once extended hospitality when they were unable to find accommodation in Venice during Carnival. He had been attracted to the daughter, Jeanne, but was forbidden by Venetian law to marry. Now that the rules of La Serenissima no longer applied to him, he and Jeanne were about to be married and he would be entering his father-in-law's banking business.

"What a letter of good news!" Marietta exclaimed when she had read it.

Then, knowing what it would mean to Domenico to have all his brothers so far away, she went to put an arm about his shoulders. "You know, we could visit him one day."

"I was thinking that. I might even extend my journey next time I'm given a mission in that direction." Domenico was frowning over the letter, which he had taken from her. Geneva was not too far away for Filippo to send hired assassins if he should ever discover Antonio's whereabouts. He could not be trusted to keep to the traditional courtesies observed by his predecessors.

Although Domenico said nothing to Marietta he was constantly watchful as far as Filippo was concerned. With Antonio out of reach and the score of the duel unsettled, it was inevitable that sooner or later he himself would be the target of a vengeful attack.

Elena also kept from Marietta the fact that she had been alerted at her homecoming to a possible plot against Domenico. She had never been admitted to any of the conferences Filippo had with his family or business colleagues, but she began to take note of all who came to the palace and she eavesdropped without the least compunction whenever he was closeted in discussion behind closed doors. Often she caught only a snatch of what was being said, but she wrote everything down with the date and time she had heard it. Her hope was that one day her notes might allow her to pass advance warnings through Marietta to Domenico.

Although she had never met Domenico, his safety had become vitally important to her on two counts, for he was both the man who Marietta loved and the foster father of her own daughter.

During this time Filippo had fully recovered his health and strength. His exasperation at Elena's continuing failure to become pregnant was fueled by a visit from his mother. She was not the woman she had been, but although she had grown frail in appearance, her tongue had not lost its viperish edge and her eyes still flashed spite.

"Elena is never going to bear children," she snapped at Filippo when they were on their own. "Free yourself and marry again."

He lowered his head and studied her warily under his lids. "What are you suggesting?"

"Use your wits! Your ancestors weren't averse to ridding themselves of a barren wife or anyone else who stood in their way. What's the matter with you? You couldn't even kill that Torrisi when you had the chance."

His outrage caused him to quiver with anger. Her derision was her own undoing. "We have come to a parting of the ways, Mother!" he declared savagely, springing from his chair. "This time when you leave you shall never return!"

He went striding away from her as she screeched after him. "Fool! You'll bring the House of Celano down about your ears!" Shakily she grabbed her cane to try to follow him. She bitterly regretted not poisoning Elena when she had had the strength and the opportunity, which would have prevented this final confrontation. "The Torrisis will prevail!"

In the corridor he met Lavinia. "Take that old hag back to her abode and never bring her here again!"

He did not turn even when he heard Lavinia cry out upon reaching the door of the salon that their mother was lying on the floor. When he was informed that the Signora had suffered another seizure he simply asked if she was still alive. Upon being told that she was, he did not retract his instructions to his sister. The Signora was borne away from the Palazzo Celano for the last time, her speech slurred and the whole of her left side paralyzed, but her eyes were as vindictive as ever as she lay on the soft pillows her son's wife had placed under her head in the gondola. Elena, returning to the palace, shivered and rubbed her arms. Curiously, the gleam in the Signora's eyes had been one of malevolent triumph.

Marietta was distressed by the invisible barrier that had arisen between her and Domenico since his return. She knew he had become aware of it, and several times he had asked her what was wrong, but she still could not speak out as she would have wished.

In his own mind Domenico believed that the change in Marietta had come about through childbirth, unlikely though that seemed. She was as loving and passionate as before, but now, he knew, she had withdrawn from him. Maybe something had happened in Adrianna's house that would never have occurred if Marietta had been at home with proper medical care. When he had thanked Adrianna for all she had done, the woman looked embarrassed and shook her head that he should thank her. What had gone wrong that he did not know about? Whatever it was, he had a right to be told. The next time Adrianna came to the house he would question her alone. She was an honest, sensible woman and should answer him as Marietta had failed to do.

His chance came on Adrianna's next visit. Marietta, carrying Elizabetta and holding the hand of Adrianna's youngest, went into another salon where she kept a bowl of sweetmeats. The other three children followed, and he was left alone with Adrianna. Experience in cross-questioning enabled him to catch her off guard with a direct and unexpected query.

"What exactly happened when Elizabetta was born?"

Her hands jerked involuntarily and a flush rose up from her neck to her cheeks. "As I told you before, there was a point when a doctor, had we been able to contact one, would probably have used forceps, but then all went well."

There was no mistaking the ring of truth in her voice or the directness of her eyes, even though that flush had looked remarkably like a guilty one. "Did Marietta come close to death? Please tell me."

"Not at all. Surely Marietta has told you that?"

He nodded. "She reassured me, but then she knows what it would mean to me to lose her."

"Have no fear on that score, Domenico."

He had to be content with what she said, for Marietta and the children could already be heard returning. Yet doubt persisted. There was something wrong, and until it was cleared up his relationship with Marietta could not be restored to what it was in those minutes before his departure for St. Petersburg. Leaving her then had been harder than he could ever have believed possible.

Gradually Marietta came to realize that in the imminence of childbirth and its tragic aftermath she had allowed her anger over the file to soar out of all proportion. She could see that Domenico was worried about her and she finally decided that must end. When they were next at the villa, which was always a place where she felt at peace, she found herself able to speak to him at last about Angela and the file. They were sitting side by side on the terrace, and he held her hand as he answered her honestly, explaining how it had all come about.

"Angela was always intrigued by any romantic situation," he said gently, "and after seeing you and the Frenchman at the ridotto she became extremely curious as to how a Pietà girl had managed to slip out of the *ospedale* on her own. That was why she wanted you watched. Never for one moment did she wish you ill. On the contrary, when she learned that the young man had left Venice she became very anxious, fearing you were deeply distressed. So now you know the whole truth. As for the letter she left me," he said in conclusion, "she wished only good for you and for me. Never suppose she would have wanted her memory to come between us even through her portraits, which is why I had them removed to my office."

"You did that for me?"

"Did you suppose otherwise? My grief had healed before I married you, even as I hoped the past had become a private memory for you too."

"It had," she said frankly, relieved and reassured by his openness. "If you wish, the portraits of Angela could be restored to their original places."

"That would have pleased her, but I leave the decision entirely to you."

She wished she could have told him the truth about Elizabetta, but that was a secret she would have to keep until her life's end. Her consolation was that he loved Elizabetta as if she were his own child.

It was for him that Elizabetta took her first steps some months later. Domenico's excited shout brought Marietta running to the scene. Laughing and happy together, they praised the child's achievement. Obligingly Elizabetta managed to toddle another two paces under the gaze of Angela's portrait, which had been restored to its place on the wall.

Elena had collected quite a dossier of overheard scraps of conversation when she warned Marietta that a plot was being hatched against Domenico.

"I don't know what is in the wind, but Maurizio has been here more often in the past three weeks than he has previously in many months. It must be something important to drag him away from his home. Maybe the others need him because he has the brains of the family. I haven't a single definite clue to offer, but I know when I catch the name Torrisi it can only be Domenico they are talking about."

"Unless Antonio's whereabouts have been discovered. But he is on guard in any case. Domenico knows from his letters that he is well aware of the danger."

"But could you find some way of telling Domenico to be more alert than ever?"

"I will," Marietta promised, "as soon as he returns. He's away again on one of his short trips."

"If ever I have something truly important to pass on I would address the whole file to him and leave it at the Pietà, marking it urgent. Then I could be sure of its reaching him without your being implicated."

Marietta decided to use Elena's warning as a means to draw still closer to Domenico. She chose a time when they were having a quiet supper together at the table under the sky-blue taffeta silk drapery of the baldachin where she had first dined with him. They had eaten a pretty green salad topped with *tartufo bianchi* and he was about to serve her with thin green pasta in a rich sauce. He liked to dine and talk alone with her after one of his absences.

The footman having been dismissed, she was able to speak freely. "On the way to the opera that evening before we were married," she said, "you spoke of your work for reform and of your many enemies. How can you be sure Filippo isn't plotting some vengeance by that route?"

"Why should you think of that now?"

"It isn't just at this minute," she said, her anxiety causing her to speak more sharply than she had intended. "I've often thought about your work. If I can be of help with it, do allow me. I might even be an extra ear to listen for danger."

"Perhaps you have been already just by suggesting I might watch in other directions for the Celano's next move, but I think that is unlikely. There's nothing subtle about Filippo. He thinks fastest when he has a rapier and a stiletto in his hands."

"But Maurizio is so often at the Palazzo Celano these days! He is the clever one of the family and could devise a cunning plan."

Domenico narrowed his eyes at her. "How would you know about those visits?" he asked, his voice dangerously soft. The food on their plates remained untouched and steaming gently.

She kept her head. "I've heard," she replied evenly, "in women's talk. There is always gossip. Rumors fly."

"I would say the source of such information could only be the young Signora Celano. Am I right?"

She stared at him defiantly. "You are!"

He leaned forward and smashed his fist down on the table with such force that everything on it jumped and rattled, a wine glass tipping to pour its contents into a crimson pool. His eyes were blazing. "You profess concern for me and yet you confer with my enemies!"

"Elena bears you no malice!" she cried back. "She has only good will toward us both!"

He was out of his chair instantly and came to seize her by the shoulders and hoist her swiftly to her feet. "Where do you meet her? At the Pietà? At Adrianna's? A coffeehouse?"

She almost screamed at him. "I'm not telling you! Find out! You have spies everywhere. Let them tell you!"

"All I asked of you when we married was that you end your friendship with Elena, because it was dangerous to me and to my house!"

"If I remember correctly," she countered caustically, "you ordered me. It was not a request."

"Then if needs must, I ask you now not to see her again."

"I will! You can't stop me!"

"Yes, I can." He released her and stepped back, breathing heavily. "I have only to inform Filippo that our wives are meeting and he will take sterner measures than I'm prepared to take with you."

"No! You don't understand!" she cried. As he turned away she threw herself at his feet in a tumble of carnation satin and lace, holding him about the leg with her arms so that he dragged her a step before he stopped. "He ill-treats her already. Her life is a misery. He might kill her in his rage!"

He looked down at her sobbing at his feet and his anger faded. Stooping, he raised her up and she leaned against him, her face buried in his shoulder while he stroked her hair. "Don't weep, my darling. I won't give the young Signora away. I have heard that Filippo has a brutal way with women. But you must realize that Celano name taints everything for me, even your friend, however well-meaning you believe her to be."

She thought of the child he loved, who was sleeping upstairs in her cradle. "You don't know what you are saying," she exclaimed desolately, her voice muffled against his silver damask coat.

"Indeed I do."

"But Elena wants to protect you." She raised her tear-wet face. "She is keeping a file of everything she can find out that might be of use in saving your life."

He looked disbelieving. "Why should she switch her loyalties?"

"She has none to the present Celanos. It was Marco whom she wanted to marry, never Filippo."

"Then it's possible that whatever she felt for Marco still binds her to his family. I don't doubt her good will toward you, but I find it impossible to believe she has any toward me."

"Is there nothing I can say to convince you?" she appealed.

He stroked the back of his fingers down the side of her face and under her chin, which he tilted as he kissed her lightly on the lips. "Nothing, Marietta." Looking into his implacable face, she knew she would willingly die to prevent his ever knowing the truth of Elizabetta's birth.

Chapter 12

The death of the Doge plunged Venice into an elaborate display of mourning and a funeral so spectacular that vast crowds, including hundreds of foreigners, gathered to witness it. It was as if the whole city were draped in black velvets and brocades. Then, almost instantly, everybody began preparing for the coronation of the new Doge. The city seemed to light up again in the glitter and gleam of rich tapestries thrown over balconies, many in cloth of gold. New masks were bought for the celebrations, sumptuous clothes ordered, and palatial salons made ready for banquets and balls.

Marietta had enough of her father's Venetian blood in her veins to be swept along by the excitement of the festivities and she marveled at the splendor of the procession when the new Doge arrived formally on the Bucintoro while bells rang and choirs sang. She had met him previously on social occasions, for he was of the Manin family, long acquainted with the Torrisis, and in government Domenico had had much to do with him. Yet she knew that his appointment did not meet with her husband's approval.

"Maybe as Doge this man will do better than you suppose," she said to Domenico after the coronation.

He shook his head grimly. "Lodovico Manin is too malleable for such a responsible position. Pleasant, but weak. Venice needs a doge far different at this time."

She thought to herself that if Domenico, as a senator, could become the Doge's adviser, he might lead him in the proper direction.

Marietta still met Elena from time to time and made no pretense to Domenico about it. She had promised him she would never mention where he was or who he saw or what his next travel arrangements might be. He was still opposed to these meetings but resigned himself to them, trusting in Marietta's good sense and her ability to keep her word. Yet she knew that by not deserting Elena she had lost whatever chance she might have had of gaining his complete confidence and knowing what he was about.

Elizabetta continued to thrive. She was a happy child, full of laughter, her hair grown into pale copper curls. By the time she was two she had begun talking well and whenever Domenico was in the palace she would trot after him, sometimes laboriously climbing one of the great staircases when she heard his voice on an upper floor. She was the only one allowed in his office when he was working. Her tantrums were saved for her nurse and Marietta, neither of whom spoiled her as he did. She was showing signs of becoming vain, for one of his games with her was to hold her up to a mirror and she had become enchanted with her own reflection. But he could see no fault in her. On her third birthday at the villa she received a pony.

Domenico had never returned from a journey, whether long or short, without bringing Marietta a gift, and now there was always one for Elizabetta as well. From St. Petersburg he had brought Marietta a golden casket, enameled and bejeweled, in which she had found, lying on a bed of crimson velvet, a parure of emeralds and diamonds made by the Empress's own jeweler. This superb set of jewels was his birthgift to her, but since she felt that she had acquired it under false pretenses, no matter how dear Elizabetta might be to him, she never wore it unless he prompted her.

"Don't you care for it?" he had asked her once.

"Of course I do. It's magnificent," she had declared. If he had caught the brittleness in her voice he made no sign. To ease his mind she had worn it to the opera that night, but afterward it had lain untouched in its casket for weeks.

It was at the opera that Marietta and Domenico came face to face with Elena and several of her friends as they passed on the main staircase. Normally this would never have happened, but Elena had discovered she had dropped her fan and two of the men in her party were descending the flight again to look for it. As Elena turned to look after them, she saw Domenico and Marietta ascending almost on her heels. She should have averted her gaze, which was the customary procedure on such occasions, but she had never been as near to Domenico before and she stared hard at him for a matter of seconds. Marietta knew instantly what was passing through her friend's mind. Elena was looking her fill at this man who all unknowingly was fostering her child. Then Domenico and even Marietta were taken completely by surprise as she inclined her head to each of them, giving her sweet smile.

"I bid you good evening, Signor and Signora Torrisi."

Marietta held her breath, and seemingly so did everyone else aware of this cameo of an encounter in the midst of an otherwise busy scene. Then Domenico, after a matter of seconds that marked his deliberation, and with his eyes hard on Elena, bowed to her as courtesy required.

"I offer our salutations to you, Signora Celano."

Then her fan was being returned to her. The incident was over and they went their separate ways along branching corridors. As soon as Marietta reached the Torrisi box she turned gladly to Domenico.

"I thank you for your tolerance on the stairs. Nobody could have appreciated your kindly acknowledgement more than Elena."

"I don't want to discuss it," he replied sharply.

Marietta bit her lip as she sat down in her chair. If Domenico knew what ordeals Elena had to suffer he would not begrudge the few words he had been obliged to speak to her. Filippo was treating her abominably. He went to her bed as a matter of routine, gratifying his own desires and, afterward, taunting and deriding her for her barrenness. More than once he had almost strangled her in a rage, and she had had to disguise the bruises on her neck with layers of gossamer scarves. Ironically, the mode had been copied by other women, who considered Elena a leader of fashion.

The door of the box was opening and Domenico stood to welcome the friends they had invited to join them that evening. Marietta was relieved to have no more conversation with him. Then an unexpected development in the opera house itself made it impossible for her to remain cross. As usual, the gallery was crammed with gondoliers, who were admitted free to await their masters or those demanding public fares at the opera's end, but on this occasion they had decided to rival the singers on the stage. With many splendid voices among them, they turned every solo into a duet and caused the auditorium to thunder in the choruses as their voices blended with those on the stage. It was all done with good will and at the end the whole audience rose in a standing ovation, the singers behind the footlights and those in the gallery taking their bows.

Elena, applauding merrily herself, glanced across at the Torrisi box. She could not quite see Domenico as Marietta and the other women were in front of the men, but she was grateful for that extraordinary encounter. In spite of the hard look he had given her, she could believe that he was a man of justice and that her daughter's future was safe in his hands.

When Elena arrived home Filippo was out. First she made sure his valet was nowhere in the vicinity and then she went through the communicating door that led from her bedchamber to Filippo's. His was a long, rectangular room with two Gothic windows overlooking the Grand Canal and a large four-poster, draped in dark green and gold brocade, set in an alcove. Among the several pieces of richly carved Venetian furniture, there was a tall cupboard with doors that opened to reveal many smaller doors with partitions and drawers where Filippo kept various items such as a pair of dueling pistols, spare silver shoe buckles, and sets of valuable buttons. But he had also allotted several sections for certain correspondence and important papers he wanted close at hand. It was these that Elena had been searching through at any opportunity, on the off chance that something from one of those meetings with his brothers might be among them.

After a final half hour of sifting through them down to the last batch, she decided that all such notes must be in Maurizio's keeping, for he always came and left on those occasions with a leather file under his arm. She had already searched everywhere else she could think of, although she was sure that if Filippo had such documentation it would be in this cupboard. She had even searched for a secret drawer, pushing and sliding and pressing the carving on every possible section. She had found one eventually, but it had contained only two articles wrapped in silk. One was an antique ring with a large jewel that sprang open to reveal a powder that might well have been poison. There were several such rings among the jewelry in the treasure room, although their contents were gone. The other item was a small erotic painting on wood, which she guessed to be even older than the ring. Since both these things were of such antiquity she wondered if Filippo even knew they were there.

As this final search had come to nothing, Elena decided she must continue to rely on her eavesdropping and trust that something would eventually be revealed. She loathed having to stoop to such means and she was in terror all the time that someone might suddenly open the door and find her there, but it was the least she could do for Domenico and through him for her child. She returned to her own room and summoned her maid to help her get ready for bed.

When Filippo entered his bedchamber later that night it seemed to his keen nostrils that Elena's lovely perfume hung faintly in the air. But then he was always acutely aware of anything that reminded him of her. It was incredible to him that he should continue to be attracted to her fair beauty even though he hated her for failing to give him children. He knew he should set himself free of her. The poison of his mother's advice had seeped into his blood as she must have known it would, and he could not rid himself of it. His conflicting emotions kept his temper constantly near the edge. There were times when he struck Elena out of fury at himself, that he should be so intoxicated by a useless wife when he could have had her life snuffed out in a score of ways that would have cast no suspicion on himself.

Yet he could not tolerate the thought of Elena's beauty being sullied in death by violence at the hands of others. Neither could he carry out the task himself. He, who had never been troubled by killing, would find it impossible ever to take a knife or a bludgeon to her. Smothering would preserve her looks, but he knew that at the sight of her spread tresses gleaming gold he would hurl away the pillow. When he had half strangled her it was in a blind rage and not from any real attempt to end her life. Never before had any woman held him in such thrall. He detested her for it and at the same time he had only to think of her to feel desire stir.

Bianca reminded him of Elena. He paused in the act of pulling off his lace cravat as he pictured her. She had the same porcelain beauty and could easily have been Elena's younger sister. Occasionally the nuns brought the girl to take refreshment with his wife. He liked to be present if he could, but these visits were usually arranged when he was at the Senate. At thirteen Bianca was like a young peach with small round breasts and a mass of silver-gilt hair that cascaded down her back under the white Pietà veil. Although shy, she never held back from talking to him and he believed he had her pity for his facial scar. He smiled to himself. That scar had the same effect on older women, and, without exception, it made them extraordinarily malleable to his wishes.

But he had other matters on his mind at present. He had told his valet not to come to put his clothes away for half an hour. He had to read a letter that had been handed to him that evening and he did not want to be disturbed. He removed his satin coat and felt in his pocket for the letter. Then he sat down in a chair and lounged back as he read. A look of intense satisfaction spread across his face: finally, a missing piece had been inserted into the most perfect case against Domenico Torrisi that could ever have been drawn up.

When he had finished reading, he rose to look at his reflection in the mirror. Slowly he drew his fingertips down the deep scar. It was to be avenged at last.

In the morning, after breakfast, Filippo went to sit at his desk for quite a while, writing a letter. When it was finished and signed he went with it to the palace of a fellow senator who added his own signature. A third name was needed, and, by arrangement, a nobleman of their acquaintance who had his own reasons for wishing Domenico out of the Senate arrived to pen his signature to the paper. A glass of wine was drunk to mark the occasion and then Filippo left for the Ducal Palace.

There, he passed through the Hall of the Bussola, pausing only briefly by a box built into the wall. This was one of many such boxes in the Ducal Palace and about the city that were known as Lion Mouths, for carved on each one was a leonine and sinister, fierce-eyed, bush-browed face with a gaping mouth above an inscription that had invited secret denunciations against traitors over the past five hundred years. The names of the three necessary accusers were never revealed. Although used less frequently than in the past, it was still a viable means of bringing suspected acts of treason to the notice of the state attorneys. Filippo slipped the letter of denunciation against Domenico through the grimacing stone lips and continued on his way.

The state attorneys who received the letter were inclined to be skeptical because of the Celano signature, yet all such cases required serious investigation. Treason was the most reviled of crimes, and one doge had been beheaded for it. The attorneys began their careful work. First of all the three signatories were interviewed, and what came to light was sufficient for the Doge to be consulted.

Domenico was leaving the Doge's Palace one afternoon when, in one of the halls, a nobleman who he knew well came forward to block his path. Domenico greeted him.

"How are you, Signor Bucello? What news? Shall you walk along with me? I'm in some haste to get home. It was a long meeting."

"I'll accompany you. Let us go this way." The nobleman indicated another direction, which led to the Hall of the Chief Inquisitor.

"That is not my route."

"I fear it is today."

Then Domenico realized that something was seriously amiss. He nodded and went with the nobleman until they reached a door, which was opened for him. He entered the square room with its gilt-leathered walls. A state attorney sat at a table with the Chief Inquisitor, their expressions grave.

"What is this, signori?" Domenico questioned sternly.

The Inquisitor rose to his feet. "I have to inform you that you are being suspended from the Senate and all your duties by order of the Doge while your political activities are being investigated. You are still a free citizen and it is asked only that you keep me informed of your whereabouts and do not attempt to leave the Republic."

"You have my word as a loyal Venetian," Domenico replied, showing nothing of the concern he felt. He did not ask any questions, since the decree was absolute and his chance would come if anything was found against him. After bowing, he turned and once more the door was swung wide for him to pass through. He breathed deeply as he continued on his way, knowing himself to be more fortunate than the countless others for whom the door of that sinister room had never opened again.

When he broke the news to Marietta she was extremely worried. He tried to reassure her. "I've not been accused of anything yet and the whole incident may pass over. As a precautionary measure I have already consulted lawyers who are fellow patricians and my friends."

"I tried to warn you—as Elena begged me—that something like this might happen!"

"I know you did."

"Filippo is the instigator of this trouble!"

"We don't know that. I admit it's likely, but we must wait and see. The investigation is likely to take some weeks. Let us go to the villa and spend the time in the countryside."

She welcomed the suggestion, always glad to be there.

They had six weeks in the tranquillity of the villa and came closer to one another than they had ever been. Then one day, having just returned from a walk with Domenico and Elizabetta, Marietta was upstairs removing her hat and cape when she heard visitors arrive. Giving a quick pat to her hair, she went downstairs to greet them. When she saw that it was three officials who had arrived with two armed guards, she froze.

"Signor Torrisi," the senior official was saying solemnly, "in the name of the Doge and the Most Serene Republic I arrest you on the charge of treason!"

Marietta suppressed a cry and flew to Domenico's side to put a hand on his arm. He was speechless. Not once had he suspected that such a monstrous charge would have been trumped up against him. He had been fully prepared for some word of his radical work to have leaked out, in which case he would have presented a full case in support of these changes for the state's own good, even though the time to speak had come upon him sooner than he had wished. It did not matter that Filippo might have been the instigator. Domenico would have seen it as an opportunity to get the better of him as Antonio's brother. But treason! Marietta had not said a word, but he could feel her trembling and put his hand over hers as he made his calm reply.

"I shall freely accompany you back to Venice in order to clear my name of this groundless charge."

He and the official bowed to one another. Then he was allowed a few minutes alone with Marietta while his valet packed some necessary items. She was deeply upset. Domenico went to a drawer and handed her a sealed document from it, before taking her in his arms.

"Listen carefully to me, Marietta. This document gives you full authority to handle Torrisi affairs in my absence. I had it drawn up as a precaution, never supposing it would be needed. I should like you to go back to the palace as soon as possible."

"I'll do anything you say."

"You must prepare yourself for a trial of long duration."

"Why should that be when you're innocent?"

"Because if Filippo is responsible—and I have no doubt any more that he is—he has presented a network of lies and false evidence convincing enough to make the state attorneys support the charge and the Council of Ten to accept it."

"Shall I be able to visit you?"

"I hope so, although in view of the severity of the charge it might not be permitted. You must draw on the courage I've always known you to have."

"I love you," she cried.

"As I love you," he said softly, looking down into her desperate up-turned face, "and will do so until my life's end."

The nurse had appeared with Elizabetta, who came running to them. Domenico turned to sweep the child up in his arms. She pointed her small finger in the direction of a mirror. "Over there, Papa! Let us play the mirror game!"

He shook his head. "You're *my* little girl today, not the mirror's." When she saw how serious he was, she poked her fingers into the corners of his mouth to turn them up. He smiled to please her and she hugged him about the neck. "I have to hand you over to Mama now, because I'm going back to Venice."

"I'll come too!" she stated imperiously, never liking to be left behind.

Marietta took her from him. "Not today, Elizabetta. I'll take you tomorrow."

He held them both within the circle of his arms. Then, after putting his lips fondly to the child's brow, he kissed Marietta long and deeply. "Take care of each other," he said as he drew away.

Marietta hurried Elizabetta to watch as he went away down the drive. He turned to look back before disappearing from their sight as he descended the steps to the waiting boat with the senior official and the guards.

Her ordeal was not over. The two officials who had stayed behind searched the villa extensively, even demanding to read the document that Domenico had given her. When she returned to Venice she found the palace had been searched as well, but no damage had been done. It had been a pointless quest since all knew that every palace had many secret places that would never be discovered by a stranger.

After long questioning by the Chief Inquisitor the date for Domenico's trial was set. It was held in the Hall of the Council of Ten in the Ducal Palace. Under its ornate and gilded ceiling, inset with a painting of the triumph of Venice, Domenico faced the court of his peers. During this time Marietta was allowed to visit him every evening for an hour, although the door was left open and a guard kept watch within earshot. On her first visit she took a miniature of herself from his bedchamber and another of Elizabetta, which she knew he would want with him.

"You must have read my mind," he said, taking them from her.

He had a comfortable room in a less distinguished part of the Ducal Palace, since the Doge had no wish for him to be confined in discomfort until his guilt or innocence was proved. The case presented by the state was that Domenico had consorted with foreign governments to undermine the security of the Republic and replace the Doge with a revolutionary regime. It was so ludicrous that Domenico did not have the least qualm about the verdict.

"It is only a matter of time before the whole charge against me is thrown out," he assured Marietta.

The trial proved to be as lengthy as he had predicted. His friends among the councillors demanded that every piece of evidence be checked and rechecked, which caused many delays. Then, gradually, everything began to take a serious turn as the work in which he had been engaged over a considerable period was misconstrued. His aim had been to encourage neighboring Italian republics and principalities to drive out foreign influences, such as that of Austria, and to form a league to strengthen themselves, which would in turn act as a buffer to protect the Venetian State.

"Temporarily this is the only means by which we can survive should any great foreign power rise up against us," he explained under cross-examination. "I saw it all as a preventative measure until La Serenissima finally loses her complaisancy and wakes up to the fact that weakness, decadence, sloth, and an exultation in rich living—always her vice—have undermined her to the point that she could fall to the first aggressor!"

There was an uproar. He had offended all but his staunchest allies. The prosecutor had to shout to make himself heard. "So you thought to hasten that end by scurrilous bribery and rabble-rousing along our very borders. I put it to you that you gave away state secrets to that end!"

"No!"

"Do you deny that you dealt in the smuggling of arms?"

"Yes! I also state that the only call to arms I have ever made has been for Venice to rise again to the forceful power she enjoyed in past centuries in order to defend what is hers against any aggressor!"

"What aggressor could possibly prove a danger? You must be aware that all neighboring states respect Venetian neutrality. That call is open to another interpretation. An incitement to riot!"

"No!" Domenico roared. "All I've ever wanted is to prevent bloodshed in the streets of the Republic. Not to cause it!"

The scales were already weighing against Domenico. He could not have been charged with treason at a worse time. It was 1789 and France was in the throes of a revolution. News had just reached Venice of the arrest of the French king and queen. Every Venetian nobleman at the trial abhorred the breakdown of law and order, which made those unconvinced by Domenico's defense even more determined that treacherous activities should be stamped out before they could take hold.

Witnesses were called. The first was the Emperor of Austria's own representative, who swore on oath that his nation had no territorial designs on the Most Serene Republic and respected its domains. Then came witnesses from some of the Italian states. Those who had been against the formation of a league spoke as unfavorably as they could of Domenico, saying his influence had been as radical, subversive, and harmful to the interests of their states as it had been to those of La Serenissima. Domenico and his lawyers were convinced that some of these witnesses had been heavily bribed, but their evidence sealed his fate. Even those of his peers who had been fully on his side now resigned themselves to his having gone too far. The guilty verdict was unanimous. Marietta, waiting with Adrianna and Leonardo outside the hall, fainted when the news was relayed to her.

Domenico could have been tortured to death or executed in the Piazzetta for all to see, but mercy prevailed and he was condemned to life imprisonment. All his property and possessions were declared forfeit to the State. In the knowledge that Marietta and Elizabetta were now homeless, he was led away to be incarcerated in one of the cells known as the leads, high up under the flat-leaded roof in the Doge's Palace, which housed only political prisoners. This time, there were no moments of farewell.

That night a great celebration was held at the Palazzo Celano as Filippo and his brothers rejoiced in the fall of the House of Torrisi. Elena was compelled to be present since there were many wives among the guests. To herself she derided her pathetic attempts to stave off the catastrophe that had occurred. No wonder Filippo had said upon her return from Paris that what he had in mind for Domenico would take a long time. How cleverly his spies had worked in their secret ways to penetrate Domenico's work. How skillfully all had been twisted to turn good into evil. Maurizio had surely done much of the spinning with that sharp intelligence of his, which she had always feared.

At Domenico's arrest she had gone through her dossier of notes and seen nothing that might help him. Yet, to be certain, she went masked to a lawyer and showed him all she had, obliterating names while presenting a seemingly hypothetical case. He had read them through and shaken his head.

"Such notes of hearsay, unsubstantiated by a second witness, and heard through a door without even sight of the speakers, are useless. Toss them away, signora. That is my advice."

Now as she watched Filippo, drunk with wine and triumph, her loathing of him made her shudder. She saw him not only as a despoiler of her own life but of Elizabetta's too. When Marietta lost her own baby it had been an unlooked-for chance for Elizabetta to grow up with loving parents. Now Filippo had smashed that family unit through his bitter vengeance.

"Why so solemn, Elena?" somebody jested, a wine-flushed face bobbing before her. "History has been made! The vendetta has come to an end!"

"So it has," she acknowledged without expression. But not as she and Marietta had wished it to end, in friendship and goodwill. She thought sadly that every dream she had ever cherished had come to nothing.

Filippo, glancing across at Elena's unsmiling face in the midst of the jubilation, scowled. He had achieved all he wanted except for an heir. Maybe for once in his life he should consider deeply the advice his mother had given him. It was still the means of disposing of Elena that was holding him back. She was his wife, and his revulsion at the thought of her being touched by any other man, even in death, had not changed.

Marietta was given twenty-four hours in which to leave the Palazzo Torrisi. When she had arrived home from the Ducal Palace after Domenico's sentencing, state officials were there ahead of her, all Domenico's keys in their possession. They allowed the treasure room, a necessity in every palace, to remain open long enough for her to remove her personal valuables, which included heirloom jewelry that Domenico had given her in addition to all the other magnificent pieces she had received from him at different times. They also allowed enough bags of money to be withdrawn from the coffers to pay off the household staff. Then the heavy doors were locked and sealed.

The packing of her own and Elizabetta's personal possessions was managed competently by Anna. The woman was sickened by the cruel turn of fate that had thrown her mistress's husband into prison and caused her to lose the best post she had ever held. She knew Signor Torrisi would have made provision for her in her old age.

In Domenico's dressing-room, Marietta took advantage of her few moments alone to gather armfuls of his clothes. She rushed with them to where Anna knelt by a large traveling box.

"Quick, Anna! Pack my husband's garments in layers between mine. He shall have good clothes and shoes even if he is a prisoner."

Domenico's wardrobe was so extensive that the absence of the few items she took would never be detected by strangers. She also included in her boxes some of his favorite books and maps. His jewelry had already been taken by the officials and sealed away, but she knew where he kept a valuable pocket-watch and took it from its hiding place. It had been his father's and he had once said to her that in time to come it should be his son's.

His son! Such a pang went through her that for the moment she could not move. How would another son, strong and healthy, be conceived now? There was the terrible possibility that she would be old and past childbearing when some merciful doge allowed the prison doors to be opened for Domenico at last.

"Signora!" A maidservant had come to find her. "The officials want to see you in the music room. The steward has told them the harpsichord there is yours."

The dispute that followed was over whether the harpsichord, which was beautifully painted with scenes of Venice and had been a birthday gift from Domenico, should remain in Marietta's possession or be forfeit to the State. Eventually it was decided that she could keep it, and she had it carried out of the palace immediately in case the favor should be revoked. It was to be transported by boat to her new address, the house where she and Elena had given birth. Leonardo, who had never made further alterations to the property, had offered the apartment to her as living accommodation, and she had gratefully accepted.

It was a sad moment for everyone in the household when Marietta, dressed for leaving, entered the ballroom to say farewell to all who had served her and her husband. She had Elizabetta, carrying a favorite doll, at her side. Even though Marietta knew from the ledgers how many were employed, she was surprised to see the full ninety of them lined up before her. The Torrisi gondoliers, who had been included on this occasion, were in their best liveries, as were all the other menservants present; the women were in fresh caps and aprons. She spoke a few words to each one, the steward following as he handed out their wages, plus extra money at her instruction, in individual leather bags. Most of the women were in tears, for they, like many of the men, were from families that had served the Torrisis through several generations.

Finally, when Marietta took Elizabetta by the hand, the head gondolier ran ahead to assist her into his gondola and take her away from her home. She did not look back. In a matter of an hour or two this palace, as well as the others that had belonged to Domenico, would be closed until the future of his properties and their contents was decided. The country villa where she had spent so many contented hours, and the one that Antonio had occupied in happier days, would similarly be locked and barred. Her gaze was set ahead. Her dual purpose in the future was to raise Elizabetta to the best of her ability and to seek clemency to reduce Domenico's sentence. Proving his innocence was her ultimate aim.

Adrianna and Leonardo were waiting to welcome her. She saw at once that they had done all they could to help her settle into her new quarters. The salon was large enough to accommodate her harpsichord without over-crowding. The kitchen, which previously had been located downstairs, had been reinstalled in the room where she had given birth, completely chang-ing its appearance, and the cooking range was as new as the woodwork and paint. She guessed that the conversion had been set in motion as soon as Domenico's trial began to turn against him.

Elena, full of remorse, arrived to see her within the first half hour. "I failed you, Marietta! I had nothing to offer in Domenico's defense and yet I knew it was all being plotted under my very nose."

"Don't reproach yourself. Domenico and I know you did your best and we're very grateful."

"How will you pass your time?" Elena looked about her in bewilder-ment. She had become so used to spacious rooms that the apartment, although large enough for Marietta's requirements, seemed even smaller to her than when she had given birth in one of its rooms. Almost without realizing it, she moved toward a half-open door on an intended tour of inspection. Then she came to an abrupt standstill as she saw Elizabetta asleep on a bed.

Marietta came to her side. "Go to her if you wish."

Elena shook her head and drew the door shut. "No," she said, putting a hand to her throat. "She is your child. I dare not let my love for her overwhelm me."

"I would never have had your strength of will."

Elena smiled ruefully. "It's cowardice. I don't think I could bear any more hurt. In future I shall try to visit you after Elizabetta's bedtime or when she is having an afternoon nap."

"Adrianna has promised that her nursemaid will take charge of her with the other children whenever I want an hour or two for myself. If we wore *bauta* masks and mantillas you and I could go for a stroll together sometimes."

"Let's do that! Do you remember I always wanted to show you where I lived with Great-Aunt Lucia and also the house where I was born? The chance has never come my way before."

They arranged to do this as soon as Marietta had time. For the present, she would be busy seeing anyone likely to help her get permission to visit Domenico. As yet he was not permitted to write to her lest he send orders in code for subversive action to those, still unidentified, who might have helped him. Marietta suspected there were many noblemen among them, but with his worthy plans uncovered and condemned out of hand, they had been unable to speak without the risk of suffering the same fate.

As she had feared, the Doge refused to grant her an audience. She approached his wife, whom she had entertained with the Doge many times at the Palazzo Torrisi, but again she was refused a hearing. There were some old friends of Domenico who did what they could for her, but as her husband had been labeled a traitor, his was a special case.

She was able to send him some furnishings since every political prisoner had the right to equip his own cell. As a result he had a rosewood table and chairs, a walnut bookcase full of volumes, two Persian rugs, a washstand that folded like a cupboard, and a comfortable bed with a supply of warm coverlets and good linen. In addition he had a chest of drawers for his clothes. He was allowed wine and whatever items of food she chose to hand in for him. Although he was not permitted to write letters she had sent him writing materials and a diary as well as a stock of candles.

She did not count the cost of anything, thankful to be able to lessen the misery of his incarceration by any means possible, but after payment had been made for these initial furnishings and supplies, she realized that what money she had would eventually run out. She had insisted on paying rent to Leonardo, and although it was a modest sum it would be needed on a regular basis. One small piece of her jewelry would keep her and Elizabetta in comfort for a long time, but she was reluctant to part with any of it in case she should have the chance to buy Domenico's freedom at any time. Prisoners had escaped from those same cells. There was a man called Casanova who had once gotten away across the roofs. With money, she and Domenico could travel with Elizabetta to safety. She had written to all his brothers to inform them of what had happened. Although there was nothing they could do at present, she was sure any one of them would come forward to help him if the chance arose.

Leonardo was not unduly surprised when Marietta asked him for work. He had expected, as she had, that her social life would soon fall away, and this had proved to be the case. All but a few close friends in her and Domenico's social circle had deserted her. Only at the Pietà nothing had changed, even though Domenico had been automatically deposed as a governor. A Pietà girl would always be one of the flock, no matter what pattern her life followed, even though there was no longer the letter P branded on her foot.

"I need to earn my living," Marietta explained to Leonardo. "I've lost none of my skills, as you know from my work on the mask that was your marriage gift to Adrianna. Do you need an extra hand in the workshop?"

"I'm always wanting hands of the standard I maintain," he replied, sitting back in his chair, "but I've a business proposition to put to you. If I hadn't been so busy I would have seen to opening the shop next to my home as I had planned some time ago. Now I'm prepared to have the alterations done if it would suit you to run the shop and its workshop for me."

"It would indeed!" she exclaimed. "How soon will the alterations start?"

"I'll seek estimates for the work tomorrow."

Although he could not write, Domenico was able to receive letters. She wrote a little to him every day, delivering the finished letter herself once a week to a prison guard. Domenico would be interested to learn of her return to mask-making and would see this as proof that she was measuring up to her new circumstances, as he had been sure she would. Yet she had many dark hours when she broke down in her sorrow, even though she reminded herself each time how much worse it was for him. At least she had Elizabetta and good friends and the freedom to go about Venice, whereas he had only four walls and a barred window that would show nothing but the nearby roofs. If only she could visit him it would be something to which they both could look forward.

While the alterations to Leonardo's property were underway, Marietta met Elena by a jeweler's shop in the arcades of St. Mark's Square. Both were *bauta*-masked as arranged, and they went on foot through the narrow *calli* and squares of Elena's childhood.

"That was my window!" Elena exclaimed, pointing to one on the third floor of an ancient house from which the pale terra-cotta plaster had come away in vast flakes to reveal the mellow, deeper-toned brickwork beneath.

They went into the church that Elena had attended and saw the bridge where once she had tripped on the steps in her excitement and torn her Carnival gown. It was as if the two of them were recapturing their own youthful Pietà days together. When they parted it was with the arrangement that they would stroll again together when the chance arose.

There was little spare time for Marietta once the new shop and its workshop were finished. In order to launch it into the public eye, Leonardo had been saving some of his most spectacular masks to dazzle in its window. When the stock arrived, Marietta chose advantageous places to display the most vivid and ornate of the masks. With so much glitter and color covering the many pegs in the walls, she felt as if she were standing in the middle of a jewel-walled cave.

There were five workers in the workshop, who would be concentrating on creating the most unusual masks. It was Leonardo's intention to make this shop different from the one in St. Mark's Square where he stocked a selection of everything. Marietta missed her old favorites—Pantelone and Pulcinella and pig-like Ganga and all the rest that had been her first toys—but the commercial quality of the new designs appealed to her business instincts. As an incentive to sell well, she was to receive a bonus for sales above a certain figure, but even without it she would have faced her new task with enthusiasm. There was comfort for her in handling so many masks again. In a way it was as if she were back to her origins and beginning to build up her life once more. The difference this time was that Domenico's future was also hers.

Leonardo did not intend the opening of his new shop to pass unnoticed. A drummer and a trumpeter in extraordinary costumes appeared in St. Mark's Square, and when attention had been drawn by the fanfare a third man, even more outstandingly dressed, made an announcement about the new shop in the Calle della Madonna. This performance was repeated in the Merceria, at the Rialto, and in many other busy places throughout the day.

Venetians, with their love of rich clothes and passion for Carnival, were not hard to coax into visiting the shop. Marietta had risen to the occasion by wearing one of her grand gowns in emerald satin with a matching mask of sequins to which were attached long silk curls of the same sharp green, which covered her own hair completely and cascaded to her shoulders. Many of the dandies who she greeted applauded her appearance as they swarmed about the shop, tilting quizzing-glasses at the wares or trying on the masks as she poured coffee for them into little gilded cups.

In no way was her mask meant as a disguise on this day, for it had become known that she would be in charge of the new enterprise. All addressed her as the Flame of the Pietà, which was a way of ignoring the scandal of her husband's treason and speaking to her without embarrassment. Some people who had kept their distance since the trial now came either out of curiosity or to try and mend the breach with her personally. She was courteous but cool toward these people, who had never been more than acquaintances in the round of social events she had shared with Domenico. All good friends she greeted warmly. Most of them had known Domenico for many years, some since childhood, and none believed him guilty. It was one of them, Sebastiano Dandolo, to whom she first spoke of the possibility of arranging Domenico's escape.

She had been invited to dine by him and his wife, Isabella. It was a small gathering of people she knew well. When the chance came she drew Sebastiano aside to put her query to him. He regarded her compassionately and shook his head slowly.

"Don't build your hopes in that direction, Marietta. Domenico is regarded as too much of a danger to be given any leeway in his incarceration. I happen to know there are never fewer than two guards at his door and there was a second row of bars installed at his window."

"What of bribery?" she questioned, refusing to accept defeat.

"It wouldn't be worth taking the risk for any guard, no matter what you offered. It is death by torture to allow a traitor to escape."

"But what can I do?" Her cry was desperate.

"Nothing except to be patient. We must trust that eventually this Doge or his successor will show some leniency. At the present time that chance is far beyond the horizon. Your husband is the victim of these unsettled times, with all Europe taking France's turmoil as a warning. Yet Domenico could have been the best Doge La Serenissima ever had."

"I thank you for that, Sebastiano." She was moved, for the statement was the highest praise that could have been given to Domenico. Her memory stirred and a long-ago prediction that she would marry a doge returned to her. Maybe, although said in jest, it had foretold that she would have a husband with the qualities of judgement such a position required. If the tide turned for Domenico, who could predict his future? Perhaps the very foresight he had shown would win him the golden corno one day.

The shop did well. During Carnival it became the place to visit for masks of unusual design and beauty. There were a few slack periods during which Marietta took a turn in the workshop, molding or painting masks or attaching some of the new gloriously shaded plumes that had been her idea. The success of these masks had been phenomenal. St. Mark's Square, during that Carnival of 1790, was a multicolored forest of Savoni plumes.

When the intense heat of summer arrived, Marietta thought back to the cool, sweet days at the villa and could scarcely begin to imagine the conditions endured by Domenico, high under the roof of the Ducal Palace. She sent him one of the plainer fans made for men and some freshening essences that could be added to his bathing water. Memories flooded back of times when they had bathed together. She hugged her arms, bowed over by the yearning ache within. So many months had passed since she had felt his embrace or experienced the total ecstasy with which his passionate body had filled hers. She felt as if she were withering up inside, becoming only half a woman instead of a whole one.

Another eighteen months passed. It was a dramatic and upsetting period, for an abortive attempt was made to rescue Domenico through the roof of the Ducal Palace itself. Nobody knew how long the unknown conspirators had been working night after night to open a way down through the lead roof and the obstructive timber and brickwork beneath to reach his cell. He would have gotten away without a trace if a piece of brick had not fallen onto the cell floor, alerting the guards on patrol in the corridor. They had burst into the cell even as Domenico was being hoisted into mid-air by those hauling him up from above. The guards hurled themselves at him and their combined weight tore the rope from the grasp of his rescuers, bringing one of them down with it. The unfortunate man broke his neck upon impact, while his confederates took flight, escaping over the roofs in the darkness.

The identity of the dead man was never discovered and there was nothing in his pockets or on his person to give a clue. Domenico was questioned closely by the Chief Inquisitor, but he steadfastly refused to say who he believed his would-be rescuers to be and he answered truthfully that the man who had died was a stranger to him. Since this Inquisitor was more merciful than his predecessors Domenico was not taken to torture, but a number of privileges were withdrawn, including the receipt of letters.

"I'm also having you removed from the leads," the Inquisitor concluded, "to the greater security of the Wells."

It was a terrible blow for Domenico. The prison on the opposite side of the canal from the Ducal Palace had gotten its name from the narrowness of its cells, the lack of ventilation, and the humidity created by the stone walls. There he would be shut away from sunlight and the sight of gulls and other birds skimming across the sky. Above all else, he would be denied his link with Marietta through her letters and the written messages from Elizabetta, who had drawn pictures for his wall even before she could read and write.

Black despair settled on him as he was escorted from his cell by the guards who would take him to the dungeon. Yet he moved lithely, the result of the number of paces he took each day around his cell to keep himself fit. An archway opened to the stone steps that led to the bridge, which was like an enclosed narrow corridor spanning the canal some depth below. Mercifully the wall on the south side had two apertures set with ornamental stonework in a design he had always found pleasing when he viewed this arched bridge from a distance. Now the openings brought clean fresh air that fanned his face, and he realized that he must be following the behavior pattern of all prisoners who passed this way when he rushed to the first aperture to press his hands flat against the stonework and gaze at the outside world, perhaps for the last time. A gondola was just passing out of the canal under the humpbacked Paglia Bridge, and in the Basin beyond he could see many ships and a thousand blues and greens all blended together in the silken ripples of the water. On the far side of the Basin lay the island of San Giorgio where the pearl-like dome of Palladio's church was cradled in a faint mist. He knew he would remember this perfect vista from this dreadful viewpoint until his dying day.

A guard spoke. "That's long enough."

With a deep sigh Domenico released his hold on the stonework. Foreign visitors to the city leaned their arms on the balustrade of the Paglia as they gazed in morbid interest at the notorious bridge that he was slowly crossing. The design of the stonework prevented him and his escort from being seen, but he wondered if by some trick of sound his sigh had reached them. Maybe it had echoed in the breeze through the stonework, taking up the countless sighs of others condemned to a living death in the Wells before him. As if his musing thoughts were right, he saw one of those bystanders turn up his coat collar as if suddenly chilled, and a woman drew her velvet domino more closely about her.

Domenico threw a last lingering look over his shoulder through the second aperture and then the gloom of the prison swallowed him up.

When Sebastiano broke the news to Marietta, she turned ashen and sank down into a chair, her head bowed.

"Is there to be no end to this cruel punishment of an innocent man?"

He took the chair beside her. "I wish I could have brought you the tidings for which I had hoped."

She looked up at him through her tears. "You were among those who tried to free him! I'll always appreciate that you tried. It is no fault of yours that things went so disastrously wrong. Neither could you have foreseen the outcome."

"When you first spoke to me about a possible escape, I gave you no encouragement because I didn't want to raise your hopes about what several of us already had in mind. But now it is with great regret I have to tell you there is no more hope along those lines. Further attempts are out of the question. The prison is far too secure and the guards will be alerted from now on."

She was desolated.

Elizabetta had to be told that she could no longer send drawings or letters to Domenico. In the early days of his incarceration she had cried for him, unable to understand why he was suddenly missing from her life, but she had gradually adjusted to his absence. There was a portrait of him in the salon of the apartment that Marietta had brought from the Palazzo Torrisi, so Elizabetta did not forget how he looked even if memories of her times with him faded away.

"Your papa has gone a little farther away from us," Marietta explained. "We must wait until he can receive our letters again."

"Has he left Venice?" Elizabetta asked, puzzled. At first she had not been able to understand why her father should live high up in the Doge's Palace and never come to see them. Later it was explained to her that he was having to stay where he was through no choice of his own until an important matter was cleared up. A young assistant in the mask-shop had once jeered that he was a traitor in prison. But the girl was instantly dismissed and Elizabetta was assured that her father had done no wrong.

"No, he hasn't left the city," Marietta replied, "but he has been moved to another building where it is more difficult for us to keep contact with him."

"I'll go on drawing pictures for Papa, Mama. He can have them when he comes home again."

Marietta hugged the child to her.

Filippo roared with laughter when he heard of the further misfortune that had befallen his old enemy. He and Vitale had been told about it on the Rialto Bridge where all local news flowed amid the shops and along the walkways. They immediately set off on a celebratory tour of the wineshops in the city and it was late when they staggered back to the Palazzo Celano, having gathered Alvise along the way. Elena had just returned from a Pietà concert and Filippo drunkenly bawled out the story to her.

"What a bunch of bungling fools the Torrisi had to help him! Did you ever hear the like? Now he'll rot of lung disease in the Wells and be dead sooner than later. Come and drink a toast to those who nipped his escape in the bud!"

He caught her roughly by the arm and thrust her down in a chair at the table where his brothers were already sprawled, decanters and glasses having been placed before them by hurrying servants.

Elena, who had heard about Domenico during an interval at the concert, was full of sorrow and she eyed the brothers with disgust. She could tell this was one of those occasions when they would drink themselves into a stupor, and they were well on the way already.

"Drink up!" Filippo filled her glass. When she did not immediately lift it, he snatched it up himself and rammed it against her lips, spilling the contents down her cleavage and soaking her bodice. "That's it! You should drink more wine!" His glowering, reddened face was close to hers. "It might make you fertile!"

He never lost any opportunity to taunt her. In public, he would make a great fuss over other people's offspring, although privately he disliked the company of children. He would flirt outrageously with any pregnant woman, praising her bloom, her beauty, and the sweet duty she was fulfilling for her fortunate husband. Like Marco he had a certain dangerous charm that attracted many women, and men liked the careless generosity and bonhomie that he showed when it suited him; but to Elena his false ways were transparent.

She managed to drink more wine to please him and then his attention swung away from her as Alvise, who had sent for a lute, began to sing a bawdy song. When sober, Alvise played and sang well; even in his present state he had not lost his talent, and his voice rang out as Filippo's deep baritone joined in lustily. Vitale soon followed suit. Elena seized the chance to slip away from the table to her own room upstairs. Her personal maid was waiting for her, but she did not exclaim at the sight of the wine-stained gown. Better that than more bruises on the signora's face and body.

Although at first Elena had kept resolutely to her vow not to see Elizabetta or talk about her beyond being told all was well, it had proved impossible to maintain. Elizabetta would come running into the shop when Elena happened to call, or else the child would be playing with Adrianna's children when Elena visited there. In spite of herself Elena looked forward more and more to seeing her daughter, building up a relationship like that of an aunt to a niece.

Elizabetta missed the walks she had taken with Marietta to deliver the letters and drawings to her papa. Now when they went out, it was mostly to the market to buy food. She liked to skip along and whenever they came to one of the little bridges that spanned the canals she would run up the steps on one side and hop down the steps on the other.

If it had not been for her work, Marietta did not know how she would have faced each day. When she could not sleep at night for anxiety about Domenico, she put on a robe and went downstairs to the workshop where she occupied herself until dawn by making masks. It relaxed her, restoring the peace she had always known with her mother in the workshop of their village home. She gained the strength through these quiet dark hours that enabled her to carry on with her life as Domenico would wish.

Something else came out of those nightly sessions. For a surprise she had made Elizabetta a carnival half-mask out of scraps of silk with tiny hand-made flowers. It was much admired generally and so she made others for sale. The demand increased and she began to produce a whole range of children's masks. There were plenty of children's masks to be had at any mask-shop in Venice, but her designs were original and before long she had the two women in the workshop concentrating only on these smaller products. Then she began to design adult masks as well along more dramatic lines and these also created a demand. Leonardo was immensely pleased and trebled her bonus, for before the year was out the new shop had become established as the place to go for especially original and splendid masks for all ages. In his own establishment Leonardo soon displayed only

Marietta's designs, together with samples of fabrics and trimmings, whenever a customer wanted to commission a mask that would be different from all the rest.

Marietta always found it relaxing to take walks with Elena and stop for refreshment and conversation at Florian's. They continued to go masked on these outings, for although the vendetta was virtually at an end, Filippo would never have allowed Elena to meet the wife of his vanquished enemy.

Individually, they each enjoyed visits with Bianca whenever Sisters Sylvia and Giaccomina brought her to their homes. In her own way the young girl brought comfort to her godmothers, each of whom was weighed down with troubles that her gentle company could sometimes ease.

Domenico spent almost a year in a dungeon before he fell ill and was transferred to a cell on a higher floor in another part of the prison. Sebastiano, who heard the news by chance, spoke to Marietta of what he had learned.

"First of all I will tell you that Domenico has been ill, but he has fully recovered," he began.

She did not pester him with all the anxious questions she longed to ask. "Please tell me what you know."

He gave her the facts as he had heard them. The doctor, concerned only with the health of his patient, had insisted on Domenico's being moved immediately and had attended him daily until the danger was past. But the treatment had not ended there. The doctor, being a conscientious man, had insisted to the authorities that the full rights of a political prisoner be restored to Domenico Torrisi, and that, for his health's sake, he was never to be returned to the dungeons. This was agreed on in principle, although for security reasons he could not be put back in the palace cells and visitors were still banned. At least he could again receive news-sheets and writing materials, order what he wished from outside, and enjoy other such minor benefits.

"What of letters?" Marietta asked eagerly.

Sebastiano shook his head regretfully. "The right to send or receive letters is still denied him."

It was a bitter disappointment to bear.

Marietta continued to have a basket of food delivered regularly to the prison for Domenico as she had done all the time, including wines she knew he liked. It was a familiar routine as one year gave way to the next and yet another followed.

With New Year's Eve being at the height of Carnival, Marietta always kept the shop open until the early hours. When the bells and merrymaking welcomed in 1794 she took stock as she never failed to do of the time that had elapsed since Domenico's conviction. Leaving the shop to her assistants, she went upstairs to see if Elizabetta had been awakened by the fireworks, but the child slept peacefully.

Marietta went to the bedchamber window and held back the curtain to look up at the colored stars filling the sky above the *calle*. She hoped that Domenico could see them and take heart. A new year was a new beginning and perhaps this one would bring his release. Unfortunately this Doge was proving to be a weak leader. As Domenico had predicted, he was easily swayed by others and unlikely to take up any cause in the face of opposition. It was said that he had wept with despair upon being informed of his esteemed appointment. Marietta found it hard to sustain hope, but she would never give up. Even a feeble doge would have to accept proof of a man's innocence if ever it could be found.

Chapter 13

*W*henever Marietta went to the Pietà she had to pass by the prison with its arches and white stone walls. It was five years now since Domenico had been shut away from her and she saw it as a test of her faith in him that she should face up to the sight of his place of incarceration. She always paused on the Paglia Bridge to rest her hands on the balustrade and look deliberately at that other dreadful bridge that so elegantly linked the Wells with the Doge's Palace. Always her thoughts went to the day when Domenico had crossed it. Had she known in time that it was to happen, she would have stood on this spot day and night in order that he see her. She might even have caught the flicker of his hand behind the ornamental stonework.

If only Domenico could have had a son through whom the House of Torrisi would live on. It would have given him some consolation. She did not understand why she had not conceived again after his return from St. Petersburg. Had her body needed time to heal and readjust itself after failing to bear a living child? Then, when the time was ripe again, it had been too late, Domenico already a prisoner.

She was descending the steps of the Paglia Bridge to continue along the Riva degli Schiavoni to the Pietà when she saw Captain Zeno of the prison guard. He had come into her shop a few weeks before to buy masks for his three young daughters.

"Good day, signora." The captain recognized her now and saluted smartly. Had she not been a beautiful woman elegantly dressed, he might not have noticed her in the flow of passers-by.

Marietta acknowledged his greeting and would have walked on, but instead she stopped, realizing that he might give her some news of Domenico. "Have your little girls made good use of their masks, Captain?"

"Indeed they have. The youngest of the three has been less kind to hers and I must soon buy a replacement."

She smiled. "We have a new selection. Bring the old one back and I'll exchange it free of charge. Savoni masks are well made and shouldn't surrender even to hard handling in such a short while."

"I'll bring my daughter to your shop tomorrow, Signora Torrisi."

"You know my name? You didn't reveal that when you purchased those masks."

"I thought you might ask me for news of your husband. I try to avoid such questions."

Disappointed, she smiled ruefully. "That was my intention in speaking to you now."

"I guessed as much." He regarded her good-humoredly. "But one good turn deserves another."

"I would have replaced the mask in any case."

"I realize that."

"Would you kindly tell my husband that you have seen me? Is it too much to ask? He would appreciate it so much."

The captain's gaze hardened. "I grant no favors to a traitor. Nobody converses with him. Those are my orders."

"I happen to believe implicitly in my husband's innocence!" she retorted. "If you will do nothing for him, could you at least point out his window to me?"

"His cell has no window."

She looked at the captain fiercely, her eyes aglitter with tears. "It would have been better for me if we hadn't spoken! You've given me nothing but terrible news!"

He glanced after her as she hurried away along the parade. She was as fiery as her hair, but he did not hold that against her.

Marietta did not expect to see the captain in the shop again, no matter that she had offered to exchange the mask. Yet he came, bringing his three little daughters with him. She treated him coolly, but not his children, who were full of smiles. When she was about to help the youngest choose a new mask, the captain spoke directly to her in a lowered voice.

"Couldn't an assistant deal with this? I'd like to talk to you on your own."

She gave him a speculative glance and led him to her office. Captain Zeno sat down without being invited and more slowly she took her own chair. "Well?" she asked warily.

He leaned forward. "I told you yesterday that I grant no favors to a traitor, but I would be prepared to do one for you by letting you speak for a few minutes to a certain prisoner. That is," he added after the briefest pause, "if you are willing to oblige me."

"How much?" She would not quibble over the price.

He looked taken aback and then he scowled angrily. "You misunderstand me, signora. I'm immune to bribery! It's not money I want from you."

Marietta was bewildered. "What do you want then?"

"I've an elder daughter with a sweet voice that should be trained. I could have paid for her to be a pupil at the Pietà, but she would have to be an orphan for that, as you know. What I'm asking is that you, the Flame of the Pietà, become her teacher."

"Would visits to my husband be on a regular basis?" Marietta could see how much it meant to him that she take his daughter as her pupil, and she intended to drive a hard bargain.

"That is impossible. I'll be taking a great risk as it is. What I can do is allow a letter to be delivered to him once a month."

"What of letters from him to me?"

"One a year."

"No more?" Her query was stern.

He hesitated and then nodded. "Two then." It seemed to satisfy her.

"I'll make a singer out of your daughter if she has the voice as you believe," she said, "but in return I want a whole night with my husband, with the guards kept away. If at any other time another visit should prove possible, I want your word that you would allow me to see him again. Finally, if ever he is sick in the future, I should be allowed to nurse him."

The captain looked as if he were going to explode, his whole face becoming red from the jowls up. "Impossible! That would cost me my livelihood. I have a wife and seven children to support, signora! I'm putting my head on the block as it is."

He pushed back his chair and sprang up to leave, but Marietta remained quietly seated, her heart beating wildly at the gambler's throw she had made. "I'm an experienced maestra," she said evenly. "Your daughter couldn't have a better training anywhere."

Breathing deeply he sat down again. "If the prisoner is ill," he acquiesced against his will, "you will be notified and you may send in medicines. I can't do more than that."

Marietta saw she had gained as much as she could hope for. "Bring your daughter to me tomorrow evening after the shop is closed. At the same time you can let me know which night I can come to the prison."

When he had gone, she felt enervated by the strain of the bargaining and stretched her arms across her desk to let her forehead rest on them. She was going to see Domenico again! It was almost more than she could believe.

The captain's daughter Lucretia was fourteen, a bright girl with blue-black hair and saucer-like brown eyes, who was clearly her father's pet. Her voice, although totally untrained, had promise. Marietta gave the captain her frank opinion.

"Lucretia will need many hours of practice as well as lessons from me. I'm prepared to take her on as an assistant-apprentice in my shop, which would make it possible for me to teach her whenever my time allowed."

Both father and daughter greeted this arrangement with enthusiasm. Lucretia would have her own room and would work a certain number of hours in the shop.

"I thank you, signora," Captain Zeno said, placing a folded piece of paper in Marietta's hand as he and his daughter went out. When she opened it, she saw that there was a date and a time written down with the instruction to be masked. She was to be at the prison at ten o'clock the following Thursday night.

In the interim Marietta told Sebastiano what she had arranged. "You've accomplished what nobody else has been able to do," he said, pleased for her sake. "Be sure to tell Domenico that his friends have not deserted him and are still working on his behalf."

"I will."

"I'll escort you to the prison on Thursday and meet you again in the morning."

"There's no need," she replied, although she appreciated his kind thought.

"Nevertheless, it's the least I can do for you and Domenico."

It was a velvety night full of stars when Sebastiano took Marietta to the prison. He waited until she was admitted and then left for home.

Marietta found Captain Zeno awaiting her. They bade each other good evening and he began to lead her up a flight of stone stairs.

"Were you here when my husband was in a dungeon, Captain?" she asked.

"Yes, I've held my present appointment for several years. It was I who called the prison doctor when he fell ill. It is impossible for a sick man to fight the dungeon rats for his rations and it's my duty to keep the traitor alive."

She was horrified by the insight he had given her into the conditions in which Domenico had lived all those terrible months. At the same time, fury at what the captain had called him surged through her. She halted abruptly on the stairs. "Don't ever call my husband a traitor again! I won't tolerate it!"

He paused and looked hard at her. "I could still change my mind about letting you in."

"As I could about training your daughter's voice," she countered fiercely.

After a second or two he grinned slowly with an admiring glint in his eye. "You've a sharp tongue in your head at times. I'll mind mine in future."

He moved on and she kept to his side, questioning him again. "You mentioned rations in the dungeon. Didn't my husband receive the food I sent to him?"

"The criminals there get no privileges. I daresay the guards took it all, but ever since Torrisi was moved he has had most of it handed in to him."

"Most?"

"Wine has a way of vanishing sometimes."

She understood. "In future I'll bring a bottle for the guards and another for the rightful recipient."

"That thoughtfulness will not go amiss."

They were going through what seemed a maze of chilly corridors and across small square halls where guards were playing cards or eating supper. They all stared at her as she went by. Whenever she and the captain passed barred cells, most of which were in darkness, there were either snores from the inmates or a sudden rush of movement as one or another came forward to see who was passing by. Some shouted, cursing or begging. When the fragrance of her perfume reached them there was an incredulous silence followed by a burst of shouting. One man began sobbing. Her heart went out to every one of them whatever his crime. A death sentence would have been merciful in comparison with this living hell.

"Does my husband have any of the books and furniture I sent in when he was in the palace cells?" she asked, dismayed by the bleakness of some of the cells. As far as she could see there were only wood-lined walls, carved deeply with graffiti by countless inmates, a straw mattress on a wooden block for a bed, and a table with a stool or bench.

"He didn't when he was in the dungeon, but the doctor insisted that a prisoner of the Torrisi's standing should have his reading matter, his feather mattress and bed-linen, and all his own clothes restored to him. I will say your husband is not a difficult prisoner. He's quiet enough, keeps his self-respect, and takes a razor to his chin every day. Not like most, but then political prisoners are not usually housed here." They had reached a door, one of a series that the guard had unlocked and relocked along the route. Once more the captain used a key from the bunch on his belt. "Here we are. I shall lock up again after I've let you into the cell. There's no other way into this section and nobody can intrude. I'll return promptly at six o'clock tomorrow morning. Make sure you've said your farewells and be ready to leave instantly."

"Is my husband expecting me?"

"I was not obliged to notify him. All I have done has been for you, according to our agreement."

Marietta had thought she might find Domenico asleep, but as the captain opened the door, the glow of a candle showed through the bars topping the waist-high walls of the rectangular cell that ran parallel with the patrol corridor. She was able to look in at Domenico immediately. He was ready for the night in a well-worn velvet dressing-robe as he sat writing at a table. He did not look up. His dark hair had gained some grey at the temples and was tied back with a black ribbon. There was a high window in the corridor that would give him some light by day, but he would be able to see nothing through it. The dreadful solitude of his place of imprisonment struck her like a physical blow.

Captain Zeno had gone ahead to unlock the cell door at the far end, and she pulled away her mask and mantilla as she ran to it. Domenico, hearing the swish of silk, looked up in surprise and then saw her in the doorway. The quill dropped from his fingers, spattering ink, and he turned deathly white as if he feared he must be hallucinating. Then joy flooded his face, and its color returned, as he hurled himself from the bench and rushed to meet her. She threw herself into his arms. Neither heard the relocking of the door or the one beyond.

They kissed and wept, caressed each other's faces in an unconscious desire to confirm that they were truly together. She answered his flood of questions about Elizabetta and herself, and her mask-making and selling, while he took her cape and hung it over some of his own clothes on a peg. Then, embracing her again, he led her to a bench where they sat down together.

"What visiting time have you been allowed, Marietta?" He held her close, inhaling her perfume, holding her hand and putting his lips to her cheek. "Five minutes? Ten? Dare I hope for fifteen?"

She smiled, tracing his jawline with her fingertip, her heart contracting at how thin he was, how drawn and with such a hollow look across his eyes. "We have the whole night, my love."

He gave a low moan of bliss and buried his face in her hair. Then he drew back to look at her again, his gaze traveling over her and back to her tresses. "You have your hair in a new style. I like it."

She smiled, touching her curls. The latest mode was to leave the hair unpowdered and dressed wide instead of high in a softer look that was in keeping with the latest fashions. "I wanted to look my best for you."

Then she asked him how he had fared throughout his imprisonment, and about the nature of his illness, but he dismissed his own experiences lightly and made nothing of the fever that had laid him low. He was full of questions, which she answered, and when he gave her pause she told him that in her cape pocket she had some of Elizabetta's drawings and a few little gifts as well as the letters she had been saving for him from Antonio and his other two brothers in England and America.

"All that can come later," he said huskily, looking deeply into her eyes.

"So it can," she agreed. Then she glanced down to loosen her fichu and began to unfasten the bodice of her gown. His hand closed over hers.

"Let me do that," he said softly.

When they lay down naked on his narrow bed each was possessed with such overpowering desire for the other that their lovemaking was fierce and immediate and ecstatic, making her arch and cry out intensely as if even her womb had opened and received.

It was only when they began to make love the second time that they were able to re-explore each other's bodies as they had in the past, every curve and crevice kissed and caressed, bringing exquisite tremblings of sensual delight to her and power and pleasure to him.

During the night the candle spluttered low and he lit the wick of a new one to replace it. As he returned to the bed she propped herself on an elbow to ask him how he kept himself supplied with what he needed.

"I have sold several of my coats and some gloves and shoes. The guards will purchase anything and I have a few coins in hand for laundry and candles."

"I've brought you two bags of gold coins. I sold a ring."

"One you could spare, I hope. That money is most welcome. It should last me a very long time."

She rested a hand on his shoulder. "Maybe your innocence will be proved long before you've spent a quarter of it."

"I did prove it in court through those who spoke on my behalf, but that mass of twisted evidence weighed so heavily against me that justice was crushed out. Who would have thought that here in Venice, where even the humblest citizen is entitled to free legal aid, I, an upholder of those rights, would have been the victim of perjury!"

She was pleased to see that he was full of healthy anger, showing that in spite of all he had been through his spirit had in no way been broken. "Sebastiano told me to tell you that when the time seems right he will present a petition signed with many names to the Doge on your behalf."

"Tell him I'm deeply appreciative, but I cherish no illusions."

"The Doge was your friend! Surely—"

"In his eyes I offended against him and the State. Yet what I tried to do for La Serenissima I would do again even though it has brought me to these straits."

"I know you were right." She leaned forward and kissed him on the mouth.

"Who is living in the Palazzo Torrisi these days," he wanted to know. "Not Filippo Celano, I trust."

"No! I heard that he tried to buy it, but as it is state property he was refused. It hasn't been reopened since it was officially locked and bolted a few days after I left with Elizabetta. I suppose the valuables were removed to the Doge's treasury, but the windows remain barred and shuttered. So it's safe until you can reclaim it when you're a free man again."

He shook his head. "Should I ever have my liberty restored it would be on the condition of banishment from the Republic and nothing that I owned would be returned to me."

"We'll not be penniless! I still have all my jewelry except for that one ring. By selling only a few pieces we would be able to go far away and start our lives all over again."

"So we could." He smiled to bring their talk away from dreams to the present. "Show me those gifts you mentioned."

She left the bed to empty the pockets of her cape onto the table. The drawstring purses of money clinked when she put them down. There were news sheets, which Elizabetta had tied with ribbons; there were sweetmeats, a recently published book, a pack of cards, and a set of chessmen, although no board. "I thought you might be able to mark out a bench or table."

"Wonderful!"

"I will leave you to look at everything after I'm—" She broke off. "There is one gift that I promised Elizabetta I would show you myself."

"Bring it to me."

He sat up as she knelt on the bed to hand him the gift, which was in a small leather-covered box. He opened it to find a new miniature of Elizabetta, which had been painted shortly after her ninth birthday. He studied it for quite a while in silence before he spoke.

"She is more like Elena than ever now. Do you know who fathered her?"

Marietta was so aghast that she threw up her hands to cover her face and bowed over until her head almost touched her knees, swaying in her distress. "You know! Merciful heaven! How long have you known?"

"I always knew there was something about Elizabetta's birth that was being kept from me. You were quite withdrawn at times. I thought perhaps you'd come close to death, but Adrianna reassured me about that. There was also your reluctance to wear the birthgift I brought you from Russia, and yet I heard you tell others you had never seen a more beautiful parure. Since it's not like you to make empty remarks, this was another thing that seemed odd to me. After we had talked out that spy's report and everything seemed normal again I put the matter from my mind. Then came that evening when we suddenly found ourselves face to face with Elena at the opera house."

Marietta was still unable to look at him and her voice croaked. "I think I know what you are about to say."

"That I saw the likeness? Yes, that was it. In the first instant when Elena smiled it was as if an adult Elizabetta stood before us. That was when everything began to fall into place. The next day when I danced Elizabetta in my arms in front of a mirror, I saw her mother in her as clearly as if the truth had been shouted at me."

Marietta's fingers stretched wide across her face and she drove them into her hair as her brow came to rest on her knees. "I don't know how to bear this!"

"That's just how I felt at the time."

"Yet you said nothing!"

"I loved the child. I had thought of her as my own too long to consider her in any other light. She was innocent of the game that had been played with her life. What happened to our baby? Did you miscarry?"

"He was stillborn."

"Oh, my God!" His groan racked through him.

Slowly she raised her head and shook back her hair. He sat with an updrawn knee, his arm folded across it, and his eyes were closed in anguish. Hesitantly she began to tell him how it had all come about. He neither opened his eyes nor moved. When she had finished all she had to say, even that Elizabetta had a strain of Celano blood in her veins, he still remained motionless. If only he had flown into a well-justified temper, which would have been more in character, she could have responded in kind until some sort of healing took place. It was a measure of the depth of his agony that he should be so silent. She did not dare to touch him.

"Do you hate us both?" she whispered fearfully.

He opened his eyes as he turned his head to look at her. "Any hate I've ever felt has never brushed against you or Elizabetta. I have had plenty of time during my incarceration in this place to evaluate my life and to know what matters most to me. It's been a comfort to think of your having the companionship of our daughter, for that is what she is, except for an accident of birth in more senses than one."

"I'm hoping that out of this night I shall have conceived again." She seemed unable to raise her voice above a whisper as if the momentum of all that had been revealed had affected her vocal chords. When he made no comment she turned away and pressed her fingers over her quivering mouth. Then she felt his hand slowly drawing her hair back from her face.

"If that doesn't happen," he said quietly, "it won't be through any lack of love between us."

As she looked at him again, he gave a serious smile and drew her to him, her head coming to rest against his shoulder. It was as if they had crossed a great abyss together and were resting safely on the other side.

When Captain Zeno unlocked the door at six o'clock they were both dressed and standing with their arms around each other. Obedient to the captain's instructions, Marietta and Domenico immediately exchanged a last fleeting kiss and then she went through the door with a swirl of her cape. As they had arranged, she did not look back after the key was turned on him once more. He did not want her to remember him looking through the bars at her, although he watched her out of sight.

When Marietta emerged from the prison Sebastiano was waiting for her. The tears she had kept back at her parting with Domenico now overwhelmed her and she was thankful for Sebastiano's arm as he supported her to the waiting gondola.

Afterward, as day followed day, Marietta was so haunted by Domenico's living conditions that she could scarcely eat, and at night she found it impossible to sleep. Lucretia's instruction in serving at the shop was given by an assistant and her first singing lesson postponed several times before Marietta felt duty-bound to begin teaching her. Elizabetta, as if sensing that Marietta's thoughts were elsewhere, became difficult and naughty. This added to the strain from which Marietta seemed unable to surface. Adrianna and Elena, whom she had told of her visit to the prison, became increasingly concerned about her, but none of their good advice had any effect. It was as if Marietta had willed herself into sharing Domenico's suffering.

Then, early one morning as she wearily left her bed, she experienced a queasiness that was strangely familiar. As the possible reason dawned on her she was overcome by a bout of nausea from which she emerged with rising hope. Throughout that day the improvement in her mood was marked by Adrianna and by those working with her in the shop. Before long Marietta knew beyond any doubt that she was pregnant. Only then did she write to tell Domenico. The letter she eventually received in reply confirmed that he shared her joy.

Sisters Sylvia and Giaccomina came with Bianca to call on Elena after the siesta hour one afternoon, only to discover that she was away from home. Not wanting to miss an outing, they decided to visit Adrianna instead.

Bianca was permitted to go on her own into the shop next door in search of Marietta. An assistant showed her through to the office. Marietta, looking up from the accounts, smiled with surprise and closed the ledger immediately, returning her quill pen to its stand.

"Am I interrupting your work?" Bianca asked. She had grown tall and willowy with a fine figure and a delicate beauty.

"Not at all. Sit down. I didn't expect to see you here again so soon. It's a pleasant diversion for me."

Bianca explained how the visit had come about. "Signor Celano was at the palace and invited us to stay for refreshments, but the nuns chose otherwise. He is immensely interested in my flute-playing, always inquiring about my progress. I told him that I'll be going to Padua with the orchestra soon for a concert."

"Are you? That's splendid. I went there several times to sing. It is an interesting old city."

"So Signor Celano told me." She smiled dreamily, playing absently with her Pietà medallion on its silver chain. "I would have heard more about the place if we had stayed. What a dear man he is!" A soft sigh escaped her and she leaned back in her chair. "Elena can't have a care in the world, living as she does in such a grand palace with such an attractive husband."

Marietta eyed her thoughtfully. Surely the girl was not cherishing romantic dreams of Filippo? Yet, though Bianca was eighteen, that Pietà-protected ingenuousness would make her susceptible to an experienced man's compliments and smiles, even though she was shy in male company. At a recent Pietà reception Marietta had seen her constant blushes and her swift drifting away from men eager to pay her amorous attention.

"You mustn't let yourself be deceived by appearances," Marietta advised. It was impossible to elaborate to the girl.

"I'm not," Bianca answered, believing her own words. "I've never heard Elena say a word against him."

"No, I'm sure you haven't," Marietta commented without expression. It was only to Adrianna and herself that Elena opened her heart. The keen sense of responsibility Marietta had always felt for her goddaughter, even though there were not many years between them, welled up. Maybe it was time the girl emerged from the chrysalis of the Pietà into the outside world. "I was wondering if you would like to come and work in the mask-shop. I need another assistant, and you would have your own room in my apartment. Elizabetta and I would be happy to have you with us."

Smiling, Bianca tilted her head to one side as she regarded Marietta fondly. "Dear, kind Marietta. That is what I had always hoped for when I was growing up, wanting to be your sister in a family. But things are different now." Her voice dropped a note. "My future lies at the Pietà. After another three or four years with the orchestra I shall become a full-time teacher there."

Marietta could understand how the settled routine and security of the Pietà would appeal to the girl's gentle temperament. "Is that what you really want?"

Bianca lowered her lashes. "Not exactly, but it is the only option open to me. The man I love is married to someone else."

Marietta was dismayed. What she had suspected seemed to have been confirmed. "Tell me you don't mean Filippo Celano!"

Bianca threw up her head defiantly. "I know you don't like him because of the vendetta, but how can you judge? You've never talked to him or known how brave he has been about that terrible scar. There is something so boyish about him when he is with me. I believe I understand him better than anyone else and he realizes that, but daren't tell me." She clasped her hands together in her lap. "But you needn't worry. He'll never know how I feel about him and neither will Elena. I've only told you because you're my godmother and have a right to know why I intend to stay on at the Pietà."

"Oh, my dear." Marietta felt relief. This misplaced worship from afar would soon fade. Venice was full of young men who Bianca would notice eventually and many of them visited the Pietà. "What you have said shall remain between us. It's right that nobody else should know. But if you do change your mind about coming here you have only to say. Even if by some miracle Domenico should be released from prison it would make no difference, because he was in agreement when I once mentioned I should like you to live with us one day."

"How you must miss him!" The girl's voice was full of sympathy.

"He is never out of my mind. One day he has to be free again and I live for that."

Bianca kept to herself her doubt that it would ever be.

It was Adrianna who first remarked on the increasing time lapses between Elena's visits. "I don't understand it. She never used to miss visiting on any one of the children's birthdays, but recently if those days are out of her routine calling she simply sends a gift with a servant."

"It's the same with our walks," Marietta remarked, puzzled. "She is full of reasons why she can't manage to meet me on one day or another."

Adrianna did not say any more, but it seemed to her that Elena's seeing less of the two of them dated from Marietta's telling her friends under a seal of secrecy about her pregnancy.

When Marietta next met Bianca at the Pietà she asked the girl if she saw Elena as often as before.

"Yes," Bianca replied. "In fact I'm seeing her even more because Sister Giaccomina and I are recataloguing a small section of the Celano library. She is such an authority on ancient volumes and I was her choice as an assistant."

"Doesn't the work interfere with your music?"

"I take my flute with me and practice there whenever Sister Giaccomina doesn't need me, which is quite often." Bianca's eyes danced. "I believe she would like to make the task last as long as possible. Signor Celano has as many priceless books as Domenico had in his library, according to her."

Marietta was still puzzled. "I can't understand why the Pietà should have been approached when the great library in the Piazzetta would have provided someone for the work. I suppose Elena must have suggested Sister Giaccomina to her husband."

Bianca made no comment. "Why did you ask me about Elena?"

"Neither Adrianna nor I have seen her for three weeks. She must be extremely busy."

"Is she? She often wanders into the library to see how we're getting on and sometimes she listens to me when I'm practicing on my flute in the neighboring salon and gives me guidance."

"Do you see much of Filippo?" Marietta asked directly.

"No. He came once to the library to make sure that the nun and I had settled in and had all we needed." Bianca shook her head in emphasis. "I told you all there was to tell a while ago. Nothing is amiss and it never will be."

Marietta tried to be reassured.

After she had gone, Bianca went to rehearsal. She was beginning to resent any activity that kept her away from the Palazzo Celano, for every time she went there she hoped Filippo would come again to the library. During that one short visit he had told her, out of the nun's earshot, that it made him content just to see her there. "In my hectic and somewhat troubled life, Signorina Bianca, you are like a ray of sunshine," he had said.

That was all, but she had hugged his words to her and quite often she still felt shy with pleasure at the thought of his paying her such a compliment. She had known already from Sister Giaccomina that when he had interviewed the nun at the Pietà he had suggested that his wife's goddaughter would be a good choice as her assistant.

"I'm only a kind of adopted goddaughter to Elena," Bianca had felt bound to point out to the nun.

Sister Giaccomina had held up her hands and laughed, already exulting in the honor of having been entrusted with the commission. "The way she helped Marietta look after you and nurse you when you were sick and the constant encouragement she has given you over the years in your flute-playing must give her the right to consider you her goddaughter, even if she did not actually make the vows at your baptism."

As the rehearsal dragged on, Bianca wished there was some way she could avoid these sessions, but that was impossible. Fortunately the number of music lessons she was obliged to give had been reduced to one at an early hour each day. At least Sister Giaccomina never went to the Palazzo Celano without her and they were going again that afternoon.

Elena was on her way out when they arrived. Bianca told her about Marietta's visit. "She was concerned that neither she nor Adrianna had seen you recently."

"I'm on my way to the Calle della Madonna now," Elena replied.

When Bianca and the nun had been working for two hours, a steward brought them some refreshments. Afterward, Sister Giaccomina sent her to practice in the salon that opened out from the library. As always, Bianca left the door between the two rooms ajar. She set her music on the stand she was permitted to keep there, and it was not until she came to the end of her second piece that she realized another door had opened silently to admit a listener. His applause took her by surprise and she turned swiftly. Filippo stood in the doorway several feet from her and made no move to come nearer.

"There are love-words to that traditional Venetian piece. Do you know them, Bianca?"

"I have heard them."

"Refresh my memory."

"I can't." She was flustered. To speak such passionate words to him was out of the question, even in the form of a poem, which it had been before being set to music long ago. "The words are written on the music sheet if you wish to read them."

Hastily she snatched the music sheet from the stand, scattering others to the floor, and held it out to him. He came across the room and took it from her, but before glancing at it he stooped down even as she did to gather up the fallen sheets. After these had been returned to the stand, Bianca remarking how clumsy it had been of her, he looked at the song again. She was intensely conscious of his height and powerful masculinity. She had never felt more vulnerable. Had she not formed her own judgement of him as a dear man, it might have been possible to believe that he could have snapped her spine like the stem of a flower.

"Shall I read it aloud?" he asked. "I want to please you."

"No! Read it to yourself," she insisted.

He glanced sideways at her. She was as frantic as a graceful, swanlike bird fearful of being netted. "You mustn't mind my flirting with you a little. Most women expect it."

"I like nothing false."

He was inwardly amused. "I'll remember that in future," he promised glibly. "In the meantime, would you object to my singing the song? I know it well."

She relaxed immediately. The world of song was entirely different from unembellished spoken words. "I won't offer to accompany you on my flute, but I do play the harpsichord as well."

"Then you shall sing with me!" He caught her by the hand and slid with her, as if on a frozen canal, across the marble floor to the harpsichord at one end of the room. She laughed and he with her. If he had not caught her by the arms when they came to a halt she might have fallen. His gaze went to her mouth, but she moved swiftly away to seat herself at the harpsichord. He put the music in front of her and she sang with him as she played. Their duet brought Sister Giaccomina from the library as Bianca had known it would. The nun smiled and listened attentively.

"I had not expected a concert at this hour of the day, Signor Celano," she reproved gently when the song had come to its end. "It was enjoyable, but you have interrupted Bianca's practice time. I had sent her in here for that reason."

Filippo bowed to her. "My apologies, Sister. It was remiss of me. I trust you and Bianca will both forgive me."

The syrup worked. The nun was reassured. As he left the room he held Bianca's eyes with his own. She thought she read in them all that had been conveyed by the love-song, and she spent the rest of the day in a dreamlike state. Even though he loved Elena he had deep feelings for her too. She saw Filippo and herself as two noble people turning away from temptation. At the same time she discovered that the burden of self-sacrifice could be extremely heavy.

Elena was no longer at ease with Marietta. Her friend's new pregnancy had renewed her feelings of guilt for having failed to prevent Domenico's incarceration, and this burden was eroding the bond that years of close friendship had built up. Indirectly it had affected Elena's relationship with Adrianna too, since visits to the Savoni household often meant seeing Marietta as well. Elena had begun to dread their concerned queries about her noticeable absences, which somehow she managed to fend off with excuses that she hoped sounded reasonable. It was the difficulty of keeping up this front that made her cut down even more the times she went to see them. Yet these two Pietà women were still her dearest friends, their well-being all important to her, and her feelings for them unchanged.

The drifting apart, however, could not be rectified so long as Domenico was in prison. Elena despised herself for having failed to gather anything to aid his defense during the trial. Nothing could shake her conviction that if she had used her wits better or strained her ears harder, she would have gathered some proof of the conspiracy that the Celanos had plotted against him. Her sense of shame at her failure, which had never left her, renewed itself to a point where she scarcely knew how to live with herself whenever she remembered that Marietta, now into her fifth month, was to bring up a second child without the man who should have been at her side.

Again and again Elena went back in her mind, trying to imagine what else she could have done in Domenico's cause and what her own incompetence had caused her to overlook. As well as eavesdropping at the meetings —pathetic in itself as she recalled, with a sting of embarrassment, the lawyer's almost derisive comment—she had searched through Filippo's desk and anywhere else that might have revealed papers from those conclaves of the Celano brothers. Had she been as diligent as possible in that search? How could she be sure of anything when blame weighed so heavily on her brain?

"Sister Giaccomina and Bianca are at the Palazzo Celano again this afternoon," Elena said as she sat drinking hot chocolate with her two friends at Adrianna's house.

"Are they making progress with the cataloguing?" Adrianna asked.

"Yes, and it shouldn't be a long task." Elena smiled. "Except that Sister Giaccomina sometimes becomes lost in the contents of the books! But Filippo doesn't seem to mind and I look forward to their coming. When Bianca practices her flute it's like having a little bird singing somewhere in the palace."

"She has come a long way since you started her on a reed pipe," Marietta remarked reminiscently. "If you hadn't encouraged her she might have been lost to the musical side of the Pietà."

"So did you, Marietta. You helped her far more generally than I."

Adrianna changed the subject then and Marietta, having noted that Elena's instinctive loyalty to herself was unchanged, wondered again why she never seemed relaxed when she came to see them these days. It had made Adrianna feel uncertain about calling at the Palazzo Celano, and

Elena did not ask her to visit as often as before. It could not be worry over Bianca, because Elena would have spoken openly about that.

"Do let's go for a walk again soon," Marietta suggested, hoping that when they were on their own Elena might come out with whatever it was that had brought about this change in her.

"We will," Elena agreed a trifle too eagerly, "but let's wait until the spring. You know how I feel the cold." She glanced at the clock. "I really must go."

Marietta was taken aback by the deliberate rebuff and her anger flashed. Elena had never felt the cold, always declaring herself invigorated by it. "Don't make such foolish excuses, Elena! What's the matter with you? We hardly see you these days and when you do come you're like a cat on hot bricks, watching the clock and trying to leave as soon as you possibly can!"

Elena, who had risen to leave, saw that Marietta had finally lost patience with her. Again her shame washed over her, but it was too painful to speak of; and she believed that if she did explain what was troubling her, both Adrianna and Marietta would see her as the fool and coward she was. That was a final humiliation she could not endure. She made the first excuse that came into her head. "I've met a lot of new people over the past few months and they take up my time. New friends are always so demanding."

"So are old ones when they care for you," Adrianna intervened quietly, "but that comes from the best of motives."

"I know!" Elena spoke a little wildly, looking as if she wanted to take to her heels. She had never expected this terrible situation to come to such a climax. Then, to her horror, a deep-rooted cry from her heart took her as much by surprise as it did her friends. "But what can you expect of me with my own child gone, one of you pregnant, and the other surrounded by children!"

She spun around and rushed for the door. Adrianna tried to stop her but Elena shook off the well-meaning hand in a kind of fury and tore out of the house. Marietta started to follow her, but Adrianna blocked the way.

"Elena is in no state to listen. Don't upset yourself. I'll go and talk to her tomorrow when she has calmed down."

Elena had been half expecting Adrianna and was prepared when she arrived the following day and expressed the worry that had brought her.

"I behaved badly yesterday," Elena apologized. She was seated in a velvet robe in front of her dressing-table, having slept until noon after a night of dancing.

Adrianna had a smile in her eyes. "I've seen you in a mood many times before. I've never forgotten your first days at the Pietà."

Elena gave an amused little grimace. "It's a wonder I wasn't thrown out." She twisted around on the stool to look directly at Adrianna and spoke truthfully. "I'm not in the least jealous of you and Marietta and I never have been. Nobody could be more pleased than I that she is to have another baby."

"I know that and so does she. So what is troubling you?"

Elena looked away. "Nothing that I can talk about." Her tone brooked no more questioning. "All I can say is that it's best if I stay away for a while. Maybe with time I'll feel able to come and see you both again, but meanwhile all I ask is that you both have patience with me."

"You don't even have to ask that. Are you sure there is nothing I can do to help you?"

Elena shook her head decisively. "Nothing."

Adrianna left soon afterward and Elena did not press her to stay. Both she and Marietta felt the visit had not been satisfactory, but there was nothing more to be done at the present time.

"We must just wait until she has worked out whatever problem she has and can return to us," Adrianna said philosophically. Reluctantly Marietta agreed.

Elena had not lied when she spoke of new friends. There were some among the Venetian nobility who had previously been prevented by the vendetta from having any real social contact with her. Their loyalties had been with the Torrisis, but with the ancient feud now in limbo they were able to become more closely acquainted with her, although not necessarily with Filippo. But since she and her husband now went their own ways much of the time, he did not have to be considered in any case.

Elena's social circle thus became even more extensive and there was never an hour after midday when she was free of engagements. She indulged in flirtations, but nothing more, although there were many men forever trying to have liaisons with her. Her loyalty was not to Filippo but to Nicolò, even though he had gone from her life. There was no other man who could take his place.

Among the rakes and *débauchés* of Venice, Elena's reputation as a faithful wife only added to her attraction in their eyes. They vied with one another to be the first to seduce her, but wagers laid on success were always lost. Frequently, when the company was entirely masked, Filippo would hear snippets of conversation about his wife that upheld his conviction that she would never dare to cuckold him. Yet he had finally reached the conclusion that he would have to be rid of her.

When Alessandro came on a visit from Rome, Filippo asked him what the chances were of the Pope allowing the marriage to be annulled.

"None!" Alessandro replied crisply. "Because I would oppose it. You say yourself that Elena has given you no cause for complaint beyond her failure to have children. I recently spoke to a man whose wife had given birth at the time of life when her childbearing days were ending. That was after twenty-two years of marriage."

"My patience has run out! I want an heir soon!"

"Wait another few years. Then, if the situation remains the same, legally surrender your authority to Pietro to allow him to marry."

"What!" Filippo's face was congested with temper. "You would expect me to do that?"

"It would be your duty."

"Duty be damned! I was born to be the true head of this house and I'll die as its head."

"I can assure you that Pietro would never want to live in Venice. Your creature comforts would be undisturbed."

"No!"

"I have advised you and I leave it at that for the time being," Alessandro said coolly. "I'll remind you that you have only yourself to blame for your predicament. Any other woman would probably have given you a quiverful of children, but your deadly sin of greed caused your bitter jealousy of your brother and your determination to have everything that was his, including the girl who would have been Marco's bride."

"Don't give me any pious talk," Filippo sneered. "What's happened to you? Are you aiming to be the next Venetian pope?"

Alessandro did not blink. "That is my hope," he admitted smoothly.

"So that's why you refuse to intercede on my behalf for an annulment of my marriage! You don't want your family to be involved in any hint of matrimonial trouble that might taint your chances!"

"That is correct. So let's drop the subject." Alessandro held up an authoritative hand. "I shall go to the mainland tomorrow to visit Mother. Have you seen her recently?"

Filippo had stalked to the window where he stood glaring out. "I haven't set eyes on her since she left here for the last time."

Alessandro went across to him and put a hand on his shoulder. "Come with me tomorrow. Lavinia has written that Mother is not long for this world."

"Go alone. I have nothing to say to the old woman. She would mock me with her last breath."

With a shake of his head Alessandro went from the room. Filippo thumped a fist against the window frame in angry frustration and then turned around to pace the room. His brother had destroyed his last hope for the annulment of his marriage, forcing him to turn to other means. His mother's evil advice had come often into his mind, making him loathe her more each time for she must have known that her words would remain in his blood. How satisfied the old hag would be if she knew that he had finally come across a powerful and effective antidote to the sexual attraction Elena had always had for him. As so often happens in life to a man of his age, a younger woman had eclipsed all others for him.

Many men at forty had already lost a wife or two in childbirth, giving them the chance to take a new young bride, but whereas their opportunities came by natural means his must come by violent action. He had no choice. In Bianca with her lovely face and figure, that beautiful silver-gilt hair and her enchanting girlish ways, he would recapture his youth and make a new beginning. She was already in love with him. He had only to clear the way for her.

Two hurdles to the task still remained. First, everything had to be planned to the last detail so that no suspicion would fall upon him. Secondly, only he could settle Elena's fate. It was an old resolve that could not be shifted.

When Alessandro arrived at his mother's house he was struck by how tired and old his sister looked. After nursing her mother night and day, there were few traces left to show that Lavinia had once been a pretty woman.

"How is Mother today?" he asked after they had greeted each other.

"Very poorly, but she has been looking forward to seeing you. Alvise and Vitale rarely come and Maurizio only occasionally. Pietro would travel from Padua to see her if she would allow it. He writes to me about his doctoring and I send him what family news I can."

"I have a regular correspondence with him. Recently I had some skin trouble on my hands and he sent me an ointment that cleared it up."

Lavinia knew how proud Alessandro was of his pale, long-fingered hands. "He is very skillful. I'll take you to Mother straight away. She will be annoyed if I keep you talking."

Apollina Celano, looking small and shrunken, was propped against lacy pillows in her huge bed. Her eyes glinted with pride at the fine sight her eldest son made in the scarlet brilliance of his rustling soutane. The heavy cross he wore was studded with magnificent jewels. He had grown more handsome with the years and his ambitions had kept pace. He kissed her hand and then her cheek before sitting on the chair at her bedside.

"Well, Mother, how are you?"

"You can see how I am," she snapped, envious of his strength and health. "You'll all soon be free of me. But don't start wanting to pray at my bedside. I've my own priest for that. Tell me the latest scandals from Rome."

He gave a quiet, reproving laugh. "Mother, I don't give my time to listening to idle gossip."

"Then you've become a duller fellow with the years. Why are you making a steeple of your fingertips in that affected way?"

He had not been aware of it, having become used to holding his fingers together in a saintlike pose when sitting. "I did not come here to be criticized as if I were still six years old," he said firmly. "I thought you'd like to know I've spoken firmly to Filippo about the lack of an heir. I must say it's a misfortune on our house that takes the edge off our triumph in vanquishing the Torrisis."

"The House of Torrisi still lives all the time Domenico Torrisi draws breath."

"But he will be in prison until he dies. I made a point of discussing the matter when I had an audience with the Doge, who told me the name of Torrisi had been struck from the Golden Book. The question of a pardon on one of the feast days is out of the question. Domenico was shown the only leniency that will ever be granted him in not being condemned to torture or a painful death."

Apollina's eyes flashed under their wrinkled, pigmented lids. "The Torrisi wouldn't have lived as long as this in his imprisonment if I'd been well enough to bribe poison into his food!"

"It's not so easily done these days as when you were young," Alessandro answered sternly, drawing back in his chair as if trying to disassociate himself from her venomous tongue. "In any case I would have forbidden such an act just as I refused to intercede with the Pope to help Filippo to annul his marriage."

"So he's finally waking up, is he?" It was the best news her eldest son could have brought her because it meant that Filippo had begun to think along the lines she had set him. She was glad Alessandro had refused to help with an annulment. That could sometimes drag on for years, which meant Filippo would not dare make a move against Elena in the interim lest he place himself under suspicion. "Do you know what I believe?"

"What is that?"

"The fool has always been half in love with Elena and hasn't known it."

Alessandro pondered her words. Since she had never shown love to any of her children except Marco, it was quite logical that Filippo, having grown up without affection, would be too warped to recognize love within himself. Alessandro had made a study of human nature and knew there was nothing more complex than mankind.

"I have advised Filippo," he said, "to think seriously about handing over his authority to Pietro if he is still childless in a few years time. That would not mean surrendering the Palazzo Celano or other properties or the land that normally goes with the estate. Pietro would not have need of it anyway since he seems destined to follow in my footsteps with good works, although not entering into Holy Orders yet awhile. I've advised him to bide his time over taking vows in case it proves necessary for him to shoulder the burden of becoming head of the House of Celano."

"Good works!" his mother echoed with contempt. "The only good works you have done since you left Venice have been for your own benefit. With you dealing out ecclesiastical favors at the top end of the scale, and Pietro who wastes his time on the shiftless poor at the other, a fine couple of sons you make!"

It took all Alessandro's self-control to stop him from losing his patience with this sick old woman who was also his mother. Deliberately he ignored her taunt. "I daresay when the time comes Filippo will see reason."

"He'll never do that!" she declared with conviction.

"We shall see," he said levelly, already revising his original intention to stay several days with her. Twenty-four hours would suffice.

Elena had decided to search again for whatever might have been written down at the time of the plotting against Domenico. The notion had come to her suddenly one night when she was on the point of sleep that Filippo would want a full account of his vanquishing of the Torrisis to be lodged in the family archives. His conceit would not allow him to let such an historical event escape the records for future generations. Even if Maurizio had kept their notes in his leather file, he would have had to surrender them to Filippo when all was done, even if he had kept a copy.

She sat up in bed on this enlightening thought. The most likely place to look was the treasure room. Elena wished she could leap from her bed and begin her search immediately, but that was not possible. In any case, this matter must not be rushed. As she returned her head to her pillow she pictured Marietta presenting the evidence of Filippo's plot to the Doge himself, resulting in an immediate release for Domenico. Then all would be mended and her own guilt at having failed would be wiped away. She and Marietta could take up their friendship again and her link with Adrianna would be restored.

Elena's first step was to gain access to the treasure room on a day when she and Filippo were to attend a ball. It was the most likely place to find what she was looking for, and Filippo always gave her the key without question when she wanted to select a piece of the heirloom jewelry that was kept in caskets there. She made her request for the key just as Filippo was going out so that she could count on having the whole afternoon for her search.

No one could have been more thorough. By the light of a candle-lamp she began systematically with the chests of ancient documents. Even those that were yellow with age did not remain undisturbed, for although she did not examine them she turned them over. There was always the possibility she would find newer papers underneath. She went through chest after chest and there were still many others left when finally she locked the door again. For once she had given no thought to which of the heirloom necklaces she would wear and had snatched up the first at hand on her way out. Throughout the following weeks she repeated these visits until she was absolutely sure that nothing had been overlooked. It was time to direct her efforts elsewhere.

It was the last day of the cataloguing. As Bianca penned the final entry under Sister Giaccomina's direction she was not far from tears. The past months had been the best in her whole life. She was glad she could look Elena in the eye without guilt, for never by any word or deed had she encouraged Filippo, and nothing untoward had passed between them. Yet whenever they had met, sometimes only for a matter of minutes, his every look, smile, and word was hers to mull over happily afterward.

"There!" the nun said with satisfaction as Bianca put down her pen. "That's all finished. We'll let Signor Celano know and then we can go back to the Pietà."

"I'll go and tell him." Bianca was quick to leave her chair.

"Very well. I'll start packing up."

A servant directed Bianca to a salon on another floor. She tapped on the door and then entered. Filippo was with an art dealer and studying a painting, one of several that were propped about the room, but he grinned spontaneously when he saw her.

"Good! I can have a second opinion. Come over here and tell me which of these paintings you like best."

Bianca went eagerly to help him select. He took her by the hand as she reached his side as if to be sure of keeping her close. The one he had been scrutinizing was by Longhi and showed a lady sipping hot chocolate, a lap dog on the sofa beside her. "That's charming," she said.

"There's another Longhi next to it."

They moved to view it and she liked that painting as well. In fact as they went to each in turn there was not one she did not care for. "I like them all and so can't cast a vote on your behalf."

"But if you were choosing for yourself which one would it be?" he persisted.

She did not hesitate. "That one!" It showed a young masked couple clearly in love and painted in sunshine amidst a crowd of Carnival revelers cavorting in the Piazzetta.

"Why?" Filippo asked with interest.

"Because I can see they're"—she quickly amended what she had been about to say since her own feelings for him were too near the surface—"so friendly."

Filippo laughed under his breath. "They're passionate lovers, my dear. The young woman has fair hair like yours. It's a Tiepolo and it shall be delivered to the Pietà for you."

"Oh, no!" She was embarrassed. "I couldn't possibly accept it."

"It is in appreciation of the library work you have done. Sister Giaccomina is to receive a book that I know will please her. Let there be no more argument."

"I don't know how to thank you."

"If you are pleased with it, that is all the thanks I want." He turned to the dealer. "See that the Tiepolo is delivered today and I'll take this Longhi and the Marieschi."

The art dealer bowed his appreciation of the order. Filippo put his arm familiarly about Bianca's waist and led her into the neighboring salon, closing the door behind them.

"I came to tell you that the cataloguing is finished," she said, drawing away from him.

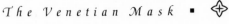

"Is it? Well done. I shall miss your pretty face, but there will be more cataloguing later on if you and Sister Giaccomina are agreeable."

"Oh, we shall be!" Her eagerness was quite transparent. "Which books would those be?"

"They're stored presently at one of my villas where they have never been read or listed."

"Sister Giaccomina and I will be honored to carry out the work."

"How obliging of you." He moved close to her and saw her alarm at his nearness blend with the love she could not hide. The next instant he pulled her into his arms and crushed his mouth down on hers, kissing her as no virgin should be kissed the first time. He felt her spine stiffen with initial shock and then she became supple and yielding, her whole body quivering. When he lifted his head again she remained motionless with her eyes downcast and he ran a gentle hand over her hair and down her face. Still without looking at him, she spoke in a soft, strangled voice.

"I'll not come here again. Someone else must help Sister Giaccomina. I can't accept the painting under any circumstances."

He copied her solemn tones. "I think that is as well. I had never expected a young woman to set out to tempt me in my own home."

Her startled eyes flew open. "I didn't!" She was flustered and at a loss for words. "I mean, how could you think such a thing?"

"Why did you come on your own to me?" He was looking suitably bewildered.

"My only intention was to deliver a message!" she cried. "You've come to see me when I've been at my flute practice."

"But then Sister Giaccomina was within earshot in the library. In this part of the palace the whole situation is different. Or perhaps you knew I had an art dealer with me?"

"No," she admitted tremulously.

"So you expected to find me alone?"

"Yes, I suppose so. Oh, I don't know what I'm saying any more!" She pressed the side of her clenched hand to her lips in distress, as if to silence any more foolish talk. "I wish I could die! I never wanted you to think such a thing of me. Don't tell Elena! She would believe her kindness to me betrayed."

He was finding the whole incident thoroughly entertaining, although in no way should she suspect it. "I suggest we pretend the kiss never happened. I'm willing to forget this whole little contretemps if you are."

She looked at him gratefully. "Could we do that?"

"Of course! We're friends, are we not?" He stretched out his hands at arm's length. With relief in her face she put hers into his.

"Then you truly believe I had no intention of causing any indirect hurt to your wife?" she asked to reassure herself.

"I do." He let her hands fall. "I'll go with you to the library. You and Sister Giaccomina shall have a glass of wine with me before leaving. Perhaps if we are fortunate Elena will have returned from calling on an acquaintance and can join us."

His fond reference to Elena reassured Bianca. With the resilience of youth she soon forgot the embarrassment she had suffered. Whenever she gazed at the Tiepolo painting on the wall of her room at the Pietà she remembered only Filippo's kiss. It was, she had decided, the one romantic encounter of her life. For that alone it would be privately treasured.

Chapter 14

E*lena continued her diligent search. She fumed at* the interruption to her task when she had to accompany Filippo to his villa from late June until the end of August. Afterward, much of her time was taken up with social arrangements such as the supervision of preparations for extravagant events at the Palazzo Celano, including one of the grandest masked balls ever seen in Venice. It was as if Filippo could not celebrate enough the defeat of the Torrisis no matter how many years slid by.

The Pietà orchestra was engaged by Filippo to play at most of these brilliant occasions. He made sure that when his many guests withdrew from the ballroom for supper, the Pietà instrumentalists had a chance to dance themselves under the nuns' supervision. Their partners were willing volunteers among the young male guests and the music was supplied by another band of musicians hired for that single purpose. Elena, busy seeing to her guests in the supper room, did not know that Filippo never failed to break away and dance at least once with Bianca.

When her careful search of Filippo's desk, shelves, and innumerable files brought forth nothing of interest, Elena turned to a number of chests of drawers and several places of concealment that she knew about. Finally she went back to the tall cupboard in Filippo's bedchamber, although the prospect of going through it again did not offer her much hope.

The task was difficult because she had to watch out that Filippo's valet did not suddenly come into the room and catch her at the cupboard. He was a sly fellow and would soon let his master know. More than once when she had searched previously she had narrowly missed being discovered. But it had to be done.

It was safest to carry out her task when Filippo dined late with only male guests. On these occasions she was not expected to make an appearance and they sat long hours at the table drinking and talking. The valet would lay out Filippo's nightshirt, fold back the sheet, and not reappear until the guests began reeling drunkenly to the water portico and their waiting gondolas.

Elena had searched all but the upper quarter of the cupboard, when an evening came on which Filippo was to hold one of these dinners. With her task in mind, she had returned from the theater early after declining to accompany her friends to a casino. A reassuring burst of raucous laughter at some bawdy joke came from the dining room as Elena went up the stairs. She could count on having the next two or three hours uninterrupted.

Her maid helped her undress and when Elena was alone again she slipped out of bed and took from a closet a velvet robe with deep pockets. She had to be sure that she could conceal quickly anything she might find. The sconces in Filippo's bedchamber were burning when she went through the communicating door. First she locked his door into the corridor. She was about to embark on the final stage of a desperate endeavor and no precaution could be overlooked. The bedchamber chairs were ornate and heavy but she pulled one to the front of the cupboard, stepped up onto it, and opened the upper doors to begin her painstaking task.

Her hope was that she would find another secret drawer like the one with the painting and the ring, and she concentrated on pushing and sliding and pressing her fingertips over every inch of wood, carved and plain. Nothing gave or moved or creaked. She let her aching arms drop to her side as she faced defeat on a wave of bitter disappointment. She had been so hopeful! But she had failed.

Wearily she was about to step down from the chair when she reconsidered the secret drawer she had discovered previously. It had been quite wide but shallow. Suppose it was a foil to hide another? Swiftly she slid up the piece of carving that concealed it. Pulling the drawer out carefully she saw that behind it there was only plain wood. Yet no sooner had she pressed it than what had appeared to be the back of the cupboard fell down like a lid to reveal a cavity. In it was a file of papers! Convinced that she had found what she was looking for at last, she drew them out. A hasty scan of the first few pages showed that she was right. Carefully she returned the file and replaced the drawer. Now that she knew where the evidence was, she could take the file just before she went out the next day. She would like to fly with it to Marietta this very night and seek a safe place to hide, but that was impossible. Servants were still moving about the palace and she dared not risk the ill chance that Filippo, drunk though he would be when he came to bed, might be in the habit of checking occasionally that the papers were safe—or, for all she knew, gloat over them now and again.

She was sliding the carved piece that concealed the drawer back into place when she heard Filippo's footsteps approaching. Panic-stricken, she sprang down from the chair but caught a foot in the folds of her robe and fell headfirst, the chair tipping with her to crash on the floor. Filippo had begun rattling the handle of his locked door and shouting.

She tried to jump to her feet but she had twisted her ankle painfully, which made her gasp as she stood up. Somehow she managed to push the doors of the cupboard shut, but before she could lift the chair upright again the communicating door from her room flew wide and Filippo stood glaring at her.

"What the devil is going on here?" He observed the nearness of the chair to the cupboard and the terror in her face.

"I was trying to catch a moth!" she cried frantically, reverting in total fear to a childlike lie. "You know how you detest them getting into your clothes."

He did not take his glinting gaze from her. His purpose in coming upstairs had been to mask and cloak himself to go with his companions to a house of orgy in which they all indulged from time to time, but this new development put that out of the question. "Set up that chair and return it to the wall," he ordered.

She obeyed as best she could, quaking so much that she could scarcely handle it. He tugged the bell-pull for his valet and then unlocked the door.

When he turned back to her she was seated on the chair, her eyes huge with fear in her white face. He said nothing, but all his longheld suspicions had been confirmed. She was a poor actress and he had seen from the start that never once had she rejoiced in his triumph over the House of Torrisi. Anger and the gravity of the situation had sobered him up, which was as well, for he needed to think straight. More than once he had had the feeling that wherever he kept ledgers and private letters someone had slightly changed their positions. The apparent disorder that he maintained in these areas meant that he alone knew exactly where everything was and not even his clerk dared to move as much as an uncut quill. Once he had even glimpsed Elena rummaging through a drawer where nothing but old bills and receipts were kept.

The valet had arrived. "Signore?"

"Tell the gentlemen downstairs that my wife is unwell and I'm unable to leave her. After that you may go to bed. I shall not require further assistance tonight."

The valet departed and Filippo locked the door after him. Normally Filippo did not trouble with keys since none would dare intrude without knocking. Elena saw this present precaution more as a way to prevent her escape than to avoid any intrusion. Filippo came across to stand in front of her. "Why were you at my cupboard?" he demanded belligerently.

"I wasn't!" she lied wildly, not far from hysteria. "I told you the reason!"

"But not the truth!" He shook his fist in her face furiously.

She cowered instinctively, but still she found the will to defy him in another lie, her only chance of escaping his brutality. "I care nothing for what you keep in your cupboard or anywhere else!"

Instantly his arm shot out and he grabbed her by the hair. She cried out in pain as he jerked her to her feet. Then he rammed her face against his chest amid the frills of his cravat and held her there. Knowing she could see nothing, he deftly opened the secret drawer with his free hand and satisfied himself that she had not discovered the file of papers within. It was far too cunning a hiding place even for a sharp-witted thief, but out of her very simplicity she might have stumbled upon it.

Although Elena guessed what he was doing, she thought he was trying to smother her against his body at the same time. She could not breathe, so hard was the force with which he held her. Then he threw her back from him, but only for his hands to seize her around the neck, his fury such that a nerve throbbed visibly in his temple.

"You think I haven't suspected your inquisitive ways?"

"I don't know what you mean!"

"Indeed you do! Your old loyalties die hard. Instead of cleaving to me, you'd like to find some written word of mine that might free the Flame of the Pietà's husband for her, wouldn't you?"

She was sure he was going to strangle her. "Yes!" she screamed out hysterically. "I would! *You* should be shut away in the Wells! Not the man who your bribery and corruption sent to prison!"

Even in the madness of his rage he knew this had to be the end of her at last, but although his hands shook to squeeze the life out of her he could not do it. There was another way, already meticulously worked out. But all along, at the back of his mind, he had hoped never to use it.

Releasing her, he stepped back to throw off his coat. Her fear had always excited him. Now, as she tried to rush past him, he picked her up and threw her onto the bed. Then, as he had done so often before, he jerked her thighs apart and raped her violently. When he had finished he seized her by the arm in a bruising grip and almost hurled her back into her own room.

"Stay there!" he roared, wagging a threatening finger at her.

She would not have had a choice in any case, for he left his own outer door locked, pocketed the key, and went out of her apartment by way of her anteroom, locking that door after him and leaving her a prisoner.

All she wanted to do was to crawl into bed and hide away, but she had to get those papers. There had not been a key in the communicating door since she had once tried to lock Filippo out, an act of defiance whose results she could not bear to recall. Now at least she could reap some good from that time. Terrified that he would return, she listened for several minutes at her anteroom door before summoning up enough courage for what she had to do. She went first to her escritoire and took out a sheaf of writing paper, which she judged to be about the amount in the secret compartment. Her next step was to go back into his room and drag a chair to the cupboard once again.

Her brain felt stultified by fear and her hands shook so much as she substituted her own papers for those in the file that they rustled as though in a wind. Her hope was that Filippo, if he should make another check on the secret compartment, would be as perfunctory as when he had crushed her face against his body. After she had closed everything up once more and replaced the chair, she went back to her bedchamber. There she took from a closet the gown she would wear when it was daylight again. She unpicked part of the deep hem and threaded in the papers one by one before she restitched it. Only when she had replaced the gown in the closet was she able to fall into bed at last. Still she did not sleep, too frightened by what she had done. It was another two hours before she heard Filippo's footsteps returning.

So far Marietta had kept her pregnancy secret from all except those she could trust. It had been easy enough with dominos and capes to disguise her figure when out of doors. In the shop she wore over her gown a sleeveless jerkin she had made, which was hung with long diamond-shaped silks that wafted concealingly about her. Daily she wore an eye-mask to pick up one of the brightest colors. With her assistants, including Lucretia, similarly attired, this was considered by customers to be a new attraction and became quite popular. A steady stream of orders came in for similar jerkins of silk for Carnival wear, adding another sideline for the workshop.

But the time was coming when nothing would disguise her condition. If it had not been that the truth might have repercussions for Domenico, putting him back in the Wells, and a possible dismissal for Captain Zeno, she would have wanted to let all of Venice know she was bearing her husband's child.

"You have no choice," Adrianna said to her, "but to go away from Venice for the birth. It's too risky to remain."

"I don't like leaving Elizabetta, and it means your taking my place in the shop."

"Elizabetta will be in my care and you must think of your baby's safety as well as your own. If you should have a son, there are hotheads among the Celanos who would want to get rid of him."

Marietta shivered. "Don't say that."

"It has to be said. A male heir for Domenico means a vengeful Torrisi to the Celanos."

Marietta bowed to the inevitable. She let it be known that she was taking a long overdue vacation and going to visit an old friend in the country. On the advice Domenico had given her during their night together, she also drew up a statement giving the date and year and the circumstances in which conception had taken place. The next time Captain Zeno called for the latest report on his child's progress, Marietta asked him to read the statement and sign it.

"What is the reason for this?" he asked with a frown.

"When the truth can be told I want to be able to prove my child's legitimacy."

"If this statement should fall into the hands of my superiors it could cause me great trouble."

"It won't, and you really have no need to worry. Much as I hope otherwise, it is possible that no one will see your signature until a son comes of age or a daughter is ready to marry."

He hesitated for a minute or two, still nervous about his own position. But although he was not a religious man, he did not want it on his conscience that he had condemned an innocent child to the stigma of bastardy. He took the pen that Marietta handed him, dipped it in the ink, and signed.

The next signature she obtained was that of Sebastiano. She was thankful she had a witness who had seen her into the prison and out again. Sebastiano gave her the same sort of warning about danger from the Celanos that Domenico and Adrianna had voiced, but what he said gave it even greater significance as he explained the situation if a son of Domenico came of age.

"The young man could lodge an appeal with the Doge for the return of the Torrisi property and the restoration of the family name in the Golden Book. I have to say such a concession is highly unlikely to be made, for it would revive the vendetta."

"That is the last thing I would ever want for any son of mine!" Marietta cried. "What an inheritance of bloodshed it would be! If there are any appeals to be made in the future, they should be solely for Domenico's release."

Adrianna and Leonardo were the next and last to sign the statement, attesting to their awareness of Marietta's visit to the prison. With this matter settled, Marietta began to make preparations for the last stages of her pregnancy.

She had a moment of alarm in the middle of one night when she had been soothing Elizabetta, who had had a nightmare. As she was returning to her bedchamber by candlelight she came face to face with Lucretia, who had fetched a drink of water from the kitchen. In silence the girl stared at Marietta's figure, revealed in her night-shift. Then the girl looked her full in the eyes.

"When I first came here," Lucretia said without expression, "my father told me I was never to discuss your private affairs with anyone. I shall continue to obey him. Good night, Signora Torrisi."

"Good night and sleep well, Lucretia," Marietta answered, full of relief.

When Marietta was only a week away from leaving Venice, it became common knowledge that Elena was suffering from melancholia and keeping to her room. Adrianna went at once to call on her, but was informed that she was receiving no visitors. Marietta met her anxiously upon her return home.

"When I was told I couldn't see Elena," Adrianna said, removing her hat and gloves, "I asked for paper and a pen to write her a note. Then I waited while it was taken to her, certain she would send for me. Instead the servant returned to say the Signora regretted she was indisposed and sent her kind regards."

Marietta's concern increased. "Oh! poor Elena. All that strangeness we noticed in her recently must have been the early signs of her illness. How could we not have guessed? We thought we were doing right by letting her take her time coming back to us, but that was a mistake. We should have persisted."

"I'll try to see her again before you go away," Adrianna promised, seeking to calm her friend.

Her second attempt proved no more successful than the first, but Adrianna did gain the information that a doctor from Verona, who specialized in the state of melancholia, had been sent for by Filippo and would be visiting Elena on the morrow. Marietta left for the mainland in the hope that Elena would soon recover. Her journey took her some distance up the River Brenta, past the shuttered Torrisi villa where she had spent so many contented hours. Her gaze lingered on it until trees hid it from sight. Eventually she reached the place where Iseppo's stepson, Giovanni, was waiting to take her by cart to his village. She had met Giovanni's wife and children on several occasions when she had called on his parents, but she had not seen him since the day she traveled as a child to Venice when he had let her ride on the barge-horse. They embraced as if they were brother and sister.

"How good to see you again, Marietta!" he exclaimed.

She was very emotional. "Dear Giovanni! It's so kind of you and your wife to take me in."

"What are old friends for if they can't help one another in time of trouble? Francesca is looking forward so much to your being with us. In spite of the three children, she gets lonely at times when I'm away on the barges for days on end." He took her baggage from the boatman and set it on his cart. Then he shouldered her large traveling box and loaded that too.

"I asked your stepfather and mother first if I could write to you," Marietta said as he assisted her up into the seat. "I was quite sure Francesca would not refuse me, but you were the one to make the decision."

"I'm glad they told you to go ahead. I don't see much of my stepfather since the pains in his joints forced his retirement, but whenever Francesca and the children go with me to Venice I try to spend a night there too. That pleases the old couple."

"I'm sure it does."

At Giovanni's house on the outskirts of a village much like the one where Marietta was born, his wife and children came out to welcome their visitor. Francesca was a kind-hearted, practical woman of thirty-five who was a midwife in her own right. She and Giovanni knew the facts of Marietta's case and their sympathies were entirely with her. In the weeks that followed, Marietta could not have received better care. Francesca made sure that her guest rested, ate well, and had fresh air and exercise. Marietta enjoyed the simple village fare of her childhood days. The house was periodically filled with the fragrance of new-baked bread, and Francesca made polenta exactly as Marietta remembered her own mother making it.

Marietta's time came upon her swiftly. The first pain seared when she was drying dishes for Francesca. Immediately the midwife in the woman came to the fore.

"It's off to bed for you," Francesca said, wiping the suds from her hands. "I'll let my neighbor know. She and I always work together and we've never yet lost a mother or a baby. It's a record we intend to maintain."

One of the children was sent with the message and the neighbor arrived soon afterward. Marietta had met her previously and liked her for having the same sensible approach to everything as did Francesca. The labor lasted five hours. At the end of it, at two o'clock in the morning on the first day of February in that year of 1795, Marietta gave birth to twins.

The babies were christened in the village church as Danilo and Melina. It was an insular village, as so many places were within the Venetian Republic, and Giovanni was the only one who ever went any distance from home. There had been local gossip about the mysterious woman who had come away from her home and family for the birth. A natural conclusion had been drawn, so nobody showed any curiosity about the babies' surname. The villagers cared little about what went on in Venice, the men being primarily concerned with the price of corn and the quality of the grape harvest, while the women kept to domestic matters. Francesca and Giovanni, together with Adrianna and Leonardo, who had traveled to the village for the occasion of the christening, stood as godparents to the twins.

"Well," Adrianna remarked with emphasis to Marietta when they were all back at Giovanni's house, "this is a fine kettle of fish. You were going to entrust your baby to Francesca for a while, but is she prepared to foster two?"

"She is, but I'm going to take Melina home with me. Even if the Celanos should suspect the truth, a girl will be no threat to them."

"I realize that, but are you aware of the scandal and gossip that will revolve around your name? Everybody will think you've had a lover."

Marietta shrugged. "People who matter to me know the truth. Venice thrives on scandal. There will be something new for them to talk about in a week or so." She leaned forward anxiously. "Tell me if you have heard anything more about Elena. She and Domenico are my chief concern."

"I think it is a little better with her, but I can't be sure. Although I've called regularly at the Palazzo Celano not once has she agreed to see me, but I happened to see her lady's maid in the Piazzetta and spoke to her."

"You knew her?"

Adrianna nodded. "I'd seen Maria in attendance on Elena several times but she is no longer employed at the Palazzo Celano. She seemed pleased to talk to me and she bears Elena no malice. She says Signor Celano was responsible for her dismissal because Elena would never have treated her so heartlessly after years of service. Maria had been with Elena since she was a bride."

"Had she noticed Elena's melancholia coming on?"

"I had no chance to ask her, because she was with two other women."

"Do you know her address? I should like to talk to her myself as soon as I return to Venice."

"No, I don't, but if I see Maria again I'll ask her for it." Adrianna then reverted to the subject of the twins. "You really should reconsider taking Melina home with you. Men have pestered you enough in the past, and the rakes will redouble their efforts when they believe you have stumbled once."

Marietta scoffed. "I can deal with them." Then her face became fiercely maternal. "I will know the joy of caring for at least one of my own babies from the moment of birth. Do you suppose I have ever forgotten the little son I lost?"

Adrianna shook her head gently. "I know you haven't. I do understand. But if you are to take one twin, you should take both."

Marietta jerked up her head as if she had been struck. "You know why I can't do that!" she cried in anguish. "It's tearing me apart to think of leaving Danilo behind."

"Then bring them both back to Venice. If you have one baby on show and another out of sight, who is to know there are two?"

Marietta's eyebrows shot up and then she laughed. "I suppose I could get away with that for a few months at least."

Adrianna laughed with her. "When you come home you'll have all my help with our little deception. To be honest, I was so sure you wouldn't be able to part with your baby, boy or girl, that I persuaded Leonardo to have a door knocked through from your place to ours."

"But there has always been a door from the shop into your hallway."

"The new door is upstairs and leads from your bedchamber into an upper room in our house that was previously a small store for masks. It will make a fine little nursery for one baby while the other will be in its crib in your room. At least neither you nor the twins will be deprived of your mutual right to be together for the first months of their lives. The Celanos have taken so much from you, Marietta. I vowed to myself they should snatch away no more."

"Dear Adrianna! What friends you and Leonardo are to me!" Marietta embraced her. Both knew that eventually Danilo would have to be returned to Francesca for fostering, but that was still in the future.

Giovanni returned Marietta with her twins and her two friends to Venice in his own boat. It was dark when he landed them at the steps a short distance from the Calle della Madonna. Both women and Leonardo were *bauta*-masked, and Marietta and Adrianna each held a baby under her cloak. Not for the first time Marietta thought how unique Venice was in having as common wear a disguise that could be used for anything, from hiding the identity of a murderer to the innocent smuggling of two babies into the safety of their own home.

The mask-shop was full of light and the assistants were busy, for Carnival was in full swing. Leonardo went to check that all was well there while his wife and Marietta entered his house. With the children already in bed there was nobody to delay them as they went swiftly up the stairs and into the new nursery. There Danilo was laid in the crib that all the Savoni babies had used, while Melina was taken next door and placed in the crib that Adrianna had had the foresight to purchase when she learned from Giovanni about the twins. Adrianna had immediately written a letter relating the joyous news and taken it to Captain Zeno, begging that it be delivered to Domenico in lieu of the regular letter Marietta had permission to write.

"I think we've been a little mad," Marietta admitted cheerfully as she and Adrianna removed masks, mantillas, and mantles, "but I'm so glad to have the twins here."

"We shall deal with each problem as it comes," Adrianna answered with equal confidence.

There were many crises and alarms, but by making a game of it all with the younger children, one particular difficulty was overcome. The older Savoni boys and their sister were able to keep what they had been told to themselves. Lucretia also promised to do so when she returned to live at the apartment after staying at her own home during Marietta's absence.

Once again Captain Zeno was persuaded to grant a small favor, much against his better judgement. He could not deny the compassion he felt for Marietta, even though he knew it was enhanced by the attraction he felt for her. As a result, at dawn one day when the twins were four weeks old, Marietta carried Danilo and Adrianna took Melina to the Paglia Bridge. There Marietta turned to face the notorious bridge of many sighs that linked the Doge's Palace to the prison. She gazed steadily at the ornamental stonework of the two apertures, wondering to which one Domenico would be brought to look out. The sky grew lighter and the canal below shone pale as shells. Suddenly she saw the flicker of his hand at the first aperture and then he pressed as close as he could to the small gaps in the stonework.

He saw Marietta raise his son high in triumph. His heir! The future of his house! The purpose of his having lived at all! In tears, he yearned to embrace his wife and his children. Marietta then handed the boy to Adrianna and held up Melina to be seen. He thought his daughter was beautiful.

Sadly Marietta watched Domenico's fingers draw away from the stonework. He was having to leave. Breaking the rule of silence that Captain Zeno had imposed on both of them she cried out.

"We are waiting for you!"

He heard her, but the swoop of shrieking gulls caused her cry to be carried across the water away from the hearing of others.

When the twins lost their birth hair Danilo's new growth was dark and Melina's became a light brown. Neither did they remain alike, and even their temperaments differed. Danilo was a difficult baby while Melina was placid. While he awoke constantly during the night, Melina slept until awakened. As a result she was always in the neighboring nursery, and in order that the Savonis not be disturbed, Marietta spent many a broken night herself with Danilo in her room. Yet she dreaded the time when she would have to part with him. Already he had such a look of Domenico about him that an independent observer would have had no difficulty guessing his parenthood. But Danilo saw the outside world much less than did Melina. At first in his bonnet and shawl he had been too much like his sister for the difference to be noticed, but now Marietta carried him out of doors only when she was *bauta*-masked so that neither her identity nor his could be guessed.

Elizabetta loved both babies equally, but she showed favoritism to Danilo, cuddling and rocking him more than Melina simply because she knew that before he could walk and talk he would have to go to a foster home. She was old enough to understand the basic reason for her father's imprisonment and trusted in her mother's firm belief that one day the truth would be revealed.

Elizabetta was always reluctant to leave her baby brother when she went out with Marietta, who followed the custom set by Leonardo of delivering masks personally to valued patrons. To ward off unwanted advances, an all too frequent occurrence that had increased considerably as Adrianna had warned, Marietta had stopped making any deliveries alone. She took Elizabetta with her or else Lucretia, who assisted in carrying the handsome satin-striped boxes with ribbon bows in which the masks were packed. To certain palaces where husbands liked to receive her at times when their wives were invariably absent, one of the young men from the workshop carried the boxes for her.

Marietta was on her way across St. Mark's Square with a mask-box, Elizabetta dancing along at her side, when a couple emerging from the Basilica caught her immediate attention.

"Look, Elizabetta!" she exclaimed. "There's Elena with her husband! Let's go nearer."

Although Elena was veiled in lace, there was no mistaking the bright gleam of her golden hair, but it was clear that she was far from well. Her head drooped sideways and she walked slowly, leaning on Filippo's arm as if it were an effort to put one foot in front of the other. Impatiently Marietta noticed how Filippo was looking at Elena with solicitous concern. It could only be for the benefit of onlookers. She found it impossible to believe he was capable of remorse for having brought Elena to such a state.

When some acquaintances tried to approach, Filippo smiled his apologies and one of the two Celano servants in attendance blocked the way, saying the Signora was not well enough to talk to anyone on her first outing.

Marietta moved swiftly with Elizabetta to a point in the Piazzetta where the couple would pass on their way to their gondola. She wanted Elena to see her and communicate in their sign language. At the right moment, when Filippo's head was turned to bow to a friend, she signed a brief message imploring Elena to receive Adrianna on her next visit. There was no response. Elena's hands remained motionless.

Elizabetta, who had Elena's own quick compassion for the sick and the unfortunate, was distressed to see the lady she knew so well in such a poor state. Elena had never hugged or kissed her as Adrianna and other good friends of her mama did, but there had been a certain warmth in Elena's look and smile that Elizabetta had always known instinctively was special for her alone. Now, forgetting all else, she darted forward before Marietta could stop her and rushed to take Elena's hand, which was hanging weakly at her side.

"It's me, Elena! Why do we never see you?"

Elena reacted as if she had been shot, snatching her hand away and turning swiftly to burrow her face in Filippo's shoulder for protection. He, recognizing both child and mother, gave a roar of rage.

"Get that Torrisi scum away from my wife!"

One of his servants rushed to obey him, grabbing Elizabetta by the arm and flinging her aside. She fell, but her burst of sobbing was from her hurt feelings and not from the graze on her hand. Marietta stooped swiftly to gather the child into her arms.

"Elena doesn't like me any more!" Elizabetta sobbed.

"Hush! Of course she does. You startled her, that's all. She's been very ill and I fear she is still a long way from recovery."

It took quite a time to console the child, and she was subdued for the rest of the walk and the delivery of the mask. Yet when they arrived home, one of the Savoni girls was waiting to play with her and the two of them were soon happy with their dolls. Marietta believed the child had recovered from the incident, but when Adrianna, after hearing what had happened, went off to the Palazzo Celano the next day, Elizabetta made a concise comment.

"Adrianna shouldn't go. Elena doesn't want to be with any of us ever again."

It was clear that nothing would shake the child's conviction, and when Adrianna's visit proved to be as futile as the rest, Marietta thought how easy it would be to accept Elizabetta's view. Still she was determined to remain convinced it was only melancholia that had laid a dark spell on Elena, and beneath it she would still be the same as she had ever been.

When the nuns brought Bianca on a visit to the Savoni household a few days later, they reported having been no more fortunate in getting to see Elena, although Filippo allowed the sisters to pray aloud for her outside her bedchamber. Marietta was not pleased when Sister Giaccomina innocently remarked on their host's kindness in taking Bianca to a salon where coffee and cakes awaited and talking to the girl until she and Sister Sylvia rejoined them.

"Did Elena take part in the prayers?" Marietta asked Sister Sylvia.

"She said them at first, but now she rarely responds."

Bianca was playing with the children in order not to be drawn into the conversation. She was afraid she would give herself away if Marietta should ask her again about her relationship with Filippo. On their most recent visit he had kissed her a second time, and she had been so distressed by his grief over Elena, who had long ceased to be a wife to him, that she had been unable to resist. When he had caressed her breasts, a liberty she should never have allowed, she thought she would melt away in his arms. He had also spoken such loving words that she would easily have been lost if her conscience had not awakened in time to prevent what she could only guess at in both fear and yearning. She felt she should have rushed to Elena and begged her forgiveness, but that had been impossible. Although loving Filippo was both wonderful and agonizing to her, it would be best if she never went to the Palazzo Celano again. But the nuns went more often now that they were saying prayers, and out of custom they took her with them, encouraging her to play her flute outside Elena's door.

"Bianca."

It was Marietta who had spoken. Bianca started uneasily. "Yes?"

"Next time you are at Elena's home, speak through the door to her when you are by yourself. She might let you in when she will receive nobody else."

Bianca felt shame that her first reaction to this request was that this would give her less time with Filippo, but she dismissed the notion sternly. "I will. Perhaps after Elena has been to the opera she will begin to take an interest in everything again."

"Did you say the opera?" Marietta asked in disbelief. Adrianna was equally astonished.

"Yes, Filippo—I mean Signor Celano—told me that he is taking her to a gala performance next week. It's a last throw. The doctor says if this doesn't work there's nothing more he can do. Elena will remain a recluse for the rest of her life." Bianca's voice cracked. "Oh, I do want her well again!"

Her cry was genuine. Apart from a heartfelt wish to see Elena restored to health, Bianca knew there was no other way she could put her own life in order.

As it happened, Marietta did not have to buy herself a seat for the gala performance in order to see Elena again. Sebastiano and his wife had already invited her, as they often did to such events as well as to occasions in their own home. Marietta felt that if Elena was well enough to attend the opera she should be able to reply in their sign language this time.

There were always nostalgic memories for Marietta when she wore one of her grand gowns again. Having kept abreast of fashion, she was not out of style even though it had been five or six years since her newest gown was made. Skirts still relied on petticoats for an abundant silhouette, fichus continued to drape necklines by day, and a scooped display of cleavage was the mode by night. In flame silk looped with silver ribbons, Marietta took her place between Sebastiano and his wife among the other guests in their box. As always her blood was stirred by the prospect of great music and splendid singing, but it saddened her to see strangers in the box where she and Domenico had sat so often and which, prior to his imprisonment, had been exclusive to the Torrisi family since the opera house was built.

As usual there was a huge buzz of conversation in the auditorium and every box glowed with candlelight and sparkled with the jewels of those chatting within. The Celano box was empty. Then, just as Marietta was beginning to fear her friend had been unable to come, Filippo appeared in the box with Elena and assisted her into a chair. She was wearing one of her favorite eye-masks studded with diamonds and a gown of oyster satin. Slowly her gaze began to travel over the faces in the boxes and she acknowledged those nodding or bowing to her with a slight dip of her head.

Marietta was certain Elena was looking for her, and she took up the little ivory and gold opera spy-glass that Domenico had once given her and put it to her eye. Elena leapt into focus, but it was impossible to read her expression for the eye-mask she wore had a frill of lace that hid the lower half of her face. Her hair was dressed in the latest style, soft and full with a single love-lock resting on her shoulder. There was a roundness to her neck, arms, and bosom that showed that if she had lost weight during her deep melancholia she was beginning to put it back on again. Yet there was a listlessness in the way she held herself and in the droop of her hand holding a fan that indicated all was still far from well.

Lowering the spy-glass, Marietta waited eagerly for Elena's eyes to find hers. When it happened, Marietta's folded fan changed directions in a call for attention and her fingers flicked a plea for a meeting. But Elena's gaze passed on without the briefest acknowledgement. Marietta was overwhelmed by disappointment. Was the doctor giving her some potion that made her less alert, or had her curious illness severed a friendship that had seemed destined to last a lifetime?

The overture ended and the curtain was going up on an elaborate set with a castle and mountains, knights in armor on every rocky ledge. Marietta tried to concentrate on the performance, for the singing was magnificent, but her attention strayed constantly to the Celano box. Elena was slumping more in her chair all the time, as if whatever energy she had was ebbing fast. Marietta gave an involuntary cry as she saw her finally tilt forward in her chair and disappear from sight. Filippo sprang up with such haste that a program resting on the velvet-covered ledge went fluttering down like a white bird into the pit, causing many in the audience to shift their gaze from the singers to the Celano box. Filippo stooped to gather Elena in his arms and carried her out of the box. It was like seeing a smaller drama enacted in unison with that on the stage.

Marietta was already on her feet, her cry having alerted those with her, who moved their chairs to let her pass. Sebastiano caught her by the wrist.

"Is it wise to go to Elena now?"

"I must!"

He followed as Marietta ran, her skirts billowing, down the narrow red-walled corridor to the stairs that descended in two flights to the foyer. They reached it before Filippo, with Elena seemingly in a swoon, came rushing from the opposite stairway preceded by a Celano servant with another following behind. Marietta ran forward.

"In mercy's name, let me come with you, Signor Celano! Elena has always been as close as a sister to me."

He looked at her with such blazing fury that she believed he would have struck her to the ground if he had not been carrying Elena. "Keep away! My wife is dying day by day! No Torrisi by name shall ever come near her." Both servants paused belligerently, ready to deal with any attempt by Marietta or Sebastiano to hinder their master's progress. Doors swung wide for him as he carried Elena out to the steps and his waiting gondola. Then the servants ran out after him. Something odd registered at the back of Marietta's mind, but for the present she was too upset to think what it might be. Sebastiano was sympathetic.

"I'm sure you'd like to go home."

She nodded. "I would. Please give my apologies to Isabella and your guests."

"They'll understand."

Afterward Marietta was not alone in fearing the worst possible news of her friend, but it seemed that Elena continued to linger.

Filippo was not affected in the least by the message from Lavinia that their mother had died, but he went ahead with preparations for a grand funeral. As he had half expected when he arrived at the country house to inform his sister about the arrangements, he found her quite disoriented. Gowned in black, she sat completely at a loss with her hands in her lap.

"I don't know what to do," she said tragically. "I've looked after Mother for so long I still seem to hear her calling for me all the time. Could I come to the Palazzo Celano after the funeral and nurse Elena?"

"No!" He spoke so sharply that she was startled. "Her doctor says she must have no change in her routine. Her final collapse at the opera house put her beyond all hope of recovery."

Lavinia wrung her hands. "How tragic! That lovely girl! I remember the first day she came to the palace. She made me think of a beautiful butterfly. So happy! So much in love with Marco!" She realized she had not been tactful. "I'm sorry, Filippo."

He looked bored. "It's of no consequence. I've done everything possible for Elena, but to no avail. I'm resigned to this dreadful deterioration."

"Pietro could see her when he comes to the funeral. With his healing hands—"

"He's not coming. I'm not notifying him of Mother's death until she has been buried. She never liked him. She resented his visits and I intend to do everything just as she would have wished. However, it is unfortunate that Alessandro cannot be present. I heard from him a short while ago that the Pope was sending him immediately on an important mission to Paris, and he could not possibly receive my letter in time to return for the funeral."

Lavinia did not argue about Pietro. She had been conditioned over a long period to be obedient to those in authority. "You said once I could live with you at the Palazzo Celano if anything should happen to Mother," she reminded him timidly. "Does that still apply?"

"In time, but it's not convenient at present. You can stay overnight at Alvise's place when you come to Venice for the funeral."

She read his refusal to let her be accommodated for one night as a negation of his promise. But suddenly it did not matter so much any more. Without Elena's sweet company what would the palace offer her? But if she remained in this house she would hear her mother bullying her until the end of her days and would become even more frightened of the Signora dead than when she was alive. Lavinia knew herself to be in a state of limbo, but she had never made a decision for herself in her whole life and did not know how to start now.

"You shall have this house and everything in it," Filippo continued. "Mother told me long ago that she would be leaving this house and its contents to you in her will. But I will take her antique books. I'm having those from the Celano villa brought to the palace for cataloguing and these can be done at the same time."

Lavinia sighed inwardly. The books were all she would have chosen to keep if she had been asked. She loved the beautifully illustrated works, and once on the library shelves of the Palazzo Celano they would never be opened by Filippo and would have to wait for another generation to rediscover their marvels.

The acquisition of the extra volumes pleased Filippo since they would extend the work of the nun and Bianca when they began the cataloguing again. The girl had no notion of how he lusted after her or how easily he could take her if he wished. It was regrettable that Elena was taking such a long time to die, but still he could not raise a hand to hasten the end for her. It had to come of its own accord.

Elizabetta was growing fast. Her shoes seemed to last no time at all. She had had two new pairs not long before the birth of the twins and already they were beginning to press on her toes.

"We'll go to the shoemaker's later today," Marietta promised the child. "Then you'll have a best pair ready for the Festival of the Redentore."

It was one of Venice's great feast days, when the whole city joined in the celebration of its delivery from the plague some three centuries before. It would be an outing for Marietta and Elizabetta with Adrianna and Leonardo and their children. The twins would be left with the trustworthy Savoni nursemaid, whose fear of Celano harm to Danilo made her protective on all counts.

It was as the shoemaker was taking measurements and commenting on the length of Elizabetta's toes that it occurred to Marietta that the child must be like her father in that respect. Elena had such small feet and dainty toes, and was always more than a little conceited about them. Something stirred again at the back of Marietta's mind but just then the shoemaker produced swatches of colored leathers for selection, and the thought did not surface. Marietta allowed the child's choice of bright red, but dissuaded her from a courtesan's purple.

The main excitement for the children at the festival was to see the bridge of boats thrown across the Guidecca Canal, which the Doge would pass over on his way to attend the celebration of High Mass at the Church of the Redentore. Marietta and her friends set out early to ensure a good view of the proceedings. On the way she had glanced in the direction of the prison, for her thoughts were constantly with Domenico and never more than on a special day such as this. On this day in years past she had crossed the bridge with him in his senator's scarlet robes as members of the Doge's procession.

"The Doge is coming!" Elizabetta exclaimed, dancing with excitement. A fanfare of trumpets was heralding his approach. He was a dazzling sight in his corno and cloth of gold robes, jewels sparkling as he advanced with great dignity under a tasseled canopy. It was a day of such tremendous heat that there was a shimmer to everything and the whole procession resembled figures woven in tapestry, with those at the end almost lost in the haze. Not only was every inch of space crowded with spectators, but hundreds more had taken to gondolas and other vessels to watch the event from the flower-strewn water. When the Doge stepped onto the first of the boats that formed the bridge, a thunderous cheer went up to blend with the church bells. Marietta thought how Domenico would hear them and be picturing the splendor of this day.

From the position she and her party had secured they were able to see the first steps that each member of the procession took onto the bridge, and it was a constant flash of gold and silver and jeweled buckles. All thirteen hundred members of the Great Council in their brilliant robes were already forming a ribbon of color across the canal in the wake of the Doge. Filippo was easy to pick out with his scarred face and his height, which rivaled Domenico's. Elena should have been with the wives on this great occasion. Marietta observed the ruby glitter of his shoe buckle as he went onto the bridge and that momentary glimpse jarred violently at her memory, making her catch her breath.

Before she could think it through, Adrianna plucked at her sleeve to introduce her to a woman in the crowd. "This is Maria Fondi, who was Elena's lady's maid. I've told her who you are."

Marietta addressed her eagerly. "What good fortune meeting you here, Signora Fondi. I want so much to talk to you about Signora Celano."

Maria looked doubtful. "I know you and my former mistress were good friends over many years, Signora Torrisi, but I'm still bound by her confidence even if I'm no longer in her employ."

"I want none of Elena's secrets, although I doubt she kept many from me before she became melancholic. It's the circumstances of your dismissal I'm interested in, and anything you could tell me about how I might save the Signora from the results of her illness, even at this late hour."

"Then, signora, you may count on my trying to help you in any way I can. When shall I call on you?"

"Let's waste no time. Would this evening be convenient?"

It suited Maria and an hour was fixed just in time, for they were soon separated as people began surging forward to cross the bridge as soon as the last of the dignitaries and their wives were past the first boat. Marietta and her friends kept the children close in case they should be swept away in the crush, but everything went smoothly. It was as they reached the other side and were going up the steps of the great church for the service of thanksgiving that Marietta comprehended fully why the sight of Filippo's shoe buckle should finally have fired her memory. She recalled clearly the image of the unconscious Elena being borne out of the opera house in his arms. Amid the lace petticoats, Elena's feet had been visible in white satin shoes with sparkling diamond buckles—but the shoes were much larger than the size she normally wore.

That evening, when there was music and celebrating everywhere on the Grand Canal, Maria arrived to see Marietta. Upstairs in the salon they sat down.

"There are so many questions I want to ask," Marietta began, "but I'll ask only one or two and then let you tell me all you can about your last days in the Celano employ and how your dismissal came about."

"One moment," Maria interrupted. "Neither you nor Signora Savoni have questioned the unfairness of my dismissal. How is it you don't suppose I was at fault in any way?"

"Because Elena once told us she could trust you implicitly. Apart from us, you were the only one to know of her meetings with Nicolò Contarini."

"I could never have betrayed her!" Maria's eyes were angry. "If you knew only a quarter of what she had to endure at the hands of that brute,

Celano! She never complained to me, but I saw the evidence often enough for myself."

"My questions center on the last weeks you were with her. What were the signs of her lapsing into her present condition?"

"She was troubled in her mind. I could always tell. I think she had lost something and couldn't remember where she had put it. Several times I found her searching in cupboards, and she went into little-used rooms in the palace where to my knowledge she had never been before. I offered to help her find whatever she had mislaid, but she denied she had lost anything and said she was just curious about the contents of the palace. She was downcast during this time. I found her having a few private tears more than once, but that was not entirely unusual. There were times when she was desperately unhappy."

"Had she ever searched about like that before?"

"Not that I ever noticed." Maria then went on to tell of how her dismissal came about. "Everything was as usual that last evening. My signora was going to the theater and the signor was having some of his friends to dine. She was always happier when he was out of the way and then she would cheer up and be her usual self, at least on the surface. Normally she and her friends would go on to a casino or supper room after the performance, but the signora told me she would be coming straight home and I supposed she was coming near the time of the month when she often felt tired. So when she came home I saw her into bed and bade her good-night. She had told me a silk rose was loose on the gown she had worn that evening and I took it away with me to mend in the morning, because she had spoken of wearing it to a private party the following week."

On the way to her own room Maria had heard the dining-room doors open and had looked over the banisters in time to see Filippo and his friends making a move as if they had changed their minds about remaining at the table until the early hours. The next morning she was up at her usual time when the steward sent for her.

"I'm sorry to have to tell you, Maria," he had said when she stood before his desk, "that your services are no longer required by the Signora." Then, as she stood stricken and unable to believe what she had heard, he added, "The Signor has arranged an immediate replacement, who has already arrived at the palace. You are to go straight to your room and pack."

"But I must speak to the Signora first!"

"No, the Signor has forbidden it. You would only plead for reinstatement and that can't be allowed."

"After so many years—"

He took up a folded testimonial from his desk and withdrew a bag of money from a drawer, both of which he handed to her. "You will have no difficulty finding another post with the recommendation I have given you, and you have three months' wages plus a bonus to tide you over."

She lost her temper completely. "It's just one more cruel act of Filippo Celano against my Signora! Just because she has been satisfied with my work all this time she is now to be upset by a change!"

The steward rose to his feet. "No more of this, Maria. I can't listen to you."

"You know the truth for all that!" she flared out. "May that hateful man rot in hell!"

In her room she could hardly see to pack for angry tears. It was a long task, for she had made a little home for herself in her own quarters with small items she had collected from market stalls over the years and any number of framed prints as well as paintings, which impoverished artists sold cheaply, on her walls. Eventually the task was done. Fortunately her married sister lived in Venice and she could go there until she secured a new post. But she could not and would not go without saying farewell to her Signora.

She tapped on Elena's door and tried to enter, but it was locked. She heard footsteps approaching from within and the new maid, who was dark-haired and about her own age of thirty, opened the door.

"Yes?"

"I've come to speak to the Signora."

"I can guess who you are. Go away. I'm in charge here now." When Maria tried to push past into the anteroom, the woman gave her a great thrust back into the corridor. "No, you don't! Clear off or I'll ring for help. You were told to stay away."

Maria was determined not to give up. "Signora!" she shouted at the top of her voice, certain Elena would come to investigate, but the door into the bedchamber remained closed.

"I told you," the maid hissed, and slammed the outer door in Maria's face.

Marietta listened attentively to the whole account. Elena's failure to answer Maria's cry could have been through fear of Filippo, who had been determined to sever the relationship with her loyal servant at a single stroke. Yet there was something that weighed against this.

"Can you think of anything else at all that is as strange as what happened to you?" she asked.

"Only that the Signora's hairdresser was stopped from attending her on the same day. I went to see him, hoping he would give her a goodwill message from me, but when he arrived at the palace at his usual hour he was told that his services were no longer required. Apparently the new maid is good at dressing hair. His pride was hurt and he was quite furious as he told me about it, fluttering his fan as if he might swoon."

"Do you ever see any of the servants from the Palazzo Celano?"

"I've spoken to one of the footmen and two of the maidservants. Nobody is allowed to go near the Signora. When the rooms are cleaned the curtains of her bed are kept closed and the new maid stands guard to see they are not disturbed. She also waits on the Signora with all trays."

"How often does the doctor call now?"

"He's stopped coming. It appears there is nothing more he can do. A couple more doctors came from away somewhere on the mainland and were of the same opinion. Do you think you'll be able to save my Signora from this melancholia that is dragging her down?" Maria's voice quavered. "If you can't, it will only be a question of time."

"I shall do my very best. I thank you for being so helpful. If you hear anything more, will you let me know without delay?"

"You may count on that."

When the woman had gone Marietta took a few quiet minutes to mull everything over before she went into the shop, which was open late on this festival night. She had come to a firm conclusion and nothing would shake her from it. In the morning she would disclose her conviction to Adrianna and Leonardo. She would need their help with what had to be done.

Chapter 15

*W*hen *Marietta* went next door, the *Savoni* family was just finishing breakfast. While Adrianna immediately took a fresh cup to pour her some hot chocolate, Leonardo greeted her with a business question.

"How did the musical side do yesterday?"

He had recently agreed to her suggestion that a section of the shop, previously unused, be opened by an archway to a display of musical instruments, which were as much a part of Venice as masks. She had then employed a young man with a pleasing voice to be an assistant. When he played a lute and sang, customers were drawn into the shop; this invariably led to extra sales of masks even if no instrument was purchased.

"Very well," Marietta responded. "There was also a run on the music and song sheets. I must order more."

"That's good. If that side continues to be so promising I might consider expanding into music myself if one of the shops next to mine should ever become empty."

Marietta nodded. "But I didn't come to report on business. Something very important has come up and I need to discuss it with you and Adrianna."

"We'll go into the salon," he said.

There he remained standing and tamped tobacco into the bowl of his long-stemmed pipe. Adrianna did not allow him to smoke in the salon, but it would be ready when he left after hearing what Marietta had to say.

"I have a theory about Elena to put to you both," she began. "You may find what I'm about to say difficult to believe, but hear me out."

"I hope I can make a fair judgement," Leonardo remarked amiably, although he glanced at the clock. In twenty minutes he should be opening his shop and Marietta unlocking hers.

"First of all I'll tell you everything Maria Fondi told me yesterday evening," she began. When this was done, she spoke about the day she and Elizabetta had seen Elena near the Basilica. "Filippo could not have taken her to a more public place for prayers. I wondered at the time why they hadn't gone to the Pietà church, which is so familiar to her."

"Has he ever done anything to please her?" Leonardo queried drily.

Adrianna turned sharply toward him from her chair. "Hush! Let Marietta finish."

Marietta inclined her head. "I admit that your remark is apt, Leonardo. Filippo has never considered Elena's feelings, but neither would I expect him to wish to be seen with a sick woman, even if she is his wife. It seems out of character to me. Then there was Elena's reaction to Elizabetta, who she loves dearly. The child glimpsed hatred in her eyes, which was as alien as it could be to Elena's true feelings."

Adrianna forgot she had told her husband not to interrupt. "But melancholia can do strange things to people and I'll remind you that Bianca told us the doctor wanted Elena to emerge again into public life."

"With regard to the visit to the Basilica that's as may be, but nothing could ever make Elena glare viciously at any child, and this was her own."

Adrianna allowed the point for the time being. "What else?"

"The night I saw them at the opera she failed to acknowledge my message in a sign language that she and I have used since our early Pietà days. Suppose it wasn't because she was ill, but because she didn't recognize my gestures?"

"Maybe she was in too poor a state to think clearly," Adrianna suggested.

"Yet she was acknowledging nods and bows."

"Automatically perhaps."

"Perhaps," Marietta conceded. "But when Elena slipped from her chair to the floor of the box, Filippo ensured the notice of most of the audience by letting a program go fluttering down as he sprang to her assistance. Then, when I ran downstairs in time to see him carry her out, I saw her shoes. They were at least two sizes larger than any Elena could wear with her small feet!"

Leonardo's eyes narrowed incredulously and Adrianna threw up her hands. "Are you expecting us to believe that another woman is masquerading as Elena?" she cried.

Marietta nodded vehemently. "Don't you see? It all adds up with the immediate dismissal of the maid and the hairdresser, as well as the doctors being called in from far away. They would never have met Elena before."

"But if this is the truth," Adrianna gasped in fear, "it means that Elena may be dead or locked up in some distant place where she could never be found."

"No, I don't think Elena can be dead, because then there would be no point in Filippo's maintaining an impostor. My terrible fear is that, if we don't act quickly, sooner or later Elena will be produced in her coffin. Then the other woman and her maid will be whisked away as swiftly as they came, which must have been during the night between the time of Maria's last seeing Elena and her dismissal in the morning."

"Whatever can we do?" Adrianna questioned anxiously. All this time Leonardo had remained silent, with nothing in his expression to indicate whether he supported Marietta's theory or not.

"I'm going to make use of a Lion's Mouth," Marietta said, "to deposit an accusation against Filippo that he has incarcerated his wife against her will to the point of endangering her life. Will you be my fellow accusers?"

"Of course we will!" Adrianna answered promptly.

Leonardo spoke heavily with a shake of his head. "You've presented a good case, Marietta, but the Lions' Mouths are for accusations of treason and treacherous acts against the state. Suspicion of this kind, however foul the deed that is involved, doesn't come into that category. You would have to go through the channels of the keepers of the peace, but you've no proof to offer, only speculation."

"I realize that, which makes the Lion's Mouth my only chance of an investigation. Murder could be interpreted as an act against the state since it is breaking one of its most stringent laws."

Again Leonardo shook his head. "You are a Torrisi by marriage and no charge you present against a Celano will be accepted without proof. It would be taken as a feeble attempt to maintain the vendetta on your imprisoned husband's behalf."

"We can't let Elena die!" Marietta protested fiercely.

"Indeed not, but the right path has to be followed. I know the Chief of Police very well. I'll have a talk with him, putting forward a hypothetical case of incarceration, and we'll see what advice we receive."

Adrianna gave him an order. "See the man today!"

Giving his word that he would, Leonardo left his wife and Marietta to continue talking over Elena's plight. "I keep trying to think how I might discover her whereabouts," Marietta said with a sigh. "Isn't it tragically ironic that two of the people I care most about should both be shut away where I'm powerless to help them?"

"But your friend Sebastiano was presenting a petition to the Doge yesterday on the Festival of the Redentore. Some are granted on every feast day in Venice. Domenico has a chance of clemency."

"I wish I could believe that," Marietta confessed, her head dipping desolately, "but there are always so many wanting ducal favors at such times. Domenico has so much stacked against him."

"We must hope. It may take a few days before you hear anything." Adrianna's thoughts turned again to Elena. "Do you suppose she might be hidden somewhere in the Palazzo Celano?"

Marietta raised her head, her eyes sharpening. "I've wondered that myself. If Filippo is expecting her to die, where could be more convenient than under his own roof?"

Adrianna considered and then rejected the idea. "No. The servants would have heard or noticed something and we know from Maria that nobody at the Palazzo Celano is suspicious of anything. Even she herself questioned only the unfairness of her dismissal and nothing more."

"But suppose there is a secret room somewhere. Domenico told me once that many of the old palaces on the Grand Canal and elsewhere in Venice would have such a place. If only I could gain entrance to the Palazzo Celano, I could look for Elena."

"But not for long," Adrianna stated wisely. "You would soon be discovered, and from what we know of Filippo, he wouldn't hesitate to have you arrested as an intruder and a thief."

Marietta sprang from her chair and went restlessly to the window. "What a black day for hope this is!"

It grew even blacker as the hours went by. Sebastiano came to tell Marietta that his petition for Domenico's freedom had been rejected without a glance, the name of Torrisi condemning its chances instantly. Later, when Leonardo came home from his shop, he had nothing good to tell of his meeting with the Chief of Police. Proof of some kind had to be produced before any steps could be taken. There was still more bad news to come the following evening.

"Filippo Celano came into my shop today," Leonardo told Marietta. "It was to place his usual order at this time of year for new and splendid masks for the start of Carnival in October. He ordered masks for his sick wife as well in the hope that she will have recovered by then. He said he was about to have her conveyed by boat to his summer villa to get her away from the heat."

"That could mean that Elena has been at the villa all along and not at the Palazzo Celano. She might be close to death! Suppose he plans to return to Venice with her body!"

Leonardo pitied Marietta's distress and took her by the shoulders. "We don't know. The truth is we don't know anything for sure!"

She threw up her head angrily. "You might still have doubts, but I don't. When are they leaving? I'll get close enough to that impostor to tear the mask from her face and reveal her for all Venice to see!"

"They left early this evening," Leonardo replied, dashing her last hope.

It was drawing near summer's end when Marietta heard in the shop that a Celano had died. She was seized with fear, but it was Maurizio Celano who had finally succumbed to the ill health that had dogged him since child-hood.

This bereavement brought Filippo back to Venice in late August, and once more the impostor was installed in Elena's rooms. To Marietta it was a sign that Elena was still alive and it confirmed her belief that without doubt she was hidden somewhere within the Palazzo Celano.

It was strange to Elena that she should have survived so long in this dark, dank mezzanine room where Filippo had confined her, but weakness and a painful cough were catching up with her at last. Soon death would release her and she would welcome the turn of its key. Maybe it would be so silent that she would hear nothing and meet it in her sleep.

She had been full of fear that night when she had heard Filippo returning along the corridor. To her relief he had gone into his own room and she had believed she would not see him again until morning. But she had been mistaken. There had been an odd creaking sound like a little-used door being opened and then silence for a while. She had not dared to investigate, but had stayed huddled in bed with a candle left burning. Then to her astonishment she had heard women's voices. Almost at once the communicating door between her room and Filippo's had opened and he entered still in his outdoor cloak.

"Get dressed!" he had ordered.

She had sat up in bed. "Who are those women in your room?"

He had not answered her, but had turned back the bedclothes and pulled her from the bed. "Do as I say! Take a warm cape. You'll need it."

She had dressed swiftly, putting on the gown with the papers sewn in the hem. He was taking her somewhere and she was at a loss to know where that might be. She was allowed no time to dress her hair so she put a comb into her pocket. Lastly she snatched up her purse, in which she had placed some of her most costly jewelry, for it was her intention never to return to this palace once the papers were safely in Marietta's hands.

"Not in that direction," he said when she moved toward the door into her anteroom. "Leave your purse. You'll not be needing that."

Nervously she obeyed him and he had opened the communicating door again. In seconds Elena took in the two women staring at her with blatant curiosity. One had hair as golden as her own and eyes almost as blue, although there the resemblance ended. But Elena also observed the cupboard that had caused her such trouble. It had been swung forward like a huge door to reveal a narrow lobby beyond with an ancient door standing wide. She realized instantly that although Filippo had returned home by the usual water entrance, he had fetched these two women by this secret way. As Filippo began propelling her toward this opening, total panic seized her. She began to scream and cry to the women for help, but Filippo clapped his hand over her mouth and hauled her, kicking and struggling, into the lobby and through the door beyond. She glimpsed a large salon far below in the light of a three-branched candelabrum on a table. The chill of this secret place rose up to meet her. Filippo forced her down into a sitting position to prevent her from losing her balance on a steep flight of stairs. Then he slammed the door shut after her and turned the key. She heard the cupboard close back into place.

All that was several months ago. Restlessly Elena stirred on the broad couch that was her bed and opened her eyes to the room, which was illumined by the candelabrum and diffused moonlight. At first she was terrified there would be rats, but there were none. Neither had a mouse ever found its way into these quarters, although sometimes she could hear them scampering somewhere above the ceiling, and she liked their company so long as they remained at a distance.

She had no idea how long she had screamed and cried and given way to despair in the early days of her imprisonment, for she had never liked to be alone, always loving to be with people and never happier than in a crowd. Her shrieking torment had been even worse by night, until she had forced herself under control in order not to be insane when finally Filippo relented and set her free again. Whereupon, since most of her creature comforts were provided by a female warden, she had asked the woman for cleaning materials and had washed and scrubbed and polished, ridding the room of dust and spiders as if she were back at the Pietà again and doing penance for some misdeed.

When the manic mood had passed she settled into a calmer routine even though bouts of panic had plagued her periodically. She had sung every song she could remember, read the book of devotions and prayers she had requested, all other reading matter being denied her, and had drawn on an inner resilience she never before recognized in herself. She had come to realize it was what had enabled her spirits to revive constantly throughout her dreadful marriage, which had been a prison of another kind. But with her ration of food getting sparser and her physical strength evaporating, hope of ever getting out of this place had faded into preparation for death.

Once this salon must have been very elegant. By day the light came through a solitary little gothic window set high in the wall and fitted with curiously strong opaque glass protected by an intricate inner grille that made it impossible to break. She had tried to break it many times by climbing precariously onto the top of a cupboard. Sunshine had revealed there was a similar outer grille the depth of a wall away.

Yet it was by candlelight that the full splendor of the salon came to light, and that had been by design. Its pilastered walls and its floor were of rose marble deepening to crimson while the ornamentation of the ceiling still retained some gleam of its gold, though it had been darkened by time. It was the same with the gold frame of an elaborate mirror, whose looking-glass—like the panels of such glass set into the ceiling—had become so spotted with damp that it gave back almost no reflection. The handsome furniture had also suffered deterioration and the chairs at the table were rickety, the gilt tassels of their velvet cushions black as night.

The precipitous staircase, leading sharply down from the door through which Filippo had thrust her, was built against the wall and flanked on its open side by a floor-to-ceiling curtain of such richness and quality that only in parts had it rotted from its rings. It had a double purpose, for it also concealed the entrance to an ornate alcove that was a latrine with an outlet to the water beneath the palace. When new, the curtain must have given exotic color to the well-proportioned and elegant room that had undoubtedly once been a place of passionate liaisons. Several paintings on the walls were darkened by time, but enough of their subject matter was discernible to show that each depicted a highly erotic scene.

There was only one other door out of the salon. She had run to it that first night, thinking she might get out, but it was locked. There were two small flaps that had opened to reveal what appeared to be a black hole beyond, but which she now knew to be a narrow flight of stairs down to an iron-studded door that opened to the side canal. Once, when a high tide had made the waters of Venice rise, the hallway and lower steps had been flooded and for four days her female warden, who came to her by way of the canal and the outside door, had been unable to reach her. She had been without food or drinking water during that time and thought she was going to die more quickly than by Filippo's method, which was to have her meager rations systematically reduced to ensure a slow death. The woman never entered the rose marble room, but handed her food and water and everything else through the small opening in the door. Laundry had to come through in a long thin bundle.

Elena knew now that this was the secret room Marco had told her about when they went on their tour of the palace, stopping to kiss and embrace frequently along the way. He said it had been shut up since a murder was committed there; remembering his words, she tried not to let herself dwell on what act of lust or jealousy had resulted in that awful crime. At least her own death seemed destined to be without violence.

Hearing a sharp knock at the outer door, Elena lifted her head wearily. Her warden, *bauta*-masked and hooded, always came by night, entering from a gondola drawn up alongside the iron-studded door. Once only lovers, courtesans, and maybe debauched rakes and their women came by that route, up the narrow marble stairs and through the second door into this room of liaisons, to join the signor of the palace in sexual pleasures.

The knock came again. With an effort Elena pushed back the bedclothes and put her feet into slippers. Holding on to the wall, scarcely able to drag herself across the room, she made her way slowly to the door. Through the small aperture she saw the *bauta*-masked face. The woman spoke only when necessary.

"I bid you good evening," Elena said as she always did, for although this deliverer of food and water was strict and hostile, she was Elena's last contact with the outside world. Elena took the covered bowl of food handed to her, and although it was not heavy her legs gave way as she set it on the side table she had long ago moved closer to the door to save time at these deliveries. Her fear had always been that if she took too long, she might not get all she had been brought. Then she took up an emptied container and passed it through the aperture in exchange.

"Judging by the moonlight it must be a wonderful night," Elena remarked, eager for speech. "I should like to be lingering on the Rialto to watch the candlelit gondolas passing to and fro and listen to the music and the songs." Whenever she conjured up one of these familiar scenes, the woman showed only impatience. Despite this indifference, however, Elena persisted. "We would stand there sometimes, my friends and I, when we were on our way to dance or play cards."

"Make haste," the woman snapped, handing through a squat flagon of water, but Elena had doubled up in such a paroxysm of coughing that she was helpless. The woman sighed with impatience and rested her arm with the flagon on the rim of the aperture. When Elena was finally able to take it from her with shaking hands the woman spoke roughly.

"Make this last. In future I'll be looking in at you every day, but bringing food and water only once a week instead of twice." She was unmoved by the quick glitter of tears in the prisoner's tragic eyes.

"So I'm overstaying my time," Elena said croakingly. Then her strength failed, and the bundle of clean laundry being passed to her fell through her arms to the floor. She often wondered why Filippo was so determined that she die with clean sheets and the other conveniences suited to her fastidious nature. As the woman turned away Elena called after her, "Good night. Sleep well."

She watched through the aperture as the woman silently went down the narrow flight by the glow of a lantern. A lovely glimmer of moonlight fell like cobwebs over her as she opened the outer door and went out. Then it closed with a thud and was locked.

Elena stood for a while by the opening. A grille somewhere out of her range of vision gave fresh air through to the stairs, although there was also a vent in the room. She often thought of Domenico, who was also shut away from all he loved. He was the cause of her being here, although maybe Filippo had simply used her search of his cupboard as a final excuse to get rid of her. She would like to tell him with her dying breath that she had had a child and it was his seed that had no life-giving power. Yet it would not be out of revenge, only a wish to spare some other woman from having to endure his goading and bullying and hateful sexual demands.

Marietta had told her how Domenico walked around his cell and did exercises to keep fit. Until her health had begun to fail Elena had followed his example and she believed it was why she had survived as long as she had. But now she was too sick to fight any longer and spent most of her time lying on her bed.

Another bout of coughing racked her through and when it was over she sank down into a chair to rest for a few minutes, leaning her head back against the top rail. She wondered what Filippo would do when the warden reported her death. He would no longer have any need of the golden-haired woman who had clearly arrived that night to take her place. And what of her companion with black curls? Thinking back, Elena remembered that the darker woman had been wearing a plain grey silk gown. The logical conclusion was that she had replaced Maria as lady's maid.

Elena found it hard to understand how two women could watch cold-bloodedly while one of their own sex was committed to unlawful incarceration and eventual death. How could any amount of gold appease their consciences? Perhaps they had none. But maybe that was not surprising in Venice with its secret police, its spies, its feared Council of Three and its torture chambers, a city where anyone could pay to have an enemy knifed or drowned in a canal.

Earlier on, Elena had tried to work out how Filippo would manage to pass off the impostor as his wife. Eventually she concluded that he must be keeping her in total seclusion. What could be easier than saying a sick woman must not be disturbed? It would then seem natural when a doctor was called in to confirm her demise, for no woman recently seen in public as healthy could change overnight into the thin and wasted creature Elena knew herself to be. She thought bitterly that the usurper and the maid were like ghouls sitting out the long hours of isolation as they awaited news of her death. She could visualize them in her apartment, yawning, playing games of chance, and wishing her life away.

Elena rose slightly, supporting herself on the arms of the chair. Before going back to bed, she lifted the lid of the food container. Two slices of bread, a peach, and three plums were all she had been given. It was well that she was past having an appetite. Then she frowned, realizing there were no candles this time. Were they to be reduced too? Something of her old panic seized her and she stumbled across to the table where she snuffed out two of the three flames of the candelabrum. Perhaps she should rely on the moonlight this night and snuff out the third. Suppose she got no more candles! Steeling herself to this frightening possibility, she snuffed out the third flame and began to tremble. It had to be done. She did not want to die in the dark!

Marietta pondered how she might get into the Palazzo Celano to search for Elena. Every kind of wild scheme was considered and rejected. Should she go with a book for Sister Giaccomina when she and Bianca resumed their library cataloguing? Or would it be better to appear with some lengths of silk from her own workshop and say she was to measure a sofa for new upholstery? Could she get temporary work in the kitchen? But none of these plans would work. She was too well known for the Celano servants not to recognize her. Neither would they admit a masked stranger arriving on some flimsy pretext. Even if she did gain admittance somehow, the likelihood of discovery by a vigilant steward was immense. And Filippo would not hesitate to have her arrested for unlawful trespass. Yet she could not give up the idea of trying to find Elena.

It helped her to have other things to think about. The rejection of the petition for Domenico's release had been devastating, even though she had tried not to raise false hopes. Her letters to her husband continued to be encouraging and loving, but she could guess how downcast he must be. At least she could be sure he would not break under the duress of his imprisonment, but Elena did not have his stamina. It was to Elena's credit that Filippo had had to continue his play-acting so long, but she could not hold on to life indefinitely, and every day that passed brought her that much closer to death.

Marietta also had Danilo to think about. She had not intended him to go to his foster parents until later in the year, but his bellow at eight months was so much louder and stronger than Melina's gentle cry that she feared her deception would soon be discovered. So far the assistants in the shop had made no comment, but it would take only one to ask a question, and then speculation would be rife among staff and customers alike. If only Domenico could have seen their son once more before she had to send him away. Adrianna had promised to take Danilo to Iseppo's house next time

Francesca came to visit. Marietta knew she could not bring herself to hand him over to another's care.

Every day she was preparing Lucretia for her first public performance. It was to be at a charity concert and the audience would be distinguished. No professional singers or musicians were taking part, and a responsive audience would give Lucretia the confidence she presently lacked. There was plenty of employment for individual singers in Venice, at social evenings and other occasions. It was to this end that Marietta was training her pupil.

On the morning of the concert Marietta went into the workshop. Leonardo had agreed to her making the masks that Filippo claimed were for Elena. The basic work had been done by others, but she had added the trimming and lined the masks herself. She had no idea if Elena would ever see them, but she had slipped a note behind the lining-silk of one. Her final task was to embroider a symbol on it that would make Elena search for the note concealed within. As she stitched, it came to her exactly how she could get into the Palazzo Celano without causing suspicion. But she would need to know her way about.

That afternoon Marietta heard Lucretia sing her solo through twice. Then she made a special visit to the Pietà to see Bianca. She found her in a rehearsal room. With a smile, Bianca set aside her flute and folded the music on the stand.

"You've come at the right time, Marietta. My practice hour is over."

"Good. What is the latest news?"

"I'm to play at a quintet concert next month."

"That's splendid." Then, as they sat down on a bench, Marietta added, "I've come to ask a favor. Would you draw a plan for me showing the rooms known to you at the Palazzo Celano and where Elena's apartments are to be found?"

"Why should you want that?" Bianca asked suspiciously. "You know you'd be the last person Filippo would ever allow at Elena's bedside."

"If you help me get into the palace without Filippo's knowledge next time you are there, I might be able to reach her."

Bianca's expression became mulish. "You always seem to suppose that you can be successful against odds that defeat everyone else. Well, you can't. Filippo has done everything in his power for Elena. The nuns have spoken to her many times through her closed door without an answer, and prayed continually for her, but in vain. I've spent my time equally futilely playing my flute and begging admittance." She drew a deep breath in defiance. "I won't offend against Filippo's generous hospitality by going behind his back for you or anyone else!"

Marietta seized her by the shoulders and shook her in exasperation. "You foolish girl! Wake up! Filippo is a lecher and a libertine! He doesn't care what happens to Elena!"

"He does!" Bianca gave back, trying to wrench herself free. "He told me how he has always cherished her!"

"What else did he tell you?" Marietta's grip tightened as she saw the guilty blush rise in the girl's cheeks. "That you are beautiful? Desirable? Can't you see that he is trying to seduce you?"

"He is too honorable a man for that!" Bianca shrieked, her face racked by anguish. "But I wish he would! It could make no difference to Elena since she never cared for him!"

Marietta released her only to strike her furiously across the face. "Never again dare to lay blame on Elena in my hearing. How could she care for a husband who used her brutally and beat her black and blue!"

"Lies! All lies!" Bianca leapt to her feet, cupping her reddened cheek, her eyes blazing. "You're jealous because I have a Celano in love with me while your Torrisi husband is locked up in prison. You'll never poison me against Filippo! You think I don't grieve for Elena's condition. I do. I love her as if she were my own kin, but I can't help it that she is never going to get better. I've done what I could to help her and I'm still trying. I'll never give up so long as there's a chance of doing some good. But I see no harm in showing friendship—and only friendship—to a sad man who sorrows for Elena as I do!"

Marietta also rose to her feet. "Then if you have such faith in him, insist that he go against Elena's wish to remain in seclusion and let you in to see her. It would be a privilege he has granted to nobody but the doctors and would enable you to make real contact with her. Test him! After all, you're so confident you've come to mean so much to him. I think you expect to be the next Signora Celano! See what your chances are!"

Bianca uttered a sharp cry and turned on her heel to rush from the room, slamming the door after her. Marietta remained standing where she was and pressed her fingertips to her closed eyes for a few minutes as she struggled to calm down. She had never before spoken angry words to Bianca, or struck her, but that final cruel taunt of hers had been deliberate. If Bianca could inveigle her way to see the impostor, or if Filippo made a switch to an ailing Elena, some good could be done.

At the concert that evening Lucretia acquitted herself well and received an encore. Captain Zeno and his wife were present at the performance, and he made a special call at the shop the next morning to thank Marietta for having brought his daughter to such heights in a matter of months.

"Lucretia has far to go yet." Marietta was pleased with her pupil's performance, but she was realistic about all the work yet to be done.

"I have something to tell you that should please you," he said with satisfaction. "I've had your husband transferred back to the palace cells. He has a window again, although the view is dull enough, and all the possessions he had there before have been restored to him."

She was overwhelmed. "How did you manage that?"

"I pointed out to the Chief Inquisitor that it was the rightful place for a political prisoner and that Torrisi should have been returned there as soon as his cell was repaired and security tightened. He agreed with me. Unfortunately there is no relaxation on visiting. The Inquisitor was adamant on that."

"But there is one too young to be bound by rules and regulations, whom you could take to visit my husband."

"I can guess." He grinned and sighed with mock resignation. "No wonder you're doing so well in your business, signora. You have a keen way of managing a deal that I respect. Fetch your son and come with me now. I'll introduce Danilo to his father."

Domenico was reading when his cell door was unlocked. He lowered the book and swiveled around in his chair to see who was about to enter, and saw Captain Zeno holding out a healthy-looking baby to him.

"Danilo Torrisi has come to see you!"

Domenico gave a surprised shout of laughter and sprang up to seize the baby from him. Exuberantly he held his son high, and Danilo, his fist in his mouth and dribble running from gums preparing for another tooth, chuckled with delight. The Captain grinned and left the two of them together. For ten minutes Domenico talked to his son, bounced him on a knee, and let Danilo grab at his hair, his watch, and his cravat. Then Captain Zeno returned. Domenico kissed the child on the brow and handed him back. As when Marietta had left his other cell, the prisoner watched through the window as his son went from his sight. Then, as before, he bowed his head and wept.

When Bianca went next to the Palazzo Celano it was with Sister Giaccomina to begin the full cataloguing of the mass of books that had been moved there from Filippo's late mother's house as well as from his villa. She was nervous. Marietta's challenge had stayed with her and she knew she had to meet it. To ignore it and let matters run their course would be to pass up the chance of seeing and speaking to Elena. She regretted her barbed remark to Marietta about Domenico. Bianca was like most placid people. Once roused to anger the hurt of harsh words lingered long after the person who spoke them had been forgiven. It was also painful to remember what she had said herself.

Sister Giaccomina was so happy about the task ahead of her that she seemed almost to bounce from one stack of books to another, her plump little hands flying up in the air with delight when she discovered that most of the antique volumes were unforeseen treasures. Bianca's stomach began to flutter as the time for her flute practice drew near. She hoped the nun would forget the hour, but matters of duty never slipped Sister Giaccomina's mind.

"It's time for your practice, my dear," she said when the clock struck. "Go along to your music."

It was not long after Bianca had begun her practice that Filippo appeared. She was sure he made a point of being in the palace at this time whenever possible. He greeted her with his handsome smile, and, as always, she felt as if her bones were melting. How could Marietta accuse him of those dreadful deeds!

"So you are back, little swan, to fill my house with music every day."

She blushed at his pet name for her. "Not every day. I have my rehearsals and other duties at the Pietà."

"More's the pity! You belong here, Bianca. The palace comes alive whenever you cross the threshold."

She could hear her own heart beating. "As it will again when Elena recovers."

A sad expression fell like a shadow across his face. "I'm resigned to the inevitable. That can never be."

She left her place behind the music stand to take a step toward him. "Take me to see her. You could let me in if you wished."

"It is no longer in my hands. She lives in the darkness of her curtained room and will tolerate only her maid's presence."

"But I truly believe she would not turn from me. If you care anything for me, grant my request!"

His expression did not change, but his mind was put on alert. Who had put Bianca up to this? He could not believe it was from her own initiative, as she had always accepted the need to obey Elena's wishes and avoid upsetting her in any way. It was something of a piquant situation that this wisp of a girl should be the first and only one to challenge him on this extremely delicate ground. Yet he could turn it to his own advantage.

"Very well. It shall be as you ask, but have you the stamina?"

Stamina was a quality she would never have listed for herself, for she was quick enough to shy away from anything unpleasant or frightening. "What do you mean?" she asked warily.

"The Elena you remember is not the Elena you will see. She has grown thin almost beyond recognition, that once lovely hair of hers is lank, and she is plagued by the most dreadful cough." He was giving the description that Elena's warden had given him, for he had requested a daily report now that the end was drawing near. He still could not comprehend why he had been unable to let Elena starve quickly, but had chosen a gradual decline to make death easier for her. "Above all she will resent the intrusion."

"What you have said only stirs my sympathy," Bianca replied, full of compassion. She would put her arms around Elena and talk to her of the

Pietà days and coax her back to living. She loved this woman who had always been sweet and good to her. The fact that she loved Filippo in a different way was a heavy weight on her conscience that she longed to erase.

"Then when you have finished your practice and had your hot chocolate, ask Sister Giaccomina's permission to come with me to Elena, but I can't allow her to come as well. It would be too much."

Bianca nodded. "She will understand."

"You're a courageous girl. I'm proud to know you."

As he left her he smiled to himself. He was always entertained by the effect such remarks had on her. To witness such quaint confusion was like glimpsing the world of the cloisters, so different from the highly sophisticated and cynical circles in which he moved. No wonder men fell in love on sight with the Pietà girls. That aura of pure virginity combined with youth and beauty was irresistible.

As he went upstairs he thought what a relief it would be to get rid of the two women, Minerva and Giovanna, who had cluttered up Elena's apartment during these many weeks. He had engaged them through his most trusted agent, who had taken them from a brothel. Neither of them liked men, but they cared deeply for each other and to be together for weeks in luxury, even if it meant one of them could never go out of the apartment, was like a dream come true. As a bonus they had been promised what to them was a small fortune, which they would use to set up their own house of assignation at the end of their assignment. Anticipation of this benefit sustained them through endless hours of boredom, and they were often like two happy children as they planned how everything would be from the drapery to the chamber pots.

But Filippo had no intention of depending on their silence in time to come. Once he had brought his wife up from the rose marble room and placed her in the bed, they would depart the way they had come. A boat would be ready to transport them, but they would never set foot on land again. When the woman who made deliveries to Elena had given her last report, she and her gondolier husband, who brought her on her nightly visits, would be disposed of by a Celano agent in a slightly different way.

Opening the communicating door, Filippo found Minerva of the golden

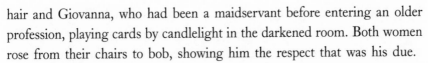

hair and Giovanna, who had been a maidservant before entering an older profession, playing cards by candlelight in the darkened room. Both women rose from their chairs to bob, showing him the respect that was his due.

"I'm bringing you a visitor," he said to Minerva.

"But you said there'd be no more since the last of the doctors left," she protested petulantly. She did not mind passing time in this apartment, for she was naturally lazy, but she had been terrified each time she had to appear in public. When a child's hand caught hold of hers outside the Basilica she had been so panic-stricken she'd almost clouted the brat about the ears. The doctors had been easy for they were only stupid men puffed up with their own importance and her mumbling and vacant stares had deceived them so completely she could have laughed in their faces. "Who is it you are bringing here? If it's another doctor I don't mind."

"Whether you mind or not is of no interest to me," he replied implacably. "You will be ready to receive the visitor in an hour's time."

Giovanna, who was the practical one of the two, bobbed again. "Tell us what we are to do, signore. You may rely on us."

"You can put that casket of sweetmeats out of sight for a start and open a window." He glanced with faint disgust about the untidy room. In Elena's time it had always smelled fragrant in here, but there was an odor about these women and a fusty atmosphere in the room for they had the same reluctance to bathe themselves as they did toward letting in fresh air. It was a relief for him to leave them, putting his scented handkerchief to his nostrils. He would have the whole apartment redecorated and refurbished after the funeral, in good time for the new bride.

Bianca finished her practice and drank her hot chocolate with Sister Giaccomina before Filippo reappeared to escort her upstairs. The nun was most anxious to be sent for if Elena should show the least sign of wishing to see her.

"A servant shall come at a run to fetch you," Filippo promised, his hand already cupped around Bianca's elbow to lead her away.

"Have you prepared Elena for my visit?" Bianca asked as they left the library.

"No. I didn't want to risk the usual refusal." He smiled reassuringly at her. "I believe we might be about to make a breakthrough. Your determination to see her might be the solution to everything. I may have been wrong to follow the advice of the doctors so implicitly. As for Elena, a patient is never a good physician and she cannot know what is best for herself."

Bianca looked at him with shining eyes. "I'm full of hope! If I could help Elena back to recovery in any way, it still wouldn't be repayment for all she's done for me."

"What a charming little swan you are," he said softly. "May you bring the same sunshine to my poor wife as you bring to me."

They had reached Elena's door and he knocked imperatively. Bianca noted that the maidservant, who must have recognized his knock, still inquired who was there. When he replied and admittance was forthcoming, he ushered Bianca ahead of him into the elegant anteroom. The maidservant looked suitably surprised to see he was not alone.

"There is no need to announce this visitor, Giovanna," he said. "You may return to your duties in the sickroom when we leave."

"Yes, signore." The woman went to the bedchamber door and opened it before drawing back. Again Filippo let Bianca precede him.

Coming from the light into the curtained room made the gloom seem very dark at first, but everything inside was still visible, including the four-poster bed on its dais, its draperies and curtains shimmering with silver threads. A slight mound in the bed showed where Elena was lying. Bianca, overjoyed that at last she could approach her friend, went slowly to the foot of the bed. She thought that if she moved to the bedside too quickly it might give Elena a shock. Gaining confidence, Bianca cast a swift glance over her shoulder and saw that Filippo had remained near the door. She smiled and he nodded encouragement. She took another step nearer the bed.

"Elena," she said softly.

There was a sudden little movement in the bed as the person lying there became alert to an alien presence. Bianca spoke Elena's name again and knew that despite the dark shadows of the bed's abundant drapery she was being heard.

Filippo gave Bianca some support. "Someone dear to your heart has come to see you, Elena," he said.

"It is I, Bianca of the Pietà. Your adopted goddaughter." Bianca began to sing softly the old Columbina song that she and Elena and Marietta had so often sung together. "Dance, Columbina, dance! See how Harlequin—"

An ear-splitting shriek from the dark-shadowed bed shattered the song as the creature lying there raised herself up in a great billowing of covers to reveal the pale glimmer of a face masked by the long, tangled snarls of still golden hair. In shock, Bianca uttered an involuntary echoing scream while pressing her clenched hands to her cheeks. Then she heard Elena hiss the cruelest possible words.

"Get out! I always hated you!"

Bianca was hysterical. She turned and ran. Filippo caught her in his arms and hastened her out through the anteroom. She neither saw nor heard where she was being taken until suddenly they were in another room where all was quiet and he was holding her cupped head against his chest and soothing her with his voice. "Hush, my little swan. My little love. My sweet. Be calm."

Her sobbing was such that she could not get her breath, huge gasps scarcely seeming to reach her lungs. She clung to him, broken-hearted. To have seen Elena turned into such a distortion of what she had been was more than she could bear and the spitting cry of hatred had cut through her like a knife.

Filippo maintained the same calm tone. "Elena's sickness has turned her brain. It was inevitable. You have learned the secret I have kept from everyone else. My hope was that you would have reawakened the past for her."

"But I did!" She was still sobbing convulsively. "You heard what she said."

He took her tear-wet face between his hands and lowered his head to bring it closer to hers. "She didn't know what she was saying. You must try to remember that."

Gently he kissed her tremulous lips. She closed her eyes. Wrapped in his protective arms, she felt as safe as if she had found some peaceful haven. Her tears would not cease, although he was trying to stem them by kissing her lids. His lips were traveling on to her temples, her cheeks, her ears, and her neck. He was unpinning her folded-back Pietà veil and she supposed he let it drift to the floor, for he was combing the fingers of one hand through her hair. How sweet his lips were.

Shock had left her in a kind of trance and she did not want to emerge from it now that all was gentle and sensual and utter bliss. To come back into the real world that lay beyond these glorious sensations would be to remember what was ugly and stressful and heartbreaking. Her gown had been unlaced and she let her head fall back while her spine arched with the pleasure of his hands and lips on her breasts.

She continued to keep her eyes shut, the better to stay locked inside herself. With a sense of floating through the air she was being lifted onto a bed. Her petticoats were being folded back up to her waist and her legs parted at an angle. Now she did not dare to open her eyes because of what was being done to her and she let herself slip again into depths of pleasure from which she never wanted to escape.

When everything became more dramatic and thrusting she knew a rise of fear and opened her eyes to Filippo's passion-ridden face. But she heard herself cry out.

"I love you!"

Then his mouth clamped over hers and ecstasy shot her through and through.

In the library, Sister Giaccomina began to look at the clock. Bianca had been absent almost an hour. It must be a good sign. She returned to her work but only for a few minutes before Bianca returned.

"What happened, my dear?" she asked eagerly, thinking the girl looked a trifle distraught. "Did you see Elena?"

"Yes. She's very ill. I'll not go again."

"Did you tell her I was here?" Sister Giaccomina was slightly piqued that she had not been sent for, considering how long a time Bianca had had at the bedside.

"Elena is past knowing or understanding anything."

The nun wrung her hands in distress, her kind eyes filling with tears. "What sad news!" Her voice quavered. "I had such hopes."

"May we go back to the Pietà now?"

"Yes. I've finished my work for today."

Bianca was silent on the way back to the Pietà. Usually she and the nun chatted together but this time Sister Giaccomina did not try to converse, misconstruing the reason for the girl's abstractedness. When the gondola brought them within sight of the Pietà, Bianca thought to herself that she had left it as a girl and was returning as a woman. She recalled Marietta's warning that Filippo was intent on her seduction, but she accepted with a curious resignation that it had been inevitable for her to surrender as she had. Her love for him had been mounting to a peak, and her natural yearnings had been undermining all the moral standards by which she had been raised. If Elena had not already been lost to this world—the sweet, laughing, buoyant Elena with kindness in her voice and her eyes, who was now changed beyond recognition—Bianca knew that her feelings at this moment would have been very different. But then she would not have been caught up in a state of anguish that had broken down all barriers. The whole incident with Filippo would never have happened.

"Here we are," Sister Giaccomina said as the gondolier brought them alongside the water entrance. "I'll tell Sister Sylvia later about your seeing Elena. She would only cross-question you and I can see you are in no state for that."

Bianca was relieved to escape to her room without making a report. She needed time on her own to think and to adjust to her new state as a woman. When Filippo had held her in his arms after making love to her, stroking her hair and her arms and kissing her hands, he said they would marry when the time was right. She had felt no shame that he should talk of marriage to her. For after what she had seen, he was to her, in all senses but one, a widower already. In no way, despite the likeness of hair and eyes, could she think of that poor soul in the bed as a living wife.

Dressing that night for an evening at the casinos, Filippo was in high spirits. Minerva had excelled herself in that little scene. The whitened face and the hissed words he had suggested were masterly touches. What he had not expected was Bianca's abandoning of herself to him in her shock and distress. That delicious girl with her spun gold hair and beautiful body had revealed an unexpected passion. There would be no more food for Elena, only a little water. She was sick enough now to drift away, and it consoled him to know he had been so merciful. He had been reminded uncannily of Elena as a bride, when he held Bianca in his arms, except that where there had been rigidness and hate he had found only willingness and love. If only he could get Bianca installed in the palace on a permanent basis prior to their marriage. He wondered if the Pietà would agree to her staying here with the nun to finish their library work more quickly. Maybe the nun would not want to move out of the Pietà even for a while? That could be the only stumbling block, but a generous donation to the Pietà would make it impossible for the governors to refuse. He would sound out Sister Giaccomina next time she came. Everyone had his or her price, and he believed the nun's would be the promised gift of a second volume of her choice from the library when the work was done.

Filippo had not whistled since he was a boy, but he broke into an involuntary tune as he left his bedchamber. It was the effect Bianca had on him, making him feel young again. Then he saw a servant look askance at him, and he was reminded of the "invalid" in Elena's bedchamber. He let his features settle into a more serious expression and went with dignity from the palace.

When Bianca and the nuns arrived on a visit, Marietta sensed immediately the hostility in her goddaughter. Clearly the girl had not forgotten what passed between them at their last meeting. It was noticeable how Bianca stood back and allowed Sister Giaccomina to be first with the news that by rights should have been hers to tell.

"Bianca has seen Elena! After all these weeks she gained admittance!" Marietta turned quickly to Bianca. "How was she?"

The girl answered quietly. "Her melancholia has destroyed her. It was exactly as we had been told. She is very ill indeed."

"Did Elena speak?"

Bianca nodded. "She said very little. Only that she should be left alone. I could tell by her expression and her voice that she did not want me there."

"How long were you with her?"

Irritably Bianca jerked her shoulders. "So many questions! I can't be sure. The curtains were drawn and the bedchamber gloomy. I wouldn't have noticed a clock even if I had looked for one."

Sister Giaccomina gave her a smile. "I can answer that for you. I noted by the clock in the library that you were with her for almost an hour."

"An hour?" Marietta repeated, looking keenly at Bianca. "You stayed all that time, although Elena said she wanted to be alone?"

"She didn't say that immediately," Bianca gave back on a note of defiance. "I sang a little of our Columbina song to her."

"That was a good idea. How did she react?"

"I don't think she remembered it. It didn't reach her anyhow. I've told you how ill she is. What do you expect?"

"I can see how distressed you are, Bianca," Marietta said gently, "but let me ask you one more thing and please give full thought to it before you answer. Did you feel you were once again with the Elena we knew and who was our good friend?"

"I don't have to think about that," Bianca replied without hesitation. "She has gone from us into a world of her own and what is left doesn't look or sound anything like the Elena we once knew."

"I thank you for being patient with me. You've told me all I wanted to know."

With the questions at an end, Bianca became more relaxed and the visit proceeded as usual. When Marietta mentioned the startling new masks that had been made for the Carnival, Bianca asked to see them. Sister Giaccomina went with her into the workshop, giving Marietta the chance to put a question to Sister Sylvia.

"If I gave you a pen and paper would you draw a plan for me of the route you take for prayers at Elena's door?"

The nun looked very seriously at her. "Very well. I would do anything to help Elena in her sickness."

When she had drawn the plan Marietta studied it. She would have to cross a hall into a salon that led to another, which in turn opened into the library. It was out of another door from there that the nuns went into a hallway with stairs that led to a corridor. The second door on the right led to Elena's apartment. Marietta folded the plan and put it away in a drawer.

"I thank you," she said gratefully.

Again the nun gave her a long look. "I don't know what you have in mind, Marietta," she advised, "but I beg you to think of yourself too. Your children are dependent on you."

"I'll not forget that."

For the first time in Marietta's life Sister Sylvia kissed her on both cheeks. "God be with you in your venture."

Marietta intended to go ahead at once with her attempt to discover Elena's true whereabouts. She had Sister Sylvia's plan of the Palazzo Celano, and her means of entering would be as the deliverer of the masks for Filippo. All that remained was to gain some knowledge as to where Elena was being hidden. Marietta knew she would have limited time at her disposal and it would be useless to prowl about aimlessly when Elena might be on any floor. There was only one person who might be able to enlighten her. That was Filippo's widowed sister, Lavinia.

Marietta took a boat to the mainland. There were wagonettes for hire and a driver took her on the half-hour ride to the house that had been the country home of Elena's mother-in-law before her death. As the driver boasted of knowing the district and everyone who lived there, he was willing enough to tell Marietta what he knew of the woman she had come to see.

"No, none of her brothers is there at the present time, signora. Since the funeral of the late Signora Celano she has been living alone in that grand house."

At the gates Marietta asked him to wait. It was a charming house that came into view as she went up the drive. Its stone walls had been mellowed by time and covered with creeping vines. When a servant answered the door Marietta asked to see the mistress of the house.

"Your name, signora?"

"Tell her I'm a friend of Elena's."

The maidservant returned almost immediately to show her through to a salon. Lavinia, pale and gowned in black, rose from a chair, clearly pleased to receive a visitor until uncertainty flooded her face and her smile of welcome faded.

"I don't think—I can't remember—surely we are not acquainted?" she said hesitantly.

"I am Marietta Torrisi."

"Signora Torrisi!" Lavinia gasped in dismay.

"Please don't turn me away," Marietta said firmly. "I've come on a mission for Elena's well-being. She needs your help desperately."

Lavinia looked even more puzzled and confused, but she invited Marietta to sit down. "I wanted to go to Venice to nurse Elena," she said falteringly, "but my brother Filippo didn't think that necessary." Hope lifted her voice. "Does she want my care after all?" Then she swayed back almost defensively in her chair. "But how would you know what she wants? You and Elena may have been Pietà friends, but Filippo would never have let you be her messenger."

"I believe you're very fond of your sister-in-law."

Lavinia nodded, still wanting her question answered. "She is a sweet, kindly woman and was always a friend to me. I worry about her being so deep in her melancholia that she is wasting away. But you haven't explained anything to me."

"I have much to tell you and a great favor to ask. Elena's life may depend on you."

Lavinia, well trained to listen when others were talking, took in every word of the dreadful evidence that was presented to her. The color drained from her face and she clenched her hands in her lap. She did not want to believe Filippo capable of such a terrible deed, but all she knew of his cruelty and his ruthlessness weighed heavily against him. He had always been merciless toward those who stood in the way of anything he wanted, in this case the heir that Elena had failed to give him. She recalled the times in earlier years when he and Marco had quarreled so fiercely that she had been afraid Filippo would one day run his brother through in a duel just to gain headship of the family. When it was finally his, and Elena became part of the prize, Lavinia had been sure that he often punished his lovely little bride for having loved his brother as she could not love him. There were times when Elena's courageous attempts to be happy, to laugh and chatter while she tried to hide a bruise on her neck or a pain in her side, had torn at Lavinia's heart, but always her mother had been in the palace to prevent all but the briefest show of friendship.

Lavinia put a trembling hand to her brow. Marietta had reached the end of what she came to say and was looking at her with such intense appeal that it frightened her. How could she do what she was being asked with her mother screaming in her ears?

"Please," Marietta urged again, "tell me how to find the place where Elena might be concealed. You must be able to think of somewhere. Is there a secret room? For mercy's sake, tell me! Don't let Elena die!"

Lavinia's whole body shook in agitation. She feared her teeth might begin to chatter in fright at the terrible dilemma into which she had been plunged. But she couldn't let that little butterfly of a girl die. Her head bobbed as if she were a puppet on a string and the words seemed to jump disjointedly out of her mouth as if by their own volition.

"There's a cupboard in Filippo's bedchamber. It conceals the double entrance to a room of ill deeds that hasn't been opened for many years." She paused to draw a deep breath and then continued while Marietta sat in silence, absorbing the rest of what Lavinia had to tell her.

When all was said, Lavinia threw her arms over her head and rocked as if she feared she was about to be beaten for having revealed a Celano secret to a Torrisi. Marietta could see that the woman was at a breaking point, but she had to press one more question on her. Elena had spoken of Filippo's adjoining room.

"Is Filippo's bedchamber next to Elena's apartment?"

"Yes." Lavinia rocked harder than before.

"I thank you with all my heart!"

Marietta hurried from the house to run to the transport that was waiting for her.

Chapter 16

$\mathcal{M}$*arietta was forced to wait two days for the* convening of the Great Council before she could go to the Palazzo Celano. She would get only one chance to save Elena and she dared not risk Filippo's appearing at an inopportune moment. An important debate, concerning measures to be taken by the Venetian Navy in view of recent developments in the fighting between the French and the Austrians, would be a lengthy affair that all councillors were expected to attend. It was no problem finding out that the debate would start at four o'clock after earlier meetings of the various committees.

Marietta prepared all she thought she might need. There was a coil of rope to be wound about her waist, a file in case Elena was chained, a sharp knife, a candle and tinderbox, scissors, a small flask of French cognac, a ring of assorted old keys she had borrowed from Leonardo to try if the one for the inner door should be in Filippo's pocket, and smelling salts. Finally, there was a small ladies' pistol that would be loaded just before she set out.

When the day came, it began upsettingly with one of the women mask-makers slipping on the floor of the workshop and breaking her wrist. Even worse, when Marietta was about to return home from the market across the Rialto Bridge she saw a crowd clustered on the Fondamento del Vin, and as she passed she saw the bodies of a gondolier and a woman being lifted from a gondola. She heard someone say they had just been found stabbed to death in the shuttered *felze* of the man's own vessel.

Many times Marietta glanced at the clock as the hours went by. At two o'clock the great bell of the Campanile began summoning all councillors in the city to their meetings. Soon afterward she changed into a plain woolen gown with deep pockets into which she put most of what she had collected to bring. She concealed the rope under her sash, and tucked the loaded pistol into its satin folds. When she had put on a short cape, she slipped the traditional black silk mantilla over her head and fastened it under her chin. Then she donned her white *bauta* mask and her black tricorne hat.

From the workshop she collected the beribboned box that held the masks for Elena and slipped it over her arm. Those for Filippo she would pick up from Leonardo's shop, for they were so elaborate they could not be packed until the last minute.

When Marietta reached Leonardo's shop he came out with his boxes to carry them for her to a gondola. These were not heavy but they were large and bulky.

"I still think I should go to the Palazzo Celano with you," he said, reviving an argument they had had previously as they walked along side by side.

"I don't want you involved in case anything should go wrong." She smiled to make light of the chances she herself was taking. "My motive is not entirely unselfish. Adrianna has promised that Elizabetta and the twins will always have a home with you both if anything untoward should happen to me. It will be much better that you arrive blamelessly at the Palazzo Celano after I've had time to do what has to be done. Then nobody can accuse you of anything."

He remained unconvinced, but she was not to be swayed.

"Good luck!" he said, his voice gruff with concern for her as she boarded the gondola.

She gave him a little wave of reassurance and took her seat.

At the water portico of the Palazzo Celano she explained to the young footman on duty that she was the carrier of the Savoni masks and was to wait for Signor Savoni to join her later. The footman did not question her being masked and mantled, as this was suitable for anyone representing a mask-shop in Carnival, but he was reluctant to admit her.

"Signor Celano won't be back before the end of the debate in the Hall of the Great Council and that could be a long time yet. You had better go away and come back later."

She shook her head and her voice took on a friendly, conspiratorial note. "It will be my good fortune to have a little rest. Delivering masks is a welcome change from serving customers and being in the workshop. I would really appreciate this chance to sit down and enjoy a little leisure before Signor Savoni arrives to supervise the trying on of the masks."

He nodded amiably. "Very well. I know the feeling. I don't often get the chance of a rest myself." He took the two large boxes she handed to him and stood aside to let her enter. "Why were you sent ahead so early?"

"My employer is elsewhere at the present time and uncertain as to when he will arrive. My being in charge temporarily means he can come straight here without having to carry the wares around with him."

The footman began leading the way to the main staircase. "What masks are selling best this season?" He was as interested as any other Venetian, rich or poor, in the latest novelty. New masks rarely made a reappearance the following year, whereas nothing could replace the popularity of old favorites.

"There are some curiously patterned ones that people seem to like," Marietta said as they ascended the stairs. "I don't care for them much myself. But the other Savoni shop in the Calle della Madonna has some really spectacular ones that are in constant demand."

"I always go for a red Pulcinella mask myself."

She approved his traditional choice. "With the tall cone hat, the padded hump between the shoulders, and the white costume?"

"Of course. To have any mask without the rest of the outfit makes a poor show." He winked at her mischievously. "Pulcinella is expected to take liberties at Carnival and I always have a good time. I could tell you some tales, but I expect in the mask business you hear a lot."

She gave a little laugh. "I do."

The footman enjoyed chatting with tradespeople. With the nobility it was all silent bowing and scraping. Yet at Carnival time he'd upended any number of those haughty patrician women, who in their masks neither knew nor cared who he was in his disguise. There was no place in all the world to match Venice at Carnival for adventure.

"What has the Savoni workshop produced for the Signor in these boxes?" he inquired inquisitively.

"Two truly splendid creations! But I'm not allowed to describe them, because Signor Celano will want to surprise everyone when the time comes. Those were my instructions. I can tell you about those for his wife. They're—"

"She'll never wear them!"

"How can you be sure?"

He shook his head with regret. "The Signora is on her last days. Her new personal maid, Giovanna, doesn't have much contact with the rest of us, but she has kept us informed of how swiftly the poor lady has gone downhill. I never had a cross word from Signora Celano. We all liked and respected her."

"I believe most people felt that way from all I've heard. It sounds as if I should have left her masks behind."

He gave a cynical snort. "Oh, they'll be worn. No fear of that!"

"Oh? By whom?"

But he had gone ahead into a great reception hall with a huge fireplace that was flanked at a distance by double doorways. Marietta had memorized Sister Sylvia's plan, but the nun had not warned her that it showed only half this area. The footman was leading her to the other set of double doors, not the ones used by the nuns. Then Marietta paused to listen, hearing the faint but unmistakable sounds of Bianca's flute. This was another unexpected complication. She certainly did not want to run into Bianca! And it was not the day when the girl usually came with the nuns.

"Who is that playing?" she inquired casually as she drew level with the footman again.

"A girl from the Pietà. She and a nun are staying here."

"Do you mean for the day?" Marietta asked as they went through the door he held open.

"No, they moved in yesterday for a few weeks or months, depending on how long it takes them to catalogue a new section of the Celano library."

Marietta was alarmed for the girl's sake. To be under the same roof with Filippo day and night could only spell trouble for Bianca. But there were other matters to deal with at the present time.

"Doesn't the music disturb the sick Signora?"

"No. The girl plays outside her door sometimes."

"Is she doing that now?" Marietta sounded guileless.

He shook his head. "The Pietà girl is at practice in the salon next to the library. The Signora's room is on the floor above. You can wait here."

They had passed from one salon to another, which was paneled with ivory damask, and he put her boxes on a chair.

"I shall unpack the masks," she said, "and display them ready for Signor Celano's return, whenever that should be. So please don't let anyone come in here. Just show Signor Savoni up when he arrives."

"Don't worry. I'll see to that."

When the footman had left her, he went to where the Pietà girl was playing her flute. She stopped as he entered and the sudden expectant look on her face vanished. He was no fool and knew whom she had been hoping to see.

"Your pardon for disturbing you, signorina, but I have a request. Some masks have been brought from the Savoni workshop and they'll be on private display in the Ivory Salon, which means that nobody is to see them before the Signor."

"Has Signor Savoni brought them? He could wait here. I know him well."

"No. It's a woman assistant in charge. He's coming later."

The footman left again and Bianca resumed her flute playing. It had been foolish of her to expect Filippo back as yet, but he had promised to get away as soon as he had made his speech at the debate. She had scarcely seen him since she arrived the day before with Sister Giaccomina. They had dined with him, and although the nun had done most of the talking, Bianca had been aware of his eyes fixed burningly on her face, her hair, and her cleavage until she felt quite naked. There had been something a little frightening about such intensity of gaze. She realized now that he had reminded her of a leashed lion straining to get its claws into her and there were enough stone lions of St. Mark all over Venice for her to compare him with the most ferocious of them. Instinct told her that marriage would release that ferocity. But she had only to remember his tenderness and those stroking, intoxicating caresses to know that he would always cherish her. Shy color tinted her cheeks. She was so possessed by love for him that she would sacrifice her life and all she had ever known or cared about in the past on his behalf if ever such a need arose.

How badly she was playing her flute! She had too much else on her mind. All the sweet things Filippo had said and promised when he had kissed and embraced her before going to the Doge's Palace seemed to dance in place of the notes on the music sheet in front of her. She would not practice any more today.

She put her flute away in its case and folded the sheets of music on the stand. Then she wandered through to the library where Sister Giaccomina sat reading a massive volume written in Latin.

"What work do you want me to do now?" Bianca asked.

The nun flapped a hand without looking up from the page. "Sit down, child. I'll tell you in a minute when I get to the end of this paragraph."

But the end of the paragraph was reached and still the nun read on, lost to the world. When she turned the page and still continued reading, Bianca, toying with a pen in readiness, heaved a sigh. How tedious it was to be sitting here doing nothing. It made the time she had to wait for Filippo's return seem all the longer. Her thoughts drifted to the masks in the Ivory Salon and her curiosity stirred. She knew about the secrecy surrounding special orders for important patrons. The element of surprise was important at Carnival balls quite apart from the complete anonymity that a new mask, never seen before, could give to the wearer.

In the past she had been like all the Pietà girls in viewing Carnival from the outside, but in future she would be part of it all—the wild rejoicing, the candlelit suppers in a gondola while serenades were sung, the dancing in St. Mark's Square, and all the laughter and snatched kisses. She would watch the fireworks not from a window but in the open, as the night sky filled with thousands of colored stars.

Filippo wouldn't mind her seeing his new masks. She would go along to the Ivory Salon and take a peep. She might even put on one of the masks and be wearing it when he returned. He had said that she, his little swan, could only make him happy whatever she did, and this would amuse him.

"I'm going along to the Ivory Salon," she said.

Sister Giaccomina answered absently, "How nice."

Bianca sighed. It was like talking to someone totally deaf when the nun was reading. She left the library and made her way to the Ivory Salon. When she went in she found the room empty, but facing her, propped on a chair, was a glittering mask that struck home the notion she had had earlier. It was a jeweled face of the snarling lion of Venice. The fangs were silver and the mane, which would go over Filippo's head and down to his shoulders, was made up of short lengths of gilt cord that gleamed and shone. It was breathtaking. The other, on another chair, was no less dramatic, a sinister face painted a vivid scarlet from which wings of feathers dyed to the same brilliant hue soared upward. She could only begin to guess at the magnificence of the costumes he would wear with each of these masterpieces.

Then Bianca saw ranged on a sofa three very feminine masks, one eye-mask of soft blue, another of sapphire, and a third that was a more delicate replica of the scarlet winged mask. All three were for her! She darted forward and picked up the first to hold it to her eyes before a mirror. Blue to match her eyes and sewn with pearls. How extravagant of Filippo! The darker blue was equally enhancing, with a soft veil of Burano lace gathered to form a wispy cloud over the lower half of the face. But oh, the scarlet one! It was wicked and exciting and when she wore it she and Filippo would complement each other perfectly.

As she turned to try the first one on again, she noticed a faint crackle in the red mask that sounded like paper. She was curious. Surely a perfectionist like Signor Savoni would not have let any loose paper remain within the lining. She turned to the others but these did not have that same crackle of paper when she pressed the linings with her fingertips. Then she saw there was a tiny embroidered emblem on the red mask. She had her library knife in her pocket for slitting uncut pages, and the stitches gave before its blade. Drawing out the thin sheet of paper, she recognized her godmother's handwriting. The message was brief. It was to Elena, assuring her that Marietta and other friends were anxious about her condition and working toward discovering her whereabouts. It closed by imploring her to keep up her courage.

Bianca felt wrath explode inside her. How dare Marietta persist in this campaign against Filippo as if he were Elena's jailer instead of a husband who had done all in his power to restore his poor wife to health! It was so unjust! So vindictive! Then she began to wonder about the woman assistant who was supposed to be in charge of these masks until Leonardo came. Where was she? Suppose the assistant was Marietta! Had she gone upstairs to try to see Elena? Foolish Marietta if that should be the case! Giovanna would never let her in and if Elena heard her voice it would only cause her to be more upset. It was cruel to invade Elena's privacy. The time to bring her back from her melancholia had long since passed.

Bianca ran from the Ivory Salon to the staircase that rose on this side of the palace as did the other near the library. Reaching the floor above she hastened to a spot where she could see the door of Elena's apartment. A *bauta*-masked woman was listening with her ear to a panel.

"You'll hear nothing, Marietta," Bianca said coldly, keeping her voice low in order not to disturb the sick woman within.

Marietta gave a start and raised her mask to lodge it against her tricorne as she answered in a whisper. "I was checking that this is the way in to Elena's apartment."

"It is and you have no right to be here!" Bianca whispered back.

"I claim that right as a friend. Don't give me away!" Marietta begged.

"Only if you promise not to call through to her and that you'll leave."

"I can promise the first, but I beg you to tell no one that I am here. I give you my word that I shall not try to get into that apartment or make any sound. If Elena is dying, surely you can find enough compassion in your heart to let me spend a little time near my childhood friend."

Bianca considered the appeal. She knew she could trust Marietta not to break a promise, but there was the question of loyalty to Filippo. "You may stay here, but how long you stay is at your own risk. I shall watch for Filippo's return. If you haven't left by the time he comes home from the Doge's Palace I shall inform him that you're here."

"Very well." Marietta only wanted Bianca to leave her. She was not interested in the apartment where the impostor was kept, but until the girl had confirmed she was at Elena's door Marietta did not know whether she was in the right corridor. There had been no sound within. "I agree to that."

"Then I'll go, but I've warned you." With a toss of her head Bianca went back the way she had come. She did not return to the Ivory Salon but went straight to the library where the nun was still reading. Bianca went to a window and stood there looking down at the Grand Canal. She would see when Marietta left and she would also see when Filippo returned. If he should arrive before Marietta's departure she would meet him on the main staircase with what she had to tell. Filippo had made her his own and she could never go against the man to whom she belonged.

As soon as Bianca had gone, Marietta went swiftly to the neighboring door, which she knew now to be that of Filippo's bedchamber. She entered silently and scanned the large and luxurious room. A glance at the communicating door showed her it was bolted on this side and she need not fear discovery from that direction. There was still nothing to be heard from within Elena's apartment. Perhaps Bianca's angry outburst had alerted the impostor and her maid, who might well believe she was still keeping silent vigil outside their door. That is, if they were still in there! If they were not, it meant their usefulness to Filippo had come to an end, which was the worst possible indication of what Elena's condition would be.

There were three richly carved cupboards in the bedchamber, but only one fitted Lavinia's description. Marietta threw off her cape as well as her mask, mantilla, and tricorne. Having come this far there was no going back, and if she found Elena the time for disguise would be over.

The room was finely paneled in wood with a garlanded ornamentation of flowers and foliage carved on each section. She went to the one at the immediate right of the tall cupboard. Taking hold of the middle flower she turned it twice in a clockwise direction as Lavinia had instructed. There was a click and then a faint rasp as the whole cupboard swung slowly sideways into the room on its massive hinges. Behind it was a small inner lobby with a stout door. An ancient key, too large for any man's pocket, hung conveniently on a hook.

Quickly Marietta snatched up a poker from the fireplace to wedge it between the hinges and prevent the cupboard from closing back again of its own accord. Then she struck a light from her pocket tinderbox and lit the wicks of a double-branched candlestick on a bedchamber table. After jettisoning the candle and the bunch of keys from her pocket, she took the great key from its hook to insert it in the lobby door. It turned easily, as if it had been recently oiled, and she opened the door. Cold air wafted into her face from the darkness. As she stepped through the doorway the candlelight showed her a rose marble wall at her left-hand side and a rich brocade curtain at her right. Then she gasped as she saw the steepness of the marble stairs sweeping down to the floor below. There was a gilt hand-rope looped to the wall and she held on to it as she began to descend.

"Elena!" she called softly. "It is I, Marietta! Are you there, my dear friend?"

There was only silence. Sharp fear and disappointment struck at her. Had she been wrong after all, or—it was a thought she scarcely knew how to contain—had she come too late? When she reached the bottom of the stairs beyond the side curtain, the whole of the rose-red salon opened up to her. The burnt-out remains of candles in the candelabrum on a table told their own story as did the motionless figure lying on a draped couch. Calling her friend's name again, Marietta rushed forward. If it had not been for the golden hue of the tangled, unkempt hair, she might have doubted that the thin-faced woman lying there with eyes closed was Elena.

"Oh, my dear Elena! What you must have suffered!" Marietta moaned in utter grief as she took hold of the still hand lying on the coverlet. Then she caught her breath. The hand was cold, but not with the chill of death. There was still a chance! Swiftly Marietta set the candlestick on a table and slid an arm under Elena to bring her to a sitting position. Elena's lids flickered, but did not open.

"I've come for you, Elena!" Marietta cupped her sick friend's face in her hand. "Look at me! I'm taking you out of here. You're coming home to Elizabetta and Adrianna and Leonardo and me!"

Elena's eyes opened blindly. Marietta went on talking and gradually Elena's gaze began to focus. Her whisper was barely audible. "I thought I was dreaming."

"It's no dream." Marietta felt with one hand for the flask in her pocket and took it out to remove the cork. "This will do you good. Try to sip some. Then I'll help you to your feet."

She held it to Elena's lips and trickled a little of the cognac into her mouth. Elena coughed, but swallowed some more before a full paroxysm of coughing took such possession of her that Marietta feared she would have a hemorrhage. When it began to ease Marietta looked over her shoulder and glanced about to see if there was a flagon of water anywhere. She saw the gleam of a glass and put the last few drops it contained to Elena's lips. There was no more time to lose. She pushed back the bed-clothes and, anguished by her friend's skeletal form beneath the nightshift, she scooped her thin legs over the edge of the couch and started to put on her slippers.

"I can't walk," Elena whispered despairingly as she lolled against Marietta, a tear trickling down her cheek.

"I'll support you."

There was a robe at the end of the couch and Marietta helped Elena into it as if dressing a child. Then she took one of Elena's arms around her neck, gripped the thin wrist, and with her own arm tight about her friend's waist she brought her from the couch. Elena's knees gave and she sagged, but Marietta had been prepared. Even though she staggered momentarily under the sudden dead weight she became stable again almost at once. It helped to lean Elena against her hip as she took her step by step across to the foot of the stairs. There she sat Elena on the bottom tread and propped her against the wall. After swiftly uncoiling the rope from about her waist, Marietta used it to bundle up her own skirts to calf-length, wanting to make sure she did not catch her heel on a hem on the precipitous staircase. Then she stooped behind her friend to put her hands under Elena's arms and heave her gently onto the next tread. Going slowly backward, Marietta had lifted her a quarter of the way up the stairs when Elena became agitated.

"Don't be afraid, Elena. I won't let you fall," Marietta promised. But Elena refused to be reassured. Marietta crouched down beside her, in-tending further words of comfort, but Elena was trying to communicate. Marietta leaned closer to catch the words. "Papers? Behind the mirror?"

Then, as if summoning up some last strength in her voice, Elena gave a little cry. "For Domenico!"

Marietta did not hesitate. She had no idea what those papers might be, but she went down again to the marble room and ran to the mirror on the wall. Taking hold of the bottom edge of the frame she raised it slightly away from where it was hanging. Two bundles of papers, one tied with a strip of petticoat lace, fell to the floor at her feet. She snatched them up, thrusting one bundle into her pocket and the other into her sash. Then as she turned back she saw to her dismay that Elena had gently slithered down the stairs again almost to the last tread. Marietta rushed back to her and began once more the process of getting her up the flight. But they had ascended no more than half a dozen treads when Filippo's wrathful voice boomed down at them, seeming to echo back from every corner.

"What is happening here!"

Although shocked and frightened, Marietta released Elena carefully to let her slump safely against the wall where she could not slip again. Then she whirled about to glare up at Filippo in a blazing rage equal to his. He was a daunting sight, standing rock-like in the doorway high above, his height and breadth silhouetted against the fading daylight in the bedchamber beyond.

"You have no need to ask such a question!" she stormed. "See for yourself, Celano. I'm taking Elena out of here to nurse her back to health!"

"You're too late. She'll not live the night!"

"That's what you would like! Then you'd be free to marry Bianca. I knew you were a cruel man, but I never supposed you would stoop to such evil depths. Step away! I'm bringing Elena up from this hell-hole!"

"Stay where you are!" he ordered thunderously as she turned back to start lifting Elena again. "You're never coming out of there alive. Since you're so concerned about Elena you shall take her place in fair exchange!"

Marietta pulled the pistol out of her sash and cocked it as she faced him again. "I'll not hesitate to shoot you, so just withdraw to allow me to get out of here and raise the alarm."

He saw by her resolute expression that she meant what she said. The idea that this Torrisi woman should try to ruin all his plans at the last moment was almost beyond belief. He had left the debate sooner than he should have, simply because this was the night he was planning to wind up his affairs. Minerva and Giovanna were ready to leave as soon as it was dark, and the warden, after giving her final report to his agent, had been disposed of with her husband. All that remained was to bring Elena back to her bedchamber. It had been agreeable to him that she draw her last breath in her own bed.

Marietta was slowly ascending the stairs. "Go backward into your bed-chamber, Celano. Do as I say!"

He was not in the least alarmed by the threat of her pistol. His guess was that she had never fired a weapon in her life, whereas he had disarmed far stronger adversaries. At the right moment he would break her neck. It meant a quick revision of his plans. Minerva would leave the palace in this Torrisi woman's *bauta* mask and mantle, which she had conveniently left on his bed. The servants would see her depart, as would Bianca, who he had sent back to the library to watch from the window for the banishment of her former friend. No finger of suspicion would be pointed at him when Mari-etta Torrisi failed to arrive home, and his agent would silence Minerva soon enough.

"At least let me carry Elena to her apartment," he offered sharply. "Having brought her so far you can hardly wish to leave her near the foot of these cold stairs. It was my intention all along that she should die in comfort."

"You'll not lay a hand on her ever again!" It scared Marietta afresh as she drew still nearer that he should be so dangerously in control of himself, making no attempt to move from his secure position. Her heart was thump-ing and the trembling of her hand made her fear that even though he was such a solid target she might only wound him if she was compelled to fire the pistol. "You're an evil man and impossible to trust!"

"Even under the threat of your pistol?" he challenged angrily, spreading his arms wide to indicate his defenselessness. "You could easily shoot and put me out of your way."

"No, I want you brought to justice for the attempted murder of your wife."

He took a step down to her so swiftly that she was caught unawares. The side of his hand struck her wrist such a blow that the pistol dropped from her grasp and went rattling away down the stairs. In terror she flung herself back against the wall, seeing murder in his eyes. In the same instant a shadow moved in behind him and he sensed another presence, wheeling about even as Bianca lunged at him with a library knife.

"In the devil's name!" he roared as she fell against him, the blade missing its target completely in the swiftness of his reaction and falling harmlessly from her hand. But she had brought him off balance and his heel slipped on the edge of a tread as together they almost toppled. Instinctively Bianca grabbed at the gilt hand-cord along the wall while he clutched at the curtain. He could still have saved himself as she had done, but with a jangling of curtain rings the age-rotted fabric tore free under the force of his weight. He uttered a terrible shout that was echoed by Bianca's hysterical scream as he reeled back over the side of the stairs to land with a heavy thud on the marble floor. A deep groan told them he was not dead.

Marietta stared at the little knife still spinning on the stair where it had fallen, and then at Bianca lying half-sprawled, her knuckles showing pearl-white from her frozen grasp on the hand-cord, her eyes wide and dark and unfocused. For a matter of seconds both she and Marietta remained motionless with shock. Then Marietta flew into action.

"Help me carry Elena out of here, Bianca! There's no time to lose. Filippo may only be stunned." Marietta had run down again to Elena, expecting the girl to follow her. But that was not the case, for Bianca had merely edged her way up to her feet from where she had fallen and stood transfixed with her back pressed against the wall.

"Come, Bianca! Now!"

There was no response. Marietta, seeing that she could expect no assistance from that source, began lifting Elena more quickly and inevitably more roughly than before. But she had drawn her sick friend no higher than three treads when Elena was almost jerked from her grasp. Filippo had reared up with a terrible cry of pain to grab his wife by the ankle. Marietta screamed, struggling to keep hold of her as he began to draw Elena over the side.

Then came a rush of movement. Bianca, spurred into action by Marietta's scream, had snatched off her shoe and was jabbing the heel hard into the back of Filippo's hand, drawing blood. His tenacious clasp relaxed and he fell back again with a roar of agony on bones that had been broken in his original fall.

Marietta hauled Elena away from the side. "Take Elena by the ankles, Bianca!" she instructed.

This time the girl flew to obey her. Together they soon had Elena up the stairs and through the lobby into Filippo's bedchamber. There they laid her on the bed. Even as Marietta leaned over the sick woman Bianca spun about to dash back through the secret doors as if she regretted the violence she had used on her lover and intended to help him. Marietta's cry for her to come back went unanswered.

Filippo, still partly entangled in the heavy folds of the curtain, breathed with relief when he saw Bianca standing over him, the candlelight making a pale aura of her hair. He was in a cold sweat of pain for he had broken a leg in his fall, and the daggers in his hip suggested that he had severely cracked it, as well as a rib or two. Somehow he managed a smile for her, unaware that it became twisted into a grimace of agony.

"My dear little swan, I knew you'd come to me. I forgive your angry attempt to knife me, even though it has brought me to this." He lifted a hand in appeal. "You must pardon me in your turn for keeping Elena out of the way. In any case the blame is yours. You made me fall in love with you until I could think of nothing but having you for my wife. Go at once and fetch help, my sweeting. Summon my valet and the servants by the bell-pulls in my bedchamber." Still she had not spoken, staring down at him with huge blue eyes that did not seem to blink. "Make haste, little swan."

Obediently she turned away, but it was not to fetch help. She went across to the branched candlestick that Marietta had set down by Elena's prison bed and blew out the flames. Only then, guided by the diminishing daylight showing through the door from the bedchamber above, did she ascend the stairs, picking up the pistol and the library knife to put both into her pocket as she went.

Filippo gave a despairing shout as it dawned on him what she was about to do. "No, Bianca!"

But she had gone through the door and shut it after her. In disbelief

Filippo heard the key turn before it was withdrawn. Seconds later there came a muffled thud as the cupboard swung back into place. He was left, consumed by pain and alarm, in total darkness.

Marietta, who had tucked Elena under the covers and given her another sip of the cognac, saw Bianca rush to the window. Before she could stop her, Bianca had opened it and flung the key to the hidden door far out through the gathering dusk into the Grand Canal.

"There was no need for that!" Marietta protested. "Filippo can't be left in that place."

Bianca's eyes flashed. "I heard what he said to you. I would leave him there forever!"

Then she rushed to the door between Filippo's bedchamber and Elena's apartment. It had been Marietta's intention that the impostor and the maid, if they were still in there, be exposed before witnesses, but already Bianca had shot back the bolt and flung the door wide.

Giovanna, who had been trying to overhear what was happening in the neighboring bedchamber, drew back swiftly, expecting to see Filippo. Instead she and Minerva saw the taut, white-faced girl with Elena in the bed behind her and Marietta darting to the nearest bell-pull.

"You wicked creatures!" Bianca shrieked at them.

Both Giovanna and Minerva were dressed to leave, and their hand-baggage was packed as they had been instructed. They were aware that something had gone awry, but Giovanna did not believe there was any situation from which it was not possible to wriggle out unscathed. Bluff was an invaluable weapon.

"Now look here," she began, "Signor Celano would never allow anyone to speak in such a manner to my mistress."

"Be silent!" Bianca took a threatening step forward, her fists clenched by her sides. Never in her life had she experienced the fury that consumed her at this moment. "The truth is known! The Council of Three shall throw you both into their torture chambers!"

The two women, Venetian to the bone, were immediately seized by terror at this dreadful threat. They snatched up their dominoes, which they had put ready for their leaving, flung the garments about their shoulders, and grabbed their hand-baggage. Minerva made little pleading cries for mercy like a mewling cat as they fled the apartment. One piece of baggage had been overlooked in their panic. Bianca rushed to catch it up and hurl it after them. The women heard it fall in their wake, but neither stopped to retrieve it. Giovanna, the more intelligent of the two, had deliberately investigated ways out of the palace in case of any emergency, and now she led her companion at a run to a little-used stairway that led down to a flower-room with a gardener's door. Since they had lost all the promised renumeration for many tedious weeks of boredom, she grabbed whatever small items of value were available en route and shoved them into her pockets. Minerva was too panic-stricken to follow her example.

Marietta went to Bianca, who had sagged sobbing against the door jamb, and put an arm around her. "There's no time for tears now," she urged kindly. "We have to think of Elena first."

As Marietta began to guide Bianca back to the bedside, Filippo's valet arrived. He was instantly belligerent, demanding to know why a stranger was in the Signor's bedchamber and for what reason the sick woman had been moved from her own apartment. Marietta gave back in the same vein, brooking no argument.

"Signora Celano is at death's door and her apartment is a pigsty! Fetch her own doctor immediately if you don't want to be blamed for her demise! Go! Dr. Grassi lives near here in the russet-red house on the Calle Bernardo." He left hurriedly as a footman arrived from another direction, puzzled to see her there. She spoke as urgently to him. "Two women are fleeing from the palace! Catch them! There is little time. They were in Signora Celano's apartment and may have stolen something!"

Other servants appeared. Some were urged to give chase with the footman while a maid was sent to fetch Sister Giaccomina in haste from the library. Marietta's stormy presence and imperious orders brought almost instant results. Another bedchamber on the other side of the palace was made ready for Elena. While this was being done Marietta and Sister Giaccomina bathed her in warm water, Bianca handing them the towels and the nun gently bewailing the terrible state to which one of her dear Pietà daughters had been reduced. They also gave Elena small spoonfuls of goat's milk that had been rushed from the kitchen, and sips of water to relieve the dryness of her mouth.

A footman returned to report that the woman named Minerva had been caught and detained in a locked storeroom off the kitchen, but her companion had escaped. When he wanted to know if the police should be called, Marietta shook her head and said that would be decided later.

When the steward of the palace arrived at the bedchamber door he was outraged to find that a Torrisi woman, who had come into the palace under false pretenses, should be commandeering his staff. It was Sister Giaccomina who beat him back with strong words. "Disgrace" and "neglect" and "ought to be ashamed of yourself" were some that she used to make him retreat. Fuming to himself, knowing the wrath he would have to face when Signor Celano reappeared from wherever he had gone, he vented his ill temper on those who were preparing the new apartment for the Signora.

Dr. Grassi, who had not been called to care for Elena since she had suffered a spate of headaches two years before, gave her his most solicitous attention when he arrived breathless from hurrying up so many stairs. After examining her and propping her up during a coughing attack, he gave her a spoonful of black liquid to ease her lungs. Then he had her carefully carried by two footmen to the bed that had been prepared for her, which was being warmed with heated bricks wrapped in linen. As the nun and Bianca attended to her, Dr. Grassi drew Marietta aside.

"This is a case of extreme malnutrition complicated by an infection of the lungs."

"What are her chances, Doctor?" Marietta asked anxiously.

He looked very grave and made a weighing motion with his hands. "It is touch and go, that's all I can say at the moment. It is utterly disgraceful that Signora Celano's state of melancholia—which I assure you I would have checked long ago had I been consulted—should have been allowed to go to such lengths."

"She was never melancholic, Doctor," Marietta said. Then she told him the whole story. He was outraged by the treatment Elena had suffered.

"Yet however much I decry Signor Celano's action, he must be released at once," he insisted, "and I will treat whatever injuries he has sustained in his fall."

"That won't be quickly done. In the confusion of Elena's release the key was lost. It will take male servants with crowbars a long time to break open the door."

"At least a start must be made. Show me where it is."

Marietta led the doctor to Filippo's bedchamber. She showed him the device that sent the cupboard swinging back on its hinges. Then Dr. Grassi himself summoned the steward, who put his strongest footmen to work. Marietta, leaving the doctor to watch the proceedings, returned to the sickroom.

Elena's breathing was labored, and with Bianca's help Marietta propped her higher with another pillow. Sister Giaccomina was waiting to give her a spoonful of the dark liquid the doctor had left on the side-table.

"Bianca has told me everything." The nun sighed deeply as she carefully tipped the liquid between Elena's colorless lips. "To think that this dear girl was locked up in such misery while I was contentedly dealing with that wicked man's library. What is to be the outcome of all this?"

"My hope is that the Church will allow an annulment of Elena's marriage and that she can be moved away from Filippo in the meantime. We have never needed your support more."

The nun dabbed with a napkin at a trickle of medicine that had escaped Elena's mouth. "You have it, my dears. All three of you, just as you have always had my blessings."

Marietta kissed her soft cheek. "I just remembered that Leonardo should have arrived downstairs two hours or more ago."

"Go and see him. Poor man! He'll be wondering whatever has happened."

Bianca followed Marietta out of the bedchamber. "I'm so ashamed," she cried. "If I'd taken notice of how much you distrusted Filippo I could have uncovered that imposture myself! Then Elena need not have come quite so near death's door." She bit deep into her tremulous lip. "I've been so stupid about everything!"

Marietta put a hand on the girl's shoulder. "I'm sure most people have felt like that at some time in their lives, and I include myself. What matters is that you saved Elena's life and mine by your action. She and I might both have been locked in that awful room if it hadn't been for you."

"When Filippo told me to go to the library and watch from the window to see you being evicted, I was suddenly afraid for you and for what I had done. I had never seen him flare into a rage before, and although he didn't speak sharply to me, I knew he would treat you roughly. I couldn't have endured that! It's why I followed him upstairs. I intended to stand between the two of you. Please believe me!"

"I do, Bianca."

They hugged each other then, and Bianca commented on the crackle of paper in Marietta's sash. "What are you hiding? Not a message for a new mask?"

Marietta smiled. "You found that, did you?" She dived a hand into her sash and then into her pocket to bring out the collection of papers she had hidden there. "Elena made me fetch these from behind the mirror in that room. I'll take them downstairs with me and look at them with Leonardo."

In the corridor she met the steward cloaked for outdoors. "I'm going to fetch Signor Alvise Celano," he said stiffly. "An axe has had to be taken to that door and still it is proving impossible to open. He may have a second key."

Nodding briefly, she left him and hurried on to the Ivory Salon. Leonardo jumped up from a chair as she entered and came to meet her, relief written clearly on his face.

"What's been happening?" When she had explained, he rubbed his chin thoughtfully. "It's as well that Bianca just gave the villain a push. Had she used the library knife on him it would not have been taken lightly. Nevertheless it's my guess that Filippo Celano will make much of that push!"

"As I shall make of Elena's incarceration!"

"Naturally. But you must remember, it is generally accepted that a husband may chastise his wife and cool her temper or a nagging tongue by shutting her up for a while."

"Not to starve her to death!"

"Indeed not! That would be murder."

"I saw no food in the room and Elena was too weak even to have put the last of the water to her lips." Marietta clenched her fists at her sides, her expression agonized. "I never thought I could heap blame on Venice, but I do now. There is something about this marvelous and beautiful city that corrupts the truth and forces deceit and bluff and falsehood on us all. You and I are greatly responsible for that state of affairs, Leonardo."

"In what way?"

"With our mask-making! It's not enough that Carnival demands constant illusion, but that fiendish *bauta* mask gives license to all people throughout the rest of the year to evade the consequences of their own actions! Without masks such as ours many infidelities and vengeful acts and infamous crimes would not go undiscovered. Filippo could never have presented that impostor at the Basilica or the opera house without a mask. Then this current dreadful situation would never have arisen."

"Well, it has," Leonardo stated phlegmatically, "and you and I will have to deal with it."

She closed her eyes for a second or two and ran her fingers through her hair as she recovered herself before speaking again. "You're right," she agreed in level tones, reorganizing her thoughts. "As I told you, the impostor herself is in custody. Minerva is the flaw in any defense Filippo might present."

"Be wary, Marietta. The first thing Filippo is likely to do when he comes out of that marble room will be to check whether those two women have slipped away. His best policy would be to have Minerva released immediately."

"Not if we get a signed confession first! Would you get that for me?"

"Gladly, if it can be done. Where is she?"

"I'll have you taken to her. At the moment she is being held as a thief and was badly frightened when Bianca threatened her."

"What are those papers on the table?"

Marietta picked up the bundle she had placed there. "Elena had hidden them. She seemed to think they had some connection with Domenico."

She spread the papers out and Leonardo moved candlelight closer to read them. But whatever had been written was no longer decipherable. They had been shut up too long behind the heavy mirror without light or air. Damp had blotched the ink and mildewed the paper. Here and there parts of sentences remained, but nothing that made any sense.

"If these papers were to be of some benefit to Domenico," Marietta said with a catch in her voice, "that chance has gone. We shall have to wait for Elena to recover before we know their importance."

Leonardo gathered up the papers for her, but he knew as she did that if Elena died whatever information had been written there would be lost forever.

"I'll show these to Sebastiano," she said emotionally as she took the bundle from him. "There may be something that can be deciphered."

Leonardo's lack of optimism showed in his failure to endorse her hope. Marietta passed a hand falteringly across her eyes. Then she straightened up and summoned a servant to take him to the impostor.

Alvise was absorbed in a news-sheet when his brother's steward arrived. France was at war with Austria and fighting was taking place on Italian soil. He read that General Bonaparte was driving all before him while sending back to France all the treasures he could lay his hands on. The Venetian Republic kept meeting his requests for food and other supplies for his army, but he was slow at paying for anything. The Doge must have a stack of unsettled accounts with the Corsican upstart! Alvise was like most Venetians in viewing everything that happened beyond their borders as brash, foolhardy, and at times almost pitiable. These wars were not for Venice. The Bride of the Sea was inviolate.

When the steward was shown into the room Alvise put down the news-sheet and rose to stand with his back to the ornate marble fireplace, feet apart, hands clasped behind him. He thought he knew the reason for the steward's coming.

"Is my sister-in-law dead?"

"No, signore, although a doctor was called urgently to the palace early this evening and it doesn't seem as if it will be long. I have come about Signor Celano. According to Signora Torrisi, your brother became locked in the secret room that leads out of his bedchamber."

"What!" Alvise's eyes narrowed incredulously. "Are you telling me a tale I'm expected to believe?"

The steward was offended. "Signore! I'm a responsible servant of the House of Celano! I'm saying only what I have seen or believe to be true.

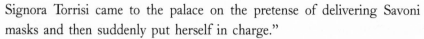
Signora Torrisi came to the palace on the pretense of delivering Savoni masks and then suddenly put herself in charge."

"The devil she did!"

"Do you have another key to that door within a door? Even with a crowbar, we have been unable to break the lock."

"No, I haven't." Alvise strode away from the fireplace. "Come along. You can tell me the rest on the way."

After watching the servants' futile onslaught with axes on the door, and speaking to the doctor, who fully described to him all that had happened, Alvise went along to the sickroom. At least he could get rid of the Torrisi woman and see that the impostor was set free. Filippo would need his help getting out of this mess. There was also Alessandro to be considered. Alvise knew his brother the Cardinal would abhor any scandal tainting the name of Celano. This was the late eighteenth century, not some earlier time when bloody deeds had done little harm and sometimes even enhanced a family's reputation.

Sister Giaccomina opened the sickroom door to Alvise and stepped forward immediately, closing it behind her.

"The doctor is allowing Elena no visitors," she said firmly.

"I'm not here for that. Signora Torrisi must leave immediately."

It was then that Sister Giaccomina did battle with him. The only time she could be roused to anger was when she needed to defend the rights of one of her Pietà girls. Now she stated flatly that she was in charge of the patient with Dr. Grassi's authority and that she needed Marietta, a former Pietà girl experienced in nursing, to assist her. "I'll not find a better aide anywhere and this is a matter of life and death! Do you wish to finish what your wicked brother started and put Elena in her coffin?"

He accepted defeat for the time being. This round little nun, bouncing on her heels with indignation, could be a powerful witness against Filippo, and it might be foolhardy to antagonize her still more.

He left her and went to see the impostor, a sniveling creature of quite comely appearance with beautiful hair as like Elena's as was possible.

"I've told everything," she sobbed, terrified by his threats and regretting bitterly the signed confession she had given to that other man, which this new interrogator had yet to mention. "It's not my fault Signor Celano wanted to murder his wife by such a crazy method. He told us he wanted to punish her without disgracing her name in public and that he would set her free when she had learned to be obedient."

"Don't lie!"

Her blue eyes flowed with a river of tears. "I'm not. I swear it! Signor Celano said it wouldn't be for long. Do you think I wanted to be shut up all that time in that apartment as if it were I who was being punished? I nearly went mad with boredom. It wasn't so bad for Giovanna—she could leave the palace sometimes. I only had two outings and then I was terrified, because I'd been threatened with prison on some trumped-up charge if I gave myself away. Your brother is a very frightening man!"

He could tell that the stupid creature had been a victim of Filippo's cunning, but still he persisted. "You must have begun to suspect that something was seriously amiss."

Her gaze shifted. "No! I deny I ever did!"

He had no more patience. She had told him all he needed to know. He opened the door wide for her. "Get out!"

She blinked for a moment in disbelief and then darted forward. But he grabbed a handful of her domino about her throat and jerked her close, half choking her. "One word of what you have seen or done in this palace and you'll be found floating in one of the canals."

Then he threw her from him and she staggered for a few steps before she ran with her domino billowing behind her.

In the rose marble room Filippo soon moved from where he had fallen. In spite of excruciating pain he had managed to disentangle himself from the folds of the curtain and felt his way along, hauling his broken limbs inch by agonizing inch to the foot of the stairs. He knew his injuries were far from fatal, but was aware that he would be incapacitated for a long while to come. If it had not been for the curtain cradling him as he fell, he would most likely have broken his back.

He was no stranger to pain, and he had the courage to bear it. His last encounter with Antonio Torrisi had brought agony no less than this. His strength of will, as well as his powerful forearms, enabled him to hoist himself up the stairs at a snail's pace while his legs dragged helplessly after him, a bone protruding from one that left a trail of blood.

Fear and fury also spurred him on. The damage done to his hip was only made worse by what he was being compelled to do. He planned every kind of revenge against Bianca, who had betrayed him, and against Marietta Torrisi, whose untimely interference was going to cost him a fortune in lawyers' fees. At least it was unlikely that Elena would survive to give damaging evidence against him.

With a groan he let his brow rest on his forearm as pain seared up through him like a furnace to swallow his brain and confuse his thoughts. It seemed to him he must have been cut down after hanging by his thumbs between the rose columns of the Doge's Palace—was it coincidence that much of this salon was in the same hue?—or else maybe he had been stretched on some ancient rack. Periodically, oblivion eased these curious tricks of the mind until he became aware of where he was again. Then he would concentrate once more on the overwhelming task of hoisting himself up one more tread.

His aim was to reach the top of the stairs, where he could keep up a persistent knocking until eventually a servant would hear him. He never went anywhere without a sheathed dagger in his coat-tail and its handle would make a resounding rap. It was his hope that the steward would send for Alvise. Their father had told each of his sons, with the exception of Pietro, who had been sent away by that time, the secret of the cupboard and where the door behind it led. Since the rose marble salon was mainly for the indulgences of the head of the House of Celano, daughters were never informed. But Marco had once let Lavinia in on the secret when he feared his older brothers might shut him in there as a cruel prank. She could have worked the mechanism if she had been in the palace now, and Filippo regretted, in view of his present circumstances, that he had refused her a home. He closed his eyes on a new shaft of agony.

The sudden crash of the first crowbar against the door made him think for a few light-headed moments that the walls were collapsing about him. Then it dawned on him what it was. Somehow he must signal to his rescuers to make haste. He was constantly in fear of not keeping close enough to the wall in this inky darkness. Fumbling, he drew his brocade coat-tail forward to slide out the dagger.

As he brought his arm back again this extra effort brought on a new wave of agony that drew him again into unconsciousness. The dagger slipped from his fingers and he slithered back down a few treads in the blood that had been pouring from his leg. Then he opened his eyes as he tilted over the side of the stairs once more and knew he was falling. This time the curtain did not break his fall. His head struck the marble floor and he lay still.

It was as Alvise was returning to Filippo's bedchamber from the kitchen quarters that the steward met him halfway.

"We managed to get the door open, signore. I regret to tell you that we found your brother dead!"

Chapter 17

*A*lvise notified *A*lessandro in *R*ome and *P*ietro in Padua of their brother's demise. Vitale, deep in his cups as usual, blubbered like a baby when told, although he and Filippo had never liked each other. A widow of the family's acquaintance offered to fetch Lavinia to Venice since she was reluctant to leave the house on her own.

Having the shortest distance to come, Lavinia was first to arrive for the funeral. She wrung her hands when she saw how ill Elena was after her ordeal. Only once did she and Marietta speak about Filippo.

"If you hadn't told me how to get into that hidden room," Marietta said when they were alone, "Elena would still be there, but no longer alive."

"Then I'm thankful I did, although Mother was furious with me."

"But she has gone, Lavinia."

Lavinia looked down at her nervous hands in her lap. "No. In that house she will always be alive."

Alessandro was the next to arrive. Alvise had given him a short account of events in the letter he sent by a fast messenger, but now he wanted to know all the remaining details. When he had heard them, Alessandro left his chair and paced across to the window. "What a catastrophe! How much of it has leaked out?"

Alvise booted a half-fallen log back into the fire. "Beyond the palace? I would say nothing. The servants know better than to let their tongues wag and the doctor is discreet. I've announced Filippo's death as an unfortunate accident, which indeed it was. The circumstances are nobody else's business."

"What of Signora Torrisi? Is she wanting to cause trouble?"

"She could do so if she wished. She has the impostor's signed confession in her possession, but that is not her intention. Now that Elena is a widow Marietta Torrisi's only concern is to avoid any scandal because it would only harm Elena, who has been through so much already." Alvise strolled across to stand by his brother. "What I can't understand is why Filippo didn't approach you to help him get an annulment."

Alessandro sighed. "He did and I forbade it."

"Ah!" Alvise raised an eyebrow and leaned a shoulder against the wall. "I'm puzzled as well to know why Filippo let Elena stay alive over such a long period. One of his agents must have kept her supplied with food and water and other things she needed. I went down to the secret salon to look around."

The Cardinal made a fist and thumped it against the window frame. "It's obvious to me! He lacked the stomach to make her end swift."

"But why? Filippo was not a man of sensitivity."

"That is true, but there was a weakness in him that he never acknowledged," Alessandro said as he moved away from the window. It was pointless to expound his theory that Filippo had loved Elena in a complicated way. "What of this girl Bianca whom you also wrote about in your letter? Where is she?"

"Still here and helping to nurse Elena. It was obvious to me that Filippo had made up his mind to marry Bianca as soon as he was free. I saw him with her a couple of times when I called, and he could not take his eyes from her. It's why he had her moved into the palace."

"Did you tell Pietro all this in your message to him?"

"I did."

"It will be up to him how soon she goes. All decisions will be his from the time of his arrival, but how he will tear himself away from Padua to settle in Venice I do not know. It was after the duel with the Torrisi that

Filippo had a change of heart about making Pietro his heir in the event of his remaining childless. He had looked death in the face and then our youngest brother healed his wounds. Up until then you were to inherit."

"I'm not in the least disappointed. The last thing I want is to be burdened with the headship of the family and all the duties that devolve upon a senator. But Mother must be turning in her grave."

Alessandro frowned. "Let us not speak of that. Where is Elena? I want to see her."

As they mounted the stairs together, Alessandro spoke with annoyance of the delay he had experienced coming through encampments of the French army not far from the Republic's border. An officer had checked his papers to make sure he was not a spy. Alessandro's indignation knew no bounds. Alvise left him at the sickroom door.

When Alessandro came to Elena's bedside he scarcely recognized the skeletal woman lying there. For all his pride and ambition he was capable of deep compassion at times.

"My poor child," he said sorrowfully, leaning over to place a hand on Elena's brow.

She gave him a little smile that still held the sweetness of her nature in it. "I'm getting better," she whispered.

He knelt by the bedside and prayed for her while Marietta, who was the only other person in the bedchamber, knelt on the opposite side of the bed. When he rose to his feet again and had blessed Elena, he drew Marietta to one side.

"I appreciate that your concern for Elena has ruled out any scandalous aftermath. There's no doubt Elena owes her life to you."

"I'm only one of three," Marietta replied.

"Nevertheless, it is a fitting end to the vendetta."

"That can never be over so long as my husband is unjustly imprisoned."

"No Celano had anything to do with that."

"I happen to believe otherwise," Marietta stated implacably.

"Have you any proof to support that belief?"

"Unfortunately no."

"Then let no more ever be said on the matter." Alessandro's face was stern. "I advise you to let that Torrisi aggression you have adopted fade away and devote your thoughts to more womanly matters. You have two daughters, I believe."

"What if I had had a son?"

"It is well for you that is a hypothetical question. At the present time his life would not have been worth a ducat. Filippo never heeded my words of peace and there are Celanos who would not tolerate the resurgence of the House of Torrisi. It is unlikely Pietro will be able to change matters immediately. As the new head of the family, he'll have much else to think about for a long time to come."

His words chilled her through.

Whenever possible Marietta made visits to see her children in Adrianna's care. She was not prepared one morning when she found Danilo's crib empty.

"Where is he?" she cried, swinging around to face Adrianna, who had followed her into the room.

"Francesca was in Venice visiting her parents-in-law. She has taken Danilo home with her." Adrianna put a consoling arm around Marietta's shoulders. "It had to be."

Marietta dropped her face into her hands.

Kinfolk from far afield began to arrive at the Palazzo Celano for the funeral. At first each new arrival was outraged to hear that a Torrisi woman was in charge of Filippo's sick wife, but Alessandro soon quelled this open opposition, even though angry resentment continued to simmer. The general opinion was that when Pietro arrived he would soon send Signora Torrisi packing. In the meantime, although the gathering relatives wore mourning clothes, they enjoyed many lively reunions. Some were accommodated by Alvise, and a few of the more distant cousins were housed with Vitale, who had one of the best wine cellars in Venice, which compensated to a degree for his somewhat noisy and boisterous company.

Bianca was crossing the reception hall when servants appeared from the main staircase carrying baggage that denoted the arrival of yet another Celano relative. She paused in order not to present her departing back to the traveler. Then in the doorway she saw a tall young man of comparatively good looks, with alert hazel eyes under peaked brows, thick brown hair that would have rippled into waves if it had not been drawn back severely into the customary bow at the back of his neck, and a well-cut mouth. A general family likeness stamped him before he spoke.

"Good day, signorina. I'm Dr. Pietro Celano."

He had guessed her identity even as she had his. This exquisite girl with the withdrawn look in her long-lashed eyes, her fair hair softly dressed, attired as she was in what he knew to be the scarlet gown of Pietà girls, was the indirect reason for Elena's incarceration and his brother's death.

"I'm Bianca," she said coolly, wanting to distance herself from all Cela-nos, "a flutist at the Pietà. At present I'm helping to nurse Elena."

He had come forward. "How is she?"

"Still very ill."

"I hope I may be of some service to her."

"She already has a good doctor attending her." It was a rebuff.

"I'm sure she has." He noticed that a manservant was waiting to show him to his room and he bowed to her. "We shall meet at dinner, no doubt."

She did not trouble to tell him that she and Marietta and the nun took their meals in a small salon adjoining the sickroom.

Within a half hour of his arrival Pietro, bathed and changed from his journey, was at Elena's bedside. Although she did not know him, for they had never met, she gave him a little smile.

"I'm Pietro, Elena."

"You have come to see me," she whispered, no strength in her voice. "How kind." She closed her eyes again.

He glanced inquiringly across at Marietta, who sat by the opposite side of the bed with Bianca. Marietta shook her head to show that as yet Elena knew nothing of Filippo's death. Dr. Grassi had advised against it.

At that moment a gathering rasping of breath that signaled the onset of a coughing bout began to convulse Elena, and although Marietta sprang to her Pietro was first, holding her in his arms until it was over. Then he asked Marietta to support Elena while he took a doctor's listening device from his pocket and put his ear to one end as he placed the other to Elena's chest and then her back. When she had been lowered back onto her pillows, he stood looking at her while Marietta drew the covers about her again.

"How long has Elena been plagued by this coughing?"

"Ever since she was brought out of captivity," Marietta told him.

"In her condition her heart won't stand the strain much longer. What is she taking?" He took the bottle of black liquid that Bianca handed to him, uncorked it and smelled the contents. "This is useless."

He left the bedchamber only to return a few minutes later with a gold-colored physic of his own mixing. Elena received a small spoonful from him.

"Repeat the dose every three hours," he instructed Marietta. Then to Bianca he added, "You are the expert at opening windows, I believe. Would you set one open now? It does a patient no good to be closeted in airless conditions."

Bianca looked warily at him. "What do you mean by an expert?"

He strolled across to her. "Nobody seems to know how or why the key to the marble salon disappeared the night Filippo fell. Marietta had her hands full with Elena and my guess is that it was someone else who locked him in and threw away the key. If the Grand Canal could be dredged, do you think it might be found?"

Her eyes flashed. "You know it was me, don't you! Yes, I did throw it away. I wanted him shut in where he could never harm anyone again!"

Anxiously Marietta took a step forward. "It all happened in the heat of the moment!"

"I'm sure it did," he acknowledged evenly, his glance piercing. Then he turned to leave, saying that he would return later.

Bianca opened the window, wondering how much more he would guess.

Pietro came back after dinner. Both Marietta and Sister Giaccomina could see he was extremely anxious about Elena's condition. He felt her pulse and asked that the cool damp cloths Bianca laid across her forehead be constantly changed. Before retiring to bed he appeared again.

"Call me in the night if Elena gets any worse," he said to Marietta.

At two o'clock in the morning Bianca went for him at a run, bursting into his room and waking him up with a shake. "Please come!" she cried frantically. "We fear Elena is dying."

He hurled himself from the bed, threw on a robe, snatched up his medical bag, and ran with her. For the rest of the night they all labored together to save Elena.

"She's not fighting!" he exclaimed once.

Just before dawn Elena became weaker, as if finally ready to slip away. Marietta gathered the thin hands into hers. "No, Elena! No! Think of Elizabetta! Think of Nicolò! Don't leave them never knowing each other!"

Sister Giaccomina and Bianca always declared afterward that Elena had heard Marietta's appeal. Marietta had no doubts about it herself, and it was the moment when she knew what Elizabetta's future must be. Pietro saw only that Marietta's cry had coincided with the breaking of the fever, but whatever the cause, Elena turned the corner.

"It doesn't mean that she is out of danger," Pietro said to Marietta later in the day. "The possibility of a relapse is ever present. She must have absolute quiet and constant nursing."

"I should like to reinstate Elena's personal maid, who was dismissed when the imposture began."

"Most certainly."

"In that case Bianca could go back to the Pietà."

He shook his head. "I want you to retain the team you have."

Bianca's feelings were mixed when she was told. She wanted to help nurse Elena, but she also longed to be away from the Palazzo Celano and never set foot in it again.

Immediately after the funeral Pietro made his presence felt throughout the palace. He never raised his voice or spoke sharply, but all respected his authority. Servants scuttled to obey his orders, seeing him at first as a younger Filippo, but it soon became clear to everyone that he was a very different man. Dr. Grassi, who had heard all about Pietro's achievements, was willing to accept his tactful suggestions as to how Elena's treatment might be improved. Her cough had eased with Pietro's medicine and she slept better at night. Some other herbal concoction that Pietro gave her stimulated her appetite and gradually she was able to digest light meals. Sometimes Pietro went to the kitchen and produced something for her himself.

It had been Marietta's conviction that Elena remembered nothing of her rescue, but the day came when the tell-tale question was asked.

"Where is Filippo?"

Marietta leaned over her. "He is not here any more."

"Did that fall kill him?"

"It is believed he struggled up the stairs and fell a second time."

Elena closed her eyes frowningly. "How terrible!"

"Try not to think about it."

Another day Elena asked where Domenico was. "Why hasn't he come to see me?"

"He can't," Marietta replied sadly. "Domenico is still in prison. I sent a letter today telling him that I'm here nursing you."

"But those papers!" Elena tried to sit up. "They told everything. I read them through until I knew every word. Take them to the Doge!"

Elena became so distressed that Marietta, despairing at what had been lost, had difficulty in calming her. "When you are well enough we shall put everything together again."

That seemed to settle Elena, but Marietta could not see that her friend's evidence would hold any weight in their present condition.

Alessandro stayed long enough to advise Pietro on many of the business and family matters that would now be his responsibility. Then, the day before he began his journey back to Rome, he had a talk with Lavinia. "As you know," he began, "I'm leaving tomorrow."

She nodded unhappily. "Are you taking me back to Mother on the way?"

He understood. "Your duties in that respect are at an end, Lavinia. Pietro has made a suggestion to me about your future. We know that when you were a girl you wanted to take the veil. It is not too late. There's a convent on the outskirts of Rome that stands in beautiful and peaceful grounds. The nuns grow food for the hungry and flowers to sell in aid of the poor. Would you like to go there?"

Her face grew radiant and she clasped her hands together excitedly. "Could I, Alessandro? May I never go back to that hateful house?"

"You are free of it. We'll leave for Rome together."

"I have always loved to garden. Pietro knows that," she exclaimed joyfully. "But Mother never approved of my soiling my hands and kept me from it."

"Tell your maidservant to pack whatever you need."

It was a relief to Alessandro when he delivered Lavinia to the convent.

All along the journey she had chatted incessantly about the digging and planting and hoeing and sowing she would do, as well as the flowers she loved best and what vegetables gave the richest crops. He realized she must have been reading gardening books for years.

Had Dr. Grassi still been in charge, Elena would have lain in bed for months, but one morning Pietro lifted her out of it and sat her by the fire in a cushioned chair. Bianca was quick to put a blanket over her legs.

Elena smiled at him. "How good this feels! I thought I would have to remain boxed in by the bed draperies for ages yet."

"This will be only for ten minutes today," he said, resting his hands on the arms of her chair as he grinned at her. "We'll increase the time gradually if you don't get too tired."

"I won't," she promised. When he had gone, she rested her head back on the cushion. "What a dear man he is! It can't be just that he was sent away from the rest of the Celano family when he was young, because Lavinia has the same kind nature."

Bianca, who was the only one in the room with her, said nothing.

Adrianna had been the only visitor allowed to see Elena to date. As the invalid grew a little stronger, Elizabetta began to visit her too in Adrianna's company. It had been Marietta's suggestion. She had explained to the child beforehand that it had not been Elena who treated her so roughly outside the Basilica, but the explanation had hardly been necessary. Upon entering the room and seeing Elena smiling at her, Elizabetta had run to her joyfully with outstretched arms.

"You're back, Elena! Please don't go away again!"

Between tears and laughter, Elena, in her chair, had embraced and kissed her daughter for the first time since she was newborn.

It did not take Elena long to discover that much had been happening politically during her illness and that the situation was accelerating during her convalescence. The French had signed an armistice with the Austrians, and General Bonaparte's attitude toward the Venetian Republic was becoming decidedly more aggressive. Elena expected to hear more from Pietro when he returned from taking his place for the first time in the Hall of the Great Council. Bianca, who was attending her, withdrew when he entered, leaving them alone together.

"How did everything go?" Elena inquired eagerly.

Pietro smiled ruefully and shook his head. "I was far from impressed by the Doge in council. He's nervous and worried and indecisive. Venice should have a strong leader at this vital time."

"He is voted in for life," she pointed out.

"More's the pity. La Serenissima is in great danger. I can see it coming nearer all the time."

"Marietta's husband warned of that."

"Thus fell the House of Torrisi," he remarked drily.

She leaned forward. "Domenico was a true patriot and never a traitor! Filippo plotted and connived and even bribed false witnesses to get him thrown into prison. I found papers to prove it, but Marietta told me only a few days ago that the dampness has obliterated the evidence."

Pietro regarded her steadily for a few moments before he spoke. "Tell me what you know." When she had concluded, he asked if Marietta would let him have the papers.

"Yes, I think she would. But her friend Sebastiano has just returned them to her as being quite useless even with all I was able to remember from reading them. What more could you do?"

"I've a friend in Padua who is an expert at deciphering writing believed to be lost. Naturally his work is on ancient manuscripts, but I see no reason why he should not try his luck with the papers you took from Filippo's cupboard. I suppose those you put in their place are still there."

Before Pietro went to bed he followed Elena's instructions and discovered that Filippo had never checked the papers again. One of those that had been switched had the beginnings of a letter by Elena to someone called Nicolò.

Marietta fetched the bundle of papers for Pietro, but before she handed them over she asked him a very direct question. "What is your ultimate purpose in letting these papers be studied? Are you genuinely interested in clearing the name of Torrisi, which has always been anathema to the Celanos, or do you want to convince yourself of your late brother's guilt and then destroy the findings?"

He was not offended by her directness. On the contrary he welcomed it. "If your husband has been unjustly imprisoned through the action of a Celano, it is my moral duty to put the matter right, whatever the cost."

She believed him. Since first meeting Pietro she had felt he was his own man, not bound in any way by Celano traditions. "You will have my ever-lasting gratitude if you can prove Domenico's innocence. What if I told you the vendetta still lives?"

"Then I would say you had a son. I trust you have him somewhere safe."

She nodded. "Can you not ensure his safety for me?"

Pietro tapped the papers that he held. "If the truth can be coaxed from these, I will be in an unassailable position to denounce the vendetta on grounds of the shame brought down on the name of Celano by Filippo's actions, and by the need to make amends to Domenico Torrisi. Only then can harmony be ensured and all threat removed from your son's life."

"You're a good man," she said huskily.

Pietro dispatched the papers in the charge of a special messenger, and Elena was delighted to hear they were on their way.

"Who is Nicolò?" he asked her one day during a lull in their conversation.

She flushed. "Someone I loved once. I used to write him letters that I never sent."

"The one I glimpsed was dated shortly before your incarceration. Is he the father of Elizabetta?"

Her eyes widened. "Why should you think that?"

"On the night we almost lost you, Marietta urged you not to die and prevent Elizabetta and Nicolò ever knowing each other." He leaned his arms on the back of a chair as he stood watching her. "I've also seen the child several times. Elizabetta bears a certain likeness to you now that I think about it. Yesterday Marietta asked if the child might stay at the palace for the time being. I thought then that she wanted one of her children with her. Now I realize it is to let you have more time with your own daughter."

"I gave her to Marietta," Elena said brokenly. "I shouldn't be seeing her."

"Maybe Marietta is giving her back to you now that Filippo has gone." Elena bowed her head and spread a hand over her face. "It's a gift I can't accept."

Pietro, giving her time to recover herself, took the chair by its top-rail and swung it forward to sit down close to her. "Was Nicolò married?"

She let her hand drop. "No, but he will be by now. It's been a long time."

He listened as she told him the whole story. His expression was that of a listener who had paid close attention to many revelations. When she finished by revealing that Nicolò had extracted a final promise that she would contact him if ever she were free to do so, he gave an encouraging nod.

"Then why not write to him in friendship when you feel able? I will see that the letter is sent."

If Pietro had judged that it had been no more than a fleeting affair between Elena and Nicolò he would never have given her that advice. She had endured so much, this woman who had been a young and innocent Pietà girl tossed like a parcel from one man to the next and used most cruelly in her marriage. She had been forced to part with her newborn infant and then had not been spared seeing her grow up with no knowledge of their relationship. If some shred of happiness could be salvaged for Elena it would be no more than her due. Marietta's unselfish wish to share Elizabetta fully with her real mother showed that she also felt the time had come for Elena to be compensated for fate's hard turns against her.

Pietro's suggestion remained with Elena, although she did nothing about it. She had lost her looks and her figure and was no longer the woman Nicolò had loved. Her incarceration had changed her. Inwardly she was stronger than she had ever been, even if her physical weakness denied it. Her thoughts went to Domenico. If his innocence should be proved through the papers that Marietta had handed over to Pietro, how would Domenico and Marietta pick up the pieces of their lives and begin again? He too would be changed, even as Marietta had become a new person with a developed business sense and the ability to support herself and her family.

Elena's improvement became noticeable during the time of Elizabetta's sojourn in the palace. The sight of the child's bright face peeping around the door at her before she entered the room, the little jokes between them, and their reading together filled Elena's days with happiness. Between visits Elena rested or slept while the child went out with a nursemaid or played with her toys in the library where Sister Giaccomina, at Pietro's request, had resumed the cataloguing of the books.

Maria Fondi, reinstated as the patient's lady's maid, was a reliable standby now that intensive nursing had given way to daily care, which enabled Marietta to spend some time at the shop and to be with Melina as well as giving Lucretia her lessons. At night Marietta and the nun took turns sleeping on a truckle bed in Elena's room, for she often needed reassurance when she woke in distress from a nightmare that she was still incarcerated.

"Mama says you and she are both my mamas," Elizabetta said to Elena one morning. "Just as you are both godmothers to Bianca. So I will call you Mama Elena."

Elena, deeply moved, cupped the child's face in her hands and kissed her.

When at last Marietta was able to move back home, Elizabetta stayed on at the palace for a while. The child enjoyed the full attention she received, for at home she had either to share it with Melina or be one among Adrianna's children. The mask-shop was continuing to do well and Marietta was well satisfied with the new musical section. Recently Leonardo's hopes had been realized when the shop neighboring his became vacant, and he soon opened it for the sale of musical instruments.

While Sister Giaccomina was content to combine caring for Elena with her library work, it was time for Bianca to return to the Pietà. Pietro made the decision.

"Bianca should return to her musical studies," he said to Marietta, who agreed. Bianca's feelings were mixed once more. She did not want to stay any longer in the palace, but she had lost interest in her flute-playing. Her life had been jarred and disrupted and changed about so much that she did not seem to belong anywhere, probably least of all at the Pietà.

Pietro spoke to Bianca privately before she left. "I've been able to see that this palace is far from the best environment for you. I can only guess at some of the unpleasant associations it has for you, and what I do know should never have happened. I'm no more at ease here than you are." He raised his hands expressively and let them fall to his sides again. "I don't want to live an idle life of pleasure, putting in an obligatory appearance at the Hall of the Great Council now and again. I'm not a statesman or I would aim toward high office. My talents lie elsewhere. Medicine is my calling and as soon as I am able to do it, the Palazzo Celano will be closed and I shall return to my hospital in Padua."

"Why are you telling me all this?" she questioned, although she believed she knew.

"I want you to have the facts and to understand why I wish you to return to the Pietà."

Sister Sylvia came to escort Bianca. As the *ospedale* came into view from the gondola, Bianca saw it in a new light. It had become for her a place of waiting.

Bianca had been back at the Pietà for a month when on an April day a French ship on patrol in the Adriatic sailed into Venetian waters to seek shelter from a storm. With tension growing daily over French intentions, the commander of the Venetian fort ordered warning shots to be fired across the intruder's bow. As a result, a Venetian ship in the vicinity took up the fire. Several French seamen were killed, the vessel was taken into custody, and the survivors were clapped into irons.

The incident acted like a spark to tinder. Napoleon Bonaparte became a madman in his fury. Venetian envoys arriving at his camp to discuss the matter with him were subject to outrageous insults and verbal abuse. He shook his fist in their faces.

"I shall be an Attila the Hun to the State of Venice!" he roared.

The envoys returned with demands that made the Doge shake, completely at a loss in the face of such a violent threat. His confusion and lack of guidance threw the Senate into a similar state. Pietro, attending a gathering of the Great Council, was appalled at the total lack of initiative. He tried to make his voice heard, but few listened and none took heed. Rumors flew. Word came that French troops were marching toward Venice.

Early on the first day of May, Pietro went to the Hall of the Great Council again to hear the final ultimatum the Doge had received from the French on the previous day. He was dismayed by the depleted number of councillors present, many nobles having fled during the night after getting wind of what was in the offing. When the Doge entered in his corno and robes he was weeping. Almost in disbelief Pietro heard him announce that the French had set up cannons on the mainland to fire upon Venice and that a vast number of enemy troops had mustered near the lagoon. The French minister in Venice was demanding that Venetian ships under French command should convey these same troops to strategic points throughout the city. It was an implacable call for total surrender.

Even as the Doge called upon all those present to cast their votes in favor of accepting these terms, there came a spate of gunshots outside. Immediately there was an undignified rush to cast votes and disperse. Only a few councillors remained, Pietro and Sebastiano among them.

Tearfully the Doge spoke his last official words. "The Most Serene Republic of Venice is no more!"

Pietro bowed along with the others as the Doge slowly walked from the chamber, looking neither to right or left. When he reached his private apartments, he removed the golden corno from his head and handed it to his servant.

"Never again will this be needed."

Pietro emerged from the palace to pause in the sunshine at the top of the great flight of stone steps he would probably never ascend again. In the thirteen hundred years since its founding, Venice had never before known a conqueror. From a great maritime nation whose trade and riches were the envy of the world, it had destroyed itself through hedonism and excess, becoming no more than a decadent oligarchy that had fallen and split apart like an over-ripe plum. The French were about to descend on it like a swarm of wasps. A glorious, unmatched era was at an end.

The French moved in swiftly. The *barnabotti*, who had long harbored grievances and jealousies against the powerful nobility upon whose charitable generosity they existed, welcomed the invaders like brothers. Most other Venetians knew only a degrading sense of shame that La Serenissima should have been delivered into the hands of the French without a fight. Many had wanted to take up arms and had already banded into groups with workers from the arsenal, only to discover it was too late.

Soon Marietta had a new kind of customer in her mask-shop. French officers tried to flirt with her, inviting her to supper, to the theater, and to other entertainments still available in the fallen city. She refused them all. They bought masks and had them boxed as gifts for wives and sweethearts at home. She loathed serving them, seeing each one as a despoiler of all that was Venetian. They tied up their horses to the columns of the Doge's Palace and stacked bales of hay within the colonnade itself. In St. Mark's Square a Tree of Liberty had been set up in readiness for a celebration on Whit Sunday. A scarlet Phrygian cap, symbol of the French Revolution and the new regime in France, topped it arrogantly. The Golden Book with all the noble names of Venice had already been destroyed, for Bonaparte's colonel in command of the city was carrying out the imperious orders he had been given without delay. Some of the greatest paintings, as well as church plate, sculptures, manuscripts, and other priceless treasures, were being officially removed in readiness for shipment to France.

The only good news for Marietta was from Lucretia who came running into the shop one day after an errand.

"Signora Torrisi! I've just heard that all the political prisoners are about to be released by the French officer in command of the city!"

Marietta was in the middle of serving a customer and without a word she snatched a handful of coins from the money drawer and ran as she was from the shop, hatless and with a mask still in her hand. She tried to hail a gondola, but joy-riding French troops seemed to be occupying every one.

On she ran across the Rialto Bridge, throwing the mask away as she went. People turned to stare at her as she flew by, her rich red hair tumbling from its pins and streaming after her. When she failed to get transport from the Riva del Carbòn, she gave up trying and plunged through the *calli*. Now and again she had to stop, doubled over and leaning against a wall, to catch her breath. Finally she reached St. Mark's Square, came to the Piazzetta, and passed the main entrance to the Doge's Palace to arrive at the door leading to the cells. A crowd had already gathered but she thrust her way through in time to see a few men emerging and waving exuberantly as they came.

Her guess was that these were Francophiles, arrested after the first

French threats and put out of harm's way. There were several joyful reunions and then the crowd began to disperse.

Immediately she realized that Domenico had probably been among the first let out and she had missed him. Seeing Captain Zeno about to go back into the palace she called to him.

"Captain Zeno! Please wait!"

He turned and came back a few paces to meet her, shaking his head. "You shouldn't be here, signora."

"Which way did Domenico go? Did he take a gondola?"

"I can't tell you how sorry I am, but the French officer in command of the city won't allow him to be released."

"Why not?" she cried in disbelief.

"He abhors traitors. Since your husband did no service to France through his actions against the deposed Venetian Republic, he says Domenico must remain in prison."

Marietta collapsed and he caught her as she fell.

The French-organized celebrations took place on Whit Sunday with full stands and crowds to watch a procession, led by French troops, of Venetian children carrying flowers and people dancing and singing, their numbers swelled by the *barnabotti* bearing the tricolor. There was dancing around the Tree of Liberty with the former Doge, devoid of his ceremonial robes, joining in. Countless Venetians were aghast at the general support of what they saw as the most tragic day in the history of La Serenissima. It seemed as if their fellow citizens were viewing the festivities as just another celebration day and that on the morrow they would wake up to find their city back to normal and the French gone.

That was far from the case. On the seventeenth day of May Marietta was calling at Leonardo's shop when a commotion in St. Mark's Square drew them outside. General Bonaparte had arrived. He stood with several officers, a short, stolid figure in his uniform, surveying the glittering gold and mosaic façade of the Basilica with its four bronze horses above the magnificent entrance, and then slowly he turned to view the grandeur of the entire square.

"This is the finest drawing-room in Europe!" he declared in admiration.

If Venetians needed final evidence of the conqueror's heel, it came when a crane was set up at the Basilica to lower the four gilded horses from the position they had held on its façade since the middle of the twelfth century. As they were loaded one by one onto wagons for shipment to France, it was as if the heart of Venice had been cut out.

Pietro came to see Marietta on the day this operation commenced. She had closed the shop temporarily because the French commander, carrying out Bonaparte's orders, had announced the abolishment of Carnival. The wearing of masks was no longer permitted. Pietro found Marietta and her assistants busily packing away masks and installing displays of musical instruments instead.

"I can't make this shop pay with masks anymore," she explained, "so it's fortunate I had already established a musical section."

"I'd like to speak to you alone," he said after describing what he had just witnessed at the Basilica.

Marietta took him upstairs to her salon. "What else has happened?" she asked anxiously when they were seated, for she was able to see that he had nothing good to tell.

"Those papers were returned to me from Padua."

"Don't say it was a task in vain," she implored.

"No, quite the reverse. From the indentations of the quill pens, slight though they were, my friend produced an exact copy of all that had been written. From the samples I sent, he was able to confirm that the original writings were in Maurizio's hand. It was all exactly as Elena had told me. Domenico was innocent of any treachery toward La Serenissima as you have always upheld. The papers hold full accounts of plans made, bribes paid to induce perjury by witnesses, and so forth."

If he had shown the least enthusiasm for what had been uncovered, Marietta would have taken heart, but his expression was grave. "So?" she breathed guardedly.

"When I received all this evidence I went with it at once to the French commander, who declined to see me. I tried again when General Bonaparte came, since he talks of justice for the common man, but I was informed he was too busy to grant interviews. I handed a copy of the evidence to his staff, asking that it be shown to him before he left the city, but nothing came of that request. I doubt it was ever brought to his attention."

Marietta was daunted that such determined attempts had met with rejection. Her eyes were tragic. "I can only thank you for what you have tried to do for Domenico."

"There is still one more thing I can do. I have paid for some special pamphlets that will be circulated throughout Venice starting tomorrow. Printed on them will be the main points of the evidence of Filippo's trickery, revealing to all that Domenico was unjustly imprisoned. There is also an apology from me as the head of the House of Celano for such shameful action against an innocent man. The final paragraph is my command that the vendetta be at an end forevermore and that friendship exist hereafter between our two families, starting with myself and Domenico and his legitimate heir, Danilo."

She could hardly speak for the rush of her tears. "It will mean everything to Domenico to have his name cleared and his son acknowledged. He has never wanted a pardon that would leave a web of lies around him. Even if the French refuse to listen, all Venetians will know the truth."

"Tomorrow these pamphlets will be handed to every member of the new municipality when they meet at the ducal palace. They should be able to engage the French commander's ear on the matter. All is not yet lost."

It was to no avail. The new municipality had no voice except on minor matters, the French officer in command of the city deciding all important governmental issues. Suspicious of all things Venetian, he saw the taking up of the Torrisi case by three or four of the members as a challenge to his authority. Since it was also linked to the old decadence of Venice and the deposed patrician families, he saw it as some trick to regain power and undermine French law and order. The Torrisi case was struck off the agenda.

Marietta saw all that she and her friends had striven for finally and irrevocably fade beyond hope. And as if that were not enough, the French colonel forbade the Torrisi prisoner all privileges, including letters. Captain Zeno, who dared to protest, was dismissed from his post, but not before he had handed in one of the pamphlets to Domenico.

———

Elena's first outing was to visit her old friends at the house in the Calle della Madonna. Pietro was invited too. Adrianna and Marietta had arranged a little party to celebrate Elena's return to health. Despite the shadow cast by Domenico's continued incarceration, Marietta was determined to make it a happy occasion, as he would wish. It was a double celebration, for Pietro's decree to all Celanos had enabled Marietta to fetch Danilo home, and he and Melina were toddling about her skirts.

"Welcome back to us here!" Adrianna cried joyfully as she and Leonardo embraced Elena and made Pietro feel at home. Everybody wanted to greet Elena, but Elizabetta was the first of the children to exchange hugs and kisses with her. When the two nuns had taken their turn, Bianca found herself facing Pietro.

"How are you, Bianca?"

"Existing," she replied hesitantly. "Nothing more."

"That will change."

Those were the only words of conversation they were to exchange throughout the party, but neither forgot them.

They all sat down at a long table decked with the best Savoni damask and silverware. Leonardo was an excellent host and there were toasts to Elena and Pietro as well as a special one for Domenico. It was by following Marietta's example and expanding into a music shop that Leonardo had been saved from financial ruin. The market for masks had collapsed. Foreign travelers were staying away from Venice, and this, combined with General Bonaparte's abolishment of Carnival and other festivals, was bringing many mask-makers to bankruptcy.

For the three former Pietà girls and Bianca the party was a time for the gathering up of old threads. Their friendship had been through fire and emerged stronger than ever. Yet nothing was the same. Adrianna had been only indirectly affected by the events that had reshaped the lives of Marietta, Elena, and Bianca, but in her own mind she ranged herself alongside them in sharing their present hopes and difficulties.

Each of the children had made Elena a little gift, and after the repast they gathered in the salon where she unwrapped them all with exclamations of genuine delight. The children crowded around her to explain how this or that had been sewn or carved or otherwise taken shape. When the excitement had died down, Leonardo made a presentation to Elena on behalf of the adults. He bowed as he held out the slim wooden box to her.

"May this bring music and happiness back into your life!"

Elena knew what it was even as she took it from him and opened the lid. It was a new flute. Everyone applauded and called for her to play. Smiling, she put the instrument to her lips and her fingers danced as she began to play the well-loved Columbina tune. The children all joined in singing with the adults. Bianca, who had come prepared, waited a few minutes and then brought out her own flute to accompany Elena.

It was a warm evening and on the way home with Pietro, Elena plied the little fan that was Elizabetta's gift to her while the Celano gondolier sang as if in defiance of the changes that had been wrought on Venice. Pietro, a generous man, was talking of buying her a house on the Riva degli Schiavoni where she would be near old friends at the Pietà, as well as giving her a more than adequate allowance. She was grateful for his kindness, for above all else she longed to leave the Palazzo Celano, that place of miserable and terrifying memories. When she was settled into the new house, she would start taking Elizabetta with her to concerts at the Pietà.

From the *felze* of the gondola she glanced up at the Palazzo Manunta where she had first seen Marco. In the years since then she had danced many times in its great ballroom. Now the palace had been rented to a Spanish grandee. So many patrician friends had moved away from Venice, uncertain if they would ever return.

"Look ahead, Elena. See those vessels coming?" Pietro remarked bitterly, for a number of boats bearing packed and crated treasures under French guard were on their way to a ship flying the tricolor in the lagoon. "There'll be nothing left soon. A Veronese panel has been removed from the ceiling of the Great Hall in the Ducal Palace, and the monastery of San Giorgio has been robbed of that same master's *Marriage at Cana*. The new French commander, who took over from his predecessor last week, is even more meticulous in looting the best and the most treasured. He has brought art experts with him to give advice."

Elena shook her head at such dedicated looting. Even the Bucintoro, the glorious state barge and symbol of Empire on which Marietta had sung for the Marriage of the Sea, had been systematically stripped of everything of beauty and value. Its hacked-off topwork had been burned in great bonfires in the Piazzetta in order that the gold could be recovered from the ashes. In a final galling act, the French had towed the hulk to be a guardship at the very place where the Doge had always thrown the gold ring into the sea in a ceremony that would never take place again.

"Shall you approach this new commander on Domenico's behalf?" Elena asked.

"I have already done so. His aide informed me that the Torrisi case was closed and would not be reopened."

"Does Marietta know?"

"It was my painful duty to tell her just before we left the Savoni house."

It seemed to Elena that the calls on Marietta's courage were without end. Her thoughts were still with her friend as she and Pietro ascended the main staircase upon their arrival back at the Palazzo Celano. A servant came to meet her.

"A visitor is awaiting you in the Tapestry Salon, signora."

"Oh? Who is it?"

"He gave his name as Signor Contarini."

Elena gasped and clutched questioningly at Pietro's arm. "Did you write to Nicolò? Because I haven't!"

"No, I wouldn't have presumed such an action without consulting you."

Without realizing what she was doing, Elena broke into a run across the reception hall; but when she reached the double doors she paused, her hand hovering, not daring to open them. Then the decision was made for her. Nicolò must have heard her swift footsteps on the marble floor, because one door was suddenly pulled open. She and Nicolò faced each other. He smiled and all her doubts melted away.

"I've come to take you home with me to Florence, Elena," he said as if they had never been apart.

Later, as they talked over supper, he explained that whenever the head of a great Venetian house died the news reached far and wide, in spite of political turmoil like that of the present time.

"I waited for you to write, Elena."

"I didn't dare. I thought you would have married, and even if not, I believed my long incarceration, about which I have told you, had changed me too much for you to still want me as your wife."

"You misjudge your own loveliness. I see no change in you and never will. Where do you wish our marriage to take place? Here or in Florence?"

"In Florence. I want to leave Venice behind me."

"Then we shall set off for home tomorrow, my love."

All Elena had withheld from him was the disclosure that they had had a lovechild. She could not risk his wanting to take Elizabetta with them, for it would be too cruel to Marietta in her present trouble and too upsetting for the child to remove her abruptly. In Florence, Nicolò would be told. Then Elizabetta could come on a visit and in time the truth would be revealed to her. When and if Elizabetta ever wanted to live with them, it must be by her own choice.

Elena saw that Nicolò was raising his glass and she took up her own. They smiled at each other, and across the table he put his hand over hers, which bore his betrothal ring. "To our future, Elena. May we never be parted again."

Marietta could not sleep that night after what Pietro had told her. But she would not give up. She tossed and turned on her pillows, constantly readjusting them and unable to gain any rest. Suppose she should go herself to the new commander?

On this thought she propped herself up on an elbow and lit the candle by her bed. Then she lay back and gazed unseeingly up at the canopy of her bed as she contemplated what she should do. It was said that this new man had an eye for attractive women, and one of the most beautiful courtesans in Venice was seen constantly in his company. Marietta thought that if she could gain entrance to the Doge's Palace the commander might listen to her pleas for her husband's release, whereas a man would have no chance of gaining his ear.

Throwing back the bedclothes, Marietta picked up the candle and took it across to the dressing table where she sat down to study her reflection. Men continued to leave her in no doubt that her sexual allure was still powerful at the age of thirty-four. She bunched handfuls of her hair about her face, considering how she might dress it in the morning. Then there was the question of what she should wear. Swiftly she went to raise the lids of chests and open the door of her closet. She would not go to him simply clad, for that would have no appeal to a man of extravagant tastes and neither would it suit her mood, for she was at the end of her tether and making a gambler's last throw.

She decided on a gown that was in the height of fashion, for although it was not new it was among those she had brought up to date to wear to the opera and other functions with Sebastiano and his wife as well as other good friends who invited her. The hat she would wear needed to have its ribbons changed to the color of the gown. When she had fetched her sewing basket, Marietta went to lift the lid of a chest where she had put many of the mask-trimmings no longer needed in the workshop. There were plumes, jars of sequins, lengths of gauze, and rolls of ribbon among other items. She took what she needed for her task. When she had finished it, she was about to go back to bed when she turned instead to a drawer and pulled it open. In it, beside her jewelry casket, lay a velvet-covered box. It held the golden mask that Domenico was wearing the first time she saw him.

Opening the box Marietta took out the mask and gazed at it fondly. She had smuggled it out on the day she left the Palazzo Torrisi. Domenico had worn the mask quite often after their marriage, and then not at all, which had told her, as she had always suspected, that it had been a special gift from his first wife. As Marietta had taken hold of his heart, so he had let the mask become a memento, stored away with memories of Angela that were private to him.

Slowly Marietta stroked its gilded surface, recalling the day in her mother's workshop when it had lain newly gilded in this same box and she had been deeply affected by the sight of it. She had not known then that this molded likeness would play such a forceful part in the course of her life. It was appropriate that she should renew contact with the mask now, when she was about to embark on a mission as dramatic and fateful as that which had brought her to Venice holding this very mask on that long-ago day.

When at last Marietta returned the mask to its box and put it away, she felt able to sleep for the few hours left to her.

Chapter 18

It was almost dawn when Marietta awoke and immediately rose from her bed. The children slept while she bathed and then donned undergarments, stockings, and shoes before putting on a robe to eat breakfast. She had heard that the new commander needed as little sleep as General Bonaparte, which was why she thought her chances of seeing him would be better in the early morning before the business of the day claimed his time. After dressing her hair, massing it in the soft style that echoed the fashionable fullness of skirts over abundant petticoats, she took the gown from where she had lain it during the night hours.

Its rich peach-pink silk dramatized her hair and the paleness of her skin. It was low-cut with a diaphanous fichu that both concealed and revealed her cleavage. The sleeves were elbow-length, and the top skirt parted to reveal a self-striped underskirt in the same lovely shade. Not to detract from the dramatic impact of this color on that of her hair, she chose simple pearl ear-drops and wore no rings except her marriage band. She gave much thought to every detail. Her flamboyant finery would proclaim to her adversary that she would not be cowed by him, whereas the pearls and the plain gold ring would emphasize her status as the wife of his prisoner, telling him that she was not offering herself in exchange for his granting her appeal.

Yet what if this commanding officer should make that demand? It had ever been the privilege of the conqueror, and by all accounts he was a passionate man. A violent shiver of dread shook her whole frame, making her feel quite faint, and she closed her eyes, gripping the top of a chair for support. Then the sensation passed. If that was the price she had to pay for Domenico's freedom, it would be done. Nothing in the world, however terrible, had the power to stop her from fulfilling this final chance to save him.

She took up her hat and carefully lowered it onto her head in front of a mirror. It had the new narrow brim covered in cream silk, the crown was veiled by bunched gauze, and broad peach-pink ribbons trailed down the left side of her face.

A padding of bare feet made her turn. Elizabetta had appeared, rubbing sleep from her eyes. When she saw how Marietta was dressed she exclaimed in astonishment.

"Mama! You look like a princess!"

Marietta smiled. "What a fine compliment to receive so early in the day! I was about to go through to the Savoni house, because everyone will be awake by now, to tell Adrianna that I'm on my way to see the colonel in command at the Doge's Palace. Now you can do that for me and explain to Lucretia when she wakes."

"Can't I come with you?"

"No. I have to go alone." Marietta stooped and kissed the child. "Be good and help Adrianna with the twins. You know what an imp Danilo can be!"

Marietta took up her silk purse and the packet of papers, which included the pamphlet and the letter from Padua that Pietro had handed to her just before his departure with Elena. He had understood that after such news she would wish to have some time to be alone.

"Wave to me at the window, Mama," Elizabetta requested.

"I will!"

Outside in the *calle*, as Marietta waved back to the child, she thought it as well that her purpose and destination should be known. If she should be arrested for any reason, at least her friends would know where she was.

As Marietta emerged from the *calle* the sun was gliding the roofs and chimney pots as well as the busy scene on the Grand Canal and its flanking parades where men and women of almost every trade were making ready for the day. She hailed a gondola and asked to be taken to the Molo. It was not long before she saw the Doge's Palace shimmering pink and gold with nothing to show at this distance that everything within was not as it always had been.

As she alighted at the Molo, French soldiers in their shirtsleeves were grooming the army horses stabled in the graceful marble colonnades of the palace, and they paused to whistle and call to her as she went by. She paid no heed, walking swiftly along the Piazzetta to the ornate gateway where sentries stood guard. Before reaching it, she noticed in a flower-seller's basket a few sprigs of pomegranate blossom among the other blooms. It evoked such memories of the Pietà that she stopped to buy a small spray, which she tucked into her cleavage like a talisman.

The sentries did not question her as she went through the gateways for there was plenty of coming and going, both military and civilian. She avoided a minor entrance where most people were stating their business. That was not for her. She went instead to ascend the Giants' Staircase, a small yet brilliant figure against the vast setting of pale marble and Renaissance grandeur. She passed through the portal at the head of the stairs and made her entry into the gilded interior of the building itself.

A sergeant on duty stepped forward. Only high-ranking officers and important personages came by this entrance, but this splendidly attired and fine-looking woman had an air about her that said she had every right to be there.

"Good day, signora."

She replied in French. "I'm here to see the commander."

"Do you have an appointment?"

"No, that's why I came early. He will see me."

The sergeant was uncertain. "What is the purpose of your visit?"

"It is a private matter." Marietta had decided before her arrival that bluff might get her through where all else would fail. "You have no right to ask."

The sergeant withdrew to speak to two lieutenants. They heard what he had to say and turned to Marietta, an appreciative look coming into their eyes. One came forward with a smile. It was easy to see that he and his fellow officer took her to be some new lady love of their commanding officer. "This way, madame," he said in his own language. "It is the hour when the colonel deals with his correspondence and there is not a great deal on his desk today. I will take you to him."

She went at his side through splendid halls and corridors, many of which she had traversed with Domenico on grander occasions. Here and there paintings were missing and she saw several empty plinths. The lieutenant engaged her in light conversation, complimenting her on her French, asking if she had lived in Venice for a long time, and expressing his own admiration of the beautiful city. When they reached the anteroom to the commander's quarters, a sergeant who was seated at a desk sprang to attention at the lieutenant's approach.

"This lady is here to see the colonel," the lieutenant said. Then he turned to her. "Your name, madame?"

"I can be announced as Signora Marietta."

The lieutenant drew his own conclusions. This was a married woman who did not want her name bandied about. "It has been an honor to meet you, madame."

He saluted and would have left her to be shown through, but the sergeant had narrowed his eyes suspiciously. "I know this woman. She runs the mask-shop in the Calle della Madonna. I bought several masks there for my wife and daughters when I first came to Venice. She's the wife of the prisoner Torrisi!"

The lieutenant's whole manner changed. "Remove her from the palace!" he snapped.

Marietta made a dash for the colonel's door, but the sergeant was quick and caught her in an iron grip. In the struggle, her packet of papers slipped from her grasp and were scattered everywhere, but she was given no chance to retrieve them. She protested furiously as she was manhandled away from the anteroom, but they had not gone far along the corridor when the lieutenant shouted after them.

"Wait, sergeant! Bring Madame Torrisi back. The colonel will see her."

Marietta could only suppose that the colonel had made inquiries as to the noise outside his door and had shown some tolerance when told what

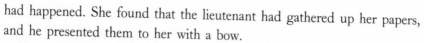

had happened. She found that the lieutenant had gathered up her papers, and he presented them to her with a bow.

"My apologies, madame."

She inclined her head in acceptance as she took them. He had only been doing his duty. The sergeant opened the door to an opulent salon and she was announced by her full name. The man she had come to see was looking out the window, his shoulders broad in the dark blue jacket of his uniform, the tricolor sash about his waist. His dark hair was cropped and well groomed in the style that was as different from the mode of powdered wigs as it could be—another rejection of anything remotely resembling the old regime in France.

"It is gracious of you to see me, Colonel."

He answered her in a well-remembered voice. "My dear Marietta, when I saw you crossing the courtyard I thought you had discovered I was here. That was foolish of me, wasn't it?"

Alix, older and more serious in mien, turned and smiled at her. Marietta stood as if transfixed. "Alix!" she exclaimed faintly. "I can scarcely believe it!"

He walked across to her. "I've finally come back to Venice as I promised, although it's not as either of us expected it would be. You are more beautiful than ever! Please take off that hat, fashionable though it is. You never used to wear one."

She made no move except to draw back a step, filled with dismay. In spite of his genial manner, this was not the Alix she had known for those few brief halcyon weeks, but the man who had rejected her for another woman and could as easily turn from her again when he heard the purpose of her visit. Was he even to be trusted with her request? He might have become more an enemy to Venice than his commander Bonaparte! "I'm not here to display myself," she said coolly.

"Forgive me," he replied more formally. "I was taking too much for granted. But do sit down. I'm more pleased to see you again than you could possibly realize." When she had arranged herself stiffly on the brocade sofa, he sat down at an angle to face her, resting an arm along the back, with one long leg crossed over the other in tight white breeches, his high black boots polished and gleaming. "I've thought about you many times and wondered how you were. Whenever an Italian opera company came to Paris I always attended the performance and scanned the program in the hope of seeing your name."

"Paris?" she queried. "What of your silk mill in Lyon?"

"That is still in full and expanding operation under my wife's management. She is an excellent businesswoman, but our marriage did not turn out for the best." He shook his head at the thought of it. "Eventually I left Louise in charge, which was what she wanted, and made the army my career. Paris became my headquarters and my home. Whenever the opportunity permits I go back to Lyon to oversee matters and to visit my children and my mother."

"I remember how important silk was to you. It must have been hard for you to give it all up."

His eyes held hers. "Nothing was as hard as losing you."

She replied stiffly. "That was a long time ago."

"Was it? Sitting here with you makes it feel like yesterday to me. Tell me about yourself. How long have you been married to Torrisi?"

"Thirteen years, but for eight of them he and I have been separated by his wrongful imprisonment."

He made no comment. "Did you never make singing your career?"

"No. I was considering touring on the concert stage whem my marriage to Domenico came about. We have a daughter and twins, a boy and a girl. And you?"

"A son, who is already determined to enter the silk business, and two daughters."

"How did your family fare in the Terror? That was a horrific time for France."

"It is a bloodstain on our noble history." There flashed through his mind's eye the sight of the guillotine in his own city of Lyon, set up on a cobbled site where he and his friends had played as boys. "There were silk-mill owners who went to the blade, but those who had always striven for better working conditions were spared along with their families. Fortunately Louise had maintained the standards I had set and none of my kin were taken."

"I included you in my prayers during that time."

"It was forgiving of you to be concerned for me in spite of everything."

"I learned in childhood that our lives are often changed by events beyond our control." She regarded him steadily. "We should have known the outcome from the start. We were Harlequin and Columbina. There never has been a happy ending for them."

He shrugged. "I doubt if I would ever have considered that notion at the time. Afterward I didn't attempt to forget you. Maybe that was unfair to Louise, although I doubt she ever cared. She became devoted to business and money-making."

"Do you like army life?"

"I've taken to it, but not to this command here in Venice. I'm a soldier, not an organized looter of treasures that should never be removed from their present site. I find that abhorrent!" He leaned forward, resting an arm across his thigh as he brought his face nearer hers. "I follow Bonaparte because I see him as the one leader who can raise my country up from the dregs of the Directory and the crimes that were perpetrated in the name of liberty. He will make France a true center of freedom and an example to the world!"

"I trust you are right, but at the present time he is a despoiler of every state he enters."

"At the Directory's orders! In Venice it is a matter of removing the best of everything in order not to leave it to the Austrians. Our recent treaty permits their taking over the city from us in a few months' time."

She threw back her head in angry frustration. "So Venice has become no more than a pawn between foreign governments! It seems to me there's no justice left anywhere. Domenico has been imprisoned all these years through a plot against him and although his innocence has now been proved beyond doubt, you and your predecessor have refused to listen. Here is the proof!" She thrust the papers toward him. "I demand his release in the name of your own revolutionary cry of *Liberté, Egalité, Fraternité!*"

He raised his hand, the palm toward her. "I don't need those. There are copies in a file I came across when I was going through my predecessor's papers."

"Have you studied them?"

"No. They did not have priority, but that doesn't mean they would not have had my attention eventually. When I glanced through the file it struck me as an interesting case."

"Please read it through now."

He smiled at her. "I have at least twelve appointments today, including meetings with two important foreign envoys and a Swiss diplomat. Tell me, Marietta, did you have a good marriage with this Torrisi?"

"I did and I will again when you set him free."

"Was it a love-match?"

She answered him straightforwardly. "No, but it came to that, and on my side sooner than his."

He nodded approvingly. "We were always honest with each other. Now I'll tell you with equal frankness that I've never loved another woman as I loved you. When I heard I was being posted to Venice I had a foolish, boyish dream that I might still find you at the Pietà and everything would be as it was then." His hand moved to cup her face tenderly. "The day after I arrived here I walked along that *calle* to the door in the wall where I used to meet you. Then I went to stare up at the windows as if you might come to one of them and see me as I saw you from this palace today."

"Did you ask for me there?"

"Yes. I met a gimlet-eyed nun who took one look at my uniform and buttoned up her mouth lest she forget her calling and tell me what she thought of my presence and that of my troops in her city. All she would say was that you had left the Pietà a long time ago."

She knew from his description that it had been Sister Sylvia he had met. "So your dream dissolved," she said quietly.

"It belonged to the past."

"That is how it should be, but on the strength of what we once felt for each other, I implore you to read the papers about Domenico's case now! I want to take him home with me when you have finished."

He looked deeply into her eyes. "You are asking me to throw away this second chance that fate has given us."

Fear of him, which had been quelled during their conversation, seemed to rise up and grip her by the throat. "What do you mean?" she asked huskily.

"I think you know," he replied evenly. "I'm not suggesting that we could recapture what we felt in the past, but on its foundation we could build a far more rewarding relationship."

Slowly she rose to her feet, not taking her eyes from him. She had been willing to submit briefly to a stranger in order to gain Domenico's freedom, but Alix was demanding a far higher price, all the more dangerous because the old look of love for her was back in his gaze. "No, Alix. That's impossible!"

He stood to take both her hands into his. "Forget the man who has been out of your life for eight years!" he urged. "I'll have him transferred to house arrest somewhere, with anything he wants except freedom! He's an enemy of France, Marietta. I cannot release him, but I can give you happiness again!"

She faced him fiercely, keeping her head at this dire moment, aware of taking the greatest gamble of her life. "Read the papers first, Alix!"

"It will make no difference," he replied inflexibly. "Torrisi must stay in prison until the end of his days."

"Read them!"

His brow gathered in a deep frown and his whole face tightened in controlled anger at her foolish persistence. Minutes seemed to tick away before he answered her. "Very well! But it will be a waste of my time and yours."

He moved sharply to summon his sergeant and told him to cancel all appointments until mid-afternoon. Then, impatiently, he took the Torrisi file from a cupboard and slapped it down on his desk. Drawing up a chair he sat down and began to read.

Marietta sank down into her seat on the sofa again, despairing that she had goaded him into this hostile mood. Domenico's chances were slim enough and she had made everything worse. How Alix had changed! Gone was the malleable youth who would have done anything for her. This was a man disillusioned with life, who was pinning his hopes for the future on a greedy conqueror. Apparently she had given him the only true happiness he had ever known, and now he hoped to find it in her arms again.

Anxiously she watched him as he read, seeking any glimpse of change in his inexorable expression. There was no sound in the room except for the turn of a page or the scratch of his nib as he made some note for himself. Now and again he would look up with a flinty glance to ask her a question, and in her high state of stress her voice quavered as she answered him. Then he would read on. An orderly brought hot chocolate in a silver pot with porcelain cups and a dish of little cakes. Alix took no more than a sip or two from his cup and then let it go cold as he continued his task. Marietta drank hers, for she was shivering as she fought against diminishing hope, almost as if the blood in her veins had turned to ice. The chocolate pot and cups had been removed again for a considerable while before Alix finally tossed down his quill and closed the file.

Instinctively Marietta rose from the sofa to face him. He looked at her soberly from where he sat.

"There has been a grave miscarriage of justice. Your husband shall be released immediately and his properties and possessions restored to him. There is an inventory in the file of the goods taken from the Palazzo Torrisi and I daresay these can be traced."

He sprang from his chair as she swayed, and caught her before she collapsed in her relief, holding her close as tears of joy choked her. Her head came to rest on his shoulder and she seemed unaware that he pressed his lips to her brow. But then, all too soon for him, she raised her grateful face to his and drew away.

"You've given Domenico back to me, Alix. I'll remember all my life what you have done for us and our children. Let Domenico know now, I beg you. He should not spend another minute as a prisoner."

"I agree." Once again Alix summoned the sergeant and spoke out of Marietta's hearing. Then he returned to her. "Domenico will be brought to a salon in what was formerly the Doge's private apartment. It is not right that you and he should meet again in grim surroundings."

"I'd like to be waiting there for him."

"I'll take you to the apartment myself."

She went at his side to the door, but before opening it he turned to her once more. It was their private moment of parting. They would not meet again.

"I wish you well, Alix," she said softly. Then she took the spray of pomegranate blossom from her cleavage and held it out to him.

He took it with a little smile. "A memento from my Pietà Columbina."

"For old times' sake."

He understood. The girl had almost been his, but never the woman, whose heart was elsewhere. Bending his head, he kissed her hand in final farewell. Then they went from the room.

In the ornate salon of the Doge's former apartment Marietta waited alone. It was quiet there except for the ticking of a magnificent gilded clock. Although she knew it would take a while before Domenico could arrive, with a maze of staircases, corridors, salons, and halls to be traversed on the way, she did not sit but wandered restlessly about the room. In her thoughts she planned how they should begin their lives together again. Now that the villa was theirs once more, the two of them would go there and spend some weeks on their own. The peace and charm of the river and countryside would help Domenico adjust to freedom again. Later the children could join them and they would become a family again.

At last she heard voices and footsteps approaching. She stayed where she was near the window as if suddenly unable to move. The door was swung open and Domenico came alone into the room, tall and gaunt, with a prison pallor on his handsome features. At the sight of her he smiled like a man newly born, holding out his arms as he crossed the floor.

"Beloved!"

With a cry she flung herself into his embrace. He crushed her to him and as they kissed wildly and hungrily and lovingly she clung to him, this man who meant more to her than life itself.

One evening several years later Marietta went out onto the balcony of the Palazzo Torrisi to gaze at the view along the Grand Canal. It was the hour of the day and the time of year when the setting sun tinted the Doge's Palace to amber and the domes of the Basilica to blazing copper before turning Venice into a city of gold. This was how she had first seen it from the barge bringing her to the Ospedale della Pietà. There was still a Pietà choir and orchestra, but the standard had fallen miserably. The other *os-*

pedali, whose choirs had contributed so much to the music of Venice, were closed.

The years since the fall of the Most Serene Republic had not been kind to Venice. After a matter of months the French had moved out to let the Austrians take their place. Then, after a while, the French took Venice back again. Whenever Bonaparte, now Emperor of France, visited the city he could look out from the windows of the palace built for him opposite the Basilica at the far west end of St. Mark's Square, which he still declared to be the finest drawing-room in Europe.

Marietta was glad that Domenico had resolved to stay on at the Palazzo Torrisi. It was one of the very few palaces on the Grand Canal still lived in by a patrician family. The nobility had melted away, unable or unwilling to conform to all the changes, and many ordinary citizens had packed up and moved elsewhere, for there was now little trade in Venice and heavy taxes had been imposed by the French. Even the sea, which had been the friend and protector of Venice ever since its first settlers had taken refuge there to escape the barbarians, had turned against her. The treacherous water lapped higher at her ancient walls and sent creeping ripples over stone steps that had once stood dry and proud.

The Palazzo Celano had suffered quite severe flooding some weeks before. Marietta wondered if the rose-red marble floor of that hidden room had been aswirl. Pietro had been the first to sell his palace. With the proceeds he had converted a former great residence in Padua into a much needed hospital. Since his marriage to Bianca, she had devoted herself with him to caring for the sick.

It was to be hoped that they would be able to spare the time to attend Elizabetta's wedding to a young Florentine banker. After many visits to Elena and Nicolò, who had had no other children, she had stayed a whole year, during which time she had become betrothed. Marietta was looking forward to traveling to Florence for the ceremony and seeing Elizabetta and Elena again. In the years since Domenico's release she had had two more daughters and another son, who would be traveling to Florence with them.

Her thoughts turned to Alix, to whom she owed so much. She had not seen him again after that day at the Doge's Palace, for when she and

Domenico returned from the villa to reside once more at the Palazzo Torrisi, he had already been posted elsewhere. She had grieved deeply when she heard that he had been killed leading a charge at the Battle of Marengo. Domenico had comforted her, expressing his own sorrow at the tragic death of their benefactor.

The sound of a step made Marietta turn. Chandeliers had been lit within the salon facing the balcony and the glow fell full upon her. Domenico had come out to join her. No matter what animosity the French aroused throughout Europe, Paris still set the fashion for both sexes, and Domenico was like most men in wearing his hair short and brushed forward. His coat collar was cut high and long, and he wore slimly cut trousers instead of the now outmoded knee breeches. Company was expected for a card party and he was exceptionally well dressed for the occasion.

"What a perfect evening," he remarked appreciatively, resting both hands on the balustrade. After those years of being shut away he appreciated freedom as never before. It saddened him that all he had warned against had come about, but he was not without hope for the future. There was a spirit of independence rising again among Venetians and mentally he carried a banner toward the day when the insurgents were finally driven out of the city. He had a vision of handing on that banner to his sons when younger men were needed to secure the final triumph.

He glanced with a smile at Marietta as she slipped an arm through his. "Our guests will soon be arriving," he reminded her.

She nodded. "Let's wait here a little longer. Do you think Carnival will ever be restored to Venice?"

"I'm sure of it, although never for so long as it was before, because that could stir up old evils from the past. Whatever made you think of that?"

"I've been reminiscing while standing here."

There came a sudden chatter of voices from the salon behind them. Adrianna and Leonardo had arrived with several other guests. Domenico moved away from the balustrade to go to them.

For a few moments Marietta lingered on, watching as the sunset faded. In spite of all that Venice had been through in recent years, its old magic was still there. The Serene City would always cast its spell over those seeing it for the first time and hold them in thrall for the rest of their lives, as it did her. Venice had laid claim to her before she'd ever seen it—on the day she had raised the lid of the box that held the golden mask.

Then she saw that Domenico was waiting for her, his hand extended and his eyes smiling. She responded, putting her fingers into his firm clasp, and re-entered the palace at his side. He was all Venice to her.